Course	Genetics, Biochemistry and Molecular Biology
Course Number	**Bio 41**
	Stanford University
	Biological Sciences

http://create.mcgraw-hill.com

ISBN-10: 1121258417   ISBN-13: 9781121258419

Contents

Credits

PART I | **Basic Principles: How Traits Are Transmitted** | CHAPTER

Mendel's Principles of Heredity

Although Mendel's laws can predict the probability that an individual will have a particular genetic makeup, the chance meeting of particular male and female gametes determines an individual's actual genetic fate.

A quick glance at an extended family portrait is likely to reveal children who resemble one parent or the other or who look like a combination of the two (**Fig. 2.1**). Some children, however, look unlike any of the assembled relatives and more like a great, great grandparent. What causes the similarities and differences of appearance and the skipping of generations?

The answers lie in our **genes,** the basic units of biological information, and in **heredity,** the way genes transmit physiological, anatomical, and behavioral traits from parents to offspring. Each of us starts out as a single fertilized egg cell that develops, by division and differentiation, into a mature adult made up of 10^{14} (a hundred trillion) specialized cells capable of carrying out all the body's functions and controlling our outward appearance. Genes, passed from one generation to the next, underlie the formation of every heritable trait. Such traits are as diverse as the presence of a cleft in your chin, the tendency to lose hair as you age, your hair, eye, and skin color, and even your susceptibility to certain cancers. All such traits run in families in predictable patterns that impose some possibilities and exclude others.

Genetics, the science of heredity, pursues a precise explanation of the biological structures and mechanisms that determine inheritance. In some instances, the relationship between gene and trait is remarkably simple. A single change in a single gene, for example, results in sickle-cell anemia, a disease in which the hemoglobin molecule found in red blood cells is defective. In other instances, the correlations between genes and traits are bewilderingly complex. An example is the genetic basis of facial features, in which many genes determine a large number of molecules that interact to generate the combination we recognize as a friend's face.

Gregor Mendel (1822–1884; **Fig. 2.2**), a stocky, bespectacled Augustinian monk and expert plant breeder, discovered the basic principles of genetics in the mid–nineteenth century. He published his findings in 1866, just seven years after Darwin's *On the Origin of Species* appeared in print. Mendel lived and worked in Brünn, Austria (now Brno in the Czech Republic), where he examined the inheritance of clear-cut alternative traits in pea plants, such as purple versus white flowers or yellow versus green seeds. In so doing, he inferred genetic laws that allowed him to make verifiable predictions about which traits would appear, disappear, and then reappear, and in which generations.

CHAPTER OUTLINE

- 2.1 Background: The Historical Puzzle of Inheritance
- 2.2 Genetic Analysis According to Mendel
- 2.3 Mendelian Inheritance in Humans

Figure 2.1 A family portrait. The extended family shown here includes members of four generations.

Figure 2.2 Gregor Mendel. Photographed around 1862 holding one of his experimental plants.

Figure 2.3 Like begets like and unlike. A Labrador retriever with her litter of pups.

Mendel's laws are based on the hypothesis that observable traits are determined by independent units of inheritance not visible to the naked eye. We now call these units *genes*. The concept of the gene continues to change as research deepens and refines our understanding. Today, a gene is recognized as a region of DNA that encodes a specific protein or a particular type of RNA. In the beginning, however, it was an abstraction—an imagined particle with no physical features, the function of which was to control a visible trait by an unknown mechanism.

We begin our study of genetics with a detailed look at what Mendel's laws are and how they were discovered. In subsequent chapters, we discuss logical extensions to these laws and describe how Mendel's successors grounded the abstract concept of hereditary units (genes) in an actual biological molecule (DNA).

Four general themes emerge from our detailed discussion of Mendel's work. The first is that variation, as expressed in alternative forms of a trait, is widespread in nature. This genetic diversity provides the raw material for the continuously evolving variety of life we see around us. Second, observable variation is essential for following genes from one generation to the next. Third, variation is not distributed solely by chance; rather, it is inherited according to genetic laws that explain why like begets both like and unlike. Dogs beget other dogs—but hundreds of breeds of dogs are known. Even within a breed, such as Labrador retrievers, genetic variation exists: Two black dogs could have a litter of black, brown, and golden puppies (**Fig. 2.3**). Mendel's insights help explain why this is so. Fourth, the laws Mendel discovered about heredity apply equally well to all sexually reproducing organisms, from protozoans to peas to people.

2.1 Background: The Historical Puzzle of Inheritance

Several steps lead to an understanding of genetic phenomena: the careful observation over time of groups of organisms, such as human families, herds of cattle, or fields of corn or tomatoes; the rigorous analysis of systematically recorded information gleaned from these observations; and the development of a theoretical framework that can explain the origin of these phenomena and their relationships. In the mid–nineteenth century, Gregor Mendel became the first person to combine data collection, analysis, and theory in a successful pursuit of the true basis of heredity. For many thousands of years before that, the only genetic practice was the selective breeding of domesticated plants and animals, with no guarantee of what a particular mating would produce.

Artificial selection was the first applied genetic technique

A rudimentary use of genetics was the driving force behind a key transition in human civilization, allowing hunters and gatherers to settle in villages and survive as shepherds and farmers. Even before recorded history, people practiced applied genetics as they domesticated plants and animals for their own uses. From a large litter of semitamed wolves, for example, they sent the savage and the misbehaving to the stew pot while sparing the alert sentries and friendly companions for longer life and eventual mating. As a result of this **artificial selection**—purposeful control over mating by choice of parents for the next generation—the domestic dog (*Canis lupus familiaris*) slowly arose from ancestral wolves (*Canis lupus*). The oldest bones identified indisputably as dog (and not wolf) are a skull excavated from a 20,000-year-old Alaskan settlement. Many millennia of evolution guided by artificial selection have produced massive Great Danes and minuscule Chihuahuas as well as hundreds of other modern breeds of dog. By 10,000 years ago, people had begun to use this same kind of genetic manipulation to develop economically valuable herds of reindeer, sheep, goats, pigs, and cattle that produced life-sustaining meat, milk, hides, and wools.

Farmers also carried out artificial selection of plants, storing seed from the hardiest and tastiest individuals for the next planting, eventually obtaining strains that grew better, produced more, and were easier to cultivate and harvest. In this way, scrawny weedlike plants gradually, with human guidance, turned into rice, wheat, barley, lentils, and dates in Asia; corn, squash, tomatoes, potatoes, and peppers in the Americas; yams, peanuts, and gourds in Africa. Later, plant breeders recognized male and female organs in plants and carried out artificial pollination. An Assyrian frieze carved in the ninth century B.C., pictured in **Fig. 2.4,** is the oldest known visual record of this kind of genetic experiment. It depicts priests brushing the flowers of female date palms with selected male pollen. By this method of artificial selection, early practical geneticists produced several hundred varieties of dates, each differing in specific observable qualities, such as the fruit's size, color, or taste. A 1929 botanical survey of three oases in Egypt turned up 400 varieties of date-bearing palms, twentieth-century evidence of the natural and artificially generated variation among these trees.

Figure 2.4 The earliest known record of applied genetics. In this 2800-year-old Assyrian relief from the Northwest Palace of Assurnasirpal II (883–859 B.C.), priests wearing bird masks artificially pollinate flowers of female date palms.

Desirable traits sometimes disappear and reappear

In 1822, the year of Mendel's birth, what people in Austria understood about the basic principles of heredity was not much different from what the people of ancient Assyria had understood. By the nineteenth century, plant and animal breeders had created many strains in which offspring often carried a prized parental trait. Using such strains, they could produce plants or animals with desired characteristics for food and fiber, but they could not always predict why a valued trait would sometimes disappear and then reappear in only some offspring. For example, selective breeding practices had resulted in valuable flocks of merino sheep producing large quantities of soft, fine wool, but at the 1837 annual meeting of the Moravian Sheep Breeders Society, one breeder's dilemma epitomized the state of the art. He possessed an outstanding ram that would be priceless "if its advantages are inherited by its offspring," but "if they are not inherited, then it is worth no more than the cost of wool, meat, and skin." Which would it be? According to the meeting's recorded minutes, current breeding practices offered no definite answers. In his concluding remarks at this sheep-breeders meeting, the

Abbot Cyril Napp pointed to a possible way out. He proposed that breeders could improve their ability to predict what traits would appear in the offspring by finding the answers to three basic questions: What is inherited? How is it inherited? What is the role of chance in heredity?

This is where matters stood in 1843 when 21-year-old Gregor Mendel entered the monastery in Brünn, presided over by the same Abbot Napp. Although Mendel was a monk trained in theology, he was not a rank amateur in science. The province of Moravia, in which Brünn was located, was a center of learning and scientific activity. Mendel was able to acquire a copy of Darwin's *On the Origin of Species* shortly after it was translated into German in 1863. Abbot Napp, recognizing Mendel's intellectual abilities, sent him to the University of Vienna—all expenses paid—where he prescribed his own course of study. His choices were an unusual mix: physics, mathematics, chemistry, botany, paleontology, and plant physiology. Christian Doppler, discoverer of the Doppler effect, was one of his teachers. The cross-pollination of ideas from several disciplines would play a significant role in Mendel's discoveries. One year after he returned to Brünn, he began his series of seminal genetic experiments. **Figure 2.5** shows where Mendel worked and the microscope he used.

Mendel devised a new experimental approach

Before Mendel, many misconceptions clouded people's thinking about heredity. Two of the prevailing errors were particularly misleading. The first was that one parent contributes most to an offspring's inherited features; Nicolaas Hartsoeker, one of the earliest microscopists, contended in 1694 that it was the male, by way of a fully formed "homunculus" inside the sperm (**Fig. 2.6**). Another deceptive notion was the concept of *blended inheritance,* the idea that parental traits become mixed and forever changed in the offspring, as when blue and yellow pigment merge to green on a painter's palette. The theory of blending may have grown out of a natural tendency for parents to see a combination of their own traits in their offspring. While blending could account for children who look like a combination of their parents, it could not explain obvious differences between biological brothers and sisters nor the persistence of variation within extended families.

The experiments Mendel devised would lay these myths to rest by providing precise, verifiable answers to the three questions Abbot Napp had raised almost 15 years earlier: What is inherited? How is it inherited? What is the role of chance in heredity? A key component of Mendel's breakthrough was the way he set up his experiments.

Figure 2.5 Mendel's garden and microscope. (a) Gregor Mendel's garden was part of his monastery's property in Brno. **(b)** Mendel used this microscope to examine plant reproductive organs and to pursue his interests in natural history.

(a)

(b)

Figure 2.6 The homunculus: A misconception. Well into the nineteenth century, many prominent microscopists believed they saw a fully formed, miniature fetus crouched within the head of a sperm.

What did Mendel do differently from those who preceded him? First, he chose the garden pea *(Pisum sativum)* as his experimental organism (**Figs. 2.7a** and **b**). Peas grew well in Brünn, and with male and female organs in the same flower, they were normally self-fertilizing. In **self-fertilization** (or *selfing*), both egg and pollen come from the same plant. The particular anatomy of pea flowers, however, makes it easy to prevent self-fertilization and instead to **cross-fertilize** (or *cross*) two individuals by brushing pollen from one plant onto a female organ of another plant, as illustrated in **Fig. 2.7c.** Peas offered yet another advantage. For each successive generation, Mendel could obtain large numbers of individuals within a relatively short growing season. By comparison, if he had worked with sheep, each mating would have generated only a few offspring and the time between generations would have been several years.

Second, Mendel examined the inheritance of clear-cut alternative forms of particular traits—purple versus white flowers, yellow versus green peas. Using such "either-or" traits, he could distinguish and trace unambiguously the transmission of one or the other observed characteristic, because there were no intermediate forms. (The opposite of these so-called *discrete traits* are *continuous traits,* such as height and skin color in humans. Continuous traits show many intermediate forms.)

Third, Mendel collected and perpetuated lines of peas that bred true. Matings within such **pure-breeding lines** produce offspring carrying specific parental traits that remain constant from generation to generation. Mendel observed his pure-breeding lines for up to eight generations. Plants with white flowers always produced offspring with white flowers; plants with purple flowers produced only offspring with purple flowers. Mendel called constant but mutually exclusive, alternative traits, such as purple versus white flowers or yellow versus green seeds, "antagonistic pairs" and settled on

Figure 2.7 Mendel's experimental organism: The garden pea. (a) Pea plants with white flowers. **(b)** Pollen is produced in the anthers. Mature pollen lands on the stigma, which is connected to the ovary (which becomes the pea pod). After landing, the pollen grows a tube that extends through the stigma to one of the ovules (immature seeds), allowing fertilization to take place. **(c)** To prevent self-fertilization, breeders remove the anthers from the female parents (here, the white flower) before the plant produces mature pollen. Pollen is then transferred with a paintbrush from the anthers of the male parent (here, the purple flower) to the stigma of the female parent. Each fertilized ovule becomes an individual pea (mature seed) that can grow into a new pea plant. All of the peas produced from one flower are encased in the same pea pod, but these peas form from different pollen grains and ovules.

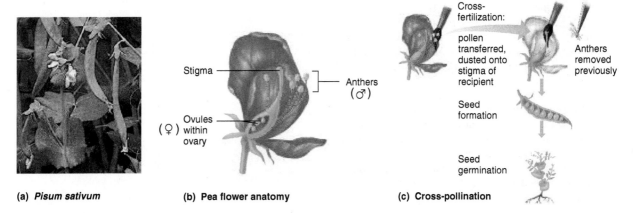

(a) *Pisum sativum*

(b) Pea flower anatomy

(c) Cross-pollination

seven such pairs for his study (**Fig. 2.8**). In his experiments, he not only perpetuated pure-breeding stocks for each member of a pair, but he also cross-fertilized pairs of plants to produce **hybrids,** offspring of genetically dissimilar parents, for each pair of antagonistic traits. Figure 2.8 shows the appearance of the hybrids he studied.

Fourth, being an expert plant breeder, Mendel carefully controlled his matings, going to great lengths to ensure that the progeny he observed really resulted from the specific fertilizations he intended. Thus he painstakingly prevented the intrusion of any foreign pollen and assured self- or cross-pollination as the experiment demanded. Not only did this allow him to carry out controlled breedings of selected traits, he could also make **reciprocal crosses.** In such crosses, he reversed the traits of the male and female parents, thus controlling whether a particular trait was transmitted via the egg cell within the ovule or via a sperm cell within the pollen. For example, he could use pollen from a purple flower to fertilize the eggs of a white flower and also use pollen from a white flower to fertilize the eggs of a purple flower. Because the progeny of these reciprocal crosses were similar, Mendel demonstrated that the two parents contribute equally to inheritance. "It is immaterial to the form of the hybrid," he wrote, "which of the parental types was the seed or pollen plant."

Fifth, Mendel worked with large numbers of plants, counted all offspring, subjected his findings to numerical analysis, and then compared his results with predictions based on his models. He was the first person to study inheritance in this manner, and no doubt his background in physics and mathematics contributed to this quantitative approach. Mendel's careful numerical analysis revealed patterns of transmission that reflected basic laws of heredity.

Finally, Mendel was a brilliant practical experimentalist. When comparing tall and short plants, for example, he made sure that the short ones were out of the shade of the tall ones so their growth would not be stunted. Eventually he focused on certain traits of the pea seeds themselves, such as their color or shape, rather than on traits of the plants arising from the seeds. In this way, he could observe many more individuals from the limited space of the monastery garden, and he could evaluate the results of a cross in a single growing season.

In short, Mendel purposely set up a simplified "black-and-white" experimental system and then figured out how it worked. He did not look at the vast number of variables that determine the development of a prize ram nor at the origin of differences between species. Rather, he looked at discrete traits that came in two mutually exclusive forms and asked questions that could be answered by observation and computation.

Figure 2.8 The mating of parents with antagonistic traits produces hybrids. Note that each of the hybrids for the seven antagonistic traits studied by Mendel resembles only one of the parents. The parental trait that shows up in the hybrid is known as the "dominant" trait.

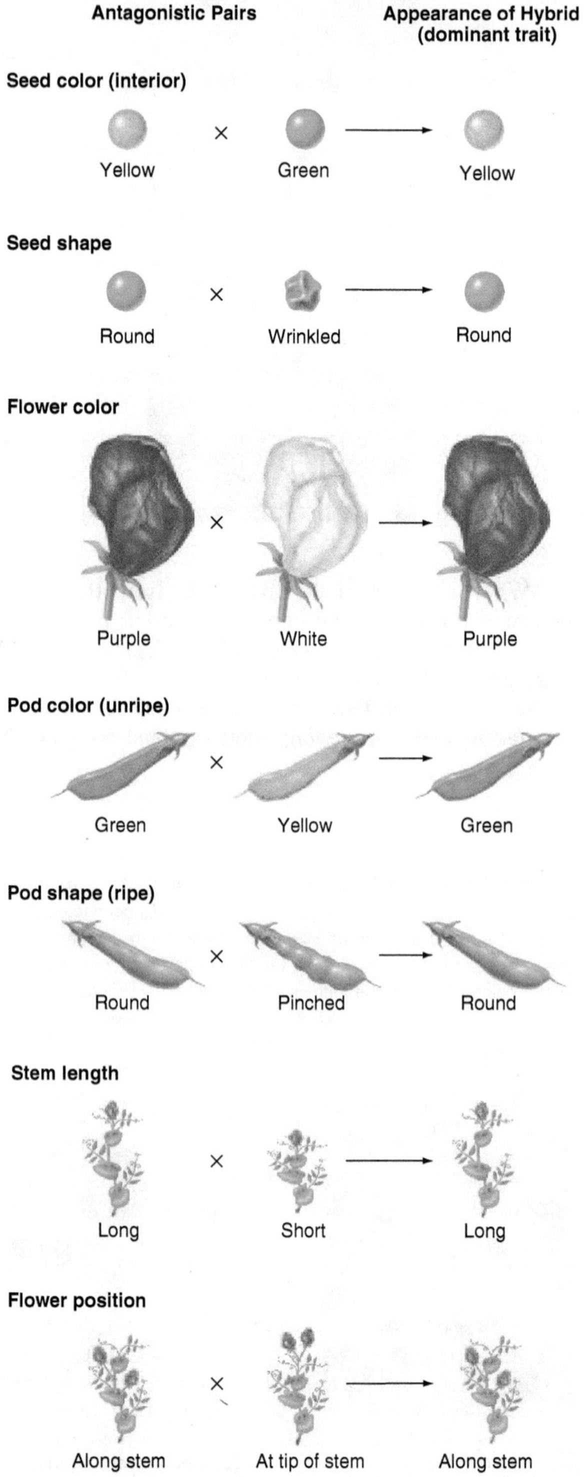

Antagonistic Pairs			Appearance of Hybrid (dominant trait)

Seed color (interior)
Yellow × Green → Yellow

Seed shape
Round × Wrinkled → Round

Flower color
Purple × White → Purple

Pod color (unripe)
Green × Yellow → Green

Pod shape (ripe)
Round × Pinched → Round

Stem length
Long × Short → Long

Flower position
Along stem × At tip of stem → Along stem

Gregor Mendel performed genetic crosses in a systematic way, using mathematics to analyze the data he obtained and to predict outcomes of other experiments.

2.2 Genetic Analysis According to Mendel

In early 1865 at the age of 43, Gregor Mendel presented a paper entitled "Experiments on Plant Hybrids" before the Natural Science Society of Brünn. Despite its modest heading, it was a scientific paper of uncommon clarity and simplicity that summarized a decade of original observations and experiments. In it Mendel describes in detail the transmission of visible characteristics in pea plants, defines unseen but logically deduced units (genes) that determine when and how often these visible traits appear, and analyzes the behavior of genes in simple mathematical terms to reveal previously unsuspected principles of heredity.

Published the following year, the paper would eventually become the cornerstone of modern genetics. Its stated purpose was to see whether there is a "generally applicable law governing the formation and development of hybrids." Let us examine its insights.

Monohybrid crosses reveal units of inheritance and the law of segregation

Once Mendel had isolated pure-breeding lines for several sets of characteristics, he carried out a series of matings between individuals that differed in only one trait, such as seed color or stem length. In each cross, one parent carries one form of the trait, and the other parent carries an alternative form of the same trait. **Figure 2.9** illustrates one such mating. Early in the spring of 1854, for example, Mendel planted pure-breeding green peas and pure-breeding yellow peas and allowed them to grow into the **parental (P) generation**. Later that spring when the plants had flowered, he dusted the female stigma of "green-pea" plant flowers with pollen from "yellow-pea" plants. He also performed the reciprocal cross, dusting "yellow-pea" plant stigmas with "green-pea" pollen. In the fall, when he collected and separately analyzed the progeny peas of these reciprocal crosses, he found that in both cases, the peas were all yellow.

These yellow peas, progeny of the P generation, were the beginning of what we now call the **first filial (F$_1$)** generation. To learn whether the green trait had disappeared entirely or remained intact but hidden in these

Figure 2.9 Analyzing a monohybrid cross. Cross-pollination of pure-breeding parental plants produces F$_1$ hybrids, all of which resemble one of the parents. Self-pollination of F$_1$ plants gives rise to an F$_2$ generation with a 3:1 ratio of individuals resembling the two original parental types. For simplicity, we do not show the plants that produce the peas or that grow from the planted peas.

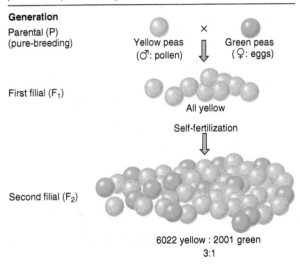

Generation

Parental (P)
(pure-breeding)   Yellow peas   ×   Green peas
                    (♂: pollen)   (♀: eggs)

First filial (F$_1$)

All yellow

Self-fertilization

Second filial (F$_2$)

6022 yellow : 2001 green
3:1

F$_1$ yellow peas, Mendel planted them to obtain mature F$_1$ plants that he allowed to self-fertilize. Such experiments involving hybrids for a single trait are often called **monohybrid crosses**. He then harvested and counted the peas of the resulting **second filial (F$_2$)** generation, progeny of the F$_1$ generation. Among the progeny of one series of F$_1$ self-fertilizations, there were 6022 yellow and 2001 green F$_2$ peas, an almost perfect ratio of 3 yellow : 1 green. F$_1$ plants derived from the reciprocal of the original cross produced a similar ratio of yellow to green F$_2$ progeny.

Reappearance of the recessive trait

The presence of green peas in the F$_2$ generation was irrefutable evidence that blending had not occurred. If it had, the information necessary to make green peas would have been irretrievably lost in the F$_1$ hybrids. Instead, the information remained intact and was able to direct the formation of 2001 green peas actually harvested from the second filial generation. These green peas were indistinguishable from their green grandparents.

Mendel concluded that there must be two types of yellow peas: those that breed true like the yellow peas of the P generation, and those that can yield some green offspring like the yellow F$_1$ hybrids. This second type somehow contains latent information for green peas. He called the trait that appeared in all the F$_1$ hybrids—in this

▶▶ FAST FORWARD

Genes Encode Proteins

Genes determine traits as disparate as pea shape and the inherited human disease cystic fibrosis. We now know that genes encode the proteins that cells produce and depend on for structure and function. As early as 1940, investigators had uncovered evidence suggesting that some genes determine the formation of enzymes, the proteins that catalyze specific chemical reactions. But it was not until 1991, 126 years after Mendel published his work, that a team of British geneticists was able to identify the gene for pea shape and to pinpoint how the enzyme it specifies influences a seed's round or wrinkled contour. About the same time, medical researchers in the United States identified the cys-

tic fibrosis gene. They discovered how a mutant allele causes unusually sticky mucus secretion and a susceptibility to respiratory infections and digestive malfunction, once again, through the protein the gene determines.

The pea shape gene encodes an enzyme known as SBE1 (for starch-branching enzyme 1), which catalyzes the conversion of amylose, an unbranched linear molecule of starch, to amylopectin, a starch molecule composed of several branching chains (**Fig. A**). The dominant *R* allele of the pea shape gene causes the formation of active SBE1 enzyme that functions normally. As a result, *RR* homozygotes produce a high proportion of branched

Figure A Round and wrinkled peas: How one gene determines an enzyme that affects pea shape. The *R* allele of the pea shape gene directs the synthesis of an enzyme that converts unbranched starch to branched starch, indirectly leading to round pea shape. The *r* allele of this gene determines an inactive form of the enzyme, leading to a buildup of linear, unbranched starch that ultimately causes seed wrinkling. The photograph at right shows two pea pods, each of which contains wrinkled (arrows) and round peas; the ratio of round to wrinkled in these two well-chosen pods is 9:3 (or 3:1).

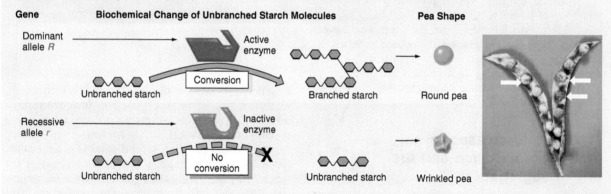

case, yellow seeds—**dominant** (see Fig. 2.8) and the "antagonistic" green-pea trait that remained hidden in the F_1 hybrids but reappeared in the F_2 generation **recessive.** But how did he explain the 3:1 ratio of yellow to green F_2 peas?

Genes: Discrete units of inheritance

To account for his observations, Mendel proposed that for each trait, every plant carries two copies of a unit of inheritance, receiving one from its maternal parent and the other from the paternal parent. Today, we call these units of inheritance *genes*. Each unit determines the appearance of a specific characteristic. The pea plants in Mendel's collection had two copies of a gene for seed color, two copies of another for seed shape, two copies of a third for stem length, and so forth.

Mendel further proposed that each gene comes in alternative forms, and combinations of these alternative forms determine the contrasting characteristics he was studying. Today we call the alternative forms of a single gene **alleles.** The gene for pea color, for example, has yellow and green alleles; the gene for pea shape has round and wrinkled alleles. (The Fast Forward box "Genes Encode Proteins" on this page describes the biochemical and molecular mechanisms by which different alleles determine different forms of a trait.) In Mendel's monohybrid crosses, one allele of each gene was dominant, the other recessive. In the P generation, one parent carried two dominant alleles for the trait under consideration; the other parent, two recessive alleles. The F_1 generation hybrids carried one dominant and one recessive allele for the trait. Individuals having two different alleles for a single trait are **monohybrids.**

starch molecules, which allow the peas to maintain a rounded shape. In contrast, the enzyme determined by the recessive *r* allele is abnormal and does not function effectively. In homozygous recessive *rr* peas, sucrose builds up because less of it is converted into starch. The excess sucrose modifies osmotic pressure, causing water to enter the young seeds. As the seeds mature, they lose water, shrink, and wrinkle. The single dominant allele in *Rr* heterozygotes apparently produces enough of the normal enzyme to prevent wrinkling. In summary, a specific gene determines a specific enzyme whose activity affects pea shape.

The human disease of cystic fibrosis (CF) was first described in 1938, but doctors and scientists did not understand the biochemical mechanism that produced the serious respiratory and digestive malfunctions associated with the disease. As a result, treatments could do little more than relieve some of the symptoms, and most CF sufferers died before the age of 30.

In 1989, molecular geneticists found that the normal allele of the cystic fibrosis gene determines a protein that forges a channel through the cell membrane (**Fig. B**). This protein, called the <u>c</u>ystic <u>f</u>ibrosis <u>t</u>ransmembrane conductance <u>r</u>egulator (CFTR), controls the flow of chloride ions into and out of the cell. The normal allele of this gene produces a CFTR protein that correctly regulates the back-and-forth exchange of ions, which, in turn, determines the cell's osmotic pressure and the flow of water through the cell membrane. In people with cystic fibrosis, however, the two recessive alleles produce only an abnormal form of the CFTR protein. The abnormal protein cannot be inserted into the cell membranes, so patients lack functional CFTR chloride channels. The cells thus retain water, and a thick, dehydrated mucus builds up outside the cells. In cells lining the airways and the ducts of secretory organs such as the pancreas,

Figure B The cystic fibrosis gene encodes a cell membrane protein. A model of the normal CFTR protein that regulates the passage of chloride ions through the cell membrane. A small change in the gene that codes for CFTR results in an altered protein that prevents proper flow of chloride ions, leading to the varied symptoms of cystic fibrosis.

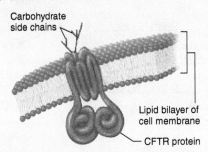

this single biochemical defect produces clogging and blockages that result in respiratory and digestive malfunction.

Identification of the cystic fibrosis gene brought not only a protein-based explanation of disease symptoms but also the promise of a cure. In the early 1990s, medical researchers placed the normal allele of the gene into respiratory tissue of mice with the disease. These mice could then produce a functional CFTR protein. Such encouraging results in these small mammals suggested that in the not-too-distant future, gene therapy might bestow relatively normal health on people suffering from this once life-threatening genetic disorder. Unfortunately, human trials of CFTR gene therapy have not yet achieved clear success.

The law of segregation

If a plant has two copies of every gene, how does it pass only one copy of each to its progeny? And how do the offspring then end up with two copies of these same genes, one from each parent? Mendel drew on his background in plant physiology and answered these questions in terms of the two biological mechanisms behind reproduction: gamete formation and the random union of gametes at fertilization. **Gametes** are the specialized cells—eggs within the ovules of the female parent and sperm cells within the pollen grains—that carry genes between generations. He imagined that during the formation of pollen and eggs, the two copies of each gene in the parent separate (or *segregate*) so that each gamete receives only one allele for each trait (**Fig. 2.10a**). Thus, each egg and each pollen grain receives only one allele for pea color (either yellow or green). At fertilization, pollen with one or the other allele unites at random with an egg carrying one or the other allele, restoring the two copies of the gene for each trait in the fertilized egg, or **zygote** (**Fig. 2.10b**). If the pollen carries yellow and the egg green, the result will be a hybrid yellow pea like the F_1 monohybrids that resulted when pure-breeding parents of opposite types mated. If the yellow-carrying pollen unites with a yellow-carrying egg, the result will be a yellow pea that grows into a pure-breeding plant like those of the P generation that produced only yellow peas. And finally, if pollen carrying the allele for green peas fertilizes a green-carrying egg, the progeny will be a pure-breeding green pea.

Mendel's **law of segregation** encapsulates this general principle of heredity: *The two alleles for each trait separate (segregate) during gamete formation, and then unite at random, one from each parent, at fertilization.* Throughout this book, the term **segregation** refers to

Figure 2.10 The law of segregation. (a) The two identical alleles of pure-breeding plants separate (segregate) during gamete formation. As a result, each pollen grain or egg carries only one of each pair of parental alleles. **(b)** Cross-pollination and fertilization between pure-breeding parents with antagonistic traits result in F₁ hybrid zygotes with two different alleles. For the seed color gene, a *Yy* hybrid zygote will develop into a yellow pea.

(a) **The two alleles for each trait separate during gamete formation.**

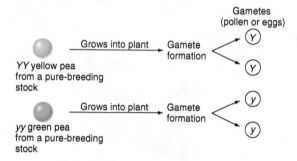

(b) **Two gametes, one from each parent, unite at random at fertilization.**

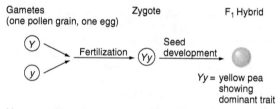

Y = yellow-determining allele of pea color gene
y = green-determining allele of pea color gene

Figure 2.11 The Punnett square: Visual summary of a cross. This Punnett square illustrates the combinations that can arise when an F₁ hybrid undergoes gamete formation and self-fertilization. The F₂ generation should have a 3:1 ratio of yellow to green peas.

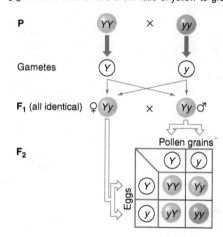

such *equal segregation* in which one allele, and only one allele, of each gene goes to each gamete. Note that the law of segregation makes a clear distinction between organisms, whose cells have two copies of each gene, and gametes, which bear only a single copy of each gene.

The Punnett square

Figure 2.11 shows a simple way of visualizing the results of the segregation and random union of alleles during gamete formation and fertilization. Mendel invented a system of symbols that allowed him to analyze all his crosses in the same way. He designated dominant alleles with a capital *A, B,* or *C* and recessive ones with a lowercase *a, b,* or *c.* Modern geneticists have adopted this convention for naming genes in peas and many other organisms, but they often choose a symbol with some reference to the trait in question—a *Y* for yellow or an *R* for round. Throughout this book, we present gene symbols in italics. In Fig. 2.11, we denote the dominant yellow allele by a capital *Y* and the recessive green allele by a lower

case *y.* The pure-breeding plants of the parental generation are either *YY* (yellow peas) or *yy* (green peas). The *YY* parent can produce only *Y* gametes, the *yy* parent only *y* gametes. You can see from the diagram why every cross between *YY* and *yy* produces exactly the same result—a *Yy* hybrid—no matter which parent (male or female) contributes which particular allele.

Next, to visualize what happens when the *Yy* hybrids self-fertilize, we set up a Punnett square (named after British mathematician Reginald Punnett, who introduced it in 1906; Fig. 2.11). The square provides a simple and convenient method for tracking the kinds of gametes produced as well as all the possible combinations that might occur at fertilization. As the Punnett square shows, each hybrid produces two kinds of gametes, *Y* and *y,* in a ratio of 1:1. Thus, half the pollen and half the eggs carry *Y,* the other half *y.* At fertilization, 1/4 of the progeny will be *YY,* 1/4 *Yy,* 1/4 *yY,* and 1/4 *yy.* Since the gametic source of an allele (egg or pollen) for the traits Mendel studied had no influence on the allele's effect, *Yy* and *yY* are equivalent. This means that 1/2 of the progeny are yellow *Yy* hybrids, 1/4 *YY* true-breeding yellows, and 1/4 true-breeding *yy* greens. The diagram illustrates how the segregation of alleles during gamete formation and the random union of egg and pollen at fertilization can produce the 3:1 ratio of yellow to green that Mendel observed in the F₂ generation.

Mendel's law of segregation states that alleles of genes separate during gamete formation and then come together randomly at fertilization. The Punnett square is one tool for analyzing allele behavior in a cross.

Mendel's results reflect basic rules of probability

Though you may not have realized it, the Punnett square illustrates two simple rules of probability—the product rule and the sum rule—that are central to the analysis of genetic crosses. These rules predict the likelihood that a particular combination of events will occur.

The product rule

The **product rule** states that the probability of two or more *independent events* occurring together is the *product* of the probabilities that each event will occur by itself. With independent events:

Probability of event 1 *and* event 2 =

Probability of event 1 × probability of event 2

Consecutive coin tosses are obviously independent events; a heads in one toss neither increases nor decreases the probability of a heads in the next toss. If you toss two coins at the same time, the results are also independent events. A heads for one coin neither increases nor decreases the probability of a heads for the other coin. Thus, the probability of a given combination is the product of their independent probabilities. For example, the probability that both coins will turn up heads is

$$1/2 \times 1/2 = 1/4$$

Similarly, the formation of egg and pollen are independent events; in a hybrid plant, the probability is 1/2 that a given gamete will carry Y and 1/2 that it will carry y. Because fertilization happens at random, the probability that a particular combination of maternal and paternal alleles will occur simultaneously in the same zygote is the product of the independent probabilities of these alleles being packaged in egg and sperm. Thus, to find the chance of a Y egg (formed as the result of one event) uniting with a Y sperm (the result of an independent event), you simply multiply 1/2 × 1/2 to get 1/4. This is the same fraction of YY progeny seen in the Punnett square of Fig. 2.11, which demonstrates that the Punnett square is simply another way of depicting the product rule.

The sum rule

While we can describe the moment of random fertilization as the simultaneous occurrence of two independent events, we can also say that two different fertilization events are mutually exclusive. For instance, if Y combines with Y, it cannot also combine with y in the same zygote. A second rule of probability, the **sum rule,** states that the probability of either of two such *mutually exclusive events* occurring is the *sum* of their individual probabilities. With mutually exclusive events:

Probability of event 1 *or* event 2 =

Probability of event 1 + probability of event 2

To find the likelihood that an offspring of a Yy hybrid self-fertilization will be a hybrid like the parents, you add 1/4 (the probability of maternal Y uniting with paternal y) and 1/4 (the probability of the mutually exclusive event where paternal Y unites with maternal y) to get 1/2, again the same result as in the Punnett square. In another use of the sum rule, you could predict the ratio of yellow to green F_2 progeny. The fraction of F_2 peas that will be yellow is the sum of 1/4 (the event producing YY) plus 1/4 (the mutually exclusive event generating Yy) plus 1/4 (the third mutually exclusive event producing yY) to get 3/4. The remaining 1/4 of the F_2 progeny will be green. So the yellow-to-green ratio is 3/4 to 1/4, or more simply, 3:1.

In the analysis of a genetic cross, the product rule multiplies probabilities to predict the chance of a particular fertilization event. The sum rule adds probabilities to predict the proportion of progeny that share a particular trait such as pea color.

Further crosses verify the law of segregation

Although Mendel's law of segregation explains the data from his pea crosses, he performed additional experiments to confirm its validity. In the rigorous check of his hypothesis illustrated in **Fig. 2.12,** he allowed self-fertilization of all the plants in the F_2 generation and counted the types of F_3 progeny. Mendel found that the plants that developed from F_2 green peas all produced only F_3 green peas, and when the resulting F_3 plants self-fertilized, the next generation also produced green peas (not shown). This is what we (and Mendel) would expect of pure-breeding lines carrying two copies of the recessive allele. The yellow peas were a different story. When Mendel allowed 518 F_2 plants that developed from yellow peas to self-fertilize, he observed that 166, roughly 1/3 of the total, were pure-breeding yellow through several generations, but the other 352 (2/3 of the total yellow F_2 plants) were hybrids because they gave rise to yellow and green F_3 peas in a ratio of 3:1.

It took Mendel years to conduct such rigorous experiments on seven pairs of pea traits, but in the end, he was able to conclude that the segregation of dominant and recessive alleles during gamete formation and their random union at fertilization could indeed explain the 3:1 ratios he observed whenever he allowed hybrids to self-fertilize. His results, however, raised yet another question,

Figure 2.12 Yellow F₂ peas are of two types: Pure breeding and hybrid. The distribution of a pair of contrasting alleles (*Y* and *y*) after two generations of self-fertilization. The homozygous individuals of each generation breed true, whereas the hybrids do not.

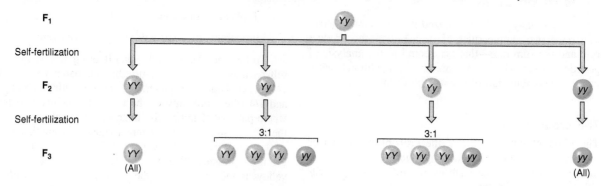

one of some importance to future plant and animal breeders. Plants showing a dominant trait, such as yellow peas, can be either pure-breeding (*YY*) or hybrid (*Yy*). How can you distinguish one from the other? For self-fertilizing plants, the answer is to observe the appearance of the next generation. But how would you distinguish pure-breeding from hybrid individuals in species that do not self-fertilize?

Testcrosses: A way to establish genotype

Before describing Mendel's answer, we need to define a few more terms. An observable characteristic, such as yellow or green pea seeds, is a **phenotype,** while the actual pair of alleles present in an individual is its **genotype.** A *YY* or a *yy* genotype is called **homozygous,** because the two copies of the gene that determine the particular trait in question are the same. In contrast, a genotype with two different alleles for a trait is **heterozygous;** in other words, it is a hybrid for that trait (**Fig. 2.13**). An individual with a homozygous genotype is a **homozygote;** one with a heterozygous genotype is a **heterozygote.** Note that the

phenotype of a heterozygote (that is, of a hybrid) defines which allele is dominant: Because *Yy* peas are yellow, the yellow allele *Y* is dominant to the *y* allele for green. If you know the genotype and the dominance relation of the alleles, you can accurately predict the phenotype. The reverse is not true, however, because some phenotypes can derive from more than one genotype. For example, the phenotype of yellow peas can result from either the *YY* or the *Yy* genotype.

With these distinctions in mind, we can look at the method Mendel devised for deciphering the unknown genotype, we'll call it *Y–*, responsible for a dominant phenotype; the dash represents the unknown second allele, either *Y* or *y*. This method, called the **testcross,** is a mating in which an individual showing the dominant phenotype, for instance, a *Y–* plant grown from a yellow pea, is crossed with an individual expressing the recessive phenotype, in this case a *yy* plant grown from a green pea. As the Punnett squares in **Fig. 2.14** illustrate, if the dominant phenotype in question derives from a homozygous

Figure 2.13 Genotype versus phenotype in homozygotes and heterozygotes. The relationship between genotype and phenotype with a pair of contrasting alleles where one allele (*Y*) shows complete dominance over the other (*y*).

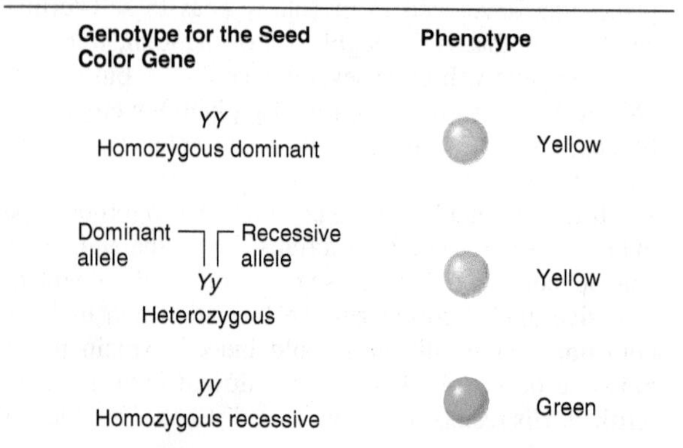

Figure 2.14 How a testcross reveals genotype. An individual of unknown genotype, but dominant phenotype, is crossed with a homozygous recessive. If the unknown genotype is homozygous, all progeny will exhibit the dominant phenotype, (*cross A*). If the unknown genotype is heterozygous, half the progeny will exhibit the dominant trait, half the recessive trait (*cross B*).

Genotype for the Seed Color Gene		Phenotype
YY Homozygous dominant		Yellow
Dominant allele ⌐ ⌐ Recessive allele *Yy* Heterozygous		Yellow
yy Homozygous recessive		Green

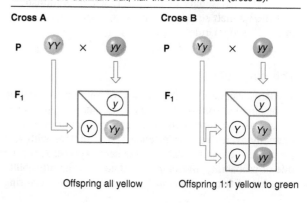

YY genotype, all the offspring of the testcross will show the dominant yellow phenotype. But if the dominant parent of unknown genotype is a heterozygous hybrid (*Yy*), 1/2 of the progeny are expected to be yellow peas, and the other half green. In this way, the testcross establishes the genotype behind a dominant phenotype, resolving any uncertainty.

As we mentioned earlier, Mendel deliberately simplified the problem of heredity, focusing on traits that come in only two forms. He was able to replicate his basic monohybrid findings with corn, beans, and four-o'clocks (plants with tubular, white or bright red flowers). As it turns out, his concept of the gene and his law of segregation can be generalized to almost all sexually reproducing organisms.

> The results of a testcross, in which an individual showing the dominant phenotype is crossed with an individual showing the recessive phenotype, indicate whether the individual with the dominant phenotype is a homozygote or a heterozygote.

Dihybrid crosses reveal the law of independent assortment

Having determined from monohybrid crosses that genes are inherited according to the law of segregation, Mendel turned his attention to the simultaneous inheritance of two or more apparently unrelated traits in peas. He asked how two pairs of alleles would segregate in a **dihybrid** individual, that is, in a plant that is heterozygous for two genes at the same time.

To construct such a dihybrid, Mendel mated true-breeding plants grown from yellow round peas (*YY RR*) with true-breeding plants grown from green wrinkled peas (*yy rr*). From this cross he obtained a dihybrid F₁ generation (*Yy Rr*) showing only the two dominant phenotypes, yellow and round (**Fig. 2.15**). He then allowed these F₁ dihybrids to self-fertilize to produce the F₂ generation. Mendel could not predict the outcome of this mating. Would all the F₂ progeny be **parental types** that looked like either the original yellow round parent or the green wrinkled parent? Or would some new combinations of phenotypes occur that were not seen in the parental lines, such as yellow wrinkled or green round peas? New phenotypic combinations like these are called **recombinant types**. When Mendel counted the F₂ generation of one experiment, he found 315 yellow round peas, 101 yellow wrinkled, 108 green round, and 32 green wrinkled. There were, in fact, yellow wrinkled and green round recombinant phenotypes, providing evidence that some shuffling of the alleles of different genes had taken place.

Figure 2.15 A dihybrid cross produces parental types and recombinant types. In this dihybrid cross, pure-breeding parents (P) produce a genetically uniform generation of F₁ dihybrids. Self-pollination or cross-pollination of the F₁ plants yields the characteristic F₂ phenotypic ratio of 9:3:3:1.

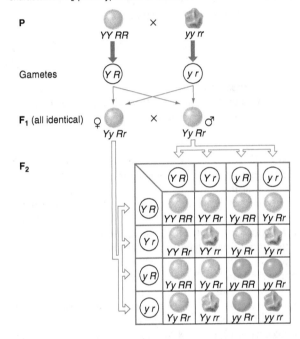

Type	Genotype	Phenotype		Number	Phenotypic Ratio
Parental	*Y– R–*	yellow round		315	9/16
Recombinant	*yy R–*	green round		108	3/16
Recombinant	*Y– rr*	yellow wrinkled		101	3/16
Parental	*yy rr*	green wrinkled		32	1/16

Ratio of yellow (dominant) to green (recessive) = 12:4 or 3:1
Ratio of round (dominant) to wrinkled (recessive) = 12:4 or 3:1

The law of independent assortment

From the observed ratios, Mendel inferred the biological mechanism of that shuffling—the **independent assortment** of gene pairs during gamete formation. Because the genes for pea color and for pea shape assort independently, the allele for pea shape in a *Y* carrying gamete could with equal likelihood be either *R* or *r*. Thus, the presence of a particular allele of one gene, say, the dominant *Y* for pea color, provides no information whatsoever about the allele of the second gene. Each dihybrid of the F₁ generation can therefore make four kinds of gametes: *Y R*, *Y r*, *y R*, and *y r*. In a large number of gametes, the four kinds will appear in an almost perfect ratio of 1:1:1:1, or put another way, roughly 1/4 of the eggs and 1/4 of the pollen will contain each of the four possible combinations of alleles. That "the different kinds of germinal cells [eggs or pollen] of a hybrid are produced on the average in equal numbers" was yet another one of Mendel's incisive insights.

At fertilization then, in a mating of dihybrids, 4 different kinds of eggs can combine with any 1 of 4 different kinds of pollen, producing a total of 16 possible zygotes. Once again, a Punnett square is a convenient way to visualize the process. If you look at the square in Fig. 2.15, you will see that some of the 16 potential allelic combinations are identical. In fact, there are only nine different genotypes—*YY RR, YY Rr, Yy RR, Yy Rr, yy RR, yy Rr, YY rr, Yy rr,* and *yy rr*—because the source of the alleles (egg or pollen) does not make any difference. If you look at the combinations of traits determined by the nine genotypes, you will see only four phenotypes—yellow round, yellow wrinkled, green round, and green wrinkled—in a ratio of 9:3:3:1. If, however, you look at just pea color or just pea shape, you can see that each trait is inherited in the 3:1 ratio predicted by Mendel's law of segregation. In the Punnett square, there are 12 yellow for every 4 green and 12 round for every 4 wrinkled. In other words, the ratio of each dominant trait (yellow or round) to its antagonistic recessive trait (green or wrinkled) is 12:4, or 3:1. This means that the inheritance of the gene for pea color is unaffected by the inheritance of the gene for pea shape, and vice versa.

The preceding analysis became the basis of Mendel's second general genetic principle, the **law of independent assortment**: *During gamete formation, different pairs of alleles segregate independently of each other* (**Fig. 2.16**). The independence of their segregation and the subsequent random union of gametes at fertilization determine the phenotypes observed. Using the product rule for assessing the probability of independent events, you can see mathematically how the 9:3:3:1 phenotypic ratio observed in a dihybrid cross derives from two separate 3:1 phenotypic ratios. If the two sets of alleles assort independently, the yellow-to-green ratio in the F_2 generation will be 3/4 : 1/4, and likewise, the round-to-wrinkled ratio will be 3/4 : 1/4. To find the probability that two independent events such as yellow and round will occur simultaneously in the same plant, you multiply as follows:

Probability of yellow round = 3/4 × 3/4 = 9/16

Probability of yellow wrinkled = 3/4 × 1/4 = 3/16

Probability of green round = 1/4 × 3/4 = 3/16

Probability of green wrinkled = 1/4 × 1/4 = 1/16

Thus, in a population of F_2 plants, there will be a 9:3:3:1 phenotypic ratio of yellow round to yellow wrinkled to green round to green wrinkled.

Branched-line diagrams

A convenient way to keep track of the probabilities of each potential outcome in a genetic cross is to construct a **branched-line diagram** (**Fig. 2.17**), which shows all the possibilities for each gene in a sequence of columns. In Fig. 2.17, the first column shows the two possible pea color phenotypes; and the second column demonstrates that each pea color can occur with either of two pea shapes. Again, the 9:3:3:1 ratio of phenotypes is apparent.

Testcrosses with dihybrids

An understanding of dihybrid crosses has many applications. Suppose, for example, that you work for a wholesale nursery, and your assignment is to grow pure-breeding plants guaranteed to produce yellow round peas. How would you proceed? One answer would be to plant the peas

Figure 2.16 The law of independent assortment. In a dihybrid cross, each pair of alleles assorts independently during gamete formation. In the gametes, *Y* is equally likely to be found with *R* or *r* (that is, *Y R* = *Y r*); the same is true for *y* (that is, *y R* = *y r*). As a result, all four possible types of gametes (*Y R, Y r, y R,* and *y r*) are produced in equal frequency among a large population.

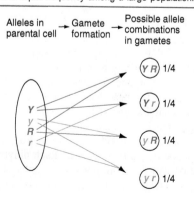

Figure 2.17 Following crosses with branched-line diagrams. A branched-line diagram, which uses a series of columns to track every gene in a cross, provides an organized overview of all possible outcomes. This branched-line diagram of a dihybrid cross generates the same phenotypic ratios as the Punnett square in Fig. 2.15, showing that the two methods are equivalent.

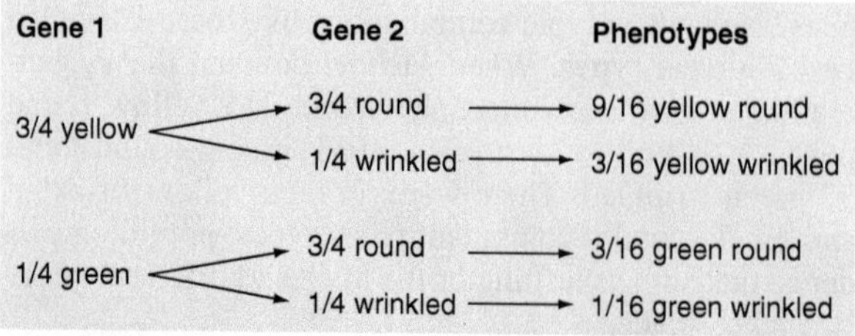

Gene 1	Gene 2	Phenotypes
3/4 yellow	3/4 round	9/16 yellow round
	1/4 wrinkled	3/16 yellow wrinkled
1/4 green	3/4 round	3/16 green round
	1/4 wrinkled	1/16 green wrinkled

Figure 2.18 Testcrosses on dihybrids. Testcrosses involving two pairs of independently assorting alleles yield different, predictable results depending on the tested individual's genotype for the two genes in question.

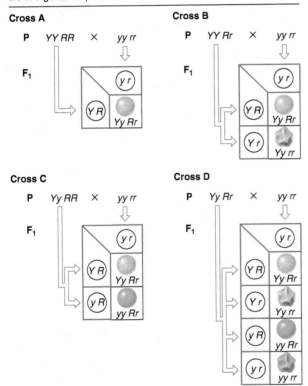

produced from a dihybrid cross that have the desired yellow round phenotype. Only one out of nine of such progeny—those grown from peas with a *YY RR* genotype—will be appropriate for your uses. To find these plants, you could subject each yellow round candidate to a testcross for genotype with a green wrinkled (*yy rr*) plant, as illustrated in **Fig. 2.18.** If the testcross yields all yellow round offspring (testcross A), you can sell your test plant, because you know it is homozygous for both pea color and pea shape. If your testcross yields 1/2 yellow round and 1/2 yellow wrinkled (testcross B), or 1/2 yellow round and 1/2 green round (testcross C), you know that the candidate plant in question is genetically homozygous for one trait and heterozygous for the other and must therefore be discarded. Finally, if the testcross yields 1/4 yellow round, 1/4 yellow wrinkled, 1/4 green round, and 1/4 green wrinkled (testcross D), you know that the plant is a heterozygote for both the pea color and the pea shape genes.

The law of independent assortment states that the alleles of genes for different traits segregate independently of each other during gamete formation.

Geneticists use Mendel's laws to calculate probabilities and make predictions

Mendel performed several sets of dihybrid crosses and also carried out **multihybrid crosses:** matings between the F_1 progeny of true-breeding parents that differed in three or more unrelated traits. In all of these experiments, he observed numbers and ratios very close to what he expected on the basis of his two general biological principles: the alleles of a gene segregate during the formation of egg or pollen, and the alleles of different genes assort independently of each other. Mendel's laws of inheritance, in conjunction with the mathematical rules of probability, provide geneticists with powerful tools for predicting and interpreting the results of genetic crosses. But as with all tools, they have their limitations. We examine here both the power and the limitations of Mendelian analysis.

First, the power: Using simple Mendelian analysis, it is possible to make accurate predictions about the offspring of extremely complex crosses. Suppose you want to predict the occurrence of one specific genotype in a cross involving several independently assorting genes. For example, if hybrids that are heterozygous for four traits are allowed to self-fertilize—*Aa Bb Cc Dd* × *Aa Bb Cc Dd*—what proportion of their progeny will have the genotype *AA bb Cc Dd*? You could set up a Punnett square to answer the question. Because for each trait there are two different alleles, the number of different eggs or sperm is found by raising 2 to the power of the number of differing traits (2^n, where n is the number of traits). By this calculation, each hybrid parent in this cross with 4 traits would make $2^4 = 16$ different kinds of gametes. The Punnett square depicting such a cross would thus contain 256 boxes (16 × 16). This may be fine if you live in a monastery with a bit of time on your hands, but not if you're taking a 1-hour exam. It would be much simpler to analyze the problem by breaking down the multihybrid cross into four independently assorting monohybrid crosses. Remember that the genotypic ratios of each monohybrid cross are 1 homozygote for the dominant allele, to 2 heterozygotes, to 1 homozygote for the recessive allele = 1/4 : 2/4 : 1/4. Thus, you can find the probability of *AA bb Cc Dd* by multiplying the probability of each independent event: *AA* (1/4 of the progeny produced by *Aa* × *Aa*); *bb* (1/4); *Cc* (2/4); *Dd* (2/4):

$$1/4 \times 1/4 \times 2/4 \times 2/4 = 4/256 = 1/64$$

The Punnett square approach would provide the same answer, but it would require much more time.

If instead of a specific genotype, you want to predict the probability of a certain phenotype, you can again use the product rule as long as you know the phenotypic ratios produced by each pair of alleles in the cross. For example, if in the multihybrid cross of *Aa Bb Cc Dd* × *Aa Bb Cc Dd*, you want to know how many offspring will show the dominant A trait (genotype *AA* or *Aa* = 1/4 + 2/4, or 3/4), the recessive b trait (genotype *bb* = 1/4), the dominant C trait (genotype *CC* or *Cc* = 3/4), and the dominant D trait (genotype *DD* or *Dd* = 3/4), you simply multiply

$$3/4 \times 1/4 \times 3/4 \times 3/4 = 27/256$$

In this way, the rules of probability make it possible to predict the outcome of very complex crosses.

You can see from these examples that particular problems in genetics are amenable to particular modes of analysis. As a rule of thumb, Punnett squares are excellent for visualizing simple crosses involving a few genes, but they become unwieldy in the dissection of more complicated matings. Direct calculations of probabilities, such as those in the two preceding problems, are useful when you want to know the chances of one or a few outcomes of complex crosses. If, however, you want to know all the outcomes of a multihybrid cross, a branched-line diagram is the best way to go as it will keep track of the possibilities in an organized fashion.

Now, the limitations of Mendelian analysis: Like Mendel, if you were to breed pea plants or corn or any other organism, you would most likely observe some deviation from the ratios you expected in each generation. What can account for such variation? One element is chance, as witnessed in the common coin toss experiment. With each throw, the probability of the coin coming up heads is equal to the likelihood it will come up tails. But if you toss a coin 10 times, you may get 30% (3) heads and 70% (7) tails, or vice versa. If you toss it 100 times, you are more likely to get a result closer to the expected 50% heads and 50% tails. The larger the number of trials, the lower the probability that chance significantly skews the data. This is one reason Mendel worked with large numbers of pea plants. Mendel's laws, in fact, have great predictive power for populations of organisms, but they do not tell us what will happen in any one individual. With a garden full of self-fertilizing monohybrid pea plants, for example, you can expect that 3/4 of the F_2 progeny will show the dominant phenotype and 1/4 the recessive, but you cannot predict the phenotype of any particular F_2 plant. In Chapter 5, we discuss mathematical methods for assessing whether the chance variation observed in a sample of individuals within a population is compatible with a genetic hypothesis.

> Branched-line diagrams or direct calculations of probabilities are often more efficient methods than Punnett squares for the analysis of genetic crosses involving two or more genes.

Mendel's work was unappreciated before 1900

Mendel's insights into the workings of heredity were a breakthrough of monumental proportions. By counting and analyzing data from hundreds of pea plant crosses, he inferred the existence of genes—independent units that determine the observable patterns of inheritance for particular traits. His work explained the reappearance of "hidden" traits, disproved the idea of blended inheritance, and showed that mother and father make an equal genetic contribution to the next generation. The model of heredity that he formulated was so specific that he could test predictions based on it by observation and experiment.

With the exception of Abbot Napp, none of Mendel's contemporaries appreciated the importance of his research. Mendel did not teach at a prestigious university and was not well known outside Brno. Even in Brno, members of the Natural Science Society were disappointed when he presented "Experiments on Plant Hybrids" to them. They wanted to view and discuss intriguing mutants and lovely flowers, so they did not appreciate his numerical analyses. Mendel, it seems, was far ahead of his time. Sadly, despite written requests from Mendel that others try to replicate his studies, no one repeated his experiments. Several citations of his paper between 1866 and 1900 referred to his expertise as a plant breeder but made no mention of his laws. Moreover, at the time Mendel presented his work, no one had yet seen the structures within cells, the *chromosomes*, that actually carry the genes. That would happen only in the next few decades (as described in Chapter 4). If scientists had been able to see these structures, they might have more readily accepted Mendel's ideas, because the chromosomes are actual physical structures that behave exactly as Mendel predicted.

Mendel's work might have had an important influence on early debates about evolution if it had been more widely appreciated. Charles Darwin (1809–1882), who was unfamiliar with Mendel's work, was plagued in his later years by criticism that his explanations for the persistence of variation in organisms were insufficient. Darwin considered such variation a cornerstone of his theory of evolution, maintaining that natural selection would favor particular variants in a given population in a given environment. If the selected combinations of variant traits were passed on to subsequent generations, this transmission of variation would propel evolution. He could not, however, say how that transmission might occur. Had Darwin been aware of Mendel's ideas, he might not have been backed into such an uncomfortable corner.

TOOLS OF GENETICS

Plants as Living Chemical Factories

For millenia, farmers used selective breeding to obtain crop plants or domestic animals with desired phenotypic characteristics, such as hardiness, improved yields, or better taste. Then, beginning in the early twentieth century, breeders were able to apply Mendel's laws to the inheritance of many traits and to make probability-based predictions about the outcomes of crosses. Even with the application of these basic rules of genetics, however, plant and animal breeders cannot always achieve their goals. Desired phenotypes often result from complex interactions involving many genes whose cumulative effects are difficult to predict. Geneticists are also limited by the availability of useful alleles, because most mutations generating new alleles of genes occur extremely rarely.

Beginning in the 1980s, a revolution in genetics took place that made it possible to overcome these limitations. Scientists developed techniques that allowed them to study and then manipulate DNA, the molecule of which genes are made. You will learn about these methods later in this book. These new tools of genetic engineering allow researchers to remove a specific gene from an organism, change the gene in virtually any way they desire, and even move a gene from one organism to an individual of a different species.

Genetic engineering has two major advantages over selective breeding programs. First, genetic engineering is extremely efficient in that researchers can specifically target a gene they think might have an interesting effect on phenotype. Second, investigators can now use their imaginations to make new alleles of genes (or even new genes!) that could otherwise never be found.

One of the most exciting potential applications of these new tools is the genetic engineering of plants to convert them into factories that inexpensively make useful biomolecules such as pharmaceutical drugs or vaccines. Consider, for example, potato plants containing a foreign gene (a *transgene*) from the hepatitis B virus that specifies a protein found on the viral surface. If the potatoes could use this gene to make a large amount of the viral protein, then people who ate these potatoes might develop an immune response to that protein. The immune response would protect them from infection by hepatitis B; in other words, such potatoes would act as an "edible vaccine"

against the virus. Edible vaccines can be grown in a field rather than made in a laboratory; they do not require refrigeration; and they can be administered orally, instead of being injected by medical personnel. The basic idea of an edible vaccine appears to be feasible: Volunteers eating such genetically engineered potatoes have mounted an immune response against hepatitis B, but many technical difficulties remain. For example, the immune response in different people has been quite variable. In addition, cooking the potatoes destroys the vaccine, and few volunteers have been eager to eat sizeable helpings of raw potatoes.

Plants genetically engineered in other ways have already had a huge economic impact. Crop plants such as corn and cotton have been genetically engineered to express the gene for a protein called Bt. This protein, made naturally by the bacterium *Bacillus thuringiensis,* is lethal to insect larvae that ingest it but not to other animals. If an insect pest such as a corn borer eats part of a corn plant making the Bt protein, the corn borer will die. In this sense, the engineered corn manufactures its own insecticide, reducing the need for costly chemical pesticides that may damage the environment. This approach has already shown itself to be very successful: Approximately one-third of all corn currently grown in the United States contains *Bt* transgenes.

Despite its promise, many people are uncomfortable with the concept of genetically modified (GM) crops. Some critics, for example, have raised concerns about this technology's potential negative effects on human health, agricultural communities (particularly in developing countries), and the environment. Researchers who are developing GM crops respond that prior to the advent of genetic engineering, plant breeders altered crops in astonishing ways simply by mating various plants together, and that the occasional exchange of genetic information between different species has occurred naturally throughout evolution.

In the Genetics and Society box on p. 304 of Chapter 9, we describe one way to evaluate GM crops such as Bt corn. This method balances potential benefits against dangers that are calculated relative to risks associated with traditional agricultural products long accepted by society.

For 34 years, Mendel's laws lay dormant—untested, unconfirmed, and unapplied. Then in 1900, 16 years after Mendel's death, Carl Correns, Hugo de Vries, and Erich von Tschermak independently rediscovered and acknowledged his work (**Fig. 2.19**). The scientific community had finally caught up with Mendel. Within a decade, investigators had coined many of the modern terms we have been using: phenotype, genotype, homozygote, heterozygote, gene, and genetics, the label given

to the twentieth-century science of heredity. Mendel's paper provided the new discipline's foundation. His principles and analytic techniques endure today, guiding geneticists and evolutionary biologists in their studies of genetic variation. The Tools of Genetics box on this page explains how modern-day "genetic engineers" apply Mendel's laws to help them artificially manipulate genes and genomes in new ways not achieved by natural evolution on earth.

Figure 2.19 The science of genetics begins with the rediscovery of Mendel. Working independently near the beginning of the twentieth century, Correns, de Vries, and von Tschermak each came to the same conclusions as those Mendel summarized in his laws.

(a) Gregor Mendel

(b) Carl Correns

(c) Hugo de Vries

(d) Erich von Tschermak

2.3 Mendelian Inheritance in Humans

Although many human traits clearly run in families, most do not show a simple Mendelian pattern of inheritance. Suppose, for example, that you have brown eyes, but both your parents' eyes appear to be blue. Because blue is normally considered recessive to brown, does this mean that you are adopted or that your father isn't really your father? Not necessarily, because eye color is influenced by more than one gene.

Like eye color, most common and obvious human phenotypes arise from the interaction of many genes.

In contrast, single-gene traits in people usually involve an abnormality that is disabling or life-threatening. Examples are the progressive mental retardation and other neurological damage of Huntington disease and the clogged lungs and potential respiratory failure of cystic fibrosis. A defective allele of a single gene gives rise to Huntington disease; defective alleles of a different gene are responsible for cystic fibrosis. There were roughly 4300 such single-gene traits known in humans in 2009, and the number continues to grow as new studies confirm the genetic basis of more traits. **Table 2.1** lists some of the most common single-gene traits in humans.

TABLE 2.1	Some of the Most Common Single-Gene Traits in Humans	
Disease	**Effect**	**Incidence of Disease**
Caused by a Recessive Allele		
Thalassemia (chromosome 16 or 11)	Reduced amounts of hemoglobin; anemia, bone and spleen enlargement	1/10 in parts of Italy
Sickle-cell anemia (chromosome 11)	Abnormal hemoglobin; sickle-shaped red cells, anemia, blocked circulation; increased resistance to malaria	1/625 African-Americans
Cystic fibrosis (chromosome 7)	Defective cell membrane protein; excessive mucus production; digestive and respiratory failure	1/2000 Caucasians
Tay-Sachs disease (chromosome 15)	Missing enzyme; buildup of fatty deposit in brain; buildup disrupts mental development	1/3000 Eastern European Jews
Phenylketonuria (PKU) (chromosome 12)	Missing enzyme; mental deficiency	1/10,000 Caucasians
Caused by a Dominant Allele		
Hypercholesterolemia (chromosome 19)	Missing protein that removes cholesterol from the blood; heart attack by age 50	1/122 French Canadians
Huntington disease (chromosome 4)	Progressive mental and neurological damage; neurologic disorders by ages 40–70	1/25,000 Caucasians

Pedigrees aid the study of hereditary traits in human families

Determining a genetic defect's pattern of transmission is not always an easy task because people make slippery genetic subjects. Their generation time is long, and the families they produce are relatively small, which makes statistical analysis difficult. They do not base their choice of mates on purely genetic considerations. There are thus no pure-breeding lines and no controlled matings. And there is rarely a true F_2 generation (like the one in which Mendel observed the 3:1 ratios from which he derived his rules) because brothers and sisters almost never mate.

Geneticists circumvent these difficulties by working with a large number of families or with several generations of a very large family. This allows them to study the large numbers of genetically related individuals needed to establish the inheritance patterns of specific traits. A family history, known as a **pedigree,** is an orderly diagram of a family's relevant genetic features, extending back to at least both sets of grandparents and preferably through as many more generations as possible. From systematic pedigree analysis in the light of Mendel's laws, geneticists can tell if a trait is determined by alternative alleles of a single gene and whether a single-gene trait is dominant or recessive. Because Mendel's principles are so simple and straightforward, a little logic can go a long way in explaining how traits are inherited in humans.

Figure 2.20 shows how to interpret a family pedigree diagram. Squares (□) represent males, circles (○) are females, diamonds (◇) indicate that the sex is unspecified; family members affected by the trait in question are indicated by a filled-in symbol (for example, ■). A single horizontal line connecting a male and a female (□—○) represents a mating, a double connecting line (□═○) designates a **consanguineous mating,** that is, a mating between relatives, and a horizontal line above a series of symbols (○□○) indicates the children of the same parents (a *sibship*) arranged and numbered from left to right in order of their birth. Roman numerals to the left or right of the diagram indicate the generations.

To reach a conclusion about the mode of inheritance of a family trait, human geneticists must use a pedigree that supplies sufficient information. For example, they could not determine whether the allele causing the disease depicted at the bottom of Fig. 2.20 is dominant or recessive solely on the basis of the simple pedigree shown. The data are consistent with both possibilities. If the trait is dominant, then the father and the affected son are heterozygotes, while the mother and the unaffected son are homozygotes for the recessive normal allele. If instead the trait is recessive, the father and affected son are homozygotes for the recessive disease-causing allele, while the mother and the unaffected son are heterozygotes.

Several kinds of additional information could help resolve this uncertainty. Human geneticists would particularly want to know the frequency at which the trait in question is found in the population from which the family came. If the trait is rare in the population, then the allele giving rise to the trait should also be rare, and the most likely hypothesis would require that the fewest genetically unrelated people carry the allele. Only the father in Fig. 2.20 would need to have a dominant disease-causing allele, but both parents would need to carry a recessive disease-causing allele (the father two copies and the mother one). However, even the information that the trait is rare does not allow us to draw the firm conclusion that it is inherited in a dominant fashion. The pedigree in the figure is so limited that we cannot be sure the two parents are themselves unrelated. As we discuss later in more detail, related parents might have both received a rare recessive allele from their common ancestor. This example illustrates why human geneticists try to collect family histories that cover several generations.

We now look at more extensive pedigrees for the dominant trait of Huntington disease and for the recessive condition of cystic fibrosis. The patterns by which these traits appear in the pedigrees provide important clues that can indicate modes of inheritance and allow geneticists to assign genotypes to family members.

A vertical pattern of inheritance indicates a rare dominant trait

Huntington disease is named for George Huntington, the New York physician who first described its course. This illness usually shows up in middle age and slowly destroys its victims both mentally and physically. Symptoms include intellectual deterioration, severe depression, and jerky, irregular movements, all caused by the progressive death of nerve cells. If one parent develops the symptoms, his or her children have a 50% probability of suffering from the disease, provided they live to adulthood. Because symptoms are not present at birth and manifest themselves only

Figure 2.20 Symbols used in pedigree analysis. In the simple pedigree at the bottom, I.1 is the father, I.2 is the mother, and II.1 and II.2 are their sons. The father and the first son are both affected by the disease trait.

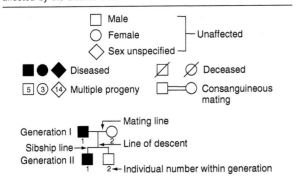

G E N E T I C S   A N D   S O C I E T Y

Developing Guidelines for Genetic Screening

In the early 1970s, the United States launched a national screening program for carriers of sickle-cell anemia, a recessive genetic disease that afflicts roughly 1 in 600 African-Americans. The disease is caused by a particular allele, called $Hb\beta^S$, of the β-globin gene; the dominant normal allele is $Hb\beta^A$. The protein determined by the β-globin gene is one component of the oxygen-carrying hemoglobin molecule. $Hb\beta^S\,Hb\beta^S$ homozygotes have a decrease in oxygen supply, tire easily, and often develop heart failure from stress on the circulatory system.

The national screening program for sickle-cell anemia was based on a simple test of hemoglobin mobility: normal and "sickling" hemoglobins move at different rates in a gel. People who participated in the screening program could use the test results to make informed reproductive decisions. A healthy man, for example, who learned he was a carrier (that is, that he was a $Hb\beta^S\,Hb\beta^A$ heterozygote), would not have to worry about having an affected child if his mate was a noncarrier. If, however, they were both carriers, they could choose either not to conceive or to conceive in spite of the 25% risk of bearing an afflicted child.

In the 1980s, newly developed techniques allowing direct prenatal detection of the fetal genotype provided additional options. Depending on their beliefs, a couple could decide to continue a pregnancy only if the fetus was not a homozygote for the $Hb\beta^S$ allele, or knowing that their child would have sickle-cell anemia, they could learn how to deal with the symptoms of the condition.

The original sickle-cell screening program, based on detection of the abnormal hemoglobin protein, was not an unqualified success, largely because of insufficient educational follow-through. Many who learned they were carriers mistakenly thought they had the disease. Moreover, because employers and insurance companies obtained access to the information, some $Hb\beta^S\,Hb\beta^A$ heterozygotes were denied jobs or health insurance for no acceptable reason. Problems of public relations and education thus made a reliable screening test into a source of dissent and alienation.

Today, at-risk families may be screened for a growing number of genetic disorders, thanks to the ability to evaluate genotypes directly. The need to establish guidelines for genetic screening thus becomes more and more pressing. Several related questions reveal the complexity of the issue.

1. *Why carry out genetic screening at all?* The first reason for screening is to obtain information that will benefit individuals. For example, if you learn at an early age that you have a genetic predisposition to heart disease, you can change your lifestyle if necessary to include more exercise and a low-fat diet, thereby improving your chances of staying healthy. You can also use the results from genetic screening to make informed reproductive decisions that reduce the probability of having children affected by a genetic disease. In Brooklyn, New York, for example, a high incidence of a fatal neurodegenerative syndrome known as Tay-Sachs disease was found among a community of Hasidic Jews of Eastern European descent. In this traditional, Old World community, marriages are arranged by rabbis or matchmakers. With confidential access to test results, a rabbi could counsel against marriages between two carriers.

   The second reason for genetic screening, which often conflicts with the first, is to benefit groups within society. Insurance companies and employers, for example, would like to be able to find out who is at risk for various genetic conditions.

2. *Should screening be required or optional?* This is partly a societal decision because the public treasury bears a large part of the cost of caring for the sufferers of genetic diseases. But it is also a personal decision. For most inherited diseases, no cures currently exist. Because the psychological burden of anticipating a fatal late-onset disease for which there is no treatment can be devastating, some people

---

later in life, Huntington disease is known as a **late-onset** genetic condition.

How would you proceed in assigning genotypes to the individuals in the Huntington disease pedigree depicted in **Fig. 2.21**? First, you would need to find out if the disease-producing allele is dominant or recessive. Several clues suggest that Huntington disease is transmitted by a dominant allele of a single gene. Everyone who develops the disease has at least one parent who shows the trait, and in several generations, approximately half of the offspring are affected. The pattern of affected individuals is thus vertical: If you trace back through the ancestors of any affected individual, you would see at least one affected person in each generation, giving a continuous line of family members with the disease. When a disease is rare in the population as a whole, a vertical pattern is strong evidence that a dominant allele causes the trait; the alternative would require that many unrelated people

Figure 2.21 Huntington disease: A rare dominant trait.
All individuals represented by filled-in symbols are heterozygotes (except I-1, who could have been homozygous for the dominant *HD* disease allele); all individuals represented by open symbols are homozygotes for the recessive *HD⁺* normal allele. Among the 14 children of the consanguineous mating, DNA testing shows that some are *HD HD*, some are *HD HD⁺*, and some are *HD⁺ HD⁺*. The diamond designation masks personal details to protect confidentiality.

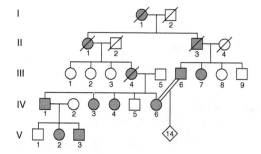

might decide not to be tested. Others may object to testing for religious reasons, or because of confidentiality concerns. On the other hand, timely information about the presence of an abnormal allele that causes a condition for which therapy is available can save lives and reduce suffering. Timely information may also affect childbearing decisions and thereby reduce the incidence of a disease in the population.

3. *If a screening program is established, who should be tested?* The answer depends on what the test is trying to accomplish as well as on its expense. Ultimately, the cost of a procedure must be weighed against the usefulness of the data it provides. In the United States, only one-tenth as many African-Americans as Caucasians are affected by cystic fibrosis, and Asians almost never have the disease. Should all racial groups be tested or only Caucasians? Because of the expense, DNA testing for cystic fibrosis and other relatively rare genetic diseases has not yet been carried out on large populations. Rather it has been reserved for couples or individuals whose family history puts them at risk.

4. *Should private employers and insurance companies be allowed to test their clients and employees?* Some employers advocate genetic screening to reduce the incidence of occupational disease, arguing that they can use data from genetic tests to make sure employees are not assigned to environments that might cause them harm. People with sickle-cell disease, for example, may be at increased risk for a life-threatening episode of severe sickling if exposed to carbon monoxide or trace amounts of cyanide. Critics of this position say that screening violates workers' rights, including the right to privacy, and increases racial and ethnic discrimination in the workplace. Many critics also oppose informing insurance companies of the results of genetic screening, as these companies may deny coverage to people with inherited medical problems or just the possibility of developing such problems. In 2008, President George W. Bush signed into law the Genetic Information Non-discrimination Act, which prohibits insurance companies and employers in the United States from discriminating (through reduced insurance coverage or adverse employment decisions) on the basis of information derived from genetic tests.

A recent high-profile case illustrates some of these issues. The Chicago Bulls, before signing a contract with the basketball player Eddy Curry, wanted him to take a DNA test to find out if he had a genetic predisposition for hypertrophic cardiomyopathy (a potentially fatal condition). The Bulls requested this test because Curry had suffered from episodes of heart arrythmia. Curry refused, citing privacy issues and stating that the test would not be in his or his family's best interest. After a battery of health exams—but not the DNA test—Curry was deemed fit to play, but he was traded to another team and eventually signed a six-year, $56 million contract with the New York Knicks.

5. *Finally, how should people be educated about the meaning of test results?* In one small-community screening program, people identified as carriers of the recessive, life-threatening blood disorder known as β-thalassemia were ostracized; as a result, carriers ended up marrying one another. This only made medical matters worse as it greatly increased the chances that their children would be born with two copies of the defective allele and thus the disease. By contrast, in Ferrara, Italy, where 30 new cases of β-thalassemia had been reported every year, extensive screening was so successfully combined with intensive education that the 1980s passed with no more than a few new cases of the disease.

Given all of these considerations, what kind of guidelines would you like to see established to ensure that genetic screening reaches the right people at the right time, and that information gained from such screening is used for the right purposes?

carry a rare recessive allele. (A recessive trait that is extremely common might also show up in every generation; we examine this possibility in Problem 34 at the end of this chapter.)

In tracking a dominant allele through a pedigree, you can view every mating between an affected and an unaffected partner as analogous to a testcross. If some of the offspring do not have Huntington's, you know the parent showing the trait is a heterozygote. You can check your genotype assignments against the answers in the caption to Fig. 2.21.

No effective treatment yet exists for Huntington disease, and because of its late onset, there was until the 1980s no way for children of a Huntington's parent to know before middle age—usually until well after their own childbearing years—whether they carried the Huntington disease allele (*HD*). Children of Huntington's parents have a 50% probability of inheriting *HD* and, before they are diagnosed, a 25% probability of passing the defective allele on to one of their children. In the mid-1980s, with new knowledge of the gene, molecular geneticists developed a DNA test that determines whether an individual carries the *HD* allele. Because of the lack of effective treatment for the disease, some young adults whose parents died of Huntington's prefer not to be tested so that they will not prematurely learn their own fate. However, other at-risk individuals employ the test for the *HD* allele to guide their decisions about having children. If someone whose parent had Huntington disease does not have *HD*, he or she has no chance of developing the disease or of transmitting it to offspring. If the test shows the presence of *HD*, the at-risk person and his or her partner might chose to conceive a child, obtain a prenatal diagnosis of the fetus, and then, depending on their beliefs, elect an abortion if the fetus is affected. The Genetics and Society box "Developing Guidelines for Genetic Screening" on the two previous pages discusses significant social and ethical issues raised by information obtained from family pedigrees and molecular tests.

> If an individual is affected by a rare dominant trait, the trait should also affect at least one of that person's parents, one of that person's grandparents, and so on.

A horizontal pattern of inheritance indicates a rare recessive trait

Unlike Huntington disease, most confirmed single-gene traits in humans are recessive. This is because, with the exception of late-onset traits, deleterious dominant traits are unlikely to be transmitted to the next generation. For example, if people affected with Huntington disease died by the age of 10, the trait would disappear from the population. In contrast, individuals can carry one allele for a recessive trait without ever being affected by any symptoms. **Figure 2.22** shows three pedigrees for cystic fibrosis (CF), the most commonly inherited recessive disease among Caucasian children in the United States. A double dose of the recessive *CF* allele causes a fatal disorder in which the lungs, pancreas, and other organs become clogged with a thick, viscous mucus that can interfere with breathing and digestion. One in every 2000 white Americans is born with cystic fibrosis, and only 10% of them survive into their 30s.

Figure 2.22 Cystic fibrosis: A recessive condition. In **(a)**, the two affected individuals (VI-4 and VII-1) are *CF CF*; that is, homozygotes for the recessive disease allele. Their unaffected parents must be carriers, so V-1, V-2, VI-1, and VI-2 must all be *CF CF⁺*. Individuals II-2, II-3, III-2, III-4, IV-2, and IV-4 are probably also carriers. We cannot determine which of the founders (I-1 or I-2) was a carrier, so we designate their genotypes as *CF⁺–*. Because the *CF* allele is relatively rare, it is likely that II-1, II-4, III-1, III-3, IV-1, and IV-3 are *CF⁺CF⁺* homozygotes. The genotype of the remaining unaffected people (VI-3, VI-5, and VII-2) is uncertain (*CF⁺–*). **(b** and **c)** These two families demonstrate horizontal patterns of inheritance. Without further information, the unaffected children in each pedigree must be regarded as having a *CF⁺–* genotype.

There are two salient features of the CF pedigrees. First, the family pattern of people showing the trait is often horizontal: The parents, grandparents, and great-grandparents of children born with CF do not themselves manifest the disease, while several brothers and sisters in a single generation may. A horizontal pedigree pattern is a strong indication that the trait is recessive. The unaffected parents are heterozygous **carriers:** They bear a dominant normal allele that masks the effects of the recessive abnormal one. An estimated 12 million Americans are carriers of the recessive *CF* allele. **Table 2.2** summarizes some of the clues found in pedigrees that can help you decide whether a trait is caused by a dominant or a recessive allele.

The second salient feature of the CF pedigrees is that many of the couples who produce afflicted children are blood relatives; that is, their mating is consanguineous (as indicated by the double line). In Fig. 2.22a, the consanguineous mating in generation V is between third cousins. Of course, children with cystic fibrosis can also have unrelated carrier parents, but because relatives share genes, their offspring have a much greater than average chance of receiving two copies of a rare allele. Whether or not they are related, carrier parents are both heterozygotes. Thus among their offspring, the proportion of unaffected to affected children is expected to be 3:1. To look at it another way, the chances are that one out of four children of two heterozygous carriers will be homozygous CF sufferers.

You can gauge your understanding of this inheritance pattern by assigning a genotype to each person in Fig. 2.22 and then checking your answers against the caption. Note that for several individuals, such as the generation I individuals in part (a) of the figure, it is

TABLE 2.2	How to Recognize Dominant and Recessive Traits in Pedigrees

Dominant Traits

1. Affected children always have at least one affected parent.

2. As a result, dominant traits show a *vertical pattern* of inheritance: the trait shows up in every generation.

3. Two affected parents can produce unaffected children, if both parents are heterozygotes.

Recessive Traits

1. Affected individuals can be the children of two unaffected carriers, particularly as a result of consanguineous matings.

2. All the children of two affected parents should be affected.

3. *Rare* recessive traits show a *horizontal pattern* of inheritance: the trait first appears among several members of one generation and is not seen in earlier generations.

4. Recessive traits may show a vertical pattern of inheritance if the trait is extremely common in the population.

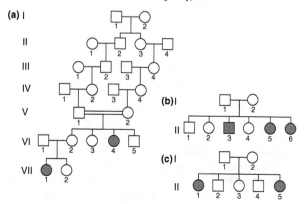

impossible to assign a full genotype. We know that one of these people must be the carrier who supplied the original *CF* allele, but we do not know if it was the male or the female. As with an ambiguous dominant phenotype in peas, the unknown second allele is indicated by a dash.

In Fig. 2.22a, a mating between the unrelated carriers VI-1 and VI-2 produced a child with cystic fibrosis. How likely is such a marriage between unrelated carriers for a recessive genetic condition? The answer depends on the gene in question and the particular population into which a person is born. As Table 2.1 on p. 30 shows, the incidence of genetic diseases (and thus the frequency of their carriers) varies markedly among populations. Such variation reflects the distinct genetic histories of different groups. The area of genetics that analyzes differences among groups of individuals is called *population genetics*, a subject we cover in detail in Chapter 19. Notice that in

Fig. 2.22a, several unrelated, unaffected people, such as II-1 and II-4, married into the family under consideration. Although it is highly probable that these individuals are homozygotes for the normal allele of the gene (CF^+CF^+), there is a small chance (whose magnitude depends on the population) that any one of them could be a carrier of the disease.

Genetic researchers identified the cystic fibrosis gene in 1989, but they are still in the process of developing a gene therapy that would ameliorate the disease's debilitating symptoms (review the Fast Forward box "Genes Encode Proteins" on pp. 20–21).

> If an individual is affected by a rare recessive trait, it is likely that none of that person's ancestors displayed the same trait. In many cases, the affected individual is the product of a consanguineous mating.

Connections

Mendel answered the three basic questions about heredity as follows: To "What is inherited?" he replied, "alleles of genes." To "How is it inherited?" he responded, "according to the principles of segregation and independent assortment." And to "What is the role of chance in heredity?" he said, "for each individual, inheritance is determined by chance, but within a population, this chance operates in a context of strictly defined probabilities."

Within a decade of the 1900 rediscovery of Mendel's work, numerous breeding studies had shown that Mendel's laws hold true not only for seven pairs of antagonistic characteristics in peas, but for an enormous diversity of traits in a wide variety of sexually reproducing plant and animal species, including four-o'clock flowers, beans, corn, wheat, fruit flies, chickens, mice, horses, and humans. Some of these same breeding studies, however, raised a challenge to the new genetics. For certain traits

in certain species, the studies uncovered unanticipated phenotypic ratios, or the results included F_1 and F_2 progeny with novel phenotypes that resembled those of neither pure-breeding parent.

These phenomena could not be explained by Mendel's hypothesis that for each gene, two alternative alleles, one completely dominant, the other recessive, determine a single trait. We now know that most common traits, including skin color, eye color, and height in humans, are determined by interactions between two or more genes. We also know that within a given population, more than two alleles may be present for some of those genes. Chapter 3 shows how the genetic analysis of such complex traits, that is, traits produced by complex interactions between genes and between genes and the environment, extended rather than contradicted Mendel's laws of inheritance.

ESSENTIAL CONCEPTS

1. Discrete units called genes control the appearance of inherited traits.

2. Genes come in alternative forms called alleles that are responsible for the expression of different forms of a trait.

3. Body cells of sexually reproducing organisms carry two copies of each gene. When the two copies of a gene are the same allele, the individual is homozygous for that gene. When the two copies of a gene are different alleles, the individual is heterozygous for that gene.

4. The genotype is a description of the allelic combination of the two copies of a gene present in an individual. The phenotype is the observable form of the trait that the individual expresses.

5. A cross between two parental lines (P) that are pure-breeding for alternative alleles of a gene will produce a first filial (F_1) generation of hybrids that are heterozygous. The phenotype expressed by these hybrids is determined by the dominant allele of the pair, and this phenotype is the same as that expressed by individuals homozygous for the dominant allele. The phenotype associated with the recessive allele will reappear only in the F_2 generation in individuals homozygous for this allele. In crosses between F_1 heterozygotes, the dominant and recessive phenotypes will appear in the F_2 generation in a ratio of 3:1.

6. The two copies of each gene segregate during the formation of gametes. As a result, each egg and each sperm or pollen grain contains only one copy, and thus, only one allele, of each gene. Male and female gametes unite at random at fertilization. Mendel described this process as the law of segregation.

7. The segregation of alleles of any one gene is independent of the segregation of the alleles of other genes. Mendel described this process as the law of independent assortment. According to this law, crosses between *Aa Bb* F_1 dihybrids will generate F_2 progeny with a phenotypic ratio of 9 (*A– B–*) : 3 (*A– bb*) : 3 (*aa B–*) : 1 (*aa bb*).

On Our Website   www.mhhe.com/hartwell4

Annotated Suggested Readings and Links to Other Websites

- More about Mendel and the early history of genetics
- More on the practice of human genetics
- An online database of human genetic diseases (OMIM)

Specialized Topics

- The binomial expansion: application of an advanced statistical method to genetics
- Conditional probabilities (Bayesian analysis): application of another advanced statistical method to genetic analysis

---

Solved Problems

Solving Genetics Problems

The best way to evaluate and increase your understanding of the material in the chapter is to apply your knowledge in solving genetics problems. Genetics word problems are like puzzles. Take them in slowly—don't be overwhelmed by the whole problem. Identify useful facts given in the problem, and use the facts to deduce additional information. Use genetic principles and logic to work toward the solutions. The more problems you do, the easier they become. In doing problems, you will not only solidify your understanding of genetic concepts, but you will also develop basic analytical skills that are applicable in many disciplines.

Solving genetics problems requires more than simply plugging numbers into formulas. Each problem is unique and requires thoughtful evaluation of the information given and the question being asked. The following are general guidelines you can follow in approaching these word problems:

a. Read through the problem once to get some sense of the concepts involved.

b. Go back through the problem, noting all the information supplied to you. For example, genotypes or phenotypes of offspring or parents may be given to you or implied in the problem. Represent the known information in a symbolic format—assign symbols for alleles; use these symbols to indicate genotypes; make a diagram of the crosses including genotypes and phenotypes given or implied. Be sure that you do not assign different letters of the alphabet to two alleles of the same gene, as this can cause confusion. Also, be careful to discriminate clearly between the upper- and lowercases of letters, such as $C(c)$ or $S(s)$.

c. Now, reassess the question and work toward the solution using the information given. Make sure you answer the question being asked!

d. When you finish the problem, check to see that the answer makes sense. You can often check solutions by working backwards; that is, see if you can reconstruct the data from your answer.

e. After you have completed a question and checked your answer, spend a minute to think about which major concepts were involved in the solution. This is a critical step for improving your understanding of genetics.

For each chapter, the logic involved in solving two or three types of problems is described in detail.

I. In cats, white patches are caused by the dominant allele *P,* while *pp* individuals are solid-colored. Short hair is caused by a dominant allele *S,* while *ss* cats have long hair. A long-haired cat with patches whose mother was solid-colored and short-haired mates with a short-haired, solid-colored cat whose mother was long-haired and solid-colored. What kinds of kittens can arise from this mating, and in what proportions?

Answer

The solution to this problem requires an understanding of dominance/recessiveness, gamete formation, and the independent assortment of alleles of two genes in a cross.

First make a representation of the known information:

Mothers:	solid, short-haired	solid, long-haired
Cross:	cat 1	cat 2
	patches, long-haired ×	solid, short-haired

What genotypes can you assign? Any cat showing a recessive phenotype must be homozygous for the recessive allele. Therefore the long-haired cats are *ss;* solid cats are *pp.* Cat 1 is long-haired, so it must be homozygous for the recessive allele (*ss*). This cat has the dominant phenotype of patches and could be either *PP* or *Pp,* but because the mother was *pp* and could only contribute a *p* allele in her gametes, the cat must be *Pp.* Cat 1's full genotype is *Pp ss.* Similarly, cat 2 is solid-colored, so it must be homozygous for the recessive allele (*pp*). Because this cat is short-haired, it could have either the *SS* or *Ss* genotype. Its mother was long-haired (*ss*) and could only contribute an *s* allele in her gamete, so cat 2 must be heterozygous *Ss.* The full genotype is *pp Ss.*

The cross is therefore between a *Pp ss* (cat 1) and a *pp Ss* (cat 2). To determine the types of kittens, first establish the types of gametes that can be produced by each cat and then set up a Punnett square to determine the genotypes of the offspring. Cat 1 (*Pp ss*) produces *Ps* and *ps* gametes in equal proportions. Cat 2 (*pp Ss*) produces *pS* and *ps* gametes in equal proportions. *Four types of kittens can result from this mating with equal probability:* Pp Ss *(patches, short-haired),* Pp ss *(patches, long-haired),* pp Ss *(solid, short-haired),* and pp ss *(solid, long-haired).*

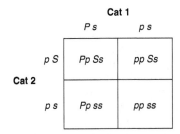

You could also work through this problem using the product rule of probability instead of a Punnett square. The principles are the same: gametes produced in equal amounts by either parent are combined at random.

Cat 1 gamete		Cat 2 gamete		Progeny
1/2 *P s*	×	1/2 *p S*	→	1/4 *Pp Ss* patches, short-haired
1/2 *P s*	×	1/2 *p s*	→	1/4 *Pp ss* patches, long-haired
1/2 *p s*	×	1/2 *p S*	→	1/4 *pp Ss* solid-colored, short-haired
1/2 *p s*	×	1/2 *p s*	→	1/4 *pp ss* solid-colored, long-haired

II. In tomatoes, red fruit is dominant to yellow fruit, and purple stems are dominant to green stems. The progeny from one mating consisted of 305 red fruit, purple stem plants; 328 red fruit, green stem plants; 110 yellow fruit, purple stem plants; and 97 yellow fruit, green stem plants. What were the genotypes of the parents in this cross?

Answer

This problem requires an understanding of independent assortment in a dihybrid cross as well as the ratios predicted from monohybrid crosses.

Designate the alleles:

R = red, *r* = yellow

P = purple stems, *p* = green stems

In genetics problems, the ratios of offspring can indicate the genotype of parents. You will usually need to total the number of progeny and approximate the ratio of offspring in each of the different classes. For this problem, in which the inheritance of two traits is given, consider each trait independently. For red fruit, there are 305 + 328 = 633 red-fruited plants out of a total of 840 plants. This value (633/840) is close to 3/4. About 1/4 of the plants have yellow fruit (110 + 97 = 207/840). From Mendel's work, you know that a 3:1 phenotypic ratio results from crosses between plants that are hybrid (heterozygous) for one gene. Therefore, the genotype for fruit color of each parent must have been *Rr.*

For stem color, 305 + 110 or 415/840 plants had purple stems. About half had purple stems, and the other half (328 + 97) had green stems. A 1:1 phenotypic ratio occurs when a heterozygote is mated to a homozygous recessive (as in a testcross). The parents' genotypes must have been *Pp* and *pp* for stem color.

The complete genotype of the parent plants in this cross was Rr Pp × Rr pp.

III. Tay-Sachs is a recessive lethal disease in which there is neurological deterioration early in life. This disease is rare in the population overall but is found at relatively high frequency in Ashkenazi Jews from Central Europe. A woman whose maternal uncle had the disease is trying to determine the probability that she and her husband could have an affected child. Her father does not come from a high-risk population. Her husband's sister died of the disease at an early age.
   a. Draw the pedigree of the individuals described. Include the genotypes where possible.
   b. Determine the probability that the couple's first child will be affected.

Answer

This problem requires an understanding of dominance/recessiveness and probability. Designate the alleles:

T = normal allele; *t* = Tay-Sachs allele

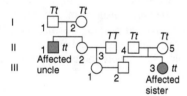

The genotypes of the two affected individuals, the woman's uncle (II-1) and the husband's sister (III-3) are *tt*. Because the uncle was affected, his parents must

have been heterozygous. There was a 1/4 chance that these parents had a homozygous recessive (affected) child, a 2/4 chance that they had a heterozygous child (carrier), and a 1/4 chance they had a homozygous dominant (unaffected) child. However, you have been told that the woman's mother (II-2) is unaffected, so the mother could only have had a heterozygous or a homozygous dominant genotype. Consider the probability that these two genotypes will occur. If you were looking at a Punnett square, there would be only three combinations of alleles possible for the normal mother. Two of these are heterozygous combinations and one is homozygous dominant. There is a 2/3 chance (2 out of the 3 possible cases) that the mother was a carrier. The father was not from a high-risk population, so we can assume that he is homozygous dominant. There is a 2/3 chance that the wife's mother was heterozygous and if so, a 1/2 chance that the wife inherited a recessive allele from her mother. Because both conditions are necessary for inheritance of a recessive allele, the individual probabilities are multiplied, and the probability that the wife (III-1) is heterozygous is 2/3 × 1/2.

The husband (III-2) has a sister who died from the disease; therefore, his parents must have been heterozygous. The probability that he is a carrier is 2/3 (using the same rationale as for II-2). The probability that the man and woman are both carriers is 2/3 × 1/2 × 2/3. Because there is a 1/4 probability that a particular child of two carriers will be affected, *the overall probability that the first child of this couple (III-1 and III-2) will be affected is 2/3 × 1/2 × 2/3 × 1/4 = 4/72, or 1/18.*

Problems

Interactive Web Exercise

The National Center for Biotechnology Information (NCBI) at the National Institutes of Health maintains several databases that are a treasure trove for geneticists. One of these databases is Online Mendelian Inheritance in Man (OMIM), which catalogs information about inherited conditions in humans and the genes involved in these syndromes. Our website at www.mhhe.com/hartwell4 contains a brief exercise to introduce you to the use of this database; once at the website, go to Chapter 2 and click on "Interactive Web Exercise."

Vocabulary

1. For each of the terms in the left column, choose the best matching phrase in the right column.

   a. phenotype
      1. having two identical alleles of a given gene
   b. alleles
      2. the allele expressed in the phenotype of the heterozygote
   c. independent assortment
      3. alternate forms of a gene
   d. gametes
      4. observable characteristic
   e. gene
      5. a cross between individuals both heterozygous for two genes
   f. segregation
      6. alleles of one gene separate into gametes randomly with respect to alleles of other genes
   g. heterozygote
      7. reproductive cells containing only one copy of each gene
   h. dominant
      8. the allele that does not contribute to the phenotype of the heterozygote
   i. F₁
      9. the cross of an individual of ambiguous genotype with a homozygous recessive individual
   j. testcross
      10. an individual with two different alleles of a gene
   k. genotype
      11. the heritable entity that determines a characteristic
   l. recessive
      12. the alleles an individual has
   m. dihybrid cross
      13. the separation of the two alleles of a gene into different gametes
   n. homozygote
      14. offspring of the P generation

Section 2.1

2. During the millennia in which selective breeding was practiced, why did breeders fail to uncover the principle that traits are governed by discrete units of inheritance (that is, by genes)?

3. Describe the characteristics of the garden pea that made it a good organism for Mendel's analysis of the basic principles of inheritance. Evaluate how easy or difficult it would be to make a similar study of inheritance in humans by considering the same attributes you described for the pea.

Section 2.2

4. An albino corn snake is crossed with a normal-colored corn snake. The offspring are all normal-colored. When these first generation progeny snakes are crossed among themselves, they produce 32 normal-colored snakes and 10 albino snakes.
   a. Which of these phenotypes is controlled by the dominant allele?
   b. In these snakes, albino color is determined by a recessive allele *a*, and normal pigmentation is determined by the *A* allele. A normal-colored female snake is involved in a testcross. This cross produces 10 normal-colored and 11 albino offspring. What are the genotypes of the parents and the offspring?

5. Two short-haired cats mate and produce six short-haired and two long-haired kittens. What does this information suggest about how hair length is inherited?

6. Piebald spotting is a condition found in humans in which there are patches of skin that lack pigmentation. The condition results from the inability of pigment-producing cells to migrate properly during development. Two adults with piebald spotting have one child who has this trait and a second child with normal skin pigmentation.
   a. Is the piebald spotting trait dominant or recessive? What information led you to this answer?
   b. What are the genotypes of the parents?

7. As a *Drosophila* research geneticist, you keep stocks of flies of specific genotypes. You have a fly that has normal wings (dominant phenotype). Flies with short wings are homozygous for a recessive allele of the wing-length gene. You need to know if this fly with normal wings is pure-breeding or heterozygous for the wing-length trait. What cross would you do to determine the genotype, and what results would you expect for each possible genotype?

8. A mutant cucumber plant has flowers that fail to open when mature. Crosses can be done with this plant by manually opening and pollinating the flowers with pollen from another plant. When closed × open crosses were done, all the F$_1$ progeny were open. The F$_2$ plants were 145 open and 59 closed. A cross of closed × F$_1$ gave 81 open and 77 closed. How is the closed trait inherited? What evidence led you to your conclusion?

9. In a particular population of mice, certain individuals display a phenotype called "short tail," which is inherited as a dominant trait. Some individuals display a recessive trait called "dilute," which affects coat color. Which of these traits would be easier to eliminate from the population by selective breeding? Why?

10. In humans, a dimple in the chin is a dominant characteristic.
    a. A man who does not have a chin dimple has children with a woman with a chin dimple whose mother lacked the dimple. What proportion of their children would be expected to have a chin dimple?
    b. A man with a chin dimple and a woman who lacks the dimple produce a child who lacks a dimple. What is the man's genotype?
    c. A man with a chin dimple and a nondimpled woman produce eight children, all having the chin dimple. Can you be certain of the man's genotype? Why or why not? What genotype is more likely, and why?

11. Among native Americans, two types of earwax (cerumen) are seen, dry and sticky. A geneticist studied the inheritance of this trait by observing the types of offspring produced by different kinds of matings. He observed the following numbers:

Parents	Number of mating pairs	Offspring Sticky	Offspring Dry
Sticky × sticky	10	32	6
Sticky × dry	8	21	9
Dry × dry	12	0	42

   a. How is earwax type inherited?
   b. Why are there no 3:1 or 1:1 ratios in the data shown in the chart?

12. Imagine you have just purchased a black stallion of unknown genotype. You mate him to a red mare, and she delivers twin foals, one red and one black. Can you tell from these results how color is inherited, assuming that alternative alleles of a single gene are involved? What crosses could you do to work this out?

13. If you roll a die (singular of dice), what is the probability you will roll: (a) a 6? (b) an even number? (c) a number divisible by 3? (d) If you roll a pair of dice, what is the probability that you will roll two 6s? (e) an even number on one and an odd number on the other? (f) matching numbers? (g) two numbers both over 4?

14. In a standard deck of playing cards, there are four suits (red suits = hearts and diamonds, black suits = spades and clubs). Each suit has thirteen cards: Ace (A), 2, 3, 4, 5, 6, 7, 8, 9, 10, and the face cards Jack (J), Queen (Q), and King (K). In a single draw, what is the probability that you will draw a face card? A red card? A red face card?

15. How many genetically different eggs could be formed by women with the following genotypes?
    a. *Aa bb CC DD*
    b. *AA Bb Cc dd*
    c. *Aa Bb cc Dd*
    d. *Aa Bb Cc Dd*

16. What is the probability of producing a child that will phenotypically resemble either one of the two parents in the following four crosses? How many phenotypically different kinds of progeny could potentially result from each of the four crosses?
    a. *Aa Bb Cc Dd* × *aa bb cc dd*
    b. *aa bb cc dd* × *AA BB CC DD*
    c. *Aa Bb Cc Dd* × *Aa Bb Cc Dd*
    d. *aa bb cc dd* × *aa bb cc dd*

17. A mouse sperm of genotype *a B C D E* fertilizes an egg of genotype *a b c D e*. What are all the possibilities for the genotypes of (a) the zygote and (b) a sperm or egg of the baby mouse that develops from this fertilization?

18. Galactosemia is a recessive human disease that is treatable by restricting lactose and glucose in the diet. Susan Smithers and her husband are both heterozygous for the galactosemia gene.
    a. Susan is pregnant with twins. If she has fraternal (nonidentical) twins, what is the probability both of the twins will be girls who have galactosemia?
    b. If the twins are identical, what is the probability that both will be girls and have galactosemia?

    For parts *c–g*, assume that none of the children is a twin.

    c. If Susan and her husband have four children, what is the probability that none of the four will have galactosemia?
    d. If the couple has four children, what is the probability that at least one child will have galactosemia?
    e. If the couple has four children, what is the probability that the first two will have galactosemia and the second two will not?
    f. If the couple has three children, what is the probability that two of the children will have galactosemia and one will not, regardless of order?
    g. If the couple has four children with galactosemia, what is the probability that their next child will have galactosemia?

19. Albinism is a condition in which pigmentation is lacking. In humans, the result is white hair, nonpigmented skin, and pink eyes. The trait in humans is caused by a recessive allele. Two normal parents have an albino child. What are the parents' genotypes? What is the probability that the next child will be albino?

20. A cross between two pea plants, both of which grew from yellow round seeds, gave the following numbers of seeds: 156 yellow round and 54 yellow wrinkled. What are the genotypes of the parent plants? (Yellow and round are dominant traits.)

21. A third-grader decided to breed guinea pigs for her school science project. She went to a pet store and bought a male with smooth black fur and a female with rough white fur. She wanted to study the inheritance of those features and was sorry to see that the first litter of eight contained only rough black animals. To her disappointment, the second litter from those same parents contained seven rough black animals. Soon the first litter had begun to produce F_2 offspring, and they showed a variety of coat types. Before long, the child had 125 F_2 guinea pigs. Eight of them had smooth white coats, 25 had smooth black coats, 23 were rough and white, and 69 were rough and black.
    a. How are the coat color and texture characteristics inherited? What evidence supports your conclusions?
    b. What phenotypes and proportions of offspring should the girl expect if she mates one of the smooth white F_2 females to an F_1 male?

22. The self-fertilization of an F_1 pea plant produced from a parent plant homozygous for yellow and wrinkled seeds and a parent homozygous for green and round seeds resulted in a pod containing seven F_2 peas. (Yellow and round are dominant.) What is the probability that all seven peas in the pod are yellow and round?

23. The achoo syndrome (sneezing in response to bright light) and trembling chin (triggered by anxiety) are both dominant traits in humans.
    a. What is the probability that the first child of parents who are heterozygous for both the achoo gene and trembling chin will have achoo syndrome but lack the trembling chin?
    b. What is the probability that the first child will not have achoo syndrome or trembling chin?

24. A pea plant from a pure-breeding strain that is tall, has green pods, and has purple flowers that are terminal is crossed to a plant from a pure-breeding strain that is dwarf, has yellow pods, and has white flowers that are axial. The F_1 plants are all tall and have purple axial flowers as well as green pods.
    a. What phenotypes do you expect to see in the F_2?
    b. What phenotypes and ratios would you predict in the progeny from crossing an F_1 plant to the dwarf parent?

25. The following chart shows the results of different matings between jimsonweed plants that had either purple or white flowers and spiny or smooth pods. Determine the dominant allele for the two traits and indicate the genotypes of the parents for each of the crosses.

Parents	Offspring			
	Purple Spiny	White Spiny	Purple Smooth	White Smooth
a. purple spiny × purple spiny	94	32	28	11
b. purple spiny × purple smooth	40	0	38	0
c. purple spiny × white spiny	34	30	0	0
d. purple spiny × white spiny	89	92	31	27
e. purple smooth × purple smooth	0	0	36	11
f. white spiny × white spiny	0	45	0	16

26. A pea plant heterozygous for plant height, pod shape, and flower color was selfed. The progeny consisted of 272 tall, inflated pods, purple flowers; 92 tall, inflated, white flowers; 88 tall, flat pods, purple; 93 dwarf, inflated, purple; 35 tall, flat, white; 31 dwarf, inflated, white; 29 dwarf, flat, purple; 11 dwarf, flat, white. Which alleles are dominant in this cross?

27. In the fruit fly *Drosophila melanogaster,* the following genes and mutations are known:

    Wingsize: recessive allele for tiny wings *t;* dominant allele for normal wings *T.*

    Eye shape: recessive allele for narrow eyes *n;* dominant allele for normal (oval) eyes *N.*

    For each of the following crosses, give the genotypes of each of the parents.

	Male		Female		
	Wings	Eyes	Wings	Eyes	Offspring
1	tiny	oval	× tiny	oval	78 tiny wings, oval eyes
					24 tiny wings, narrow eyes
2	normal	narrow	× tiny	oval	45 normal wings, oval eyes
					40 normal wings, narrow eyes
					38 tiny wings, oval eyes
					44 tiny wings, narrow eyes
3	normal	narrow	× normal	oval	35 normal wings, oval eyes
					29 normal wings, narrow eyes
					10 tiny wings, oval eyes
					11 tiny wings, narrow eyes
4	normal	narrow	× normal	oval	62 normal wings, oval eyes
					19 tiny wings, oval eyes

28. Based on the information you discovered in Problem 27 above, answer the following:
    a. A female fruit fly with genotype *Tt nn* is mated to a male of genotype *Tt Nn*. What is the probability that any one of their offspring will have normal phenotypes for both characters?
    b. What phenotypes would you expect among the offspring of this cross? If you obtained 200 progeny, how many of each phenotypic class would you expect?

Section 2.3

29. For each of the following human pedigrees, indicate whether the inheritance pattern is recessive or dominant. What feature(s) of the pedigree did you use to determine the inheritance? Give the genotypes of affected individuals and of individuals who carry the disease allele.

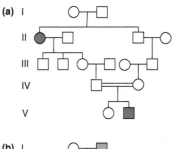

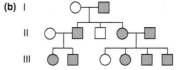

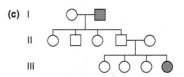

30. Consider the pedigree that follows for cutis laxa, a connective tissue disorder in which the skin hangs in loose folds.
    a. Assuming complete penetrance and that the trait is rare, what is the apparent mode of inheritance?
    b. What is the probability that individual II-2 is a carrier?
    c. What is the probability that individual II-3 is a carrier?
    d. What is the probability that individual III-1 is affected by the disease?

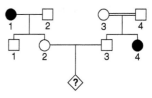

31. A young couple went to see a genetic counselor because each had a sibling affected with cystic fibrosis. (Cystic fibrosis is a recessive disease, and neither member of the couple nor any of their four parents is affected.)
    a. What is the probability that the female of this couple is a carrier?
    b. What are the chances that their child will be affected with cystic fibrosis?
    c. What is the probability that their child will be a carrier of the cystic fibrosis mutation?

32. Huntington disease is a rare fatal, degenerative neurological disease in which individuals start to show symptoms, on average, in their 40s. It is caused by a dominant allele. Joe, a man in his 20s, just learned that his father has Huntington disease.
    a. What is the probability that Joe will also develop the disease?
    b. Joe and his new wife have been eager to start a family. What is the probability that their first child will eventually develop the disease?

33. Is the disease shown in the following pedigree dominant or recessive? Why? Based on this limited pedigree, do you think the disease allele is rare or common in the population? Why?

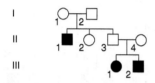

34. Figure 2.21 on p. 32 shows the inheritance of Huntington disease in a family from a small village near Lake Maracaibo in Venezuela. The village was founded by a small number of immigrants, and generations of their descendents have remained concentrated in this isolated location. The allele for Huntington disease has remained unusually prevalent there.
    a. Why could you not conclude definitively that the disease is the result of a dominant or a recessive allele solely by looking at this pedigree?
    b. Is there any information you could glean from the family's history that might imply the disease is due to a dominant rather than a recessive allele?

35. The common grandfather of two first cousins has hereditary hemochromatosis, a recessive condition causing an abnormal buildup of iron in the body. Neither of the cousins has the disease nor do any of their relatives.
    a. If the first cousins mated with each other and had a child, what is the chance that the child would have hemochromatosis? Assume that the unrelated, unaffected parents of the cousins are not carriers.
    b. How would your calculation change if you knew that 1 out of every 10 unaffected people in the population (including the unrelated parents of these cousins) was a carrier for hemochromatosis?

36. People with nail-patella syndrome have poorly developed or absent kneecaps and nails. Individuals with alkaptonuria have arthritis as well as urine that darkens when exposed to air. Both nail-patella syndrome and alkaptonuria are rare phenotypes. In the following pedigree, vertical red lines indicate individuals with nail-patella syndrome, while horizontal green lines denote individuals with alkaptonuria.
    a. What are the most likely modes of inheritance of nail-patella syndrome and alkaptonuria? What genotypes can you ascribe to each of the individuals in the pedigree for both of these phenotypes?
    b. In a mating between IV-2 and IV-5, what is the chance that the child produced would have both nail-patella syndrome and alkaptonuria? Nail-patella syndrome alone? Alkaptonuria alone? Neither defect?

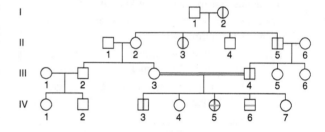

37. Midphalangeal hair (hair on top of the middle segment of the fingers) is a common phenotype caused by a dominant allele *M*. Homozygotes for the recessive allele (*mm*) lack hair on the middle segment of their fingers. Among 1000 families in which both parents had midphalangeal hair, 1853 children showed the trait while 209 children did not. Explain this result.

| PART I | Basic Principles: How Traits Are Transmitted | CHAPTER **3** |

Extensions to Mendel's Laws

In this array of green, brown, and red lentils, some of the seeds have speckled patterns, while others are clear.

Unlike the pea traits that Mendel examined, most human characteristics do not fall neatly into just two opposing phenotypic categories. These complex traits, such as skin and hair color, height, athletic ability and many others, seem to defy Mendelian analysis. The same can be said of traits expressed by many of the world's food crops; their size, shape, succulence, and nutrient content vary over a wide range of values.

Lentils (*Lens culinaris*) provide a graphic illustration of this variation. Lentils, a type of legume, are grown in many parts of the world as a rich source of both protein and carbohydrate. The mature plants set fruit in the form of diminutive pods that contain two small seeds. These seeds can be ground into meal or used in soups, salads, and stews. Lentils come in an intriguing array of colors and patterns (**Fig. 3.1**), and commercial growers always seek to produce combinations to suit the cuisines of different cultures. But crosses between pure-breeding lines of lentils result in some startling surprises. A cross between pure-breeding tan and pure-breeding gray parents, for example, yields an all-brown F_1 generation. When these hybrids self-pollinate, the F_2 plants produce not only tan, gray, and brown lentils, but also green.

Beginning with the first decade of the twentieth century, geneticists subjected many kinds of plants and animals to controlled breeding tests, using Mendel's 3:1 phenotypic ratio as a guideline. If the traits under analysis behaved as predicted by Mendel's laws, then they were assumed to be determined by a single gene with alternative dominant and recessive alleles. Many traits, however, did not behave in this way. For some, no definitive dominance and recessiveness could be observed, or more than two alleles could be found in a particular cross. Other traits turned out to be **multifactorial,** that is, determined by two or more genes, or by the interaction of genes with the environment. The seed coat color of lentils is a multifactorial trait.

Because such traits arise from an intricate network of interactions, they do not necessarily generate straightforward Mendelian phenotypic ratios. Nonetheless, simple extensions of Mendel's hypotheses can clarify the relationship between genotype and phenotype, allowing explanation of the observed deviations without challenging Mendel's basic laws.

CHAPTER OUTLINE

- 3.1 Extensions to Mendel for Single-Gene Inheritance
- 3.2 Extensions to Mendel for Multifactorial Inheritance

Figure 3.1 Some phenotypic variation poses a challenge to Mendelian analysis. Lentils show complex speckling patterns that are controlled by a gene that has more than two alleles.

One general theme stands out from these breeding studies: To make sense of the enormous phenotypic variation of the living world, geneticists usually try to limit the number of variables under investigation at any one time. Mendel did this by using pure-breeding, inbred strains of peas that differed from each other by one or a few traits, so that the action of single genes could be detected. Similarly, twentieth-century geneticists used inbred populations of fruit flies, mice, and other experimental organisms to study specific traits. Of course, geneticists cannot approach people in this way. Human populations are typically far from inbred, and researchers cannot ethically perform breeding experiments on people. As a result, the genetic basis of much human variation remained a mystery. The advent of molecular biology in the 1970s provided new tools that geneticists now use to unravel the genetics of complex human traits as described later in Chapters 9–11.

3.1 Extensions to Mendel for Single-Gene Inheritance

William Bateson, an early interpreter and defender of Mendel, who coined the terms "genetics," "allelomorph" (later shortened to "allele"), "homozygote," and "heterozygote," entreated the audience at a 1908 lecture: "Treasure your exceptions! . . . Keep them always uncovered and in sight. Exceptions are like the rough brickwork of a growing building which tells that there is more to come and shows where the next construction is to be." Consistent exceptions to simple Mendelian ratios revealed unexpected patterns of single-gene inheritance. By distilling the significance of these patterns, Bateson and other early geneticists extended the scope of Mendelian analysis and obtained a deeper understanding of the relationship between genotype and phenotype. We now look at the major extensions to Mendelian analysis elucidated over the last century.

Dominance is not always complete

A consistent working definition of dominance and recessiveness depends on the F_1 hybrids that arise from a mating between two pure-breeding lines. If a hybrid is identical to one parent for the trait under consideration, the allele carried by that parent is deemed dominant to the allele carried by the parent whose trait is not expressed in the hybrid. If, for example, a mating between a pure-breeding white line and a pure-breeding blue line produces F_1 hybrids that are white, the white allele of the gene for color is dominant to the blue allele. If the F_1 hybrids are blue, the blue allele is dominant to the white one (**Fig. 3.2**).

Mendel described and relied on complete dominance in sorting out his ratios and laws, but it is not the only kind of dominance he observed. Figure 3.2 diagrams two situations in which neither allele of a gene is completely dominant. As the figure shows, crosses between true-breeding strains can produce hybrids with phenotypes that differ from both parents. We now explain how these phenotypes arise.

Incomplete dominance: The F_1 hybrid resembles neither pure-breeding parent

A cross between pure late-blooming and pure early-blooming pea plants results in an F_1 generation that blooms in between the two extremes. This is just one of many examples of **incomplete dominance,** in which the hybrid does not resemble either pure-breeding parent. F_1 hybrids that differ from both parents often express a phenotype that is intermediate between those of the pure-breeding parents. Thus, with incomplete dominance, neither parental allele is dominant or recessive to the other; both contribute to the F_1 phenotype. Mendel observed plants that bloomed midway between two extremes when he cultivated various types of pure-breeding peas for his hybridization studies, but he did not pursue the implications. Blooming time was not one of the seven characteristics he chose to analyze in detail, almost certainly because in peas, the time of bloom was not as clear-cut as seed shape or flower color.

Figure 3.2 Different dominance relationships. The phenotype of the heterozygote defines the dominance relationship between two alleles of the same gene (here, A^1 and A^2). Dominance is complete when the hybrid resembles one of the two pure-breeding parents. Dominance is incomplete when the hybrid resembles neither parent; its novel phenotype is usually intermediate. Codominance occurs when the hybrid shows the traits from both pure-breeding parents.

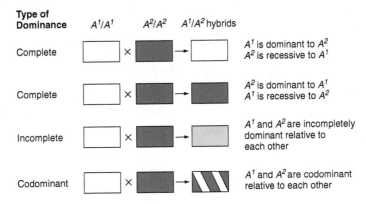

Figure 3.3 Pink flowers are the result of incomplete dominance. (a) Color differences in these snapdragons reflect the activity of one pair of alleles. **(b)** The F_1 hybrids from a cross of pure-breeding red and white strains of snapdragons have pink blossoms. Flower colors in the F_2 appear in the ratio of 1 red : 2 pink : 1 white. This ratio signifies that the alleles of a single gene determine these three colors.

(a) *Antirrhinum majus* **(snapdragons)**

(b) A Punnett square for incomplete dominance

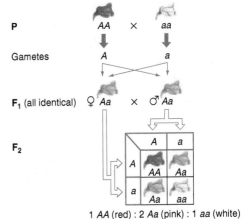

1 *AA* (red) : 2 *Aa* (pink) : 1 *aa* (white)

In many plant species, flower color serves as a striking example of incomplete dominance. With the tubular flowers of four-o'clocks or the floret clusters of snapdragons, for instance, a cross between pure-breeding red-flowered parents and pure-breeding white yields hybrids with pink blossoms, as if a painter had mixed red and white pigments to get pink (**Fig. 3.3a**). If allowed to self-pollinate, the F_1 pink-blooming plants produce F_2 progeny bearing red, pink, and white flowers in a ratio of 1:2:1 (**Fig. 3.3b**). This is the familiar *genotypic* ratio of an ordinary single-gene F_1 self-cross. What is new is that because the heterozygotes look unlike either homozygote, the *phenotypic* ratios are an exact reflection of the genotypic ratios.

The modern biochemical explanation for this type of incomplete dominance is that each allele of the gene under analysis specifies an alternative form of a protein molecule with an enzymatic role in pigment production. If the "white" allele does not give rise to a functional enzyme, no pigment appears. Thus, in snapdragons and four-o'clocks, two "red" alleles per cell produce a double dose of a red-producing enzyme, which generates enough pigment to make the flowers look fully red. In the heterozygote, one copy of the "red" allele per cell results in only enough pigment to make the flowers look pink. In the homozygote for the "white" allele, where there is no functional enzyme and thus no red pigment, the flowers appear white.

Codominance: The F₁ hybrid exhibits traits of both parents

A cross between pure-breeding spotted lentils and pure-breeding dotted lentils produces heterozygotes that are both spotted and dotted (**Fig. 3.4a**). These F₁ hybrids illustrate a second significant departure from complete dominance. They look like both parents, which means that neither the "spotted" nor the "dotted" allele is dominant or recessive to the other. Because both traits show up

Figure 3.4 In codominance, F₁ hybrids display the traits of both parents. (a) A cross between pure-breeding spotted lentils and pure-breeding dotted lentils produces heterozygotes that are both spotted and dotted. Each genotype has its own corresponding phenotype, so the F₂ ratio is 1:2:1. **(b)** The I^A and I^B blood group alleles are codominant because the red blood cells of an $I^A I^B$ heterozygote have both kinds of sugars at their surface.

(a) Codominant lentil coat patterns

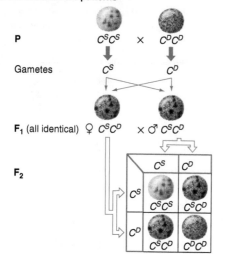

1 $C^S C^S$ (spotted) : 2 $C^S C^D$ (spotted/dotted) : 1 $C^D C^D$ (dotted)

(b) Codominant blood group alleles

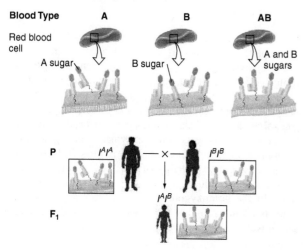

equally in the heterozygote's phenotype, the alleles are termed **codominant.** Self-pollination of the spotted/dotted F₁ generation generates F₂ progeny in the ratio of 1 spotted : 2 spotted/dotted : 1 dotted. The Mendelian 1:2:1 ratio among these F₂ progeny establishes that the spotted and dotted traits are determined by alternative alleles of a single gene. Once again, because the heterozygotes can be distinguished from both homozygotes, the phenotypic and genotypic ratios coincide.

In humans, some of the complex membrane-anchored molecules that distinguish different types of red blood cells exhibit codominance. For example, one gene (I) with alleles I^A and I^B controls the presence of a sugar polymer that protrudes from the red blood cell membrane. The alternative alleles each encode a slightly different form of an enzyme that causes production of a slightly different form of the complex sugar. In heterozygous individuals, the red blood cells carry both the I^A-determined and the I^B-determined sugars on their surface, whereas the cells of homozygous individuals display the products of either I^A or I^B alone (**Fig. 3.4b**). As this example illustrates, when both alleles produce a functional gene product, they are usually codominant for phenotypes analyzed at the molecular level.

Figure 3.2 on p. 45 summarizes the differences between complete dominance, incomplete dominance, and codominance for phenotypes reflected in color variations. Determinations of dominance relationships depend on what phenotype appears in the F₁ generation. With complete dominance, F₁ progeny look like one of the true-breeding parents. Complete dominance, as we saw in Chapter 2, results in a 3:1 ratio of phenotypes in the F₂. With incomplete dominance, hybrids resemble neither of the parents and thus display neither pure-breeding trait. With codominance, the phenotypes of both pure-breeding lines show up simultaneously in the F₁ hybrid. Both incomplete dominance and codominance yield 1:2:1 F₂ ratios.

Mendel's law of segregation still holds

The dominance relations of a gene's alleles do not affect the alleles' transmission. Whether two alternative alleles of a single gene show complete dominance, incomplete dominance, or codominance depends on the kinds of proteins determined by the alleles and the biochemical function of those proteins in the cell. These same phenotypic dominance relations, however, have no bearing on the segregation of the alleles during gamete formation.

As Mendel proposed, cells still carry two copies of each gene, and these copies—a pair of either similar or dissimilar alleles—segregate during gamete formation. Fertilization then restores two alleles to each cell without reference to whether the alleles are the same or different. Variations in dominance relations thus do not detract from Mendel's laws of segregation. Rather, they reflect differences in the way gene products control the production of phenotypes, adding a level of complexity to the tasks of interpreting the visible results of gene transmission and inferring genotype from phenotype.

> In cases of incomplete dominance or codominance, mating of F_1 hybrids produces an F_2 generation with a 1:2:1 phenotypic ratio. The reason is that heterozygotes have a phenotype different from that of either homozygote.

A gene may have more than two alleles

Mendel analyzed "either-or" traits controlled by genes with two alternative alleles, but for many traits, there are more than two alternatives. Here, we look at three such traits: human ABO blood types, lentil seed coat patterns, and human histocompatibility antigens.

ABO blood types

If a person with blood type A mates with a person with blood type B, it is possible in some cases for the couple to have a child that is neither A nor B nor AB, but a fourth blood type called O. The reason? The gene for the ABO blood types has three alleles: I^A, I^B, and i (**Fig. 3.5a**). Allele I^A gives rise to blood type A by specifying an enzyme that adds sugar A, I^B results in blood type B by specifying an enzyme that adds sugar B; i does not produce a functional sugar-adding enzyme. Alleles I^A and I^B are both dominant to i, and blood type O is therefore a result of homozygosity for allele i.

Note in Fig. 3.5a that the A phenotype can arise from two genotypes, $I^A I^A$ or $I^A i$. The same is true for the B blood type, which can be produced by $I^B I^B$ or $I^B i$. But a combination of the two alleles $I^A I^B$ generates blood type AB.

We can draw several conclusions from these observations. First, as already stated, a given gene may have more than two alleles, or **multiple alleles;** in our example, the series of alleles is denoted I^A, I^B, i.

Second, although the ABO blood group gene has three alleles, each person carries only two of the alternatives— $I^A I^A$, $I^B I^B$, $I^A I^B$, $I^A i$, $I^B i$, or ii. There are thus six possible ABO genotypes. Because each individual carries no more than two alleles for each gene, no matter how many alleles there are in a series, Mendel's law of segregation remains intact, because in a sexually reproducing organism, the two alleles of a gene separate during gamete formation.

Third, an allele is not inherently dominant or recessive; its dominance or recessiveness is always relative to a second allele. In other words, dominance relations are unique to a pair of alleles. In our example, I^A is completely dominant to i, but it is codominant with I^B. Given these dominance relations, the six genotypes possible with I^A, I^B, and i generate four different phenotypes:

Figure 3.5 ABO blood types are determined by three alleles of one gene. (a) Six genotypes produce the four blood group phenotypes. **(b)** Blood serum contains antibodies against foreign red blood cell molecules. **(c)** If a recipient's serum has antibodies against the sugars on a donor's red blood cells, the blood types of recipient and donor are incompatible and coagulation of red blood cells will occur during transfusions. In this table, a plus (+) indicates compatibility, and a minus (−) indicates incompatibility. Antibodies in the donor's blood usually do not cause problems because the amount of transfused antibody is small.

(a)

Genotypes	Corresponding Phenotypes: Type(s) of Molecule on Cell
$I^A I^A$ $I^A i$	A
$I^B I^B$ $I^B i$	B
$I^A I^B$	AB
ii	O

(b)

Blood Type	Antibodies in Serum
A	Antibodies against B
B	Antibodies against A
AB	No antibodies against A or B
O	Antibodies against A and B

(c)

Blood Type of Recipient	Donor Blood Type (Red Cells)			
	A	B	AB	O
A	+	−	−	+
B	−	+	−	+
AB	+	+	+	+
O	−	−	−	+

blood groups A, B, AB, and O. With this background, you can understand how a type A and a type B parent could produce a type O child: The parents must be $I^A i$ and $I^B i$ heterozygotes, and the child receives an i allele from each parent.

An understanding of the genetics of the ABO system has had profound medical and legal repercussions. Matching ABO blood types is a prerequisite of successful blood transfusions, because people make antibodies to foreign blood cell molecules. A person whose cells carry only A molecules, for example, produces anti-B antibodies; B people manufacture anti-A antibodies; AB individuals make neither type of antibody; and O individuals produce both anti-A and anti-B antibodies (**Fig. 3.5b**). These antibodies cause coagulation of cells displaying the foreign molecules (**Fig. 3.5c**). As a result, people with blood type O have historically been known as universal donors because their red blood cells carry no surface molecules that will stimulate an antibody attack. In contrast, people with blood type AB are considered universal recipients, because they make neither anti-A nor anti-B antibodies, which, if present, would target the surface molecules of incoming blood cells.

Information about ABO blood types can also be used as legal evidence in court, to exclude the possibility of paternity or criminal guilt. In a paternity suit, for example, if the mother is type A and her child is type B, logic dictates that the I^B allele must have come from the father, whose genotype may be $I^A I^B$, $I^B I^B$, or $I^B i$. In 1944, the actress Joan Barry (phenotype A) sued Charlie Chaplin (phenotype O) for support of a child (phenotype B) whom she claimed he fathered. The scientific evidence indicated that Chaplin could not have been the father, since he was apparently ii and did not carry an I^B allele. This evidence was admissible in court, but the jury was not convinced, and Chaplin had to pay. Today, the molecular genotyping of DNA (*DNA fingerprinting,* see Chapter 11) provides a powerful tool to help establish paternity, guilt, or innocence, but juries still often find it difficult to evaluate such evidence.

Lentil seed coat patterns

Lentils offer another example of multiple alleles. A gene for seed coat pattern has five alleles: spotted, dotted, clear (pattern absent), and two types of marbled. Reciprocal crosses between pairs of pure-breeding lines of all patterns (marbled-1 × marbled-2, marbled-1 × spotted, marbled-2 × spotted, and so forth) have clarified the dominance relations of all possible pairs of the alleles to reveal a **dominance series** in which alleles are listed in order from most dominant to most recessive. For example, crosses of marbled-1 with marbled-2, or of marbled-1 with spotted or dotted or clear, produce the marbled-1 phenotype in the F_1 generation and a ratio of three marbled-1 to one of any of the other phenotypes in the F_2. This indicates that the marbled-1 allele is completely dominant to each of the other four alleles.

Analogous crosses with the remaining four phenotypes reveal the dominance series shown in **Fig. 3.6.** Recall that dominance relations are meaningful only when comparing two alleles; an allele, such as marbled-2, can be recessive to a second allele (marbled-1) but dominant to a third and fourth (dotted and clear). The fact that all tested pairings of lentil seed coat pattern alleles yielded a 3:1 ratio in the F_2 generation (except for spotted × dotted, which yielded the 1:2:1 phenotypic ratio reflective of codominance) indicates that these lentil seed coat patterns are determined by different alleles of the same gene.

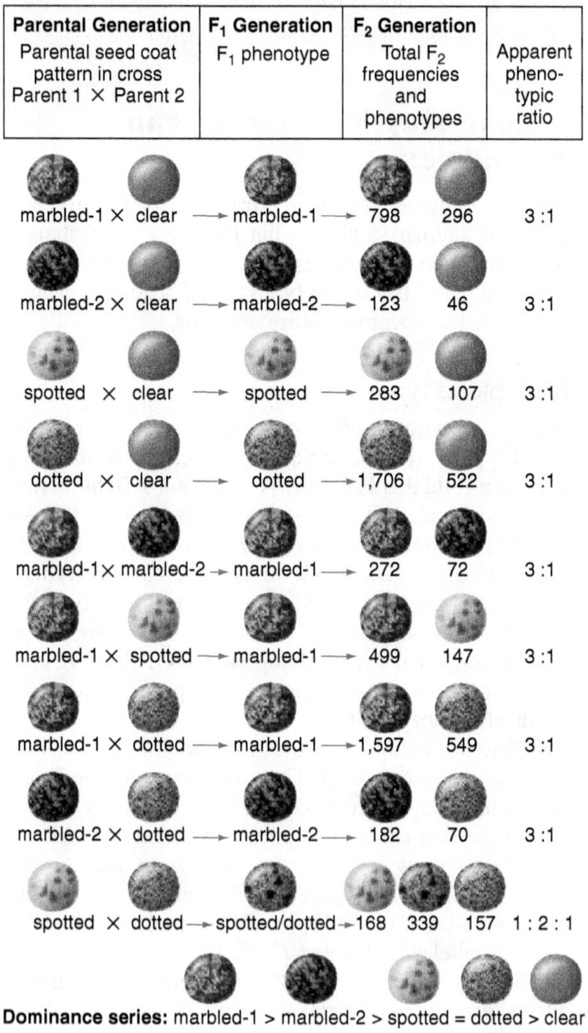

Histocompatibility in humans

In some multiple allelic series, each allele is codominant with every other allele, and every distinct genotype therefore produces a distinct phenotype. This happens particularly with traits defined at the molecular level. An extreme example is the group of three major genes that encode a

Figure 3.6 How to establish the dominance relations between multiple alleles. Pure-breeding lentils with different seed coat patterns are crossed in pairs, and the F_1 progeny are self-fertilized to produce an F_2 generation. The 3:1 or 1:2:1 F_2 monohybrid ratios from all of these crosses indicate that different alleles of a single gene determine all the traits. The phenotypes of the F_1 hybrids establish the dominance relationships (*bottom*). Spotted and dotted alleles are codominant, but each is recessive to the marbled alleles and is dominant to clear.

Parental Generation	F₁ Generation	F₂ Generation	
Parental seed coat pattern in cross Parent 1 × Parent 2	F₁ phenotype	Total F₂ frequencies and phenotypes	Apparent phenotypic ratio
marbled-1 × clear →	marbled-1 →	798 296	3:1
marbled-2 × clear →	marbled-2 →	123 46	3:1
spotted × clear →	spotted →	283 107	3:1
dotted × clear →	dotted →	1,706 522	3:1
marbled-1 × marbled-2 →	marbled-1 →	272 72	3:1
marbled-1 × spotted →	marbled-1 →	499 147	3:1
marbled-1 × dotted →	marbled-1 →	1,597 549	3:1
marbled-2 × dotted →	marbled-2 →	182 70	3:1
spotted × dotted →	spotted/dotted →	168 339 157	1:2:1

Dominance series: marbled-1 > marbled-2 > spotted = dotted > clear

family of related cell surface molecules in humans and other mammals known as **histocompatibility antigens.** Carried by all of the body's cells except the red blood cells and sperm, histocompatibility antigens play a critical role in facilitating a proper immune response that destroys intruders (viral or bacterial, for example) while leaving the body's own tissues intact. Because each of the three major histocompatibility genes (called *HLA-A, HLA-B,* and *HLA-C* in humans) has between 20 and 100 alleles, the number of possible allelic combinations creates a powerful potential for the phenotypic variation of cell surface molecules. Other than identical (that is, *monozygotic*) twins, no two people are likely to carry the same array of cell surface molecules.

> Within a population, a gene may have multiple alleles, but any one individual can have at most two of these alleles. Considered in pairs, the alleles can exhibit a variety of dominance relationships.

Mutations are the source of new alleles

How do the multiple alleles of an allelic series arise? The answer is that chance alterations of the genetic material, known as **mutations,** arise spontaneously in nature. Once they occur in gamete-producing cells, they are faithfully inherited. Mutations that have phenotypic consequences can be counted, and such counting reveals that they occur at low frequency. The frequency of gametes carrying a mutation in a particular gene varies anywhere from 1 in 10,000 to 1 in 1,000,000. This range exists because different genes have different mutation rates.

Mutations make it possible to follow gene transmission. If, for example, a mutation specifies an alteration in an enzyme that normally produces yellow so that it now makes green, the new phenotype (green) will make it possible to recognize the new mutant allele. In fact, it takes at least two alleles, that is, some form of variation, to "see" the transmission of a gene. Thus, in segregation studies, geneticists can analyze only genes with variants; they have no way of following a gene that comes in only one form. If all peas were yellow, Mendel would not have been able to decipher the transmission patterns of the gene for the seed color trait. We discuss mutations in greater detail in Chapter 7.

Allele frequencies and monomorphic genes

Because each organism carries two copies of every gene, you can calculate the number of copies of a gene in a given population by multiplying the number of individuals by 2. Each allele of the gene accounts for a percentage of the total number of gene copies, and that percentage is known as the **allele frequency.** The most common allele in a population is usually called the **wild-type allele,** often designated by a superscript plus sign ($^+$). A rare allele in the same population is considered a **mutant allele.** (A mutation is a newly arisen mutant allele.)

In mice, for example, one of the main genes determining coat color is the *agouti* gene. The wild-type allele (*A*) produces fur with each hair having yellow and black bands that blend together from a distance to give the appearance of dark gray, or agouti. Researchers have identified in the laboratory 14 distinguishable mutant alleles for the *agouti* gene. One of these (*a^t*) is recessive

Figure 3.7 The mouse *agouti* gene: One wild-type allele, many mutant alleles. (a) Black-backed, yellow-bellied (*top left*); black (*top right*); and agouti (*bottom*) mice. **(b)** Genotypes and corresponding phenotypes for alleles of the *agouti* gene. **(c)** Crosses between pure-breeding lines reveal a dominance series. Interbreeding of the F₁ hybrids (not shown) yields 3:1 phenotypic ratios of F₂ progeny, indicating that *A, a^t*, and *a* are in fact alleles of one gene.

(a) *Mus musculus* (house mouse) coat colors

(b) Alleles of the *agouti* gene

Genotype	Phenotype
A–	agouti
a^t a^t	black/yellow
aa	black
a^t a	black/yellow

(c) Evidence for a dominance series

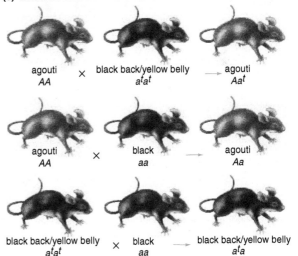

| agouti *AA* × black back/yellow belly *a^t a^t* → agouti *Aa^t* |
| agouti *AA* × black *aa* → agouti *Aa* |
| black back/yellow belly *a^t a^t* × black *aa* → black back/yellow belly *a^t a* |

Dominance series: *A > a^t > a*

to the wild type and gives rise to a black coat on the back and a yellow coat on the belly; another (*a*) is also recessive to *A* and produces a pure black coat (**Fig. 3.7**). In nature, wild-type agoutis (*AA*) survive to reproduce, while very few black-backed or pure black mutants (*a^t a^t* or *aa*) do so because their dark coat makes it hard for them to evade the eyes of predators. As a result, *A* is present at a frequency of much more than 99% and is thus the only wild-type allele in mice for the *agouti* gene. A gene with only one common, wild-type allele is **monomorphic.**

Allele frequencies and polymorphic genes

In contrast, some genes have more than one common allele, which makes them **polymorphic.** For example, in the ABO blood type system, all three alleles—I^A, I^B, and i—have appreciable frequencies in most human populations. Although all three of these alleles can be considered to be wild-type, geneticists instead usually refer to the high-frequency alleles of a polymorphic gene as *common variants.*

A rather unusual mechanism leading to the proliferation of many different alleles occurs in the mating systems of wild species of tomatoes and petunias. Evolution of an "incompatibility" gene whose alleles determine acceptance or rejection of pollen has allowed these plants to prevent self-fertilization and promote outbreeding. In this form of incompatibility, a plant cannot accept pollen carrying an allele identical to either of its own incompatibility alleles. If, for example, pollen carrying allele S_1 of the incompatibility gene lands on the stigma of a plant that also carries S_1 as one of its incompatibility alleles, a pollen tube will not grow (**Fig. 3.8**). Every plant is thus heterozygous for the incompatibility

Figure 3.8 Plant incompatibility systems prevent self-fertilization and thus promote outbreeding and allele proliferation. A pollen grain carrying a self-incompatibility allele that is identical to either of the two alleles carried by a potential female parent cannot grow a pollen tube; as a result, fertilization cannot take place.

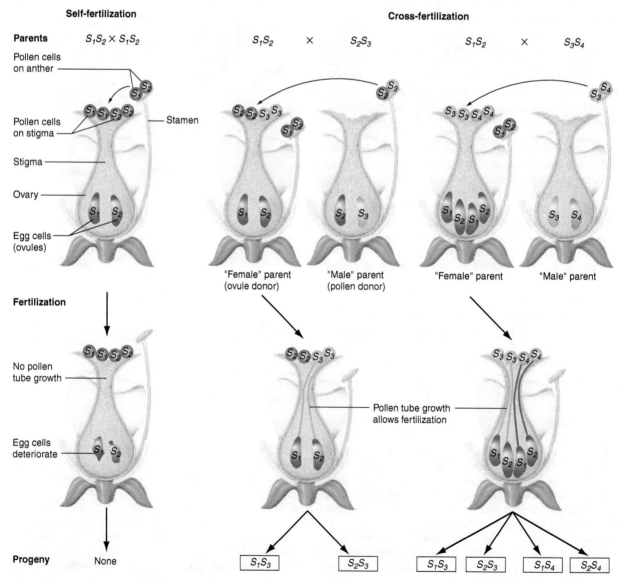

gene, since the pollen grain and female reproductive organs needed to form the plant cannot share alleles. Plants carrying rare alleles (that have arisen relatively recently by mutation and are not present in many other plants) will be able to send pollen to and receive pollen from most of the other plants in their population. In some species with this type of mating system, geneticists have detected as many as 92 alleles for the incompatibility gene. Because the incompatibility mechanism encourages the proliferation of new mutants, this is an extreme case of multiple alleles, not seen with most genes.

> Genes and alleles can be classified according to allele frequencies. A monomorphic gene has a single common allele referred to as the wild-type allele; a polymorphic gene has several common variants. Rare or newly arisen alleles of any gene are mutant alleles.

One gene may contribute to several characteristics

Mendel derived his laws from studies in which one gene determined one trait; but, always the careful observer, he himself noted possible departures. In listing the traits selected for his pea experiments, he remarked that specific seed coat colors are always associated with specific flower colors.

The phenomenon of a single gene determining a number of distinct and seemingly unrelated characteristics is known as **pleiotropy.** Because geneticists now know that each gene determines a specific protein and that each protein can have a cascade of effects on an organism, we can understand how pleiotropy arises. Among the aboriginal Maori people of New Zealand, for example, many of the men develop respiratory problems and are also sterile. Researchers have found that the fault lies with the recessive allele of a single gene. The gene's normal dominant allele specifies a protein necessary for the action of cilia and flagella, both of which are hairlike structures extending from the surfaces of some cells. In men who are homozygous for the recessive allele, cilia that normally clear the airways fail to work effectively, and flagella that normally propel sperm fail to do their job. Thus, one gene determines a protein that indirectly affects both respiratory function and reproduction. Because most proteins act in a variety of tissues and influence multiple biochemical processes, mutations in almost any gene may have pleiotropic effects.

Recessive lethal alleles

A significant variation of pleiotropy occurs in alleles that not only produce a visible phenotype but also affect viability. Mendel assumed that all genotypes are equally viable—that is, they have the same likelihood of survival. If this were not true and a large percentage of, say, homozygotes for a particular allele died before germination or birth, you would not be able to count them after birth, and this would alter the 1:2:1 genotypic ratios and the 3:1 phenotypic ratios predicted for the F_2 generation.

Consider the inheritance of coat color in mice. As mentioned earlier, wild-type agouti (*AA*) animals have black and yellow striped hairs that appear dark gray to the eye. One of the 14 mutant alleles of the *agouti* gene gives rise to mice with a much lighter, almost yellow color. When inbred *AA* mice are mated to yellow mice, one always observes a 1:1 ratio of the two coat colors among the offspring (**Fig. 3.9a**). From this result, we can draw three conclusions: (1) All yellow mice must carry the *agouti* allele even though they do not express it; (2) yellow is therefore dominant to agouti; and (3) all yellow mice are heterozygotes.

Note again that dominance and recessiveness are defined in the context of each pair of alleles. Even though, as previously mentioned, agouti (*A*) is dominant to the a^t and *a* mutations for black coat color, it can still be recessive to the yellow coat color allele. If we designate the allele for yellow as A^y, the yellow mice in the preceding cross are A^yA heterozygotes, and the agoutis, *AA* homozygotes.

Figure 3.9 A^y: **A recessive lethal allele that also produces a dominant coat color phenotype. (a)** A cross between inbred agouti mice and yellow mice yields a 1:1 ratio of yellow to agouti progeny. The yellow mice are therefore A^yA heterozygotes, and for the trait of coat color, A^y (for yellow) is dominant to *A* (for agouti). **(b)** Yellow mice do not breed true. In a yellow × yellow cross, the 2:1 ratio of yellow to agouti progeny indicates that the A^y allele is a recessive lethal.

(a) All yellow mice are heterozygotes.

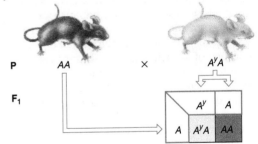

(b) Two copies of A^y cause lethality.

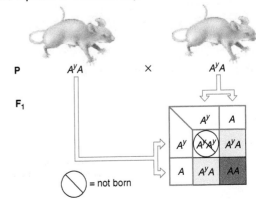

⊘ = not born

So far, no surprises. But a mating of yellow to yellow produces a skewed phenotypic ratio of two yellow mice to one agouti (**Fig. 3.9b**). Among these progeny, matings between agouti mice show that the agoutis are all pure-breeding and therefore AA homozygotes as expected. There are, however, no pure-breeding yellow mice among the progeny. When the yellow mice are mated to each other, they unfailingly produce 2/3 yellow and 1/3 agouti offspring, a ratio of 2:1, so they must therefore be heterozygotes. In short, one can never obtain pure-breeding yellow mice.

How can we explain this phenomenon? The Punnett square in Fig. 3.9b suggests an answer. Two copies of the A^y allele prove fatal to the animal carrying them, whereas one copy of the allele produces a yellow coat. This means that the A^y allele affects two different traits: It is dominant to A in the determination of coat color, but it is recessive to A in the production of lethality. An allele, such as A^y, that negatively affects the survival of a homozygote is known as a **recessive lethal allele.** Note that the same two alleles (A^y and A) can display different dominance relationships when looked at from the point of view of different phenotypes; we return later to this important point.

Because the A^y allele is dominant for yellow coat color, it is easy to detect carriers of this particular recessive lethal allele in mice, but such is not the case for the vast majority of recessive lethal mutations that do not simultaneously show a visible dominant phenotype for some other trait. Lethal mutations can arise in many different genes, and as a result, most animals, including humans, carry some recessive lethal mutations. Such mutations usually remain "silent," except in rare cases of homozygosity, which in people are often caused by consanguineous matings (that is, matings between close relatives). If a mutation produces an allele that prevents production of a crucial molecule, homozygous individuals would not make any of the vital molecule and would not survive. Heterozygotes, by contrast, with only one copy of the deleterious mutation and one wild-type allele, would be able to produce 50% of the wild-type amount of the normal molecule; this is usually sufficient to sustain normal cellular processes such that life goes on.

Delayed lethality

In the preceding discussion, we have described recessive alleles that result in the death of homozygotes prenatally, *in utero*. With some mutations, however, homozygotes may survive beyond birth and die later from the deleterious consequences of the genetic defect. An example is seen in human infants with Tay-Sachs disease. The seemingly normal newborns remain healthy for five to six months but then develop blindness, paralysis, mental retardation, and other symptoms of a deteriorating nervous system; the disease usually proves fatal by the age of six. Tay-Sachs disease results from the absence of an active lysosomal enzyme called hexosaminidase A, leading to the accumulation of a toxic waste product inside nerve cells. The approximate incidence of Tay-Sachs among live births is 1/35,000 worldwide, but it is 1/3000 among Jewish people of Eastern European descent. Reliable tests that detect carriers, in combination with genetic counseling and educational programs, have all but eliminated the disease in the United States.

Recessive alleles causing prenatal or early childhood lethality can only be passed on to subsequent generations by heterozygous carriers, because affected homozygotes die before they can mate. However, for late-onset diseases causing death in adults, homozygous patients can pass on the lethal allele before they become debilitated. An example is provided by the degenerative disease Friedreich ataxia: Some homozygotes first display symptoms of ataxia (loss of muscle coordination) at age 30–35 and die about five years later from heart failure.

Dominant alleles causing late-onset lethality can also be transmitted to subsequent generations; Figure 2.21 on p. 32 illustrates this for the inheritance of Huntington disease. By contrast, if the lethality caused by a dominant allele occurs instead during fetal development or early childhood, the allele will not be passed on, so all dominant early lethal mutant alleles must be new mutations.

Table 3.1 summarizes Mendel's basic assumptions about dominance, the number and viability of one gene's alleles, and the effects of each gene on phenotype, and then

TABLE 3.1	For Traits Determined by One Gene: Extensions to Mendel's Analysis Explain Alterations of the 3:1 Monohybrid Ratio		
What Mendel Described	**Extension**	**Extension's Effect on Heterozygous Phenotype**	**Extension's Effect on Ratios Resulting from an $F_1 \times F_1$ Cross**
Complete dominance	Incomplete dominance Codominance	Unlike either homozygote	Phenotypes coincide with genotypes in a ratio of 1:2:1
Two alleles	Multiple alleles	Multiplicity of phenotypes	A series of 3:1 ratios
All alleles are equally viable	Recessive lethal alleles	No effect	2:1 instead of 3:1
One gene determines one trait	Pleiotropy: one gene influences several traits	Several traits affected in different ways, depending on dominance relations	Different ratios, depending on dominance relations for each affected trait

compares these assumptions with the extensions contributed by his twentieth-century successors. Through carefully controlled monohybrid crosses, these later geneticists analyzed the transmission patterns of the alleles of single genes, challenging and then confirming the law of segregation.

> A mutant allele can disrupt many biochemical processes; as a result, mutations often have pleiotropic effects that can include lethality at various times in an organism's life cycle.

A comprehensive example: Sickle-cell disease illustrates many extensions to Mendel's analysis

Sickle-cell disease is the result of a faulty hemoglobin molecule. Hemoglobin is composed of two types of polypeptide chains, alpha (α) globin and beta (β) globin, each specified by a different gene: $Hb\alpha$ for α globin and $Hb\beta$ for β globin. Normal red blood cells are packed full of millions upon millions of hemoglobin molecules, each of which picks up oxygen in the lungs and transports it to all the body's tissues.

Multiple alleles

The β-globin gene has a normal wild-type allele ($Hb\beta^A$) that gives rise to fully functional β globin, as well as close to 400 mutant alleles that have been identified so far. Some of these mutant alleles result in the production of hemoglobin that carries oxygen only inefficiently. Other mutant alleles prevent the production of β globin, causing a hemolytic (blood-destroying) disease called β-thalassemia. Here, we discuss the most common mutant allele of the β-globin gene, $Hb\beta^S$, which specifies an abnormal polypeptide that causes sickling of red blood cells (**Fig. 3.10a**).

Pleiotropy

The $Hb\beta^S$ allele of the β-globin gene affects more than one trait (**Fig. 3.10b**). Hemoglobin molecules in the red blood cells of homozygous $Hb\beta^S$ $Hb\beta^S$ individuals undergo an aberrant transformation after releasing their oxygen. Instead of remaining soluble in the cytoplasm, they aggregate to form long fibers that deform the red blood cell from a normal biconcave disk to a sickle shape (see Fig. 3.10a). The deformed cells clog the small blood vessels, reducing oxygen flow to the tissues and giving rise to muscle cramps, shortness of breath, and fatigue. The sickled cells are also very fragile and easily broken.

Figure 3.10 Pleiotropy of sickle-cell anemia: Dominance relations vary with the phenotype under consideration. **(a)** A normal red blood cell (*top*) is easy to distinguish from the sickled cell in the scanning electron micrograph at the *bottom*. **(b)** Different levels of analysis identify various phenotypes. Dominance relationships between the $Hb\beta^S$ and $Hb\beta^A$ alleles of the $Hb\beta$ gene vary with the phenotype and sometimes even change with the environment.

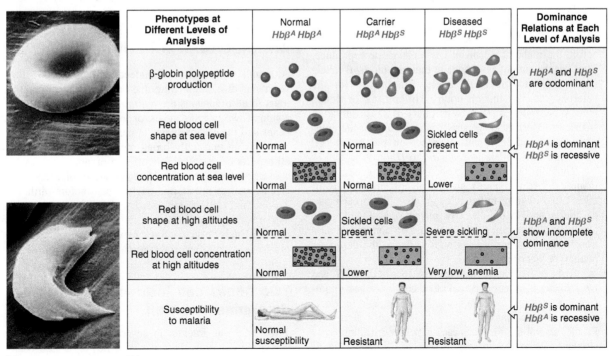

Phenotypes at Different Levels of Analysis	Normal $Hb\beta^A Hb\beta^A$	Carrier $Hb\beta^A Hb\beta^S$	Diseased $Hb\beta^S Hb\beta^S$	Dominance Relations at Each Level of Analysis
β-globin polypeptide production				$Hb\beta^A$ and $Hb\beta^S$ are codominant
Red blood cell shape at sea level	Normal	Normal	Sickled cells present	$Hb\beta^A$ is dominant $Hb\beta^S$ is recessive
Red blood cell concentration at sea level	Normal	Normal	Lower	
Red blood cell shape at high altitudes	Normal	Sickled cells present	Severe sickling	$Hb\beta^A$ and $Hb\beta^S$ show incomplete dominance
Red blood cell concentration at high altitudes	Normal	Lower	Very low, anemia	
Susceptibility to malaria	Normal susceptibility	Resistant	Resistant	$Hb\beta^S$ is dominant $Hb\beta^A$ is recessive

(a) (b)

Consumption of fragmented cells by phagocytic white blood cells leads to a low red blood cell count, a condition called anemia.

On the positive side, $Hb\beta^S Hb\beta^S$ homozygotes are resistant to malaria, because the organism that causes the disease, *Plasmodium falciparum*, can multiply rapidly in normal red blood cells, but cannot do so in cells that sickle. Infection by *P. falciparum* causes sickle-shaped cells to break down before the malaria organism has a chance to multiply.

Recessive lethality

People who are homozygous for the recessive $Hb\beta^S$ allele often develop heart failure because of stress on the circulatory system. Many sickle-cell sufferers die in childhood, adolescence, or early adulthood.

Different dominance relations

Comparisons of heterozygous carriers of the sickle-cell allele—individuals whose cells contain one $Hb\beta^A$ and one $Hb\beta^S$ allele—with homozygous $Hb\beta^A Hb\beta^A$ (normal) and homozygous $Hb\beta^S Hb\beta^S$ (diseased) individuals make it possible to distinguish different dominance relations for different phenotypic aspects of sickle-cell anemia (Fig. 3.10b).

At the molecular level—the production of β globin—both alleles are expressed such that $Hb\beta^A$ and $Hb\beta^S$ are *codominant*. At the cellular level, in their effect on red blood cell shape, the $Hb\beta^A$ and $Hb\beta^S$ alleles show *incomplete dominance*. Although under normal oxygen conditions, the great majority of a heterozygote's red blood cells have the normal biconcave shape, when oxygen levels drop, sickling occurs in some cells. All $Hb\beta^A Hb\beta^S$ cells, however, are resistant to malaria because like the $Hb\beta^S Hb\beta^S$ cells described previously, they break down before the malarial organism has a chance to reproduce. Thus for the trait of resistance to malaria, the $Hb\beta^S$ allele is *dominant* to the $Hb\beta^A$ allele. But luckily for the heterozygote, for the phenotypes of anemia or death, $Hb\beta^S$ is *recessive* to $Hb\beta^A$. A corollary of this observation is that in its effect on general health under normal environmental conditions and its effect on red blood cell count, the $Hb\beta^A$ allele is *dominant* to $Hb\beta^S$.

Thus, for the β-globin gene, as for other genes, dominance and recessiveness are not an inherent quality of alleles in isolation; rather, they are specific to each pair of alleles and to the level of physiology at which the phenotype is examined. When discussing dominance relationships, it is therefore essential to define the particular phenotype under analysis.

In the 1940s, the incomplete dominance of the $Hb\beta^A$ and $Hb\beta^S$ alleles in determining red blood cell shape had significant repercussions for certain soldiers who fought in World War II. Aboard transport planes flying troops across the Pacific, several heterozygous carriers suffered sickling crises similar to those usually seen in $Hb\beta^S Hb\beta^S$ homozygotes. The reason was that heterozygous red blood cells of a carrier produce both normal and abnormal hemoglobin molecules. At sea level, these molecules together deliver sufficient oxygen, although less than the normal amount, to the body's tissues, but with a decrease in the amount of oxygen available at the high-flying altitudes, the hemoglobin picks up less oxygen, the rate of red blood cell sickling increases, and symptoms of the disease occur.

The complicated dominance relationships between the $Hb\beta^S$ and $Hb\beta^A$ alleles also help explain the puzzling observation that the normally deleterious allele $Hb\beta^S$ is widespread in certain populations. In areas where malaria is endemic, heterozygotes are better able to survive and pass on their genes than are either type of homozygote. $Hb\beta^S Hb\beta^S$ individuals often die of sickle-cell disease, while those with the genotype $Hb\beta^A Hb\beta^A$ often die of malaria. Heterozygotes, however, are relatively immune to both conditions, so high frequencies of both alleles persist in tropical environments where malaria is found. We explore this phenomenon in more quantitative detail in Chapter 19 on population genetics.

New therapies have improved the medical condition of many $Hb\beta^S Hb\beta^S$ individuals, but these treatments have significant shortcomings; as a result, sickle-cell disease remains a major health problem. The Fast Forward box "Gene Therapy for Sickle-Cell Disease in Mice" on the following page describes recent success in using genetic engineering to counteract red blood cell sickling in mice whose genomes carry human $Hb\beta^S$ alleles. Researchers hope that similar types of "gene therapies" will one day lead to a cure for sickle-cell disease in humans.

3.2 Extensions to Mendel for Multifactorial Inheritance

Although some traits are indeed determined by allelic variations of a single gene, the vast majority of common traits in all organisms are *multifactorial,* arising from the action of two or more genes, or from interactions between genes and the environment. In genetics, the term *environment* has an unusually broad meaning that encompasses all aspects of the outside world an organism comes into contact with. These include temperature, diet, and exercise as well as the uterine environment before birth.

In this section, we examine how geneticists again used breeding experiments and the guidelines of Mendelian ratios to analyze the complex network of interactions that give rise to multifactorial traits.

Two genes can interact to determine one trait

Two genes can interact in several ways to determine a single trait, such as the color of a flower, a seed coat, a chicken's feathers, or a dog's fur, and each type of interaction

Gene Therapy for Sickle-Cell Disease in Mice

The most widespread inherited blood disorder in the United States is sickle-cell disease, which affects approximately 80,000 Americans. It is caused, as you have seen, by homozygosity for the $Hb\beta^S$ allele of the gene that specifies the β-globin constituent of hemoglobin. Because heterozygotes for this allele are partially protected from malaria, $Hb\beta^S$ is fairly common in people of African, Indian, Mediterranean, and Middle Eastern descent; 1 in 13 African-Americans is a carrier of the sickle-cell allele. Before the 1980s, most people with sickle-cell disease died during childhood. However, advances in medical care have improved the outlook for many of these patients so that about half of them now live beyond the age of 50.

The main therapies in use today include treatment with the drug hydroxyurea, which stimulates the production of other kinds of hemoglobin; and bone marrow transplantation, which replaces the patient's red-blood-cell-forming hematopoietic stem cells with those of a healthy donor. Unfortunately, these treatments are not ideal. Hydroxyurea has toxic side effects, and bone marrow transplantation can be carried out successfully only with a donor whose tissues are perfectly matched with the patient's. As a result, medical researchers are exploring an alternative: the possibility of developing gene therapy for sickle-cell disease in humans.

In 2001 a research team from Harvard Medical School announced the successful use of gene therapy to treat mice that had been genetically engineered to have sickling red blood cells. These transgenic mice (called SAD mice) express an allelic form of the human $Hb\beta$ gene, closely related to $Hb\beta^S$.

The research team began by removing bone marrow from the SAD mice and isolating the hematopoietic stem cells from the marrow. They next used genetic engineering to add an antisickling

transgene to these stem cells. The transgene was a synthetically mutated allele of the human $Hb\beta$ gene; it encoded a special β-globin protein designed to prevent sickling in red blood cells that also contain $Hb\beta^S$. When the genetically modified stem cells were transplanted back into the SAD mice, healthy, nonsickling red blood cells were produced. The new genetically modified transgene thus counteracted the effects of the Hb^S allele and prevented sickling, as predicted.

For human gene therapy, adding a transgene to hematopoietic stem cells derived from the sickle-cell patient would in theory mean no threat of tissue rejection when these engineered stem cells are transplanted back into the patient. However, researchers must overcome several potential problems. First, the method is not guaranteed to work in humans because SAD mice do not exhibit all aspects of sickle-cell disease in humans. Another difficulty is how to make sure the therapeutic gene gets into enough target cells to make a difference. The Harvard group resolved this issue in mice by using a modified version of the HIV virus causing AIDS (*Acquired Immune Deficiency Syndrome*) to transport the genetically engineered antisickling transgene into the stem cells. It has not been proven that virus-treated cells will be safe when reintroduced into the human body. Finally, successful gene therapy of this type requires that all the hematopoietic stem cells without the transgene must be removed. The Harvard researchers did this by destroying the bone marrow in the SAD mice with large doses of X-rays before putting the transgene-containing stem cells back into the mice. However, such a treatment in humans would be extremely toxic. Despite these potential complications, the successful application of gene therapy to a mouse model for sickle-cell disease suggests an exciting pathway for future clinical research.

---

produces its own signature of phenotypic ratios. In many of the following examples showing how two genes interact to affect one trait, we use big *A* and little *a* to represent alternative alleles of the first gene and big *B* and little *b* for those of the second gene.

Novel phenotypes resulting from gene interactions

In the chapter opening, we described a mating of tan and gray lentils that produced a uniformly brown F₁ generation and then an F₂ generation containing lentils with brown, tan, gray, and green seed coats. An understanding of how this can happen emerges from experimental results demonstrating that the ratio of the four F₂ colors is 9 brown: 3 tan: 3 gray: 1 green (**Fig. 3.11a**). Recall from Chapter 2 that this is the same ratio Mendel observed in his analysis of the F₂ generations from dihybrid crosses following two independently assorting genes. In Mendel's studies, each of the four classes consisted of plants that

expressed a combination of two unrelated traits. With lentils, however, we are looking at a single trait—seed coat color. The simplest explanation for the parallel ratios is that a combination of genotypes at two independently assorting genes interacts to produce the phenotype of seed coat color in lentils.

Results obtained from self-crosses with the various types of F₂ lentil plants support this explanation. Self-crosses of F₂ green individuals show that they are pure-breeding, producing an F₃ generation that is entirely green. Tan individuals generate either all tan offspring, or a mixture of tan offspring and green offspring. Grays similarly produce either all gray, or gray and green. Self-crosses of brown F₂ individuals can have four possible outcomes: all brown, brown plus tan, brown plus gray, or all four colors (**Fig. 3.11b**). The two-gene hypothesis explains why there is

- only one green genotype: pure-breeding *aa bb*, but
- two types of tans: pure-breeding *AA bb* as well as tan- and green-producing *Aa bb*, and

Figure 3.11 How two genes interact to produce seed colors in lentils. (a) In a cross of pure-breeding tan and gray lentils, all the F₁ hybrids are brown, but four different phenotypes appear among the F₂ progeny. The 9:3:3:1 ratio of F₂ phenotypes suggests that seed coat color is determined by two independently assorting genes. **(b)** Expected results of selfing individual F₂ plants of the indicated phenotypes to produce an F₃ generation, if seed coat color results from the interaction of two genes. The third column shows the proportion of the F₂ population that would be expected to produce the observed F₃ phenotypes. **(c)** Other two-generation crosses involving pure-breeding parental lines also support the two-gene hypothesis. In this table, the F₁ hybrid generation has been omitted.

(a) A dihybrid cross with lentil coat colors

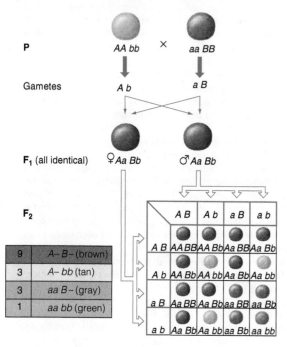

9	A– B– (brown)
3	A– bb (tan)
3	aa B– (gray)
1	aa bb (green)

(b) Self-pollination of the F₂ to produce an F₃

Phenotypes of F₂ Individual	Observed F₃ Phenotypes	Expected Proportion of F₂ Population*
Green	Green	1/16
Tan	Tan	1/16
Tan	Tan, green	2/16
Gray	Gray, green	2/16
Gray	Gray	1/16
Brown	Brown	1/16
Brown	Brown, tan	2/16
Brown	Brown, gray	2/16
Brown	Brown, gray, tan, green	4/16

*This 1:1:2:2:1:1:2:2:4 F₂ genotypic ratio corresponds to a 9 brown : 3 tan : 3 gray : 1 green F₂ phenotypic ratio.

(c) Sorting out the dominance relations by select crosses

Seed Coat Color of Parents	F₂ Phenotypes and Frequencies	Ratio
Tan × green	231 tan, 85 green	3:1
Gray × green	2586 gray, 867 green	3:1
Brown × gray	964 brown, 312 gray	3:1
Brown × tan	255 brown, 76 tan	3:1
Brown × green	57 brown, 18 gray, 13 tan, 4 green	9:3:3:1

- two types of grays: pure-breeding *aa BB* and gray- and green-producing *aa Bb,* yet
- four types of browns: true-breeding *AA BB,* brown- and tan-producing *AA Bb,* brown- and gray-producing *Aa BB,* and *Aa Bb* dihybrids that give rise to plants producing lentils of all four colors.

In short, for the two genes that determine seed coat color, both dominant alleles must be present to yield brown (*A– B–*); the dominant allele of one gene produces tan (*A– bb*); the dominant allele of the other specifies gray (*aa B–*); and the complete absence of dominant alleles (that is, the double recessive) yields green (*aa bb*). Thus, the four color phenotypes arise from four **genotypic classes,** with each class defined in terms of the presence or absence of the dominant alleles of two genes: (1) both present (*A– B–*), (2) one present (*A– bb*), (3) the other present (*aa B–*), and (4) neither present (*aa bb*). Note that the *A–* notation means that the second allele of this gene can be either *A* or *a,* while *B–* denotes a second allele of either *B* or *b.* Note also that only with a two-gene system in which the dominance and recessiveness of alleles at both genes is complete can the nine different genotypes of the F₂ generation be categorized into the four genotypic

classes described. With incomplete dominance or codominance, the F₂ genotypes could not be grouped together in this simple way, as they would give rise to more than four phenotypes.

Further crosses between plants carrying lentils of different colors confirmed the two-gene hypothesis (**Fig. 3.11c**). Thus, the 9:3:3:1 phenotypic ratio of brown to tan to gray to green in an F₂ descended from pure-breeding tan and pure-breeding gray lentils tells us not only that two genes assorting independently interact to produce the seed coat color, but also that each genotypic class (*A– B–, A– bb, aa B–,* and *aa bb*) determines a particular phenotype.

Complementary gene action

In some two-gene interactions, the four F₂ genotypic classes produce fewer than four observable phenotypes, because some of the phenotypes include two or more genotypic classes. For example, in the first decade of the twentieth century, William Bateson conducted a cross between two lines of pure-breeding white-flowered sweet peas (**Fig. 3.12**). Quite unexpectedly, all of the F₁ progeny were purple. Self-pollination of these novel hybrids produced a ratio

Figure 3.12 Complementary gene action generates color in sweet peas. (a) White and purple sweet pea flowers. **(b)** The 9:7 ratio of purple to white F$_2$ plants indicates that at least one dominant allele for each gene is necessary for the development of purple color.

(a) *Lathyrus odoratus* (sweet peas)

(b) A dihybrid cross involving complementary gene action

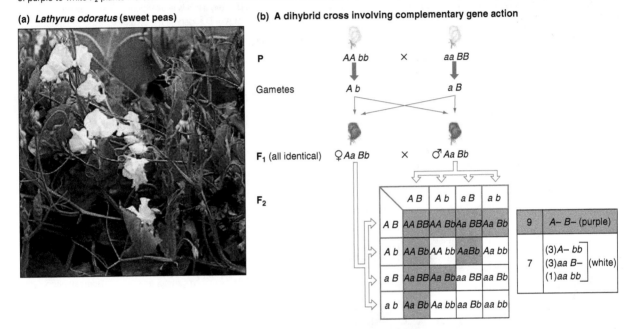

P AA bb × aa BB

Gametes A b   a B

F$_1$ (all identical) ♀ Aa Bb × ♂ Aa Bb

F$_2$

	A B	A b	a B	a b
A B	AA BB	AA Bb	Aa BB	Aa Bb
A b	AA Bb	AA bb	AaBb	Aa bb
a B	Aa BB	Aa Bb	aa BB	aa Bb
a b	Aa Bb	Aa bb	aa Bb	aa bb

9	A– B– (purple)
7	(3)A– bb (3)aa B– (white) (1)aa bb

of 9 purple : 7 white in the F$_2$ generation. The explanation? Two genes work in tandem to produce purple sweet-pea flowers, and a dominant allele of both genes must be present to produce that color.

A simple biochemical hypothesis for this type of **complementary gene action** is shown in **Fig. 3.13.** Because it takes two enzymes catalyzing two separate biochemical reactions to change a colorless precursor into a colorful pigment, only the *A– B–* genotypic class, which produces active forms of both required enzymes, can generate colored flowers. The other three genotypic classes (*A– bb, aa B–*, and *aa bb*) become grouped together with respect to phenotype because they do not specify functional forms of one or the other requisite enzyme and thus give rise to no color, which is the same as white. It is easy to see how the "7" part of the 9:7 ratio encompasses the 3:3:1 of the 9:3:3:1 ratio of two genes in action. The 9:7 ratio is the phenotypic signature of this type of complementary gene interaction in which the dominant alleles of two genes acting together (*A– B–*) produce color or some other trait, while the other three genotypic classes (*A– bb, aa B–*, and *aa bb*) do not (see Fig. 3.12b).

Epistasis

In some gene interactions, the four Mendelian genotypic classes produce fewer than four observable phenotypes because one gene masks the phenotypic effects of another. An example is seen in the sleek, short-haired coat of Labrador retrievers, which can be black, chocolate brown,

Figure 3.13 A possible biochemical explanation for complementary gene action in the generation of sweet pea color. Enzymes specified by the dominant alleles of two genes are both necessary to produce pigment. The recessive alleles of both genes specify inactive enzymes. In *aa* homozygotes, no intermediate precursor 2 is created, so even if enzyme B is available, it cannot create purple pigment.

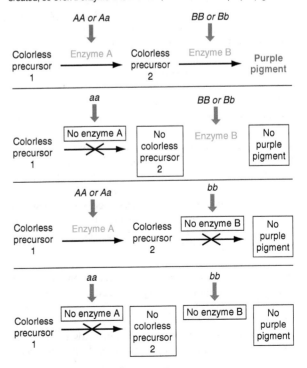

Figure 3.14 Recessive epistasis: Coat color in Labrador retrievers and a rare human blood type. (a) Golden Labrador retrievers are homozygous for the recessive *e* allele, which masks the effects of the *B* or *b* alleles of a second coat color gene. In *E–* dogs, a *B–* genotype produces black and a *bb* genotype produces brown. **(b)** Homozygosity for the *h* Bombay allele is epistatic to the *I* gene determining ABO blood types. *hh* individuals fail to produce substance H, which is needed for the addition of A or B sugars at the surface of red blood cells.

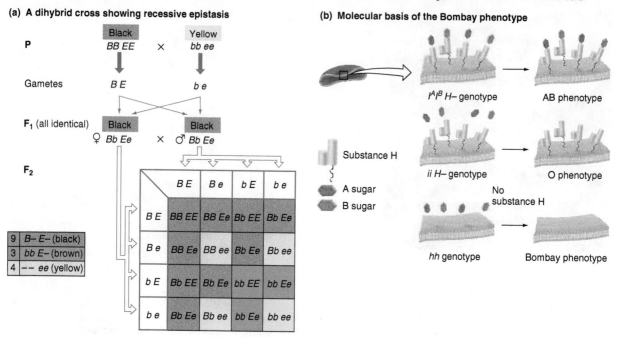

(a) A dihybrid cross showing recessive epistasis

(b) Molecular basis of the Bombay phenotype

or golden yellow. (These phenotypes may be viewed in Fig. 2.3 on p. 14) Which color shows up depends on the allelic combinations of two independently assorting coat color genes (**Fig. 3.14a**). The dominant *B* allele of the first gene determines black, while the recessive *bb* homozygote is brown. With the second gene, the dominant *E* allele has no visible effect on black or brown coat color, but a double dose of the recessive allele (*ee*) hides the effect of any combination of the black or brown alleles to yield gold. A gene interaction in which the effects of an allele at one gene hide the effects of alleles at another gene is known as **epistasis;** the allele that is doing the masking (in this case, the *e* allele of the *E* gene) is **epistatic** to the gene that is being masked (the *hypostatic gene*). In this example, where homozygosity for a recessive *e* allele of the second gene is required to hide the effects of another gene, the masking phenomenon is called **recessive epistasis** (because the allele causing the epistasis is recessive), and the recessive *ee* homozygote is considered epistatic to any allelic combination at the first gene.

Recessive Epistasis Let's look at the phenomenon in greater detail. Crosses between pure-breeding black retrievers (*BB EE*) and one type of pure-breeding golden retriever (*bb ee*) create an F₁ generation of dihybrid black retrievers (*Bb Ee*). Crosses between these F₁ dihybrids produce an F₂ generation with nine black dogs (*B– E–*) for every three

brown (*bb E–*) and four gold (*– – ee*) (Fig. 3.14a). Note that there are only three phenotypic classes because the two genotypic classes without a dominant *E* allele—the three *B– ee* and the one *bb ee*—combine to produce golden phenotypes. The telltale ratio of recessive epistasis in the F₂ generation is thus 9:3:4, with the 4 representing a combination of 3 (*B– ee*) + 1 (*bb ee*). Because the *ee* genotype completely masks the influence of the other gene for coat color, you cannot tell by looking at a golden Labrador what its genotype is for the black or brown (*B* or *b*) gene.

An understanding of recessive epistasis made it possible to resolve an intriguing puzzle in human genetics. In rare instances, two parents who appear to have blood type O, and thus genotype *ii,* produce a child who is either blood type A (genotype *IᴬI*) or blood type B (genotype *IᴮI*). This phenomenon occurs because an extremely rare trait, called the Bombay phenotype after its discovery in Bombay, India, superficially resembles blood type O. As **Fig. 3.14b** shows, the Bombay phenotype actually arises from homozygosity for a mutant recessive allele (*hh*) of a second gene that masks the effects of any ABO alleles that might be present.

Here's how it works at the molecular level. In the construction of the red blood cell surface molecules that determine blood type, type A individuals make an enzyme that adds polysaccharide A onto a base consisting of a sugar polymer known as substance H; type B individuals make an altered form of the enzyme that

Figure 3.15 Dominant epistasis produces telltale phenotypic ratios of 12:3:1 or 13:3. (a) In summer squash, the dominant *B* allele causes white color and is sufficient to mask the effects of any combination of *A* and *a* alleles. As a result, yellow (*A–*) or green (*aa*) color is expressed only in *bb* individuals. **(b)** In the F₂ generation resulting from a dihybrid cross between white leghorn and white wyandotte chickens, the ratio of white birds to birds with color is 13:3. This is because at least one copy of *A* and the absence of *B* is needed to produce color.

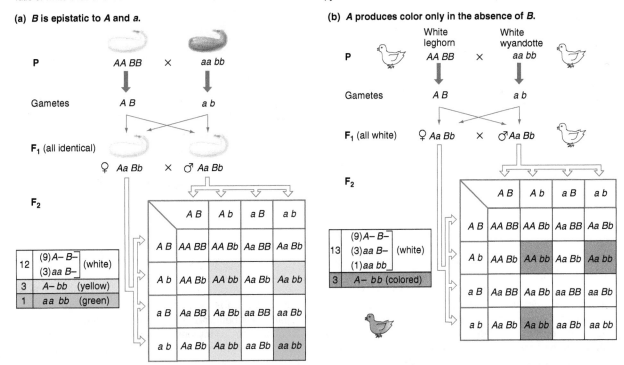

(a) *B* is epistatic to *A* and *a*.

(b) *A* produces color only in the absence of *B*.

adds polysaccharide B onto the base; and type O individuals make neither A-adding nor B-adding enzyme and thus have an exposed substance H in the membranes of their red blood cells. All people of A, B, or O phenotype carry at least one dominant wild-type *H* allele for the second gene and thus produce some substance H. In contrast, the rare Bombay-phenotype individuals, with genotype *hh* for the second gene, do not make substance H at all, so even if they make an enzyme that would add A or B to this polysaccharide base, they have nothing to add it onto; as a result, they appear to be type O. For this reason, homozygosity for the recessive *h* allele of the H-substance gene masks the effects of the *ABO* gene, making the *hh* genotype epistatic to any combination of *I^A*, *I^B*, and *i* alleles.

A person who carries *I^A*, *I^B*, or both *I^A* and *I^B* but is also an *hh* homozygote for the H-substance gene may appear to be type O, but he or she will be able to pass along an *I^A* or *I^B* allele in sperm or egg. The offspring receiving, let's say, an *I^A* allele for the ABO gene and a recessive *h* allele for the H-substance gene from its mother plus an *i* allele and a dominant *H* allele from its father would have blood type A (genotype *I^A i, Hh*), even though neither of its parents is phenotype A or AB.

Dominant Epistasis Epistasis can also be caused by a dominant allele. In summer squash, two genes influence the color of the fruit (**Fig. 3.15a**). With one gene, the dominant allele (*A–*) determines yellow, while homozygotes for the recessive allele (*aa*) are green. A second gene's dominant allele (*B–*) produces white, while *bb* fruit may be either yellow or green, depending on the genotype of the first gene. In the interaction between these two genes, the presence of *B* hides the effects of either *A–* or *aa*, producing white fruit, and *B–* is thus epistatic to any genotype of the *Aa* gene. The recessive *b* allele has no effect on fruit color determined by the *Aa* gene. Epistasis in which the dominant allele of one gene hides the effects of another gene is called **dominant epistasis**. In a cross between white F₁ dihybrids (*Aa Bb*), the F₂ phenotypic ratio is 12 white : 3 yellow : 1 green (Fig. 3.15a). The "12" includes two genotypic classes: 9 *A– B–* and 3 *aa B–*. Another way of looking at this same phenomenon is that dominant epistasis restores the 3:1 ratio for the dominant epistatic phenotype (12 white) versus all other phenotypes (4 green plus yellow).

A variation of this ratio is seen in the feather color of certain chickens (**Fig. 3.15b**). White leghorns have a doubly dominant *AA BB* genotype for feather color; white wyandottes are homozygous recessive for both

■ **TABLE 3.2**	Summary of Discussed Gene Interactions					
		F$_2$ Genotypic Ratios from an F$_1$ Dihybrid Cross				**F$_2$ Pheno-**
Gene Interaction	**Example**	**A– B–**	**A– bb**	**aa B–**	**aa bb**	**typic Ratio**
None: Four distinct F$_2$ phenotypes	Lentil: seed coat color (see Fig. 3.11a)	9	3	3	1	9:3:3:1
Complementary: One dominant allele of each of two genes is necessary to produce phenotype	Sweet pea: flower color (see Fig. 3.12b)	9	3	3	1	9:7
Recessive epistasis: Homozygous recessive of one gene masks both alleles of another gene	Retriever coat color (see Fig. 3.14a)	9	3	3	1	9:3:4
Dominant epistasis I: Dominant allele of one gene hides effects of both alleles of another gene	Summer squash: color (see Fig. 3.15a)	9	3	3	1	12:3:1
Dominant epistasis II: Dominant allele of one gene hides effects of dominant allele of another gene	Chicken: feather color (see Fig. 3.15b)	9	3	3	1	13:3

genes (*aa bb*). A cross between these two pure-breeding white strains produces an all-white dihybrid (*Aa Bb*) F$_1$ generation, but birds with color in their feathers appear in the F$_2$, and the ratio of white to colored is 13:3 (Fig. 3.15b). We can explain this ratio by assuming a kind of dominant epistasis in which *B* is epistatic to *A*; the *A* allele (in the absence of *B*) produces color; and the *a, B*, and *b* alleles produce no color. The interaction is characterized by a 13:3 ratio because the 9 *A– B–*, 3 *aa B–*, and 1 *aa bb* genotypic classes combine to produce only one phenotype: white.

So far we have seen that when two independently assorting genes interact to determine a trait, the 9:3:3:1 ratio of the four Mendelian genotypic classes in the F$_2$ generation can produce a variety of phenotypic ratios, depending on the nature of the gene interactions. The result may be four, three, or two phenotypes, composed of different combinations of the four genotypic classes. **Table 3.2** summarizes some of the possibilities, correlating the phenotypic ratios with the genetic phenomena they reflect.

Heterogeneous traits and the complementation test

Close to 50 different genes have mutant alleles that can cause deafness in humans. Many genes generate the developmental pathway that brings about hearing, and a loss of function in any part of the pathway, for instance, in one small bone of the middle ear, can result in deafness. In other words, it takes a dominant wild-type allele at each of these 50 genes to produce normal hearing. Thus, deafness is a **heterogeneous trait:** A mutation at any one of a number of genes can give rise to the same phenotype.

It is not always possible to determine which of many different genes has mutated in a person who expresses a heterogeneous mutant phenotype. In the case of deafness, for example, it is usually not possible to discover whether a particular nonhearing man and a particular nonhearing woman carry mutations at the same gene, unless they have children together. If they have only children who can hear, the parents most likely carry mutations at two different genes, and the children carry one normal, wild-type allele at both of those genes (**Fig. 3.16a**). By contrast, if all of their children are deaf, it is likely that both parents are homozygous for a mutation in the same gene, and all of their children are also homozygous for this same mutation (**Fig. 3.16b**).

This method of discovering whether a particular phenotype arises from mutations in the same or separate genes is a naturally occurring version of an experimental genetic tool called the **complementation test.** Simply put, when what appears to be an identical *recessive* phenotype arises in two separate breeding lines, geneticists want to know whether mutations at the same gene are responsible for the phenotype in both lines. They answer this question by setting up a mating between affected individuals from the two lines. If offspring receiving the two mutations—one from each parent—express the wild-type phenotype, complementation has occurred. The observation of complementation means that the original mutations affected two different genes, and for both genes, the normal allele from one parent can provide what the mutant allele of the same gene from the other parent cannot. Figure 3.16a illustrates one example of this phenomenon in humans. By contrast, if offspring receiving two recessive mutant alleles—again, one from each parent—express the mutant phenotype, complementation does not occur because the two mutations independently alter the same gene

Figure 3.16 Genetic heterogeneity in humans: Mutations in many genes can cause deafness. (a) Two deaf parents can have hearing offspring. This situation is an example of genetic complementation; it occurs if the nonhearing parents are homozygous for recessive mutations in different genes. **(b)** Two deaf parents may produce all deaf children. In such cases, complementation does not occur because both parents carry mutations in the same gene.

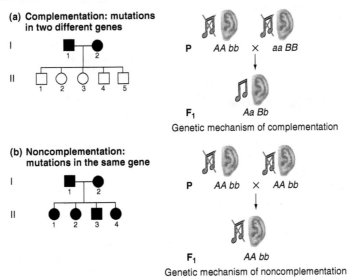

(Fig. 3.16b). Thus, the occurrence of complementation reveals genetic heterogeneity. Note that complementation tests cannot be used if either of the mutations is dominant to the wild type. Chapter 7 includes an in-depth discussion of complementation tests and their uses.

To summarize, several variations on the theme of multifactorial traits can be identified:

(1) genes can interact to generate novel phenotypes,
(2) the dominant alleles of two interacting genes can both be necessary for the production of a particular phenotype,
(3) one gene's alleles can mask the effects of alleles at another gene, and
(4) mutant alleles at one of two or more different genes can result in the same phenotype.

In examining each of these categories, for the sake of simplicity, we have looked at examples in which one allele of each gene in a pair showed complete dominance over the other. But for any type of gene interaction, the alleles of one or both genes may exhibit incomplete dominance or codominance, and these possibilities increase the potential for phenotypic diversity. For example, **Fig. 3.17** shows how incomplete dominance at both genes in a dihybrid cross generates additional phenotypic variation.

Although the possibilities for variation are manifold, none of the observed departures from Mendelian phenotypic ratios contradicts Mendel's genetic laws of segregation and independent assortment. The alleles of each gene still segregate as he proposed. Interactions between the alleles of many genes simply make it harder to unravel the complex relation of genotype to phenotype.

Figure 3.17 With incomplete dominance, the interaction of two genes can produce nine different phenotypes for a single trait. In this example, two genes produce purple pigments. Alleles *A* and *a* of the first gene exhibit incomplete dominance, as do alleles *B* and *b* of the second gene. The two alleles of each gene can generate three different phenotypes, so double heterozygotes can produce nine (3×3) different colors in a ratio of 1:2:2:1:4:1:2:2:1.

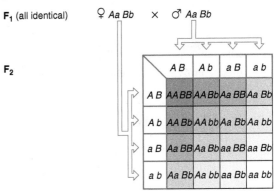

1	AA BB	purple shade 9
2	AA Bb	purple shade 8
2	Aa BB	purple shade 7
1	AA bb	purple shade 6
4	Aa Bb	purple shade 5
1	aa BB	purple shade 4
2	Aa bb	purple shade 3
2	aa Bb	purple shade 2
1	aa bb	purple shade 1 (white)

F₂ phenotypic ratios of 9:3:3:1 or its derivatives indicate the combined action of two independently assorting genes. For heterogeneous traits caused by recessive alleles of two or more genes, a mating between affected individuals acts as a complementation test, revealing whether they carry mutations in the same gene or in different genes.

Breeding studies help decide how a trait is inherited

How do geneticists know whether a particular trait is caused by the alleles of one gene or by two genes interacting in one of a number of possible ways? Breeding tests can usually resolve the issue. Phenotypic ratios diagnostic of a particular mode of inheritance (for instance, the 9:7 or 13:3 ratios indicating that two genes are interacting) can provide the first clues and suggest hypotheses. Further breeding studies can then show which hypothesis is correct. We have seen, for example, that yellow coat color in mice is determined by a dominant allele of the *agouti* gene, which also acts as a recessive lethal. We now look at two other mouse genes for coat color. Because we have already designated alleles of the *agouti* gene as *Aa,* we use *Bb* and *Cc* to designate the alleles of these additional genes.

A mating of one strain of pure-breeding white albino mice with pure-breeding brown results in black hybrids; and a cross between the black F₁ hybrids produces 90 black, 30 brown, and 40 albino offspring. What is the genetic constitution of these phenotypes? We could assume that we are seeing the 9:3:4 ratio of recessive epistasis and hypothesize that two genes, one epistatic to the other, interact to produce the three mouse phenotypes (**Fig. 3.18a**). But how do we know if this hypothesis is

Figure 3.18 Specific breeding tests can help decide between hypotheses. Either of two hypotheses could explain the results of a cross-tracking coat color in mice. **(a)** In one hypothesis, two genes interact with recessive epistasis to produce a 9:3:4 ratio. **(b)** In the other hypothesis, a single gene with incomplete dominance between the alleles generates the observed results. One way to decide between these models is to cross each of several albino F₂ mice with true-breeding brown mice. The two-gene model predicts several different outcomes depending on the − − *cc* albino's genotype at the *B* gene. The one-gene model predicts that all progeny of all the crosses will be black.

(a) Hypothesis 1 (two genes with recessive epistasis)

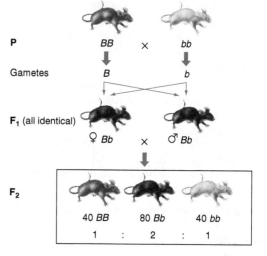

(b) Hypothesis 2 (one gene with incomplete dominance)

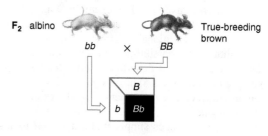

correct? We might also explain the data—160 progeny in a ratio of 90:30:40—by the activity of one gene (**Fig. 3.18b**). According to this one-gene hypothesis, albinos would be homozygotes for one allele (*bb*), brown mice would be homozygotes for a second allele (*BB*), and black mice would be heterozygotes (*Bb*) that have their own "intermediate" phenotype because *B* shows incomplete dominance over *b*. Under this system, a mating of black (*Bb*) to black (*Bb*) would be expected to produce 1 *BB* brown : 2 *Bb* black : 1 *bb* albino, or 40 brown : 80 black : 40 albino. Is it possible that the 30 brown, 90 black, and 40 albino mice actually counted were obtained from the inheritance of a single gene? Intuitively, the answer is yes: the ratios 40:80:40 and 30:90:40 do not seem that different. We know that if we flip a coin 100 times, it doesn't always come up 50 heads : 50 tails; sometimes it's 60:40 just by chance. So, how can we decide between the two-gene versus the one-gene model?

The answer is that we can use other types of crosses to verify or refute the hypotheses. For instance, if the one-gene hypothesis were correct, a mating of pure white F$_2$ albinos with pure-breeding brown mice similar to those of the parental generation would produce all black heterozygotes (brown [*BB*] × albino [*bb*] = all black [*Bb*]) (Fig. 3.18b). But if the two-gene hypothesis is correct, with recessive mutations at an albino gene (called *C*) epistatic to all expression from the *B* gene, different matings of pure-breeding brown (*bb CC*) with the F$_2$ albinos (– – *cc*) will give different results—all progeny are black; half are black and half brown; all are brown—depending on the albino's genotype at the *B* gene (see Fig. 3.18a). In fact, when the experiment is actually performed, the diversity of results confirms the two-gene hypothesis. The comprehensive example on pp. 68–69 outlines additional details of the interactions of the three mouse genes for coat color.

With humans, pedigree analysis replaces breeding experiments

Breeding experiments cannot be applied to humans, for obvious ethical reasons. But a careful examination of as many family pedigrees as possible can help elucidate the genetic basis of a particular condition.

In a form of albinism known as ocular-cutaneous albinism (OCA), for example, people with the inherited condition have little or no pigment in their skin, hair, and eyes (**Fig. 3.19a**). The horizontal inheritance pattern seen in **Fig. 3.19b** suggests that OCA is determined by the recessive allele of one gene, with albino family members being homozygotes for that allele. But a 1952 paper on albinism reported a family in which two albino parents produced three normally pigmented

Figure 3.19 Family pedigrees help unravel the genetic basis of ocular-cutaneous albinism (OCA). (a) An albino Nigerian girl and her sister celebrating the conclusion of the All Africa games. **(b)** A pedigree following the inheritance of OCA in an inbred family indicates that the trait is recessive. **(c)** A family in which two albino parents have nonalbino children demonstrates that homozygosity for a recessive allele of either of two genes can cause OCA.

(a) Ocular-cutaneous albinism (OCA)

(b) OCA is recessive

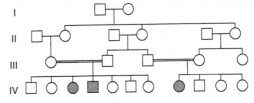

(c) Complementation for albinism

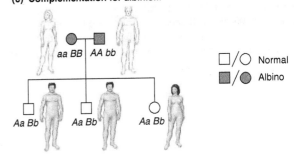

children (**Fig. 3.19c**). How would you explain this phenomenon?

The answer is that albinism is another example of heterogeneity: Mutant alleles at any one of several different genes can cause the condition. The reported mating was, in effect, an inadvertent complementation test, which showed that one parent was homozygous for an OCA-causing mutation in gene *A*, while the other parent was homozygous for an OCA-causing mutation in a different gene, *B* (compare with Fig. 3.16 on p. 61).

The same genotype does not always produce the same phenotype

In our discussion of gene interactions so far, we have looked at examples in which a genotype reliably fashions a particular phenotype. But this is not always what happens. Sometimes a genotype is not expressed at all; that is, even though the genotype is present, the expected phenotype does not appear. Other times, the trait caused by a genotype is expressed to varying degrees or in a variety of ways in different individuals. Factors that alter the phenotypic expression of genotype include modifier genes, the environment (in the broadest sense, as defined earlier), and chance.

Penetrance and expressivity

Retinoblastoma, the most malignant form of eye cancer, arises from a dominant mutation of one gene, but only 75% of people who carry the mutant allele develop the disease. Geneticists use the term **penetrance** to describe how many members of a population with a particular genotype show the expected phenotype. Penetrance can be *complete* (100%), as in the traits that Mendel studied, or *incomplete*, as in retinoblastoma (see the Genetics and Society box "Disease Prevention Versus the Right to Privacy" on p. 67 for another example of incomplete penetrance). For retinoblastoma, the penetrance is 75%.

In some people with retinoblastoma, only one eye is affected, while in other individuals with the phenotype, both eyes are diseased. **Expressivity** refers to the degree or intensity with which a particular genotype is expressed in a phenotype. Expressivity can be *variable,* as in retinoblastoma (one or both eyes affected), or *unvarying,* as in pea color. As we will see, the incomplete penetrance and variable expressivity of retinoblastoma are the result of chance, but in other cases, it is modifier genes and/or the environment that causes such variations in the appearance of phenotype.

Modifier genes

Not all genes that influence the appearance of a trait contribute equally to the phenotype. Major genes have a large influence, while **modifier genes** have a more subtle, secondary effect. Modifier genes alter the phenotypes produced by the alleles of other genes. There is no formal distinction between major and modifier genes. Rather, there is a continuum between the two, and the cutoff is arbitrary.

Modifier genes influence the length of a mouse's tail. The mutant *T* allele of the tail-length gene causes a shortening of the normally long wild-type tail. But not all mice carrying the *T* mutation have the same length tail. A comparison of several inbred lines points to modifier genes as the cause of this variable expressivity. In one inbred line, mice carrying the *T* mutation have tails that are approximately 75% as long as normal tails; in another inbred line, the tails are 50% normal length; and in a third line, the tails are only 10% as long as wild-type tails. Because all members of each inbred line grow the same length tail, no matter what the environment (for example, diet, cage temperature, or bedding), geneticists conclude it is genes and not the environment or chance that determines the length of a mutant mouse's tail. Different inbred lines most likely carry different alleles of the modifier genes that determine exactly how short the tail will be when the *T* mutation is present.

Environmental effects on phenotype

Temperature is one element of the environment that can have a visible effect on phenotype. For example, temperature influences the unique coat color pattern of Siamese cats (**Fig. 3.20**). These domestic felines are homozygous for one of the multiple alleles of a gene that encodes an enzyme catalyzing the production of the dark pigment melanin. The form of the enzyme generated by the variant *"Siamese"* allele does not function at the cat's normal body temperature. It becomes active only at the lower temperatures found in the cat's extremities, where it promotes the production of melanin, which darkens the animal's ears, nose, paws, and tail. The enzyme is thus *temperature sensitive.* Under the normal environmental conditions in temperate climates, the Siamese phenotype does not vary much in expressivity from one cat to another, but one can imagine the expression of a very different phenotype—no dark extremities—in equatorial deserts, where the ambient temperature is at or above normal body temperature.

Temperature can also affect survivability. In one type of experimentally bred fruit fly (*Drosophila melanogaster),* some individuals develop and multiply normally at temperatures between 18°C and 29°C; but if the thermometer climbs beyond that cutoff for a short time, they become reversibly paralyzed, and if the temperature remains high for more than a few hours, they die. These insects carry a temperature-sensitive allele of the *shibire* gene, which encodes a protein essential for nerve cell transmission. This type of allele is known as a **conditional lethal** because it is lethal only under certain conditions. The range of temperatures under which the insects remain viable are **permissive conditions;** the lethal temperatures above that are **restrictive conditions.** Thus, at one temperature, the allele gives rise to a phenotype that is indistinguishable from the wild type, while at another temperature, the same allele generates a mutant phenotype (in this case, lethality). Flies with the wild-type *shibire* allele are viable even at the higher temperatures. The fact that some mutations are lethal only under certain conditions clearly illustrates that the environment can affect the penetrance of a phenotype.

Figure 3.20 In Siamese cats, temperature affects coat color. (a) A Siamese cat. **(b)** Melanin is produced only in the cooler extremities. This is because Siamese cats are homozygous for a mutation that renders an enzyme involved in melanin synthesis temperature sensitive. The mutant enzyme is active at lower temperatures but inactive at higher temperatures.

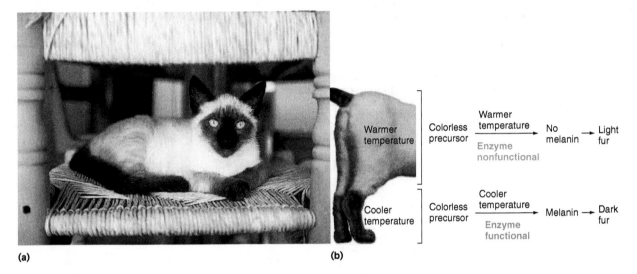

(a)

(b)

Even in genetically normal individuals, exposure to chemicals or other environmental agents can have phenotypic consequences that are similar to those caused by mutant alleles of specific genes. A change in phenotype arising in such a way is known as a **phenocopy.** By definition, phenocopies are not heritable because they do not result from a change in a gene. In humans, ingestion of the sedative thalidomide by pregnant women in the early 1960s produced a phenocopy of a rare dominant trait called *phocomelia.* By disrupting limb development in otherwise normal fetuses, the drug mimicked the effect of the phocomelia-causing mutation. When this became evident, thalidomide was withdrawn from the market.

Some types of environmental change may have a positive effect on an organism's survivability, as in the following example, where a straightforward application of medical science artificially reduces the penetrance of a mutant phenotype. Children born with the recessive trait known as phenylketonuria, or PKU, will develop a range of neurological problems, including convulsive seizures and mental retardation, unless they are put on a special diet. Homozygosity for the mutant PKU allele eliminates the activity of a gene encoding the enzyme phenylalanine hydroxylase. This enzyme normally converts the amino acid phenylalanine to the amino acid tyrosine. Absence of the enzyme causes a buildup of phenylalanine, and this buildup results in neurological problems. Today, a reliable blood test can detect the condition in newborns. Once a baby with PKU is identified, a protective diet that excludes phenylalanine is prescribed; the diet must also provide enough calories to prevent the infant's body from breaking down its own proteins,

thereby releasing the damaging amino acid from within. Such dietary therapy—a simple change in the environment—now enables many PKU infants to develop into healthy adults.

Finally, two of the top killer diseases in the United States—cardiovascular disease and lung cancer—also illustrate how the environment can alter phenotype by influencing both expressivity and penetrance. People may inherit a propensity to heart disease, but the environmental factors of diet and exercise contribute to the occurrence (penetrance) and seriousness (expressivity) of their condition. Similarly, some people are born genetically prone to lung cancer, but whether or not they develop the disease (penetrance) is strongly determined by whether they choose to smoke.

Thus, various aspects of an organism's environment, including temperature, diet, and exercise, interact with its genotype to generate the functional phenotype, the ultimate combination of traits that determines what a plant or animal looks like and how it behaves.

The effects of random events on penetrance and expressivity

Whether a carrier of the retinoblastoma mutation described earlier develops the phenotype, and whether the disease affects one or both eyes, depend on additional genetic events that occur at random. To produce retinoblastoma, these events must alter the second allele of the gene in specific body cells. Examples of random events that can trigger the onset of the disease include cosmic rays (to which humans are constantly exposed) that alter the genetic material in retinal cells or mistakes made during cell division in the retina. Chance events provide the second "hit"—a mutation in the second copy of the retinoblastoma gene—necessary to turn a normal retinal cell into a cancerous one. The phenotype of retinoblastoma thus results from a specific heritable mutation in a specific gene, but the incomplete penetrance and variable expressivity of the disease depend on random genetic events that affect the other allele in certain cells.

By contributing to incomplete penetrance and variable expressivity, modifier genes, the environment, and chance give rise to phenotypic variation. Unlike dominant epistasis or recessive lethality, however, the probability of penetrance and the level of expressivity cannot be derived from the original Mendelian principles of segregation and independent assortment; they are determined empirically by observation and counting.

> Because modifier genes, the environment, and chance events can affect phenotypes, the relationship of a particular genotype and its corresponding phenotype is not always absolute: An allele's penetrance can be incomplete, and its expressivity can be variable.

Mendelian principles can also explain continuous variation

In Mendel's experiments, height in pea plants was determined by two segregating alleles of one gene (in the wild, it is determined by many genes, but in Mendel's inbred populations, the alleles of all but one of these genes were invariant). The phenotypes that resulted from these alternative alleles were clear-cut, either short or tall, and pea plant height was therefore known as a **discontinuous trait.** In contrast, because people do not produce inbred populations, height in humans is determined by segregating alleles of many different genes whose interaction with each other and the environment produces continuous variation in the phenotype; height in humans is thus an example of a **continuous trait.** Within human populations, individual heights vary over a range of values that when charted on a graph produce a bell curve (**Fig. 3.21a**). In fact, many human traits, including height, weight, and skin color, show continuous variation, rather than the clear-cut alternatives analyzed by Mendel.

Continuous traits often appear to blend and "unblend." Think for a moment of skin color. Children of marriages between people of African and Northern European descent, for example, often seem to be a blend of their parents' skin colors. Progeny of these F₁ individuals produce offspring displaying a wide range of skin pigmentation; a few may be as light as the original Northern European parent, a few as dark as the original African parent, but most will fall in a range between the two

Figure 3.21 Continuous traits in humans. (a) Women runners at the start of a 5th Avenue mile race in New York City demonstrate that height is a trait showing continuous variation. **(b)** The skin color of most F₁ offspring is usually between the parental extremes, while the F₂ generation exhibits a broader distribution of continuous variation.

(a)

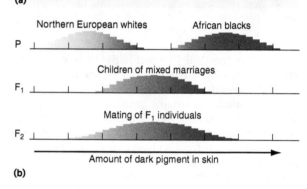

(b)

(**Fig. 3.21b**). For such reasons, early human geneticists were slow to accept Mendelian analysis. Because they were working with outbred populations, they found very few examples of "either-or" Mendelian traits in normal, healthy people.

By 1930, however, studies of corn and tobacco conclusively demonstrated that it is possible to provide a Mendelian explanation of continuous variation by simply increasing the number of genes contributing to a phenotype. The more genes, the more phenotypic classes, and the more classes, the more the variation appears continuous.

As a hypothetical example, consider a series of genes (*A, B, C, . . .*) all affecting the height of pole beans. For each gene, there are two alleles, a *"0"* allele that contributes nothing to height and a *"1"* allele that increases the height of a plant by one unit. All alleles exhibit incomplete dominance relative to alternative alleles at the same gene. The phenotypes determined by all these genes are additive. What would be the result of a two-generation cross between pure-breeding plants carrying only *0* alleles at each height gene and

G E N E T I C S   A N D   S O C I E T Y

Disease Prevention Versus the Right to Privacy

In one of the most extensive human pedigrees ever assembled, a team of researchers traced a familial pattern of blindness back through five centuries of related individuals to its origin in a couple who died in a small town in northwestern France in 1495. More than 30,000 French men and women alive today descended from that one fifteenth-century couple, and within this direct lineage reside close to half of all reported French cases of hereditary juvenile glaucoma. The massive genealogic tree for the trait (when posted on the office wall, it was over 100 feet long) showed that the genetic defect follows a simple Mendelian pattern of transmission determined by the dominant allele of a single gene (**Fig. A**). The pedigree also showed that the dominant genetic defect displays incomplete penetrance: Not all people receiving the dominant allele become blind; these sighted carriers may unknowingly pass the blindness-causing dominant allele to their children.

Unfortunately, people do not know they have the disease until their vision starts to deteriorate. By that time, their optic fibers have sustained irreversible damage, and blindness is all but inevitable. Surprisingly, the existence of medical therapies that make it possible to arrest the nerve deterioration created a quandary in the late 1980s. Because treatment, to be effective, has to begin before symptoms of impending blindness show up, information in the pedigree could have helped doctors pinpoint people who are at risk, even if neither of their parents is blind. The researchers who compiled the massive family history therefore wanted to give physicians the names of at-risk individuals living in their area, so that doctors could monitor certain patients and recommend treatment if needed. However, a long-standing French law protecting personal privacy forbids public circulation of the names in genetic pedigrees. The French government agency interpreting this law maintained that if the names in the glaucoma pedigree were made public, potential carriers of the disease might suffer discrimination in hiring or insurance.

France thus faced a serious ethical dilemma: On the one hand, giving out names could save perhaps thousands of people from blindness; on the other hand, laws designed to protect personal privacy precluded the dissemination of specific names. The solution adopted by the French government at the time was a massive educational program to alert the general public to the problem so that concerned families could seek medical advice. This approach addressed the legal issues but was only partially helpful in dealing with the medical problem, because many affected individuals escaped detection.

Figure A A pedigree showing the transmission of juvenile glaucoma. A small part of the genealogic tree: The vertical transmission pattern over seven generations shows that a dominant allele of a single gene causes juvenile glaucoma. The lack of glaucoma in V-2 followed by its reappearance in VI-2 reveals that the trait is incompletely penetrant. As a result, sighted heterozygotes may unknowingly pass the condition on to their children.

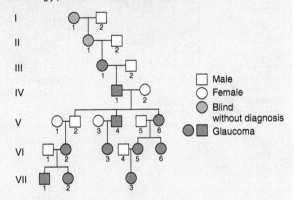

By 1997, molecular geneticists had identified the gene whose dominant mutant allele causes juvenile glaucoma. This gene specifies a protein called myocilin whose normal function in the eye is at present unknown. The mutant allele encodes a form of myocilin that folds incorrectly and then accumulates abnormally in the tiny canals through which eye fluid normally drains into the bloodstream. Misfolded myocilin blocks the outflow of excess vitreous humor, and the resulting increased pressure within the eye (glaucoma) eventually damages the optic nerve, leading to blindness.

Knowledge of the specific disease-causing mutations in the *myocilin* gene has more recently led to the development of diagnostic tests based on the direct analysis of genotype. (We describe methods for direct genotype analysis in Chapters 9 and 11.) These DNA-based tests can not only identify individuals at risk, but they can also improve disease management. Detection of the mutant allele before the optic nerve is permanently damaged allows for timely treatment. If these tests become sufficiently inexpensive in the future, they could resolve France's ethical dilemma. Doctors could routinely administer the tests to all newborns and immediately identify nearly all potentially affected children; private information in a pedigree would thus not be needed.

---

pure-breeding plants carrying only *1* alleles at each height gene? If only one gene were responsible for height, and if environmental effects could be discounted, the F₂ population would be distributed among three classes: homozygous A^0A^0 plants with 0 height (they lie prostrate on the ground); heterozygous A^0A^1 plants with a height of 1; and homozygous A^1A^1 plants with a height of 2 (**Fig. 3.22a** on p. 68). This distribution of heights

over three phenotypic classes does not make a continuous curve. But for two genes, there will be five phenotypic classes in the F₂ generation (**Fig. 3.22b**); for three genes, seven classes (**Fig. 3.22c**); and for four genes, nine classes (not shown).

The distributions produced by three and four genes thus begin to approach continuous variation, and if we add a small contribution from environmental variation,

Figure 3.22 A Mendelian explanation of continuous variation. The more genes or alleles, the more possible phenotypic classes, and the greater the similarity to continuous variation. In these examples, several pairs of incompletely dominant alleles have additive effects. Percentages shown at the *bottom* denote frequencies of each genotype expressed as fractions of the total population.

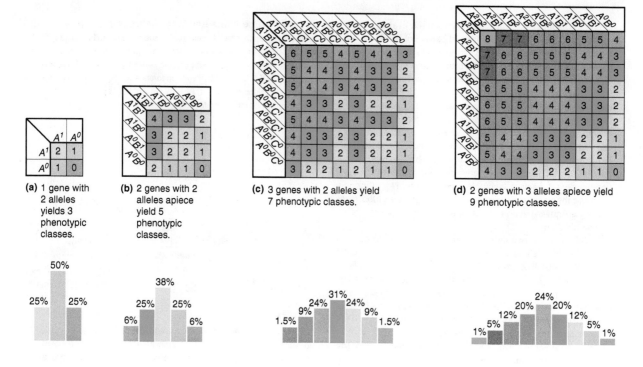

(a) 1 gene with 2 alleles yields 3 phenotypic classes.

(b) 2 genes with 2 alleles apiece yield 5 phenotypic classes.

(c) 3 genes with 2 alleles yield 7 phenotypic classes.

(d) 2 genes with 3 alleles apiece yield 9 phenotypic classes.

a smoother curve will appear. After all, we would expect bean plants to grow better in good soil, with ample sunlight and water. The environmental component effectively converts the stepped bar graph to a continuous curve by producing some variation in expressivity within each genotypic class. Moreover, additional variation might arise from more than two alleles at some genes (Fig. 3.22d), unequal contribution to the phenotype by the various genes involved (review Fig. 3.17 on p. 61), interactions with modifier genes, and chance. Thus, from what we now know about the relation between genotype and phenotype, it is possible to see how just a handful of genes that behave according to known Mendelian principles can easily generate continuous variation.

Continuous traits (also called **quantitative traits**) vary over a range of values and can usually be measured: the length of a tobacco flower in millimeters, the amount of milk produced by a cow per day in liters, or the height of a person in meters. Continuous traits are usually **polygenic**—controlled by multiple genes—and show the additive effects of a large number of alleles, which creates an enormous potential for variation within a population. Differences in the environments encountered by different individuals contribute even more variation. We discuss

the analysis and distribution of multifactorial traits in Chapter 19 on population genetics.

> The action of a handful of genes, combined with environmental effects, can produce an enormous range of phenotypic variation for a particular trait.

A comprehensive example: Mouse coat color is determined by multiple alleles of several genes

Most field mice are a dark gray (agouti), but mice bred for specific mutations in the laboratory can be gray, tan, yellow, brown, black, or various combinations thereof. Here we look at the alleles of three of the genes that make such variation possible. This review underscores how allelic interactions of just a handful of genes can produce an astonishing diversity of phenotypes.

Gene 1: Agouti or other color patterns

The *agouti* gene determines the distribution of color on each hair, and it has multiple alleles. The wild-type allele *A* specifies bands of yellow and black that give the agouti appearance; A^y gets rid of the black and thus produces solid yellow; a gets rid of the yellow and thus produces solid black; and a^t specifies black on the animal's back and yellow on the belly. The dominance series for this set of *agouti* gene alleles is $A^y > A > a^t > a$. However, although A^y is dominant to all other alleles for coat color, it is recessive to all the others for lethality: A^yA^y homozygotes die before birth, while A^yA, A^ya^t, or A^ya heterozygotes survive.

Gene 2: Black or brown

A second gene specifies whether the dark color of each hair is black or brown. This gene has two alleles: B is dominant and designates black; b is recessive and generates brown. Because the A^y allele at the *agouti* gene completely eliminates the dark band of each hair, it acts in a dominant epistatic manner to the B gene. With all other *agouti* alleles, however, it is possible to distinguish the effects of the two different B alleles on phenotype. The $A-\ B-$ genotype gives rise to the wild-type agouti having black with yellow hairs. The $A-\ bb$ genotype generates a color referred to as cinnamon (with hairs having stripes of brown and yellow); $aa\ bb$ is all brown; and $a^ta^t\ bb$ is brown on the animal's back and yellow on the belly. A cross between two F_1 hybrid animals of genotype $A^ya\ Bb$ would yield an F_2 generation with yellow ($A^ya\ -\ -$), black ($aa\ B-$), and brown ($aa\ bb$) animals in a ratio of 8:3:1. This ratio reflects the dominant epistasis

of A^y and the loss of a class of four ($A^yA^y\ -\ -$) due to prenatal lethality.

Gene 3: Albino or pigmented

Like other mammals, mice have a third gene influencing coat color. A recessive allele (c) abolishes the function of the enzyme that leads to the formation of the dark pigment melanin, making this allele epistatic to all other coat color genes. As a result, cc homozygotes are pure white, while $C-$ mice are agouti, black, brown, yellow, or yellow and black (or other colors and patterns), depending on what alleles they carry at the A and B genes, as well as at some 50 other genes known to play a role in determining the coat color of mice. Adding to the complex color potential are other alleles that geneticists have uncovered for the albino gene; these cause only a partial inactivation of the melanin-producing enzyme and thus have a partial epistatic effect on phenotype.

This comprehensive example of coat color in mice gives some idea of the potential for variation from just a few genes, some with multiple alleles. Amazingly, this is just the tip of the iceberg. When you realize that both mice and humans carry roughly 25,000 genes, the number of interactions that connect the various alleles of these genes in the expression of phenotype is in the millions, if not the billions. The potential for variation and diversity among individuals is staggering indeed.

Connections

Part of Mendel's genius was to look at the genetic basis of variation through a very narrow window, focusing his first glimpse of the mechanisms of inheritance on simple yet fundamental phenomena. Mendel worked on just a handful of traits in inbred populations of one species. For each trait, he manipulated one gene with one completely dominant and one recessive allele that determined two distinguishable, or discontinuous, phenotypes. Both the dominant and recessive alleles showed complete penetrance and negligible differences of expressivity.

In the first few decades of the twentieth century, many questioned the general applicability of Mendelian analysis, for it seemed to shed little light on the complex inheritance patterns of most plant and animal traits or on the mechanisms producing continuous variation. Simple embellishments, however, clarified the genetic basis of continuous variation and provided explanations for other apparent exceptions to Mendelian analysis. These embellishments included the ideas that dominance need not be complete; that one gene can have multiple alleles; that one gene can determine more than one trait; that several

genes can contribute to the same trait; and that the expression of genes can be affected in a variety of ways by other genes, the environment, and chance. Each embellishment extends the range of Mendelian analysis and deepens our understanding of the genetic basis of variation. And no matter how broad the view, Mendel's basic conclusions, embodied in his first law of segregation, remain valid.

But what about Mendel's second law that genes assort independently? As it turns out, its application is not as universal as that of the law of segregation. Many genes do assort independently, but some do not; rather, they appear to be linked and transmitted together from generation to generation. An understanding of this fact emerged from studies that located Mendel's hereditary units, the genes, in specific cellular organelles, the chromosomes. In describing how researchers deduced that genes travel with chromosomes, Chapter 4 establishes the physical basis of inheritance, including the segregation of alleles, and clarifies why some genes assort independently while others do not.

ESSENTIAL CONCEPTS

1. The F_1 phenotype defines the dominance relationship between each pair of alleles. One allele is not always completely dominant or completely recessive to another. With incomplete dominance, the F_1 hybrid phenotype resembles neither parent. With codominance, the F_1 hybrid phenotype includes aspects derived from both parents. Many allele pairs are codominant at the level of protein production.

2. In pleiotropy, one gene contributes to multiple traits. For such a gene, the dominance relation between any two alleles can vary according to the particular phenotype under consideration.

3. A single gene may have any number of alleles, each of which can cause the appearance of different phenotypes. New alleles arise by mutation. Common alleles in a population are considered wild types; rare alleles are mutants. When two or more common alleles exist for a gene, the gene is polymorphic; a gene with only one wild-type allele is monomorphic.

4. Two or more genes may interact in several ways to affect the production of a single trait. These interactions may be understood by observing characteristic deviations from traditional Mendelian phenotypic ratios (review Table 3.2).

5. In epistasis, the action of an allele at one gene can hide traits normally caused by the expression of alleles at another gene. In complementary gene action, dominant alleles of two or more genes are required to generate a trait. In heterogeneity, mutant alleles at any one of two or more genes are sufficient to elicit a phenotype. The complementation test can reveal whether a particular phenotype seen in two individuals arises from mutations in the same or separate genes.

6. In many cases, the route from genotype to phenotype can be modified by the environment, chance, or other genes. A phenotype shows incomplete penetrance when it is expressed in fewer than 100% of individuals with the same genotype. A phenotype shows variable expressivity when it is expressed at a quantitatively different level among individuals with the same genotype.

7. A continuous trait can have any value of expression between two extremes. Most traits of this type are polygenic, that is, determined by the interactions of multiple genes.

On Our Website   www.mhhe.com/hartwell4

Annotated Suggested Readings and Links to Other Websites

- Additional historical examples of complications in Mendelian analysis
- Recently discovered interesting genetic systems

Specialized Topics

- Use of chi-square analysis to test the likelihood that the experimental outcomes of a cross can be explained by a particular hypothesis for the mode of inheritance. (This is a different use of chi-square analysis than the one we present in Chapter 5, where we introduce the technique as a way to determine whether two genes are linked to each other.)

Solved Problems

I. Imagine you purchased an albino mouse (genotype *cc*) in a pet store. The *c* allele is epistatic to other coat color genes. How would you go about determining the genotype of this mouse at the brown locus? (In pigmented mice, *BB* and *Bb* are black, *bb* is brown.)

Answer

This problem requires an understanding of gene interactions, specifically epistasis. You have been placed in the role of experimenter and need to design crosses that will answer the question. To determine the alleles of the *B* gene present, you need to eliminate the blocking action of the *cc* genotype. Because only the recessive *c* allele is epistatic, when a *C* allele is present, no epistasis will occur. To introduce a *C* allele during the mating, the test mouse you mate to your albino can have the genotype *CC* or *Cc*. (If the mouse is *Cc,* half of the progeny will be albino and will not contribute useful information, but the nonalbinos from this cross would be informative.) What alleles of the *B* gene should the test mouse carry? To make this decision, work through the expected results using each of the possible genotypes.

Test mouse genotype		Albino mouse	Expected progeny
BB	×	*BB*	all black
	×	*Bb*	all black
	×	*bb*	all black
Bb	×	*BB*	all black
	×	*Bb*	3/4 black, 1/4 brown
	×	*bb*	1/2 black, 1/2 brown
bb	×	*BB*	all black
	×	*Bb*	1/2 black, 1/2 brown
	×	*bb*	all brown

From these hypothetical crosses, you can see that a test mouse with either the *Bb* or *bb* genotype would yield distinct outcomes for each of the three possible albino mouse genotypes. However, a *bb* test mouse would be more useful and less ambiguous. First, it is easier to identify a mouse with the *bb* genotype because a brown mouse must have this homozygous recessive genotype. Second, the results are completely different for each of the three possible genotypes when you use the *bb* test mouse. (In contrast, a *Bb* test mouse would yield both black and brown progeny whether the albino mouse was *Bb* or *bb;* the only distinguishing feature is the ratio.) *To determine the full genotype of the albino mouse, you should cross it to a brown mouse (which could be* CC bb *or* Cc bb*).*

II. In a particular kind of wildflower, the wild-type flower color is deep purple, and the plants are true-breeding. In one true-breeding mutant stock, the flowers have a reduced pigmentation, resulting in a lavender color. In a different true-breeding mutant stock, the flowers have no pigmentation and are thus white. When a lavender-flowered plant from the first mutant stock was crossed to a white-flowered plant from the second mutant stock, all the F_1 plants had purple flowers. The F_1 plants were then allowed to self-fertilize to produce an F_2 generation. The 277 F_2 plants were 157 purple : 71 white : 49 lavender. Explain how flower color is inherited. Is this trait controlled by the alleles of a single gene? What

kinds of progeny would be produced if lavender F_2 plants were allowed to self-fertilize?

Answer

Are there any modes of single-gene inheritance compatible with the data? The observations that the F_1 plants look different from either of their parents and that the F_2 generation is composed of plants with three different phenotypes exclude complete dominance. The ratio of the three phenotypes in the F_2 plants has some resemblance to the 1:2:1 ratio expected from codominance or incomplete dominance, but the results would then imply that purple plants must be heterozygotes. This conflicts with the information provided that purple plants are true-breeding.

Consider now the possibility that two genes are involved. From a cross between plants heterozygous for two genes (*W* and *P*), the F_2 generation would contain a 9:3:3:1 ratio of the genotypes *W– P–*, *W– pp*, *ww P–*, and *ww pp* (where the dash indicates that the allele could be either a dominant or a recessive form). Are there any combinations of the 9:3:3:1 ratio that would be close to that seen in the F_2 generation in this example? The numbers seem close to a 9:4:3 ratio. What hypothesis would support combining two of the classes (3 + 1)? If *w* is epistatic to the *P* gene, then the *ww P–* and *ww pp* genotypic classes would have the same white phenotype. With this explanation, 1/3 of the F_2 lavender plants would be *WW pp*, and the remaining 2/3 would be *Ww pp*. Upon self-fertilization, *WW pp* plants would produce only lavender (*WW pp*) progeny, while *Ww pp* plants would produce a 3:1 ratio of lavender (*W– pp*) and white (*ww pp*) progeny.

III. Huntington disease (HD) is a rare dominant condition in humans that results in a slow but inexorable deterioration of the nervous system. HD shows what might be called "age-dependent penetrance," which is to say that the probability that a person with the HD genotype will express the phenotype varies with age. Assume that 50% of those inheriting the *HD* allele will express the symptoms by age 40. Susan is a 35-year-old woman whose father has HD. She currently shows no symptoms. What is the probability that Susan will show symptoms in five years?

Answer

This problem involves probability and penetrance. Two conditions are necessary for Susan to show symptoms of the disease. There is a 1/2 (50%) chance that she inherited the mutant allele from her father and a 1/2 (50%) chance that she will express the phenotype by age 40. Because these are independent events, *the probability is the product of the individual probabilities, or 1/4.*

Problems

Interactive Web Exercise

PubMed is a database maintained by the National Center for Biotechnology Information (NCBI) that provides synopses of, and in many cases direct access to, published biomedical journal articles. This database is invaluable to genetics researchers, as well as all biologists and physicians. Our website at www.mhhe.com/hartwell4 contains a brief exercise introducing you to the resources at PubMed; once at the website, go to Chapter 3 and click on "Interactive Web Exercise."

Vocabulary

1. For each of the terms in the left column, choose the best matching phrase in the right column.

   a. epistasis
   b. modifier gene
   c. conditional lethal
   d. permissive condition
   e. reduced penetrance
   f. multifactorial trait
   g. incomplete dominance
   h. codominance
   i. histocompatibility antigens
   j. mutation
   k. pleiotropy
   l. variable expressivity

   1. one gene affecting more than one phenotype
   2. the alleles of one gene mask the effects of alleles of another gene
   3. both parental phenotypes are expressed in the F_1 hybrids
   4. a heritable change in a gene
   5. cell surface molecules that are involved in the immune system and are highly variable
   6. genes whose alleles alter phenotypes produced by the action of other genes
   7. less than 100% of the individuals possessing a particular genotype express it in their phenotype
   8. environmental conditions that allow conditional lethals to live
   9. a trait produced by the interaction of alleles of at least two genes or from interactions between gene and environment
   10. individuals with the same genotype have related phenotypes that vary in intensity
   11. a genotype that is lethal in some situations (for example, high temperature) but viable in others
   12. the heterozygote resembles neither homozygote

Section 3.1

2. In four-o'clocks, the allele for red flowers is incompletely dominant over the allele for white flowers, so heterozygotes have pink flowers. What ratios of flower colors would you expect among the offspring of the following crosses: (a) pink × pink, (b) white × pink, (c) red × red, (d) red × pink, (e) white × white, and (f) red × white? If you specifically wanted to produce pink flowers, which of these crosses would be most efficient?

3. A cross between two plants that both have yellow flowers produces 80 offspring plants, of which 38 have yellow flowers, 22 have red flowers, and 20 have white flowers. If one assumes that this variation in color is due to inheritance at a single locus, what is the genotype associated with each flower color, and how can you describe the inheritance of flower color?

4. In the fruit fly *Drosophila melanogaster,* very dark (ebony) body color is determined by the e allele. The e^+ allele produces the normal wild-type, honey-colored body. In heterozygotes for the two alleles, a dark marking called the trident can be seen on the thorax, but otherwise the body is honey-colored. The e^+ allele is thus considered to be incompletely dominant to the e allele.

   a. When female e^+e^+ flies are crossed to male e^+e flies, what is the probability that progeny will have the dark trident marking?
   b. Animals with the trident marking mate among themselves. Of 300 progeny, how many would be expected to have a trident, how many ebony bodies, and how many honey-colored bodies?

5. A wild legume with white flowers and long pods is crossed to one with purple flowers and short pods. The F_1 offspring are allowed to self-fertilize, and the F_2 generation has 301 long purple, 99 short purple, 612 long pink, 195 short pink, 295 long white, and 98 short white. How are these traits being inherited?

6. In radishes, color and shape are each controlled by a single locus with two incompletely dominant alleles. Color may be red (RR), purple (Rr), or white (rr) and shape can be long (LL), oval (Ll), or round (ll). What phenotypic classes and proportions would you expect among the offspring of a cross between two plants heterozygous at both loci?

7. Familial hypercholesterolemia (FH) is an inherited trait in humans that results in higher than normal serum cholesterol levels (measured in milligrams of cholesterol per deciliter of blood [mg/dl]). People with serum cholesterol levels that are roughly twice normal have a 25 times higher frequency of heart attacks than unaffected individuals. People with serum cholesterol levels three or more times higher than normal have severely blocked arteries and almost always die before they reach the age of 20.

The pedigrees below show the occurrence of FH in four Japanese families:

a. What is the most likely mode of inheritance of FH based on this data? Are there any individuals in any of these pedigrees who do not fit your hypothesis? What special conditions might account for such individuals?

b. Why do individuals in the same phenotypic class (unfilled, yellow, or red symbols) show such variation in their levels of serum cholesterol?

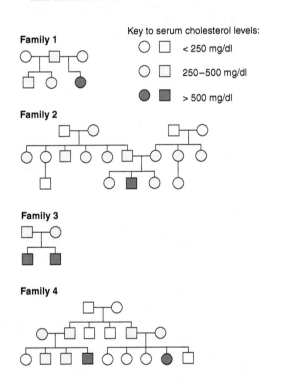

Family 1

Family 2

Family 3

Family 4

Key to serum cholesterol levels:

○ □ < 250 mg/dl

○ □ 250–500 mg/dl

● ■ > 500 mg/dl

8. Describe briefly:

a. The genotype of a person who has sickle-cell anemia.

b. The genotype of a person with a normal phenotype who has a child with sickle-cell anemia.

c. The *total* number of different alleles of the β-globin gene that could be carried by five children with the same mother and father.

9. Assuming no involvement of the Bombay phenotype:

a. If a girl has blood type O, what could be the genotypes and corresponding phenotypes of her parents?

b. If a girl has blood type B and her mother has blood type A, what genotype(s) and corresponding phenotype(s) could the other parent have?

c. If a girl has blood type AB and her mother is also AB, what are the genotype(s) and corresponding phenotype(s) of any male who could *not* be the girl's father?

10. There are several genes in humans in addition to the *ABO* gene that give rise to recognizable antigens on the surface of red blood cells. The *MN* and *Rh* genes are two examples. The *Rh* locus can contain either a positive or negative allele, with positive being dominant to negative. *M* and *N* are codominant alleles of the *MN* gene. The following chart shows several mothers and their children. For each mother–child pair, choose the father of the child from among the males in the right column, assuming one child per male.

	Mother	Child	Males
a.	O M Rh pos	B MN Rh neg	O M Rh neg
b.	B MN Rh neg	O N Rh neg	A M Rh pos
c.	O M Rh pos	A M Rh neg	O MN Rh pos
d.	AB N Rh neg	B MN Rh neg	B MN Rh pos

11. Alleles of the gene that determines seed coat patterns in lentils can be organized in a dominance series: marbled > spotted = dotted (codominant alleles) > clear. A lentil plant homozygous for the marbled seed coat pattern allele was crossed to one homozygous for the spotted pattern allele. In another cross, a homozygous dotted lentil plant was crossed to one homozygous for clear. An F_1 plant from the first cross was then mated to an F_1 plant from the second cross.

a. What phenotypes in what proportions are expected from this mating between the two F_1 types?

b. What are the expected phenotypes of the F_1 plants from the two original parental crosses?

12. In clover plants, the pattern on the leaves is determined by a single gene with multiple alleles that are related in a dominance series. Seven different alleles of this gene are known; an allele that determines the absence of a pattern is recessive to the other six alleles, each of which produces a different pattern. All heterozygous combinations of alleles show complete dominance.

a. How many different kinds of leaf patterns (including the absence of a pattern) are possible in a population of clover plants in which all seven alleles are represented?

b. What is the largest number of different genotypes that could be associated with any one phenotype? Is there any phenotype that could be represented by only a single genotype?

c. In a particular field, you find that the large majority of clover plants lack a pattern on their leaves, even though you can identify a few plants representative of all possible pattern types. Explain this finding.

13. In a population of rabbits, you find three different coat color phenotypes: chinchilla (C), himalaya (H), and albino (A). To understand the inheritance of coat

colors, you cross individual rabbits with each other and note the results in the following table.

Cross number	Parental phenotypes	Phenotypes of progeny
1	H × H	3/4 H : 1/4 A
2	H × A	1/2 H : 1/2 A
3	C × C	3/4 C : 1/4 H
4	C × H	all C
5	C × C	3/4 C : 1/4 A
6	H × A	all H
7	C × A	1/2 C : 1/2 A
8	A × A	all A
9	C × H	1/2 C : 1/2 H
10	C × H	1/2 C : 1/4 H : 1/4 A

a. What can you conclude about the inheritance of coat color in this population of rabbits?

b. Ascribe genotypes to the parents in each of the 10 crosses.

c. What kinds of progeny would you expect, and in what proportions, if you crossed the chinchilla parents in crosses #9 and #10?

14. Some plant species have an incompatibility system different from that shown in Fig. 3.8. In this alternate kind of incompatibility, a mating cannot produce viable seeds if the male parent shares an incompatibility allele with the female parent. (Just as with the kind of incompatibility system shown in Fig. 3.8, this system ensures that all plants are heterozygous for the incompatibility gene.) Five plants were isolated from a wild population of a species with this alternate type of incompatiblity. The results of matings between each pair of plants are given here (− means no seeds were produced; + means seeds were produced). How many different alleles of the incompatibility gene are present in this group of five plants? What are the genotypes of the five plants?

	1	2	3	4	5
1	−	−	−	+	−
2		−	+	+	+
3			−	+	−
4				−	−
5					−

15. Fruit flies with one allele for curly wings (Cy) and one allele for normal wings (Cy⁺) have curly wings. When two curly-winged flies were crossed, 203 curly-winged and 98 normal-winged flies were obtained. In fact, all crosses between curly-winged flies produce nearly the same curly : normal ratio among the progeny.

a. What is the approximate phenotypic ratio in these offspring?

b. Suggest an explanation for these data.

c. If a curly-winged fly was mated to a normal-winged fly, how many flies of each type would you expect among 180 total offspring?

16. Spherocytosis is an inherited blood disease in which the erythrocytes (red blood cells) are spherical instead of biconcave. This condition is inherited in a dominant fashion, with Sph^- dominant to Sph^+. In people with spherocytosis, the spleen "reads" the spherical red blood cells as defective, and it removes them from the bloodstream, leading to anemia. The spleen in different people removes the spherical erythrocytes with different efficiencies. Some people with spherical erythrocytes suffer severe anemia and some mild anemia, yet others have spleens that function so poorly there are no symptoms of anemia at all. When 2400 people with the genotype $Sph^- Sph^+$ were examined, it was found that 2250 had anemia of varying severity, but 150 had no symptoms.

a. Does this description of people with spherocytosis represent incomplete penetrance, variable expressivity, or both? Explain your answer. Can you derive any values from the numerical data to measure penetrance or expressivity?

b. Suggest a treatment for spherocytosis and describe how the incomplete penetrance and/or variable expressivity of the condition might affect this treatment.

17. In a species of tropical fish, a colorful orange and black variety called montezuma occurs. When two montezumas, are crossed, 2/3 of the progeny are montezuma, and 1/3 are the wild-type, dark grayish green color. Montezuma is a single-gene trait, and montezuma fish are never true-breeding.

a. Explain the inheritance pattern seen here and show how your explanation accounts for the phenotypic ratios given.

b. In this same species, the morphology of the dorsal fin is altered from normal to ruffled by homozygosity for a recessive allele designated f. What progeny would you expect to obtain, and in what proportions, from the cross of a montezuma fish homozygous for normal fins to a green, ruffled fish?

c. What phenotypic ratios of progeny would be expected from the crossing of two of the montezuma progeny from part b?

18. You have come into contact with two unrelated patients who express what you think is a rare phenotype—a dark spot on the bottom of the foot. According to a medical source, this phenotype is seen in 1 in every 100,000 people in the population. The two patients give their family histories to you, and you generate the pedigrees that follow.

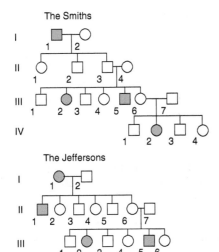

The Smiths

The Jeffersons

a. Given that this trait is rare, do you think the inheritance is dominant or recessive? Are there any special conditions that appear to apply to the inheritance?

b. Which nonexpressing members of these families must carry the mutant allele?

c. If this trait is instead quite common in the population, what alternative explanation would you propose for the inheritance?

d. Based on this new explanation (part *c*), which non-expressing members of these families must have the genotype normally causing the trait?

19. Polycystic kidney disease is a dominant trait that causes the growth of numerous cysts in the kidneys. The condition eventually leads to kidney failure. A child with polycystic kidney disease is born to a couple, neither of whom shows the disease. What possibilities might explain this outcome?

Section 3.2

20. A rooster with a particular comb morphology called walnut was crossed to a hen with a type of comb morphology known as single. The F_1 progeny all had walnut combs. When F_1 males and females were crossed to each other, 93 walnut and 11 single combs were seen among the F_2 progeny, but there were also 29 birds with a new kind of comb called rose and 32 birds with another new comb type called pea.

a. Explain how comb morphology is inherited.

b. What progeny would result from crossing a homozygous rose-combed hen with a homozygous pea-combed rooster? What phenotypes and ratios would be seen in the F_2 progeny?

c. A particular walnut rooster was crossed to a pea hen, and the progeny consisted of 12 walnut,

11 pea, 3 rose, and 4 single chickens. What are the likely genotypes of the parents?

d. A different walnut rooster was crossed to a rose hen, and all the progeny were walnut. What are the possible genotypes of the parents?

21. A black mare was crossed to a chestnut stallion and produced a bay son and a bay daughter. The two offspring were mated to each other several times, and they produced offspring of four different coat colors: black, bay, chestnut, and liver. Crossing a liver grandson back to the black mare gave a black foal, and crossing a liver granddaughter back to the chestnut stallion gave a chestnut foal. Explain how coat color is being inherited in these horses.

22. Filled-in symbols in the pedigree that follows designate individuals suffering from deafness.

a. Study the pedigree and explain how deafness is being inherited.

b. What is the genotype of the individuals in generation V? Why are they not affected?

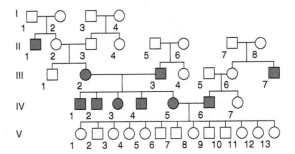

23. You do a cross between two true-breeding strains of zucchini. One has green fruit and the other has yellow fruit. The F_1 plants are all green, but when these are crossed, the F_2 plants consist of 9 green : 7 yellow.

a. Explain this result. What were the genotypes of the two parental strains?

b. Indicate the phenotypes, with frequencies, of the progeny of a testcross of the F_1 plants.

24. Two true-breeding white strains of the plant *Illegitimati noncarborundum* were mated, and the F_1 progeny were all white. When the F_1 plants were allowed to self-fertilize, 126 white-flowered and 33 purple-flowered F_2 plants grew.

a. How could you describe inheritance of flower color? Describe how specific alleles influence each other and therefore affect phenotype.

b. A white F_2 plant is allowed to self-fertilize. Of the progeny, 3/4 are white-flowered, and 1/4 are purple-flowered. What is the genotype of the white F_2 plant?

c. A purple F_2 plant is allowed to self-fertilize. Of the progeny, 3/4 are purple-flowered, and 1/4 are white-flowered. What is the genotype of the purple F_2 plant?

d. Two white F_2 plants are crossed with each other. Of the progeny, 1/2 are purple-flowered, and 1/2 are white-flowered. What are the genotypes of the two white F_2 plants?

25. Explain the difference between epistasis and dominance. How many loci are involved in each case?

26. As you will learn in later chapters, duplication of genes is an important evolutionary mechanism. As a result, many cases are known in which a species has two or more nearly identical genes.

a. Suppose there are two genes, A and B, that specify production of the same enzyme. An abnormal phenotype results only if an individual does not make any of that enzyme. What ratio of normal versus abnormal progeny would result from a mating between two parents of genotype $Aa\ Bb$, where A and B represent alleles that specify production of the enzyme, while a and b are alleles that do not?

b. Suppose now that there are three genes specifying production of this enzyme, and again that a single functional allele is sufficient for a wild-type phenotype. What ratio of normal versus abnormal progeny would result from a mating between two triply heterozygous parents?

27. "Secretors" (genotypes SS and Ss) secrete their A and B blood group antigens into their saliva and other body fluids, while "nonsecretors" (ss) do not. What would be the apparent phenotypic blood group proportions among the offspring of an $I^A I^B\ Ss$ woman and an $I^A I^A\ Ss$ man if typing was done using saliva?

28. Normally, wild violets have yellow petals with dark brown markings and erect stems. Imagine you discover a plant with white petals, no markings, and prostrate stems. What experiment could you perform to determine whether the non-wild-type phenotypes are due to several different mutant genes or to the pleiotropic effects of alleles at a single locus? Explain how your experiment would settle the question.

29. The following table shows the responses of blood samples from the individuals in the pedigree to anti-A and anti-B sera. A "+" in the anti-A row indicates that the red blood cells of that individual were clumped by anti-A serum and therefore the individual made A antigens, and a "−" indicates no clumping. The same notation is used to describe the test for the B antigens.

a. Deduce the blood type of each individual from the data in the table.

b. Assign genotypes for the blood groups as accurately as you can from these data, explaining the pattern of inheritance shown in the pedigree. Assume that all genetic relationships are as presented in the pedigree (that is, there are no cases of false paternity).

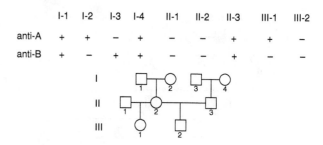

	I-1	I-2	I-3	I-4	II-1	II-2	II-3	III-1	III-2
anti-A	+	+	−	+	−	−	+	+	−
anti-B	+	−	+	+	−	−	+	−	−

30. Three different pure-breeding strains of corn that produce ears with white kernels were crossed to each other. In each case, the F_1 plants were all red, while both red and white kernels were observed in the F_2 generation in a 9:7 ratio. These results are tabulated here.

	F_1	F_2
white-1 × white-2	red	9 red : 7 white
white-1 × white-3	red	9 red : 7 white
white-2 × white-3	red	9 red : 7 white

a. How many genes are involved in determining kernel color in these three strains?

b. Define your symbols and show the genotypes for the pure-breeding strains white-1, white-2, and white-3.

c. Diagram the cross between white-1 and white-2, showing the genotypes and phenotypes of the F_1 and F_2 progeny. Explain the observed 9:7 ratio.

31. In mice, the A^y allele of the *agouti* gene is a recessive lethal allele, but it is dominant for yellow coat color. What phenotypes and ratios of offspring would you expect from the cross of a mouse heterozygous at the agouti locus (genotype $A^y A$) and also at the albino locus (Cc) to an albino mouse (cc) heterozygous at the agouti locus ($A^y A$)?

32. A student whose hobby was fishing pulled a very unusual carp out of Cayuga Lake: It had no scales on its body. She decided to investigate whether this strange nude phenotype had a genetic basis. She therefore obtained some inbred carp that were pure-breeding for the wild-type scale phenotype (body covered with scales in a regular pattern) and crossed them with her nude fish. To her surprise, the F_1 progeny consisted of wild-type fish and fish with a single linear row of scales on each side in a 1:1 ratio.

a. Can a single gene with two alleles account for this result? Why or why not?

b. To follow up on the first cross, the student allowed the linear fish from the F_1 generation to mate with each other. The progeny of this cross consisted of fish with four phenotypes: linear, wild type, nude, and scattered (the latter had a few scales scattered irregularly on the body). The ratio of these phenotypes was 6:3:2:1, respectively. How many genes appear to be involved in determining these phenotypes?

c. In parallel, the student allowed the phenotypically wild-type fish from the F_1 generation to mate with each other and observed, among their progeny, wild-type and scattered carp in a ratio of 3:1. How many genes with how many alleles appear to determine the difference between wild-type and scattered carp?

d. The student confirmed the conclusions of part *c* by crossing those scattered carp with her pure-breeding wild-type stock. Diagram the genotypes and phenotypes of the parental, F_1, and F_2 generations for this cross and indicate the ratios observed.

e. The student attempted to generate a true-breeding nude stock of fish by inbreeding. However, she found that this was impossible. Every time she crossed two nude fish, she found nude and scattered fish in the progeny, in a 2:1 ratio. (The scattered fish from these crosses bred true.) Diagram the phenotypes and genotypes of this gene in a nude × nude cross and explain the altered Mendelian ratio.

f. The student now felt she could explain all of her results. Diagram the genotypes in the linear × linear cross performed by the student (in part *b*). Show the genotypes of the four phenotypes observed among the progeny and explain the 6:3:2:1 ratio.

33. You picked up two mice (one female and one male) that had escaped from experimental cages in the animal facility. One mouse is yellow in color, and the other is brown agouti. You know that this mouse colony has animals with different alleles at only three coat color genes: the agouti or nonagouti or yellow alleles of the *A* gene, the black or brown allele of the *B* gene, and the albino or nonalbino alleles of the *C* gene. However, you don't know which alleles of these genes are actually present in each of the animals that you've captured. To determine the genotypes, you breed them together. The first litter has only three pups. One is albino, one is brown (nonagouti), and the third is black agouti.

a. What alleles of the *A, B,* and *C* genes are present in the two mice you caught?

b. After raising several litters from these two parents, you have many offspring. How many different coat color phenotypes (in total) do you expect to see expressed in the population of offspring? What are the phenotypes and corresponding genotypes?

34. Figure 3.17 on p. 61 and Fig. 3.22b on p. 68 both show traits that are determined by two genes, each of which has two incompletely dominant alleles. But in Fig. 3.17 the gene interaction produces nine different phenotypes, while the situation depicted in Fig. 3.22b shows only five possible phenotypic classes. How can you explain this difference in the amount of phenotypic variation?

35. Three genes in fruit flies affect a particular trait, and one dominant allele of *each* gene is necessary to get a wild-type phenotype.

a. What phenotypic ratios would you predict among the progeny if you crossed triply heterozygous flies?

b. You cross a particular wild-type male in succession with three tester strains. In the cross with one tester strain (*AA bb cc*), only 1/4 of the progeny are wild type. In the crosses involving the other two tester strains (*aa BB cc* and *aa bb CC*), half of the progeny are wild type. What is the genotype of the wild-type male?

36. The garden flower *Salpiglossis sinuata* ("painted tongue") comes in many different colors. Several crosses are made between true-breeding parental strains to produce F_1 plants, which are in turn self-fertilized to produce F_2 progeny.

Parents	F_1 phenotypes	F_2 phenotypes
red × blue	all red	102 red, 33 blue
lavender × blue	all lavender	149 lavender, 51 blue
lavender × red	all bronze	84 bronze, 43 red, 41 lavender
red × yellow	all red	133 red, 58 yellow, 43 blue
yellow × blue	all lavender	183 lavender, 81 yellow, 59 blue

a. State a hypothesis explaining the inheritance of flower color in painted tongues.

b. Assign genotypes to the parents, F_1 progeny, and F_2 progeny for all five crosses.

c. In a cross between true-breeding yellow and true-breeding lavender plants, all of the F_1 progeny are bronze. If you used these F_1 plants to produce an F_2 generation, what phenotypes in what ratios would you expect? Are there any genotypes that might produce a phenotype that you cannot predict from earlier experiments, and if so, how might this alter the phenotypic ratios among the F_2 progeny?

37. In foxgloves, there are three different petal phenotypes: white with red spots (WR), dark red (DR), and light red (LR). There are actually two different kinds of true-breeding WR strains (WR-1 and WR-2) that can be distinguished by two-generation intercrosses with true-breeding DR and LR strains:

	Parental	F_1	F_2		
			WR	**LR**	**DR**
1	WR-1 × LR	all WR	480	39	119
2	WR-1 × DR	all WR	99	0	32
3	DR × LR	all DR	0	43	132
4	WR-2 × LR	all WR	193	64	0
5	WR-2 × DR	all WR	286	24	74

a. What can you conclude about the inheritance of the petal phenotypes in foxgloves?

b. Ascribe genotypes to the four true-breeding parental strains (WR-1, WR-2, DR, and LR).

c. A WR plant from the F_2 generation of cross #1 is now crossed with an LR plant. Of 500 total progeny from this cross, there were 253 WR, 124 DR, and 123 LR plants. What are the genotypes of the parents in this WR × LR mating?

38. In a culture of fruit flies, matings between any two flies with hairy wings (wings abnormally containing additional small hairs along their edges) always produce both hairy-winged and normal-winged flies in a 2:1 ratio. You now take hairy-winged flies from this culture and cross them with four types of normal-winged flies; the results for each cross are shown in the following table. Assuming that there are only two possible alleles of the hairy-winged gene (one for hairy wings and one for normal wings), what can you say about the genotypes of the four types of normal-winged flies?

Type of normal-winged flies	Progeny obtained from cross with hairy-winged flies	
	Fraction with normal wings	Fraction with hairy wings
1	1/2	1/2
2	1	0
3	3/4	1/4
4	2/3	1/3

39. A married man and woman, both of whom are deaf, carry some recessive mutant alleles in three different "hearing genes": *d1* is recessive to *D1, d2* is recessive to *D2*, and *d3* is recessive to *D3*. Homozygosity for a mutant allele at any one of these three genes causes deafness. In addition, homozygosity for any two of the three genes together in the same genome will cause prenatal lethality (and spontaneous abortion) with a penetrance of 25%. Furthermore, homozygosity for the mutant alleles of all three genes will cause prenatal lethality with a penetrance of 75%. If the genotypes of the mother and father are as indicated here, what is the likelihood that a live-born child will be deaf?

Mother: *D1 d1, D2 d2, d3 d3*
Father: *d1 d1, D2 d2, D3 d3*

PART I | Basic Principles: How Traits Are Transmitted

CHAPTER 4

The Chromosome Theory of Inheritance

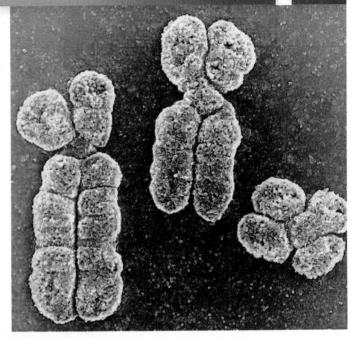

Each of these three human chromosomes carries hundreds to thousands of genes.

In the spherical, membrane-bounded nuclei of plant and animal cells prepared for viewing under the microscope, chromosomes appear as brightly colored, threadlike bodies. The nuclei of normal human cells carry 23 pairs of chromosomes for a total of 46. There are noticeable differences in size and shape among the 23 pairs, but within each pair, the two chromosomes appear to match exactly. (The only exceptions are the male's sex chromosomes, designated X and Y, which constitute an unmatched pair.)

Down syndrome was the first human genetic disorder attributable not to a gene mutation but to an abnormal number of chromosomes. Children born with Down syndrome have 47 chromosomes in each cell nucleus because they carry three, instead of the normal pair, of a very small chromosome referred to as number 21. The aberrant genotype, known as trisomy 21, gives rise to an abnormal phenotype, including a wide skull that is flatter than normal at the back, an unusually large tongue, learning disabilities caused by the abnormal development of the hippocampus and other parts of the brain, and a propensity to respiratory infections as well as heart disorders, rapid aging, and leukemia (**Fig. 4.1**).

How can one extra copy of a chromosome that is itself of normal size and shape cause such wide-ranging phenotypic effects? The answer has two parts. First and foremost, chromosomes are the cellular structures responsible for transmitting genetic information. In this chapter, we describe how geneticists concluded that chromosomes are the carriers of genes, an idea that became known as the **chromosome theory of inheritance.** The second part of the answer is that proper development depends not just on what type of genetic material is present but also on how much of it there is. Thus the mechanisms governing gene transmission during cell division must vigilantly maintain each cell's chromosome number.

Proof that genes are located on chromosomes comes from both breeding experiments and the microscopic examination of cells. As you will see, the behavior of chromosomes during one type of nuclear division called *meiosis* accounts for the segregation and independent assortment of genes proposed by Mendel. Meiosis figures prominently in the process by which most sexually reproducing organisms generate the gametes—eggs or sperm—that at fertilization unite to form the first cell of the next generation. This first cell is the fertilized egg, or *zygote.* The zygote then undergoes a second kind of nuclear division, known as *mitosis,* which continues to occur during the millions of cell divisions that propel development from a single

CHAPTER OUTLINE

- 4.1 Chromosomes: The Carriers of Genes
- 4.2 Mitosis: Cell Division That Preserves Chromosome Number
- 4.3 Meiosis: Cell Divisions That Halve Chromosome Number
- 4.4 Gametogenesis
- 4.5 Validation of the Chromosome Theory

Figure 4.1 Down syndrome: One extra chromosome 21 has widespread phenotypic consequences. Trisomy 21 usually causes changes in physical appearance as well as in the potential for learning. Many children with Down syndrome, such as the fifth grader at the center of the photograph, are able to participate fully in regular activities.

cell to a complex multicellular organism. Mitosis provides each of the many cells in an individual with the same number and types of chromosomes.

The precise chromosome-parceling mechanisms of meiosis and mitosis are crucial to the normal functioning of an organism. When the machinery does not function properly, errors in chromosome distribution can have dire repercussions on the individual's health and survival. Down syndrome, for example, is the result of a failure of chromosome segregation during meiosis. The meiotic error gives rise to an egg or sperm carrying an extra chromosome 21, which if incorporated in the zygote at fertilization, is passed on via mitosis to every cell of the developing embryo. Trisomy—three copies of a chromosome instead of two—can occur with other chromosomes as well, but in nearly all of these cases, the condition is prenatally lethal and results in a miscarriage.

Two themes emerge in our discussion of meiosis and mitosis. First, direct microscopic observations of chromosomes during gamete formation led early twentieth-century investigators to recognize that *chromosome movements parallel the behavior of Mendel's genes, so chromosomes are likely to carry the genetic material.* This chromosome theory of inheritance was proposed in 1902 and was confirmed in the following 15 years through elegant experiments performed mainly on the fruit fly *Drosophila melanogaster.* Second, the chromosome theory transformed the concept of a gene from an abstract particle to a physical reality—part of a chromosome that could be seen and manipulated.

4.1 Chromosomes: The Carriers of Genes

One of the first questions asked at the birth of an infant—is it a boy or a girl?—acknowledges that male and female are mutually exclusive characteristics like the yellow versus green of Mendel's peas. What's more, among humans and most other sexually reproducing species, a roughly 1:1 ratio exists between the two genders. Both males and females produce cells specialized for reproduction—sperm or eggs—that serve as a physical link to the next generation. In bridging the gap between generations, these gametes must each contribute half of the genetic material for making a normal, healthy son or daughter. Whatever part of the gamete carries this material, its structure and function must be able to account for the either-or aspect of sex determination as well as the generally observed 1:1 ratio of males to females. These two features of sex determination were among the earliest clues to the cellular basis of heredity.

Genes reside in the nucleus

The nature of the specific link between sex and reproduction remained a mystery until Anton van Leeuwenhoek, one of the earliest and most astute of microscopists, discovered in 1667 that semen contains spermatozoa

(literally "sperm animals"). He imagined that these microscopic creatures might enter the egg and somehow achieve fertilization, but it was not possible to confirm this hypothesis for another 200 years. Then, during a 20-year period starting in 1854 (about the same time Gregor Mendel was beginning his pea experiments), microscopists studying fertilization in frogs and sea urchins observed the union of male and female gametes and recorded the details of the process in a series of drawings. These drawings, as well as later micrographs (photographs taken through a microscope), clearly show that egg and sperm nuclei are the only elements contributed equally by maternal and paternal gametes. This observation implies that something in the nucleus contains the hereditary material. In humans, the nuclei of the gametes are less than 2 millionth of a meter in diameter. It is indeed remarkable that the genetic link between generations is packaged within such an exceedingly small space.

Genes reside in chromosomes

Further investigations, some dependent on technical innovations in microscopy, suggested that yet smaller, discrete structures within the nucleus are the repository of genetic information. In the 1880s, for example, a newly discovered combination of organic and inorganic dyes revealed the existence of the long, brightly staining, threadlike bodies within the nucleus that we call **chromosomes** (literally "colored bodies"). It was now possible to follow the movement of chromosomes during different kinds of cell division.

In embryonic cells, the chromosomal threads split lengthwise in two just before cell division, and each of the two newly forming daughter cells receives one-half of every split thread. The kind of nuclear division followed by cell division that results in two daughter cells containing the same number and type of chromosomes as the original parent cell is called **mitosis** (from the Greek *mitos* meaning "thread" and *-osis* meaning "formation" or "increase").

In the cells that give rise to male and female gametes, the chromosomes composing each pair become segregated, so that the resulting gametes receive only one chromosome from each chromosome pair. The kind of nuclear division that generates egg or sperm cells containing half the number of chromosomes found in other cells within the same organism is called **meiosis** (from the Greek word for "diminution").

Fertilization: The union of haploid gametes to produce diploid zygotes

In the first decade of the twentieth century, cytologists—scientists who use the microscope to study cell structure—showed that the chromosomes in a fertilized egg actually consist of two matching sets, one contributed by the maternal gamete, the other by the paternal gamete. The corresponding maternal and paternal chromosomes appear alike in size and shape, forming pairs (with one exception—the *sex chromosomes*—which we discuss in a later section).

Gametes and other cells that carry only a single set of chromosomes are called **haploid** (from the Greek word for "single"). Zygotes and other cells carrying two matching sets are **diploid** (from the Greek word for "double"). The number of chromosomes in a normal haploid cell is designated by the shorthand symbol n; the number of chromosomes in a normal diploid cell is then $2n$. **Figure 4.2** shows diploid cells as well as the haploid gametes that arise from them in *Drosophila*, where $2n = 8$ and $n = 4$. In humans, $2n = 46$; $n = 23$.

You can see how the halving of chromosome number during meiosis and gamete formation, followed by the union of two gametes' chromosomes at fertilization, normally allows a constant $2n$ number of chromosomes to be maintained from generation to generation in all individuals of a species. The chromosomes of every pair must segregate from each other during meiosis so that the haploid gametes will each have one complete set of chromosomes. After fertilization forms the zygote, the process of mitosis then ensures that all the cells of the developing individual have identical diploid chromosome sets.

Microscopic studies suggested that the nuclei of egg and sperm contribute equally to the offspring by providing a single set of n chromosomes. The zygote formed by the union of haploid gametes is diploid ($2n$).

Species variations in the number and shape of chromosomes

Scientists analyze the chromosomal makeup of a cell when the chromosomes are most visible—at a specific moment in the cell cycle of growth and division, just before the nucleus divides. At this point, known as *metaphase* (described in detail later), individual chromosomes have duplicated and condensed from thin threads into compact rodlike structures. Each chromosome now consists of two identical halves known as **sister chromatids** attached to each other at a specific location called the **centromere** (**Fig. 4.3**). In **metacentric** chromosomes, the centromere is more or less in the middle; in **acrocentric** chromosomes, the centromere is very close to one end. Modern high-resolution microscopy has failed to find any chromosomes in which the centromere is exactly at one end. As a result, the sister chromatids of all chromosomes

Figure 4.2 Diploid versus haploid: 2*n* versus *n*. Most body cells are diploid: They carry a maternal and paternal copy of each chromosome. Meiosis generates haploid gametes with only one copy of each chromosome. In *Drosophila*, diploid cells have eight chromosomes ($2n = 8$), while gametes have four chromosomes ($n = 4$). Note that the chromosomes in this diagram are pictured before their replication. The X and Y chromosomes determine the sex of the individual.

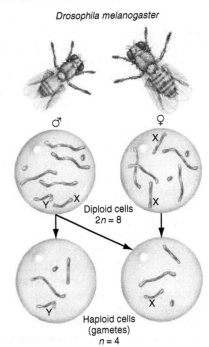

Drosophila melanogaster

Figure 4.3 Metaphase chromosomes can be classified by centromere position. Before cell division, each chromosome replicates into two sister chromatids connected at a centromere. In highly condensed metaphase chromosomes, the centromere can appear near the middle (a metacentric chromosome), very near an end (an acrocentric chromosome), or anywhere in between. In a diploid cell, one homologous chromosome in each pair is from the mother and the other from the father.

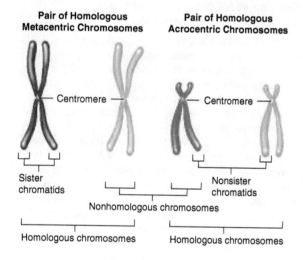

Figure 4.4 Karyotype of a human male. Photos of metaphase human chromosomes are paired and arranged in order of decreasing size. In a normal human male karyotype, there are 22 pairs of autosomes, as well as an X and a Y ($2n = 46$). Homologous chromosomes share the same characteristic pattern of dark and light bands.

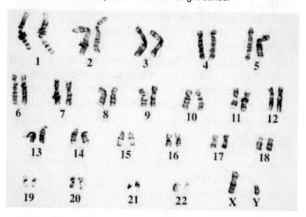

actually have two "arms" separated by a centromere, even if one of the arms is very short.

Cells in metaphase can be fixed and stained with one of several dyes that highlight the chromosomes and accentuate the centromeres. The dyes also produce characteristic banding patterns made up of lighter and darker regions. Chromosomes that match in size, shape, and banding are called **homologous chromosomes,** or **homologs.** The two homologs of each pair contain the same set of genes, although for some of those genes, they may carry different alleles. The differences between alleles occur at the molecular level and don't show up in the microscope.

Figure 4.3 introduces a system of notation employed throughout this book, using color to indicate degrees of relatedness between chromosomes. Thus, sister chromatids, which are identical duplicates, appear in the same shade of the same color. Homologous chromosomes, which carry the same genes but may vary in the identity of particular alleles, are pictured in different shades (light or dark) of the same color. *Nonhomologous chromosomes,* which carry completely unrelated sets of genetic information, appear in different colors.

To study the chromosomes of a single organism, geneticists arrange micrographs of the stained chromosomes in homologous pairs of decreasing size to produce a **karyotype.** Karyotype assembly can now be speeded and automated by computerized image analysis. **Figure 4.4** shows the karyotype of a human male, with 46 chromosomes arranged in 22 matching pairs of chromosomes and one nonmatching pair. The 44 chromosomes in matching

pairs are known as **autosomes.** The two unmatched chromosomes in this male karyotype are called *sex chromosomes,* because they determine the sex of the individual. (We discuss sex chromosomes in more detail in subsequent sections.)

Modern methods of DNA analysis can reveal differences between the maternally and paternally derived chromosomes of a homologous pair, and can thus track the origin of the extra chromosome 21 that causes Down syndrome in individual patients. In 80% of cases, the third chromosome 21 comes from the egg; in 20%, from the sperm. The Genetics and Society box on the next page describes how physicians use karyotype analysis and a technique called *amniocentesis* to diagnose Down syndrome prenatally, roughly three months after a fetus is conceived.

Through thousands of karyotypes on normal individuals, cytologists have verified that the cells of each species carry a distinctive diploid number of chromosomes. Among three species of fruit flies, for example, *Drosophila melanogaster* carries 8 chromosomes in 4 pairs, *Drosophila obscura* carries 10 (5 pairs), and *Drosophila virilis,* 12 (6 pairs). Mendel's peas contain 14 chromosomes (7 pairs) in each diploid cell, macaroni wheat has 28 (14 pairs), giant sequoia trees 22 (11 pairs), goldfish 94 (47 pairs), dogs 78 (39 pairs), and people 46 (23 pairs). Differences in the size, shape, and number of chromosomes reflect differences in the assembled genetic material that determines what each species looks like and how it functions. As these figures show, the number of chromosomes does not always correlate with the size or complexity of the organism.

Karyotyping, the analysis of stained images of all the chromosomes in a cell, reveals that different species have different numbers and shapes of chromosomes.

G E N E T I C S   A N D   S O C I E T Y

Prenatal Genetic Diagnosis

With new technologies for observing chromosomes and the DNA in genes, modern geneticists can define an individual's genotype directly. They can use this information to predict aspects of the individual's phenotype, even before these traits manifest themselves. Doctors can even use this basic strategy to diagnose, before birth, whether or not a baby will be born with a genetic condition.

The first prerequisite for prenatal diagnosis is to obtain fetal cells whose DNA and chromosomes can be analyzed for genotype. The most frequently used method for acquiring these cells is **amniocentesis (Fig. A)**. To carry out this procedure, a doctor inserts a needle through a pregnant woman's abdominal wall into the amniotic sac in which the fetus is growing; this procedure is performed about 16 weeks after the woman's last menstrual period. By using ultrasound imaging to guide the location of the needle, the physician can minimize the chance of injuring the fetus. The doctor then withdraws some of the amniotic fluid, in which the fetus is suspended, back through the needle into a syringe. This fluid contains living cells called *amniocytes* that were shed by the fetus. When placed in a culture medium, these fetal cells undergo several rounds of mitosis and increase in number. Once enough fetal cells are available, clinicians look at the chromosomes and genes in those cells. In later chapters, we describe techniques that allow the direct examination of the DNA constituting particular disease genes.

Amniocentesis also allows the diagnosis of Down syndrome through the analysis of chromosomes by karyotyping. Because the risk of Down syndrome increases rapidly with the age of the mother, more than half the pregnant women in North America who are over the age of 35 currently undergo amniocentesis. Although the goal of this karyotyping is usually to learn whether the fetus is trisomic for chromosome 21, many other abnormalities in chromosome number or shape may show up when the karyotype is examined.

The availability of amniocentesis and other techniques of prenatal diagnosis is intimately entwined with the personal and societal issue of abortion. The large majority of amniocentesis procedures are performed with the understanding that a fetus whose genotype indicates a genetic disorder, such as Down syndrome, will be aborted. Some prospective parents who are opposed to abortion still elect to undergo amniocentesis so that they can better prepare for an affected child, but this is rare.

The ethical and political aspects of the abortion debate influence many of the practical questions underlying prenatal diagnosis. For example, parents must decide which genetic conditions

Figure A Obtaining fetal cells by amniocentesis. A physician guides insertion of the needle into the amniotic sac using ultrasound imaging and extracts amniotic fluid containing fetal cells into the syringe.

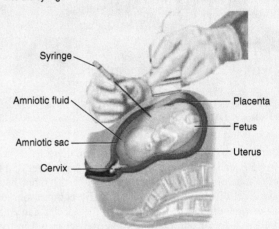

would be sufficiently severe that they would be willing to abort the fetus. They must also assess the risk that amniocentesis might harm the fetus. The normal risk of miscarriage at 16 weeks of gestation is about 2–3%; amniocentesis increases that risk by about 0.5% (about 1 in 200 procedures). From the economic point of view, society must decide who should pay for prenatal diagnosis procedures. In the United States, almost all private insurance companies and most state Medicaid programs cover at least some of the approximately $1500 cost of amniocentesis.

In current practice, the risks and costs of prenatal testing generally restrict amniocentesis to women over age 35 or to mothers whose fetuses are at high risk for a testable genetic condition because of family history. The personal and societal equations determining the frequency of prenatal testing may, however, need to be overhauled in the not-to-distant future because of technological advances that will simplify the procedures and thereby minimize the costs and risks. As one example, clinicians may soon be able to take advantage of new methods currently under evaluation to purify the very small number of fetal cells that find their way into the mother's bloodstream during pregnancy. Collecting these cells from the mother's blood would be much less invasive and expensive than amniocentesis and would pose no risk to the fetus, yet their karyotype analysis would be just as accurate.

Sex chromosomes

Walter S. Sutton, a young American graduate student at Columbia University in the first decade of the twentieth century, was one of the earliest cytologists to realize that particular chromosomes carry the information for determining sex. In one study, he obtained cells from the testes of the great lubber grasshopper (*Brachystola magna;* **Fig. 4.5**)

and followed them through the meiotic divisions that produce sperm. He observed that prior to meiosis, precursor cells within the testes of a great lubber grasshopper contain a total of 24 chromosomes. Of these, 22 are found in 11 matched pairs and are thus autosomes. The remaining 2 chromosomes are unmatched. He called the larger of these the X chromosome and the smaller the Y chromosome.

Figure 4.5 The great lubber grasshopper. In this mating pair, the smaller male is astride the female.

After meiosis, the sperm produced within these testes are of two equally prevalent types: one-half have a set of 11 autosomes plus an X chromosome, while the other half have a set of 11 autosomes plus a Y. By comparison, all of the eggs produced by females of the species carry an 11-plus-X set of chromosomes like the set found in the first class of sperm. When a sperm with an X chromosome fertilizes an egg, an XX female grasshopper results; when a Y-containing sperm fuses with an egg, an XY male develops. Sutton concluded that the X and Y chromosomes determine sex.

Several researchers studying other organisms soon verified that in many sexually reproducing species, two distinct chromosomes—known as the **sex chromosomes**—provide the basis of sex determination. One sex carries two copies of the same chromosome (a matching pair), while the other sex has one of each type of sex chromosome (an unmatched pair). The cells of normal human females, for example, contain 23 pairs of chromosomes. The two chromosomes of each pair, including the sex-determining X chromosomes, appear to be identical in size and shape. In males, however, there is one unmatched pair of chromosomes: the larger of these is the X; the smaller, the Y (Fig. 4.4 and **Fig. 4.6a**). Apart from this difference in sex chromosomes, the two sexes are not distinguishable at any other pair of chromosomes. Thus, geneticists can designate women as XX and men as XY and represent sexual reproduction as a simple cross between XX and XY.

If sex is an inherited trait determined by a pair of sex chromosomes that separate to different cells during gamete formation, then an XX × XY cross could account for both the mutual exclusion of genders and the near 1:1 ratio of males to females, which are hallmark features of sex determination (**Fig. 4.6b**). And if chromosomes carry information defining the two contrasting sex phenotypes, we can easily infer that chromosomes also carry genetic information specifying other characteristics as well.

Figure 4.6 How the X and Y chromosomes determine sex in humans. (a) This colorized micrograph shows the human X chromosome on the *left* and the human Y on the *right*. **(b)** Children can receive only an X chromosome from their mother, but they can inherit either an X or a Y from their father.

(a)

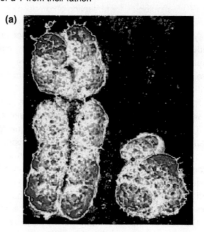

(b)

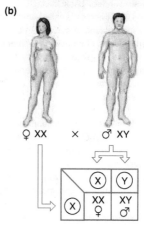

Species variations in sex determination

You have just seen that humans and other mammals have a pair of sex chromosomes that are identical in the XX female but different in the XY male. Several studies have shown that in humans, it is the presence or absence of the Y that actually makes the difference; that is, any person carrying a Y chromosome will look like a male. For example, rare humans with two X and one Y chromosomes (XXY) are males displaying certain abnormalities collectively called *Klinefelter syndrome*. Klinefelter males are typically tall, thin, and sterile, and they sometimes show mental retardation. That these individuals are males shows that two X chromosomes are insufficient for female development in the presence of a Y. In contrast, humans carrying an X and no second sex chromosome (XO) are females with *Turner syndrome*. Turner females are usually sterile, lack secondary sexual characteristics such as pubic hair, are of short stature, and have folds of skin between their necks and shoulders (webbed necks). Even though these

TABLE 4.1	Sex Determination in Fruit Flies and Humans						
	Complement of Sex Chromosomes						
	XXX	**XX**	**XXY**	**XO**	**XY**	**XYY**	**OY**
Drosophila	Dies	Normal female	Normal female	Sterile male	Normal male	Normal male	Dies
Humans	Nearly normal female	Normal female	Klinefelter male (sterile); tall, thin	Turner female (sterile); webbed neck	Normal male	Normal or nearly normal male	Dies

Humans can tolerate extra X chromosomes (e.g., XXX) better than can *Drosophila*. Complete absence of an X chromosome is lethal to both fruit flies and humans. Additional Y chromosomes have little effect in either species.

individuals have only one X chromosome, they develop as females because they have no Y chromosome.

Other species show variations on this XX versus XY chromosomal strategy of sex determination. In fruit flies, for example, although normal females are XX and normal males XY (see Fig. 4.2), it is ultimately the ratio of X chromosomes to autosomes (and not the presence or absence of the Y) that determines sex. In female *Drosophila*, the ratio is 1:1 (there are two X chromosomes and two copies of each autosome); in males, the ratio is 1:2 (there is one X chromosome but two copies of each autosome). Curiously, a rarely observed abnormal intermediate ratio of 2:3 produces intersex flies that display both male and female characteristics. Although the Y chromosome in *Drosophila* does not determine whether a fly looks like a male, it is necessary for male fertility; XO flies are thus sterile males. **Table 4.1** compares how humans and *Drosophila* respond to unusual complements of sex chromosomes. Differences between the two species arise in part because the genes they carry on their sex chromosomes are not identical and in part because the strategies they use to deal with the presence of additional sex chromosomes are not the same. The molecular mechanisms of sex determination in *Drosophila* are covered in detail in Chapter 16.

The XX = female / XY = male strategy of sex determination is by no means universal. In some species of moths, for example, the females are XX, but the males are XO. In *C. elegans* (one species of nematode), males are similarly XO, but XX individuals are not females; they are instead self-fertilizing hermaphrodites that produce both eggs and sperm. In birds and butterflies, males have the matching sex chromosomes, while females have an unmatched set; in such species, geneticists represent the sex chromosomes as ZZ in the male and ZW in the female. The gender having two different sex chromosomes is termed the **heterogametic sex** because it gives rise to two different types of gametes. These gametes would contain either X or Y in the case of male humans, and either Z or W in the case of female birds. Yet other variations include the complicated sex-determination mechanisms of bees and wasps, in which females are diploid and males haploid, and the systems of certain fish, in which sex is determined by changes in the environment, such as fluctuations in

temperature. **Table 4.2** summarizes some of the astonishing variety in the ways that different species have solved the problem of assigning gender to individuals.

In spite of these many differences between species, early researchers concluded that chromosomes can carry the genetic information specifying sexual identity—and probably many other characteristics as well. Sutton and other early adherents of the chromosome theory realized that the perpetuation of life itself therefore depends on the proper distribution of chromosomes during cell division. In the next sections, you will see that the behavior of chromosomes during mitosis and meiosis is exactly that expected of cellular structures carrying genes.

In many species, the sex of an individual correlates with a particular pair of chromosomes termed the sex chromosomes. The segregation of the sex chromosomes during gamete formation and their random reunion at fertilization explains the 1:1 ratio of the two sexes.

TABLE 4.2	Mechanisms of Sex Determination	
	♀	♂
Humans and *Drosophila*	XX	XY
Moths and *C. elegans*	XX (hermaphrodites in *C. elegans*)	XO
Birds and Butterflies	ZW	ZZ
Bees and Wasps	Diploid	Haploid
Lizards and Alligators	Cool temperature	Warm temperature
Tortoises and Turtles	Warm temperature	Cool temperature
Anemone Fish	Older adults	Young adults

In the species highlighted in *purple*, sex is determined by sex chromosomes. The species highlighted in *green* have identical chromosomes in the two sexes, and sex is determined instead by environmental or other factors. Anemone fish (bottom row) undergo a sex change from male to female as they age.

4.2 Mitosis: Cell Division That Preserves Chromosome Number

The fertilized human egg is a single diploid cell that preserves its genetic identity unchanged through more than 100 generations of cells as it divides again and again to produce a full-term infant ready to be born. As the newborn infant develops into a toddler, a teenager, and an adult, yet more cell divisions fuel continued growth and maturation. Mitosis, the nuclear division that apportions chromosomes in equal fashion to two daughter cells, is the cellular mechanism that preserves genetic information through all these generations of cells. In this section, we take a close look at how the nuclear division of mitosis fits into the overall scheme of cell growth and division.

If you were to peer through a microscope and follow the history of one cell through time, you would see that for much of your observation, the chromosomes resemble a mass of extremely fine tangled string—called **chromatin**—surrounded by the **nuclear envelope.** Each convoluted thread of chromatin is composed mainly of DNA (which carries the genetic information) and protein (which serves as a scaffold for packaging and managing that information, as described in Chapter 12). You would also be able to distinguish one or two darker areas of chromatin called *nucleoli* (singular, **nucleolus,** literally "small nucleus"); nucleoli play a key role in the manufacture of ribosomes, organelles that function in protein synthesis. During the period between cell divisions, the chromatin-laden nucleus houses a great deal of invisible activity necessary for the growth and survival of the cell. One particularly important part of this activity is the accurate duplication of all the chromosomal material.

With continued vigilance, you would observe a dramatic change in the nuclear landscape during one very short period in the cell's life history: The chromatin condenses into discrete threads, and then each chromosome compacts even further into the twin rods clamped together at the centromere that can be identified in karyotype analysis (review Fig. 4.3 on p. 82). Each rod in a duo is called a **chromatid;** as described earlier, it is an exact duplicate of the other sister chromatid to which it is connected. Continued observation would reveal the doubled chromosomes beginning to jostle around inside the cell, eventually lining up at the cell's midplane. At this point, the sister chromatids comprising each chromosome separate to opposite poles of the now elongating cell, where they become identical sets of chromosomes. Each of the two identical sets eventually ends up enclosed in a separate nucleus in a separate cell. The two cells, known as *daughter cells,* are thus genetically identical.

The repeating pattern of cell growth (an increase in size) followed by division (the splitting of one cell into two) is called the **cell cycle** (**Fig. 4.7**). Only a small part

Figure 4.7 The cell cycle: An alternation between interphase and mitosis. (a) Chromosomes replicate to form sister chromatids during synthesis (S phase); the sister chromatids segregate to daughter cells during mitosis (M phase). The gaps between the S and M phases, during which most cell growth takes place, are called the G_1 and G_2 phases. In multicellular organisms, some terminally differentiated cells stop dividing and arrest in a "G_0" stage. **(b)** Interphase consists of the G_1, S, and G_2 phases together.

(a) The cell cycle

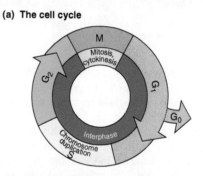

(b) Chromosomes replicate during S phase

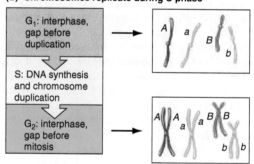

of the cell cycle is spent in division (or **M phase**); the period between divisions is called **interphase.**

During interphase, cells grow and replicate their chromosomes

Interphase consists of three parts: gap 1 (**G_1**), synthesis (**S**), and gap 2 (**G_2**) (Fig. 4.7). G_1 lasts from the birth of a new cell to the onset of chromosome replication; for the genetic material, it is a period when the chromosomes are neither duplicating nor dividing. During this time, the cell achieves most of its growth by using the information from its genes to make and assemble the materials it needs to function normally. G_1 varies in length more than any other phase of the cell cycle. In rapidly dividing cells of the human embryo, for example, G_1 is as short as a few hours. In contrast, mature brain cells become arrested in a resting form of G_1 known as **G_0** and do not normally divide again during a person's lifetime.

Synthesis (S) is the time when the cell duplicates its genetic material by synthesizing DNA. During duplication, each chromosome doubles to produce identical sister chromatids that will become visible when the chromosomes condense at the beginning of mitosis. The two sister chromatids remain joined to each other at the centromere. (Note that this joined structure is considered a single chromosome as long as the connection between sister chromatids is maintained.) The replication of chromosomes during S phase is critical; the genetic material must be copied exactly so that both daughter cells receive identical sets of chromosomes.

Gap 2 (G_2) is the interval between chromosome duplication and the beginning of mitosis. During this time, the cell may grow (usually less than during G_1); it also synthesizes proteins that are essential to the subsequent steps of mitosis itself.

In addition, during interphase an array of fine microtubules crucial for many interphase processes becomes visible outside the nucleus. The microtubules radiate out into the cytoplasm from a single organizing center known as the **centrosome,** usually located near the nuclear envelope. In animal cells, the discernible core of each centrosome is a pair of small, darkly staining bodies called **centrioles** (**Fig. 4.8a**); the microtubule-organizing center of plants does not contain centrioles. During the S and G_2 stages of interphase, the centrosomes replicate, producing two centrosomes that remain in extremely close proximity.

During mitosis, sister chromatids separate and two daughter nuclei form

Although the rigorously choreographed events of nuclear and cellular division occur as a dynamic and continuous process, scientists traditionally analyze the process in separate stages marked by visible cytological events. The artist's sketches in Fig. 4.8 illustrate these stages in the nematode *Ascaris,* whose diploid cells contain only four chromosomes (two pairs of homologous chromosomes).

Prophase: Chromosomes condense (Fig. 4.8a)

During all of interphase, the cell nucleus remains intact, and the chromosomes are indistinguishable aggregates of chromatin. At **prophase** (from the Greek *pro-* meaning "before"), the gradual emergence, or **condensation,** of individual chromosomes from the undifferentiated mass of chromatin marks the beginning of mitosis. Each condensing chromosome has already been duplicated during interphase and thus consists of sister chromatids attached at the centromere. At this stage in *Ascaris* cells, there are therefore four chromosomes with a total of eight chromatids.

The progressive appearance of an array of individual chromosomes is a truly impressive event: Interphase DNA molecules as long as 3–4 cm condense into discrete chromosomes whose length is measured in microns (millionths of a meter). This is equivalent to compacting a 200 m length of thin string (as long as two football fields) into a cylinder 8 mm long and 1 mm wide.

Another visible change in chromatin also takes place during prophase: The darkly staining nucleoli begin to break down and disappear. As a result, the manufacture of ribosomes ceases, providing one indication that general cellular metabolism shuts down so that the cell can focus its energy on chromosome movements and cellular division.

Several important processes that characterize prophase occur outside the nucleus in the cytoplasm. The centrosomes, which replicated during interphase, now move apart and become clearly distinguishable as two separate entities in the light microscope. At the same time, the interphase scaffolding of long, stable microtubules disappears and is replaced by a set of dynamic microtubules that rapidly grow from and shrink back toward their centrosomal organizing centers. The centrosomes continue to move apart, migrating around the nuclear envelope toward opposite ends of the nucleus, apparently propelled by forces exerted between interdigitated microtubules extending from both centrosomes.

Prometaphase: The spindle forms (Fig. 4.8b)

Prometaphase ("before middle stage") begins with the breakdown of the nuclear envelope, which allows microtubules extending from the two centrosomes to invade the nucleus. Chromosomes attach to these microtubules through the **kinetochore,** a structure in the centromere region of each chromatid that is specialized for conveyance. Each kinetochore contains proteins that act as molecular motors, enabling the chromosome to slide along the microtubule. When the kinetochore of a chromatid originally contacts a microtubule at prometaphase, the kinetochore-based motor moves the entire chromosome toward the centrosome from which that microtubule radiates. Microtubules growing from the two centrosomes randomly capture chromosomes by the kinetochore of one of the two sister chromatids. As a result, it is sometimes possible to observe groups of chromosomes congregating in the vicinity of each centrosome. In this early part of prometaphase, for each chromosome, one chromatid's kinetochore is attached to a microtubule, but the sister chromatid's kinetochore remains unattached.

During prometaphase, three different types of microtubule fibers together form the **mitotic spindle;** all of these microtubules originate from the centrosomes, which function as the two "poles" of the spindle apparatus. Microtubules that extend between a centrosome and the kinetochore of a chromatid are called **kinetochore microtubules,** or *centromeric fibers.* Microtubules from each centrosome that are directed toward the middle of the cell are **polar microtubules;** polar microtubules originating in opposite centrosomes interdigitate near the

Figure 4.8 Mitosis maintains the chromosome number of the parent cell nucleus in the two daughter nuclei. In the photomicrographs of newt lung cells at the left, chromosomes are stained *blue* and microtubules appear either *green* or *yellow*.

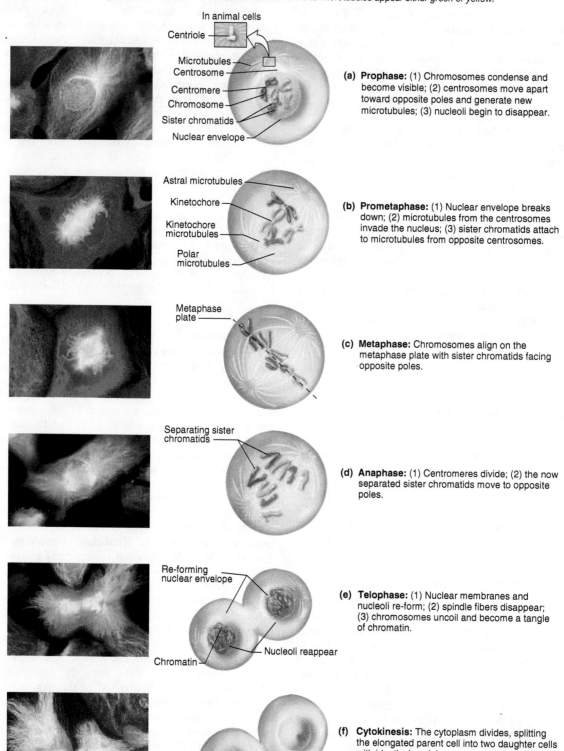

In animal cells

Centriole

Microtubules
Centrosome
Centromere
Chromosome
Sister chromatids
Nuclear envelope

(a) Prophase: (1) Chromosomes condense and become visible; (2) centrosomes move apart toward opposite poles and generate new microtubules; (3) nucleoli begin to disappear.

Astral microtubules
Kinetochore
Kinetochore microtubules
Polar microtubules

(b) Prometaphase: (1) Nuclear envelope breaks down; (2) microtubules from the centrosomes invade the nucleus; (3) sister chromatids attach to microtubules from opposite centrosomes.

Metaphase plate

(c) Metaphase: Chromosomes align on the metaphase plate with sister chromatids facing opposite poles.

Separating sister chromatids

(d) Anaphase: (1) Centromeres divide; (2) the now separated sister chromatids move to opposite poles.

Re-forming nuclear envelope

Chromatin

Nucleoli reappear

(e) Telophase: (1) Nuclear membranes and nucleoli re-form; (2) spindle fibers disappear; (3) chromosomes uncoil and become a tangle of chromatin.

(f) Cytokinesis: The cytoplasm divides, splitting the elongated parent cell into two daughter cells with identical nuclei.

cell's equator. Finally, there are short **astral microtubules** that extend out from the centrosome toward the cell's periphery.

Near the end of prometaphase, the kinetochore of each chromosome's previously unattached sister chromatid now associates with microtubules extending from the opposite centrosome. This event orients each chromosome such that one sister chromatid faces one pole of the cell, and the other, the opposite pole. Experimental manipulation has shown that if both kinetochores become attached to microtubules from the same pole, the configuration is unstable; one of the kinetochores will repeatedly detach from the spindle until it associates with microtubules from the other pole. The attachment of sister chromatids to opposite spindle poles is the only stable arrangement.

Metaphase: Chromosomes align at the cell's equator (Fig. 4.8c)

During **metaphase** ("middle stage"), the connection of sister chromatids to opposite spindle poles sets in motion a series of jostling movements that cause the chromosomes to move toward an imaginary equator halfway between the two poles. The imaginary midline is called the **metaphase plate.** When the chromosomes are aligned along it, the forces pulling and pushing them toward or away from each pole are in a balanced equilibrium. As a result, any movement away from the metaphase plate is rapidly compensated by tension that restores the chromosome to its position equidistant between the poles.

> The essence of mitosis is the arrangement of chromosomes at metaphase. The kinetochores of sister chromatids are connected to fibers from opposite spindle poles, but the sister chromatids remain held together by their connection at the centromere.

Anaphase: Sister chromatids move to opposite spindle poles (Fig. 4.8d)

The nearly simultaneous severing of the centromeric connection between the sister chromatids of all chromosomes indicates that **anaphase** (from the Greek *ana-* meaning "up" as in "up toward the poles") is underway. The separation of sister chromatids allows each chromatid to be pulled toward the spindle pole to which it is connected by its kinetochore microtubules; as the chromatid moves toward the pole, its kinetochore microtubules shorten. Because the arms of the chromatids lag behind the kinetochores, metacentric chromatids have a characteristic V shape during anaphase. The connection of sister chromatids to microtubules emanating from opposite spindle poles means that the genetic information migrating toward one pole is exactly the same as its counterpart moving toward the opposite pole.

Telophase: Identical sets of chromosomes are enclosed in two nuclei (Fig. 4.8e)

The final transformation of chromosomes and the nucleus during mitosis happens at **telophase** (from the Greek *telo-* meaning "end"). Telophase is like a rewind of prophase. The spindle fibers begin to disperse; a nuclear envelope forms around the group of chromatids at each pole; and one or more nucleoli reappears. The former chromatids now function as independent chromosomes, which decondense (uncoil) and dissolve into a tangled mass of chromatin. Mitosis, the division of one nucleus into two identical nuclei, is over.

Cytokinesis: The cytoplasm divides (Fig. 4.8f)

In the final stage of cell division, the daughter nuclei emerging at the end of telophase are packaged into two separate daughter cells. This final stage of division is called **cytokinesis** (literally "cell movement"). During cytokinesis, the elongated parent cell separates into two smaller independent daughter cells with identical nuclei. Cytokinesis usually begins during anaphase, but it is not completed until after telophase.

The mechanism by which cells accomplish cytokinesis differs in animals and plants. In animal cells, cytoplasmic division depends on a **contractile ring** that pinches the cell into two approximately equal halves, similar to the way the pulling of a string closes the opening of a bag of marbles (**Fig. 4.9a**). Intriguingly, some types of molecules that form the contractile ring also participate in the mechanism

Figure 4.9 Cytokinesis: The cytoplasm divides, producing two daughter cells. (a) In this dividing frog zygote, the contractile ring at the cell's periphery has contracted to form a cleavage furrow that will eventually pinch the cell in two. **(b)** In this dividing onion root cell, a cell plate that began forming near the equator of the cell expands to the periphery, separating the two daughter cells.

(a) Cytokinesis in an animal cell

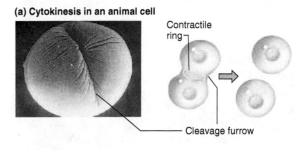

Contractile ring

Cleavage furrow

(b) Cytokinesis in a plant cell

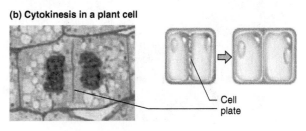

Cell plate

responsible for muscle contraction. In plants, whose cells are surrounded by a rigid cell wall, a membrane-enclosed disk, known as the **cell plate,** forms inside the cell near the equator and then grows rapidly outward, thereby dividing the cell in two (**Fig. 4.9b**).

During cytokinesis, a large number of important organelles and other cellular components, including ribosomes, mitochondria, membranous structures such as Golgi bodies, and (in plants) chloroplasts, must be parcelled out to the emerging daughter cells. The mechanism accomplishing this task does not appear to predetermine which organelle is destined for which daughter cell. Instead, because most cells contain many copies of these cytoplasmic structures, each new cell is bound to receive at least a few representatives of each component. This original complement of structures is enough to sustain the cell until synthetic activity can repopulate the cytoplasm with organelles.

Sometimes cytoplasmic division does not immediately follow nuclear division, and the result is a cell containing more than one nucleus. An animal cell with two or more nuclei is known as a **syncytium.** The early embryos of fruit flies are multinucleated syncytia (**Fig. 4.10**), as are the precursors of spermatozoa in humans and many other animals. A multinucleate plant tissue is called a **coenocyte;** coconut milk is a nutrient-rich food composed of coenocytes.

> After mitosis plus cytokinesis, the sister chromatids of every chromosome are separated into two daughter cells. As a result, these two cells are genetically identical to each other and to the original parental cell.

Figure 4.10 If cytokinesis does not follow mitosis, one cell may contain many nuclei. In fertilized *Drosophila* eggs, 13 rounds of mitosis take place without cytokinesis. The result is a single-celled syncytial embryo that contains several thousand nuclei. The photograph shows part of an embryo in which the nuclei are all dividing; chromosomes are in *red,* and spindle fibers are in *green.* Nuclei at the *upper left* are in metaphase, while nuclei toward the *bottom right* are progressively later in anaphase. Membranes eventually grow around these nuclei, dividing the embryo into cells.

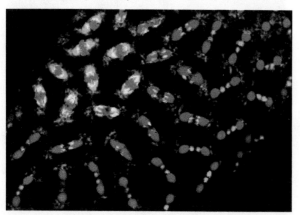

Regulatory checkpoints ensure correct chromosome separation

The cell cycle is a complex sequence of precisely coordinated events. In higher organisms, a cell's "decision" to divide depends on both intrinsic factors, such as conditions within the cell that register a sufficient size for division; and signals from the environment, such as hormonal cues or contacts with neighboring cells that encourage or restrain division. Once a cell has initiated events leading to division, usually during the G_1 period of interphase, everything else follows like clockwork. A number of **checkpoints**—moments at which the cell evaluates the results of previous steps—allow the sequential coordination of cell-cycle events. Consequently, under normal circumstances, the chromosomes replicate before they condense, and the doubled chromosomes separate to opposite poles only after correct metaphase alignment of sister chromatids ensures equal distribution to the daughter nuclei (**Fig. 4.11**).

In one illustration of the molecular basis of checkpoints, even a single kinetochore that has not attached to

Figure 4.11 Checkpoints help regulate the cell cycle. Cellular checkpoints (*red wedges*) ensure that important events in the cell cycle occur in the proper sequence. At each checkpoint, the cell determines whether prior events have been completed before it can proceed to the next step of the cell cycle. (For simplicity, we show only two chromosomes per cell.)

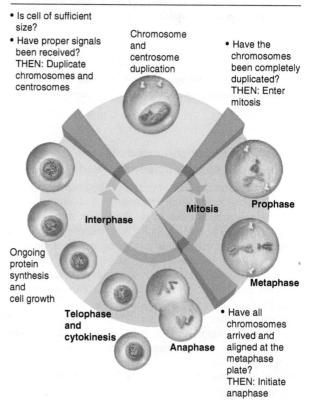

- Is cell of sufficient size?
- Have proper signals been received? THEN: Duplicate chromosomes and centrosomes

Chromosome and centrosome duplication

- Have the chromosomes been completely duplicated? THEN: Enter mitosis

Ongoing protein synthesis and cell growth

Interphase

Mitosis

Prophase

Metaphase

Telophase and cytokinesis

Anaphase

- Have all chromosomes arrived and aligned at the metaphase plate? THEN: Initiate anaphase

FAST FORWARD

How Gene Mutations Cause Errors in Mitosis

During each cell cycle, the chromosomes participate in a tightly patterned choreography that proceeds through sequential steps, synchronized in both time and space. Through their dynamic dance, the chromosomes convey a complete set of genes to each of two newly forming daughter cells. Not surprisingly, some of the genes they carry encode proteins that direct them through the dance.

A variety of proteins, some assembled into structures such as centrosomes and microtubule fibers, make up the molecular machinery that helps coordinate the orderly progression of events in mitosis. Because a particular gene specifies each protein, we might predict that mutant alleles generating defects in particular proteins could disrupt the dance. Cells homozygous for a mutant allele might be unable to complete chromosome duplication, mitosis, or cytokinesis because of a missing or nonfunctional component. Experiments on organisms as disparate as yeast and fruit flies have borne out this prediction. Here we describe the effects of a mutation in one of the many *Drosophila* genes critical for proper chromosome segregation.

Although most mistakes in mitosis are eventually lethal to a multicellular organism, some mutant cells may manage to divide early in development. When prepared for viewing under the microscope, these cells actually allow us to see the effects of defective mitosis. To understand these effects, we first present part of a normal mitosis as a basis for comparison. **Figure A** (*left panel*) shows the eight condensed metaphase chromosomes of a wild-type male fruit fly (*Drosophila melanogaster*): two pairs of large metacentric autosomes with the centromere in the center, a pair of dotlike autosomes that are so small it is not possible to see the centromere region, an acrocentric X chromosome with the centromere very close to one end, and a metacentric Y chromosome. Because most of the Y chromosome consists of a special form of chromatin known as heterochromatin, the two Y sister chromatids remain so tightly connected that they often appear as one.

Figure B (*left panel*) shows the results of aberrant mitosis in an animal homozygous for a mutation in a gene called *zw10* that encodes a component of the chromosomal kinetochores. The mutation disrupted mitotic chromosome segregation during early development, producing cells with the wrong number of chromosomes. The problem in chromosome segregation probably occurred during anaphase of the previous cell division.

Figure A (*right panel*) shows a normal anaphase separation leading to the wild-type chromosome complement. Figure B (*right panel*) portrays an aberrant anaphase separation in a *zw10* mutant animal that could lead to an abnormal chromosome complement similar to that depicted in the left panel of the same figure; you can

see that many more chromatids are migrating to one spindle pole than to the other.

The smooth unfolding of each cell cycle depends on a diverse array of proteins. Particular genes specify each of the proteins active in mitosis and cytokinesis, and each protein makes a contribution to the coordinated events of the cell cycle. As a result, a mutation in any of a number of genes can disrupt the meticulously choreographed mechanisms of cell division.

Figure A Metaphase and anaphase chromosomes in a wild-type male fruit fly.

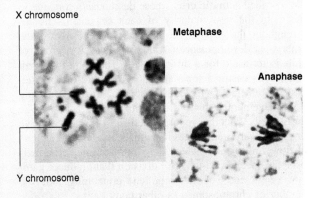

Figure B Metaphase and anaphase chromosomes in a mutant fly. These cells are from a *Drosophila* male homozygous for a mutation in the *zw10* gene. The mutant metaphase cell (*left*) contains extra chromosomes as compared with the wild-type metaphase cell in Fig. A. In the mutant anaphase cell (*right*), more chromatids are moving toward one spindle pole than toward the other.

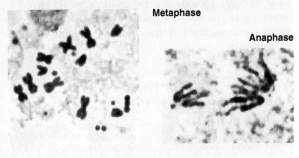

spindle fibers generates a molecular signal that prevents the sister chromatids of all chromosomes from separating at their centromeres. This signal makes the beginning of anaphase dependent on the prior proper alignment of all the chromosomes at metaphase. As a result of multiple cell-cycle checkpoints, each daughter cell reliably receives the right number of chromosomes.

Breakdown of the mitotic machinery can produce division mistakes that have crucial consequences for the cell. Improper chromosome segregation, for example, can cause serious malfunction or even the death of daughter cells. As the Fast Forward box "How Gene Mutations Cause Errors in Mitosis" explains, gene mutations that disrupt mitotic structures, such as the spindle, kinetochores, or centrosomes are one source of improper segregation. Other problems occur in cells where the normal restraints on cell division, such as checkpoints, have broken down. Such cells may divide uncontrollably, leading to a tumor. We present the details of cell-cycle regulation, checkpoint controls, and cancer formation in Chapter 17.

4.3 Meiosis: Cell Divisions That Halve Chromosome Number

During the many rounds of cell division within an embryo, most cells either grow and divide via the mitotic cell cycle just described, or they stop growing and become arrested in G_0. These mitotically dividing and G_0-arrested cells are the so-called **somatic cells** whose descendants continue to make up the vast majority of each organism's tissues throughout the lifetime of the individual. Early in the embryonic development of animals, however, a group of cells is set aside for a different fate. These are the **germ cells:** cells destined for a specialized role in the production of gametes. Germ cells arise later in plants, during floral development instead of during embryogenesis. The germ cells become incorporated in the reproductive organs—ovaries and testes in animals; ovaries and anthers in flowering plants—where they ultimately undergo meiosis, the special two-part cell division that produces gametes (eggs and sperm or pollen) containing half the number of chromosomes as other body cells.

The union of haploid gametes at fertilization yields diploid offspring that carry the combined genetic heritage of two parents. Sexual reproduction therefore requires the alternation of haploid and diploid generations. If gametes were diploid rather than haploid, the number of chromosomes would double in each successive generation such that in humans, for example, the children would have 92 chromosomes per cell, the grandchildren 184, and so on. Meiosis prevents this lethal, exponential accumulation of chromosomes.

In meiosis, the chromosomes replicate once but the nucleus divides twice

Unlike mitosis, meiosis consists of two successive nuclear divisions, logically named **division I of meiosis** and **division II of meiosis,** or simply **meiosis I** and **meiosis II.** With each round, the cell passes through a prophase, metaphase, anaphase, and telophase followed by cytokinesis. In meiosis I, the parent nucleus divides to form two daughter nuclei; in meiosis II, each of the two daughter nuclei divides, resulting in four nuclei (**Fig. 4.12**). These four nuclei—the final products of meiosis—become partitioned in four separate daughter cells because cytokinesis occurs after both rounds of division. The chromosomes

Figure 4.12 An overview of meiosis: The chromosomes replicate once, while the nuclei divide twice. In this figure, all four chromatids of each chromosome pair are shown in the same shade of the same color. Note that the chromosomes duplicate before meiosis I, but they do not duplicate between meiosis I and meiosis II.

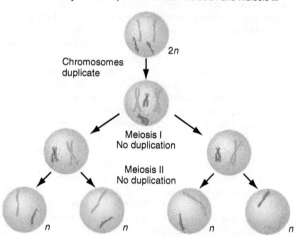

duplicate at the start of meiosis I, but they do not duplicate in meiosis II, which explains why the gametes contain half the number of chromosomes found in other body cells. A close look at each round of meiotic division reveals the mechanisms by which each gamete comes to receive one full haploid set of chromosomes.

During meiosis I, homologs pair, exchange parts, and then segregate

The events of meiosis I are unique among nuclear divisions (**Fig. 4.13**, meiosis I, pp. 94–95). The process begins with the replication of chromosomes, after which each one consists of two sister chromatids. A key to understanding meiosis I is the observation that the centromeres joining these chromatids remain intact throughout the entire division, rather than splitting as in mitosis.

As the division proceeds, homologous chromosomes align across the cellular equator to form a coupling that ensures proper chromosome segregation to separate nuclei. Moreover, during the time homologous chromosomes face each other across the equator, the maternal and paternal chromosomes of each homologous pair may exchange parts, creating new combinations of alleles at different genes along the chromosomes. Afterward, the two homologous chromosomes, each still consisting of two sister chromatids connected at a single, unsplit centromere, are pulled to opposite poles of the spindle. As a result, it is homologous chromosomes (rather than sister chromatids as in mitosis) that segregate into different daughter cells at the conclusion of the first meiotic division. With this overview in mind, let us take a closer look at the specific events of meiosis I, bearing in mind that we analyze a dynamic, flowing sequence of cellular events by breaking it down somewhat arbitrarily into the easily pictured, traditional phases.

Prophase I: Homologs condense and pair, and crossing-over occurs

Among the critical events of **prophase I** are the condensation of chromatin, the pairing of homologous chromosomes, and the reciprocal exchange of genetic information between these paired homologs. Figure 4.13 shows a generalized view of prophase I; however, research suggests that the exact sequence of events may vary in different species. These complicated processes can take many days, months, or even years to complete. For example, in the female germ cells of several species, including humans, meiosis is suspended at prophase I until ovulation (as discussed further in section 4.4).

Leptotene (from the Greek for "thin" and "delicate") is the first definable substage of prophase I, the time when the long, thin chromosomes begin to thicken (see **Fig. 4.14a** on p. 96 for a more detailed view). Each chromosome has already duplicated prior to prophase I (as in mitosis) and thus consists of two sister chromatids affixed at a centromere. At this point, however, these sister chromatids are so tightly bound together that they are not yet visible as separate entities.

Zygotene (from the Greek for "conjugation") begins as each chromosome seeks out its homologous partner and the matching chromosomes become zipped together in a process known as **synapsis**. The "zipper" itself is an elaborate protein structure called the **synaptonemal complex** that aligns the homologs with remarkable precision, juxtaposing the corresponding genetic regions of the chromosome pair (**Fig. 4.14b**).

Pachytene (from the Greek for "thick" or "fat") begins at the completion of synapsis when homologous chromosomes are united along their length. Each synapsed chromosome pair is known as a **bivalent** (because it encompasses two chromosomes), or a **tetrad** (because it contains four chromatids). On one side of the bivalent is a maternally derived chromosome, on the other side a paternally derived one. Because X and Y chromosomes are not identical, they do not synapse completely; there is, however, a small region of similarity (or "homology") between the X and the Y chromosomes that allows for a limited amount of pairing.

During pachytene, structures called **recombination nodules** begin to appear along the synaptonemal complex, and an exchange of parts between nonsister (that is, between maternal and paternal) chromatids occurs at these nodules (see **Fig. 4.14c** for details). Such an exchange is known as **crossing-over;** it results in the **recombination** of genetic material. As a result of crossing-over, chromatids may no longer be of purely maternal or paternal origin; however, no genetic information is gained or lost, so all chromatids retain their original size.

Diplotene (from the Greek for "twofold" or "double") is signaled by the gradual dissolution of the synaptonemal zipper complex and a slight separation of regions of the homologous chromosomes (see **Fig. 4.14d**). The aligned homologous chromosomes of each bivalent nonetheless remain very tightly merged at intervals along their length called **chiasmata** (singular, *chiasma*), which represent the sites where crossing-over occurred.

Diakinesis (from the Greek for "double movement") is accompanied by further condensation of the chromatids. Because of this chromatid thickening and shortening, it can now clearly be seen that each tetrad consists of four separate chromatids, or viewed in another way, that the two homologous chromosomes of a bivalent are each composed of two sister chromatids held together at a centromere (see **Fig. 4.14e**). Nonsister chromatids that have undergone crossing-over remain closely associated at chiasmata. The end of diakinesis is analogous to the prometaphase of mitosis: The nuclear envelope breaks down, and the microtubules of the spindle apparatus begin to form.

> During prophase I, homologous chromosomes pair, and recombination occurs between nonsister chromatids of the paired homologs.

Metaphase I: Paired homologs attach to spindle fibers from opposite poles

During mitosis, each sister chromatid has a kinetochore that becomes attached to microtubules emanating from opposite spindle poles. During meiosis I, the situation is different. The kinetochores of sister chromatids fuse, so that each chromosome contains only a single functional kinetochore. The result of this fusion is that sister chromatids remain together throughout meiosis I because no oppositely directed forces exist that can pull the chromatids apart. Instead, during **metaphase I** (Fig. 4.13, meiosis I), it is the kinetochores of homologous chromosomes that attach to microtubules from opposite spindle poles. As a result, in chromosomes aligned at the metaphase plate, the kinetochores of maternally and paternally derived chromosomes face opposite spindle poles, positioning the homologs to move in opposite directions. Because each bivalent's alignment and hookup is independent of that of every other bivalent, the chromosomes facing each pole are a random mix of maternal and paternal origin.

> The essence of the first meiotic division is the arrangement of chromosomes at metaphase I. The kinetochores of homologous chromosomes are connected to fibers from opposite spindle poles. The homologs are held together by chiasmata.

FEATURE FIGURE 4.13

Meiosis: One Diploid Cell Produces Four Haploid Cells

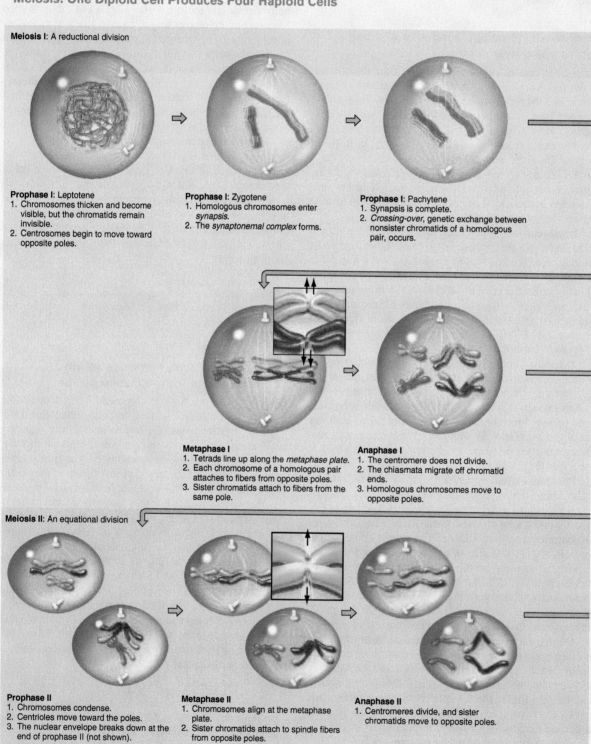

Meiosis I: A reductional division

Prophase I: Leptotene
1. Chromosomes thicken and become visible, but the chromatids remain invisible.
2. Centrosomes begin to move toward opposite poles.

Prophase I: Zygotene
1. Homologous chromosomes enter *synapsis*.
2. The *synaptonemal complex* forms.

Prophase I: Pachytene
1. Synapsis is complete.
2. *Crossing-over*, genetic exchange between nonsister chromatids of a homologous pair, occurs.

Metaphase I
1. Tetrads line up along the *metaphase plate*.
2. Each chromosome of a homologous pair attaches to fibers from opposite poles.
3. Sister chromatids attach to fibers from the same pole.

Anaphase I
1. The centromere does not divide.
2. The chiasmata migrate off chromatid ends.
3. Homologous chromosomes move to opposite poles.

Meiosis II: An equational division

Prophase II
1. Chromosomes condense.
2. Centrioles move toward the poles.
3. The nuclear envelope breaks down at the end of prophase II (not shown).

Metaphase II
1. Chromosomes align at the metaphase plate.
2. Sister chromatids attach to spindle fibers from opposite poles.

Anaphase II
1. Centromeres divide, and sister chromatids move to opposite poles.

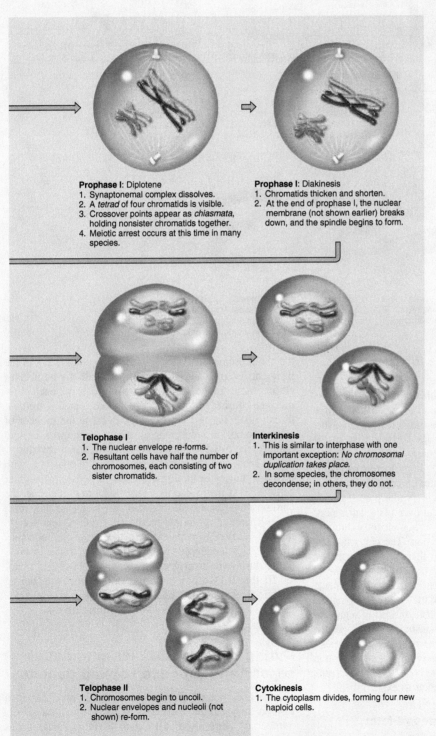

Prophase I: Diplotene
1. Synaptonemal complex dissolves.
2. A *tetrad* of four chromatids is visible.
3. Crossover points appear as *chiasmata*, holding nonsister chromatids together.
4. Meiotic arrest occurs at this time in many species.

Prophase I: Diakinesis
1. Chromatids thicken and shorten.
2. At the end of prophase I, the nuclear membrane (not shown earlier) breaks down, and the spindle begins to form.

Telophase I
1. The nuclear envelope re-forms.
2. Resultant cells have half the number of chromosomes, each consisting of two sister chromatids.

Interkinesis
1. This is similar to interphase with one important exception: *No chromosomal duplication takes place.*
2. In some species, the chromosomes decondense; in others, they do not.

Telophase II
1. Chromosomes begin to uncoil.
2. Nuclear envelopes and nucleoli (not shown) re-form.

Cytokinesis
1. The cytoplasm divides, forming four new haploid cells.

Figure 4.13 To aid visualization of the chromosomes, the figure is simplified in two ways: (1) The nuclear envelope is not shown during prophase of either meiotic division. (2) The chromosomes are shown as fully condensed at zygotene; in reality, full condensation is not achieved until diakinesis.

Figure 4.14 Prophase I of meiosis at very high magnification.

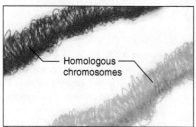

(a) Leptotene: Threadlike chromosomes begin to condense and thicken, becoming visible as discrete structures. Although the chromosomes have duplicated, the sister chromatids of each chromosome are not yet visible in the microscope.

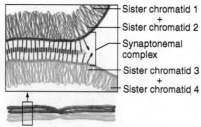

(b) Zygotene: Chromosomes are clearly visible and begin pairing with homologous chromosomes along the synaptonemal complex to form a bivalent, or tetrad.

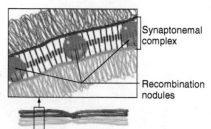

(c) Pachytene: Full synapsis of homologs. Recombination nodules appear along the synaptonemal complex.

(d) Diplotene: Bivalent appears to pull apart slightly but remains connected at crossover sites, called chiasmata.

(e) Diakinesis: Further condensation of chromatids. Nonsister chromatids that have exchanged parts by crossing-over remain closely associated at chiasmata.

Anaphase I: Homologs move to opposite spindle poles

At the onset of **anaphase I,** the chiasmata joining homologous chromosomes dissolve, which allows the maternal and paternal homologs to begin to move toward opposite spindle poles (see Fig. 4.13, meiosis I). Note that in the first meiotic division, the centromeres do not divide as they do in mitosis. Thus, from each homologous pair, one chromosome consisting of two sister chromatids joined at their centromere segregates to each spindle pole.

Recombination through crossing-over plays an important role in the proper segregation of homologous chromosomes during the first meiotic division. The chiasmata, in holding homologs together, ensure that their kinetochores remain attached to opposite spindle poles throughout metaphase. When recombination does not occur within a bivalent, mistakes in hookup and conveyance may cause homologous chromosomes to move to the same pole, instead of segregating to opposite poles. In some organisms, however, proper segregation of nonrecombinant chromosomes nonetheless occurs through other pairing processes. Investigators do not yet completely understand the nature of these processes and are currently evaluating several models to explain them.

Telophase I: Nuclear envelopes re-form

The telophase of the first meiotic division, or **telophase I,** takes place when nuclear membranes begin to form around

the chromosomes that have moved to the poles. Each of the incipient daughter nuclei contains one-half the number of chromosomes in the original parent nucleus, but each chromosome consists of two sister chromatids joined at the centromere (see Fig. 4.13, meiosis I). Because the number of chromosomes is reduced to one-half the normal diploid number, meiosis I is often called a **reductional division.**

In most species, cytokinesis follows telophase I, with daughter nuclei becoming enclosed in separate daughter cells. A short interphase then ensues. During this time, the chromosomes usually decondense, in which case they must recondense during the prophase of the subsequent second meiotic division. In some cases, however, the chromosomes simply stay condensed. Most importantly, there is no S phase during the interphase between meiosis I and meiosis II; that is, the chromosomes do not replicate during meiotic interphase. The relatively brief interphase between meiosis I and meiosis II is known as **interkinesis.**

During meiosis II, sister chromatids separate to produce haploid gametes

The second meiotic division (meiosis II) proceeds in a fashion very similar to that of mitosis, but because the number of chromosomes in each dividing nucleus has already been reduced by half, the resulting daughter cells are haploid. The same process occurs in each of the two daughter cells generated by meiosis I, producing four haploid cells at the end of this second meiotic round (see Fig. 4.13, meiosis II).

Prophase II: The chromosomes condense

If the chromosomes decondensed during the preceding interphase, they recondense during **prophase II.** At the end of prophase II, the nuclear envelope breaks down, and the spindle apparatus re-forms.

Metaphase II: Chromosomes align at the metaphase plate

The kinetochores of sister chromatids attach to microtubule fibers emanating from opposite poles of the spindle apparatus, just as in mitotic metaphase. There are nonetheless two significant features of **metaphase II** that distinguish it from mitosis. First, the number of chromosomes is one-half that in mitotic metaphase of the same species. Second, in most chromosomes, the two sister chromatids are no longer strictly identical because of the recombination through crossing-over that occurred during meiosis I. The sister chromatids still contain the same genes, but they may carry different combinations of alleles.

Anaphase II: Sister chromatids move to opposite spindle poles

Just as in mitosis, severing of the centromeric connection between sister chromatids allows them to move toward opposite spindle poles during **anaphase II.**

Telophase II: Nuclear membranes re-form, and cytokinesis follows

Membranes form around each of four daughter nuclei in **telophase II,** and cytokinesis places each nucleus in a separate cell. The result is four haploid gametes. Note that at the end of meiosis II, each daughter cell (that is, each gamete) has the same number of chromosomes as the parental cell present at the beginning of this division. For this reason, meiosis II is termed an **equational division.**

> Meiosis consists of two rounds of cell division. The first is a reductional division during which homologs segregate, producing haploid daughter cells. The second is an equational division during which sister chromatids are separated.

Mistakes in meiosis produce defective gametes

Segregational errors during either meiotic division can lead to aberrations, such as trisomies, in the next generation. If, for example, the homologs of a chromosome pair do not segregate during meiosis I (a mistake known as **nondisjunction**), they may travel together to the same pole and eventually become part of the same gamete. Such an error may at fertilization result in any one of a large variety of possible trisomies. Most autosomal trisomies, as we already mentioned, are lethal *in utero;* one exception is trisomy 21, the genetic basis of Down syndrome. Like trisomy 21, extra sex chromosomes may also be nonlethal but cause a variety of mental and physical abnormalities, such as those seen in Klinefelter syndrome (see Table 4.1 on p. 85).

In contrast to rare mistakes in the segregation of one pair of chromosomes, some hybrid animals carry nonhomologous chromosomes that can never pair up and segregate properly. **Figure 4.15** shows the two dissimilar sets of

Figure 4.15 Hybrid sterility: When chromosomes cannot pair during meiosis I, they segregate improperly. The mating of a male donkey (*Equus asinus; green*) and a female horse (*Equus caballus; peach color*) produces a mule with 63 chromosomes. In this karyotype of a female mule, the first 13 donkey and horse chromosomes are homologous and pictured in pairs. Starting at chromosome 14, the donkey and horse chromosomes are too dissimilar to pair with each other during meiosis I.

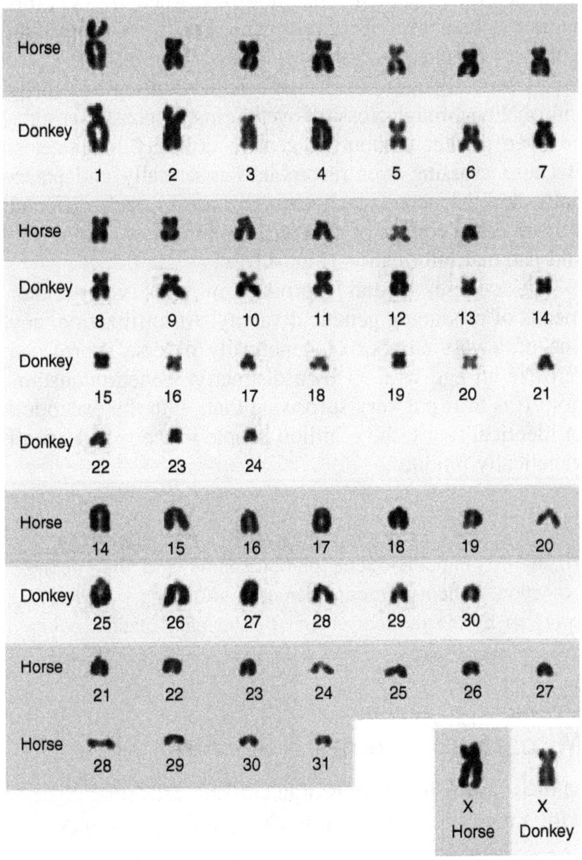

Genetics, Biochemistry and Molecular Biology

chromosomes carried by the diploid cells of a mule. The set inherited from the donkey father contains 31 chromosomes, while the set from the horse mother has 32 chromosomes. Viable gametes cannot form in these animals, so mules are sterile.

Meiosis contributes to genetic diversity

The wider the assortment of different gene combinations among members of a species, the greater the chance that at least some individuals will carry combinations of alleles that allow survival in a changing environment. Two aspects of meiosis contribute to genetic diversity in a population. First, because only chance governs which paternal or maternal homologs migrate to the two poles during the first meiotic division, different gametes carry a different mix of maternal and paternal chromosomes. **Figure 4.16a** shows how two different patterns of homolog migration produce four different mixes of parental chromosomes in the gametes. The amount of potential variation generated by this random independent assortment increases with the number of chromosomes. In *Ascaris,* for example, where $n = 2$ (the chromosome complement shown in Fig. 4.16a), the random assortment of homologs could produce only 2^2, or 4 types of gametes. In a human being, however, where $n = 23$, this same mechanism alone could generate 2^{23}, or more than 8 million genetically different kinds of gametes.

A second feature of meiosis, the reshuffling of genetic information through crossing-over during prophase I, ensures an even greater amount of genetic diversity in gametes. Because crossing-over recombines maternally and paternally derived genes, each chromosome in each different gamete could consist of different combinations of maternal and paternal information (**Fig. 4.16b**).

Of course, sexual reproduction adds yet another means of producing genetic diversity. At fertilization, any one of a vast number of genetically diverse sperm can fertilize an egg with its own distinctive genetic constitution. It is thus not very surprising that, with the exception of identical twins, the 6 billion people in the world are all genetically unique.

> Genetic diversity is ensured by the independent assortment of nonhomologous chromosomes and the recombination of homologous chromosomes during meiosis, as well as by the random union of genetically distinct sperm and eggs.

Mitosis and meiosis: A comparison

Mitosis occurs in all types of eukaryotic cells (that is, cells with a membrane-bounded nucleus) and is a conservative

Figure 4.16 How meiosis contributes to genetic diversity. (a) The variation resulting from the independent assortment of nonhomologous chromosomes increases with the number of chromosomes in the genome. **(b)** Crossing-over between homologous chromosomes ensures that each gamete is unique.

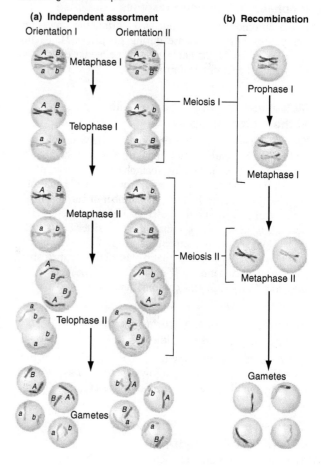

mechanism that preserves the genetic status quo. Mitosis followed by cytokinesis produces growth by increasing the number of cells. It also promotes the continual replacement of roots, stems, and leaves in plants and the regeneration of blood cells, intestinal tissues, and skin in animals.

Meiosis, on the other hand, occurs only in sexually reproducing organisms, in just a few specialized germ cells within the reproductive organs that produce haploid gametes. It is not a conservative mechanism; rather, the extensive combinatorial changes arising from meiosis are one source of the genetic variation that fuels evolution. **Table 4.3** illustrates the significant contrasts between the two mechanisms of cell division.

TABLE 4.3	**Comparing Mitosis and Meiosis**

Mitosis	**Meiosis**

Mitosis

Occurs in somatic cells
Haploid and diploid cells can undergo mitosis
One round of division

Mitosis is preceded by S phase (chromosome duplication).

Homologous chromosomes do not pair.

Genetic exchange between homologous chromosomes is very rare.

Sister chromatids attach to spindle fibers from opposite poles during metaphase.

The centromere splits at the beginning of anaphase.

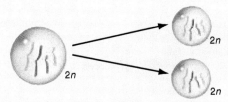

Mitosis produces two new daughter cells, identical to each other and the original cell. Mitosis is thus genetically conservative.

Meiosis

Occurs in germ cells as part of the sexual cycle
Two rounds of division, meiosis I and meiosis II
Only diploid cells undergo meiosis

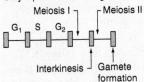

Chromosomes duplicate prior to meiosis I but not before meiosis II.

During prophase of meiosis I, homologous chromosomes pair (synapse) along their length.

Crossing-over occurs between homologous chromosomes during prophase of meiosis I.

Homologous chromosomes (not sister chromatids) attach to spindle fibers from opposite poles during metaphase I.

The centromere does not split during meiosis I.

Sister chromatids attach to spindle fibers from opposite poles during metaphase II.

The centromere splits at the beginning of anaphase II.

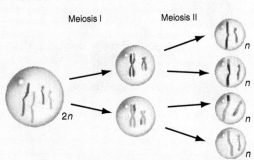

Meiosis produces four haploid cells, one (egg) or all (sperm) of which can become gametes. None of these is identical to each other or to the original cell, because meiosis results in combinatorial change.

4.4 Gametogenesis

In all sexually reproducing animals, the embryonic germ cells (collectively known as the **germ line**) undergo a series of mitotic divisions that yield a collection of specialized diploid cells, which subsequently divide by meiosis to produce haploid cells. As with other biological processes, many variations on this general pattern have been observed. In some species, the haploid cells resulting from meiosis are the gametes themselves, while in other species, those cells must undergo a specific plan of differentiation to fulfill that function. Moreover, in certain organisms, the four haploid products of a single meiosis do not all become gametes. Gamete formation, or **gametogenesis,** thus gives rise to haploid gametes marked not only by the events of meiosis per se but also by cellular events that precede and follow meiosis. Here we illustrate gametogenesis with a description of egg and sperm formation in humans. The details of gamete formation in several other organisms appear throughout the book in discussions of specific experimental studies; they also appear in the Genetic Portraits on our website (www.mhhe.com/hartwell4).

Oogenesis in humans produces one ovum from each primary oocyte

The end product of egg formation in humans is a large, nutrient-rich ovum whose stored resources can sustain the early embryo. The process, known as **oogenesis (Fig. 4.17)**, begins when diploid germ cells in the ovary, called **oogonia** (singular, *oogonium*), multiply rapidly by mitosis and produce a large number of **primary oocytes,** which then undergo meiosis.

For each primary oocyte, meiosis I results in the formation of two daughter cells that differ in size, so this division is asymmetric. The larger of these cells, the

Figure 4.17 In humans, egg formation begins in the fetal ovaries and arrests during the prophase of meiosis I. Fetal ovaries contain about 500,000 primary oocytes arrested in the diplotene substage of meiosis I. If the egg released during a menstrual cycle is fertilized, meiosis is completed. Only one of the three (rarely, four) cells produced by meiosis serves as the functional gamete, or ovum.

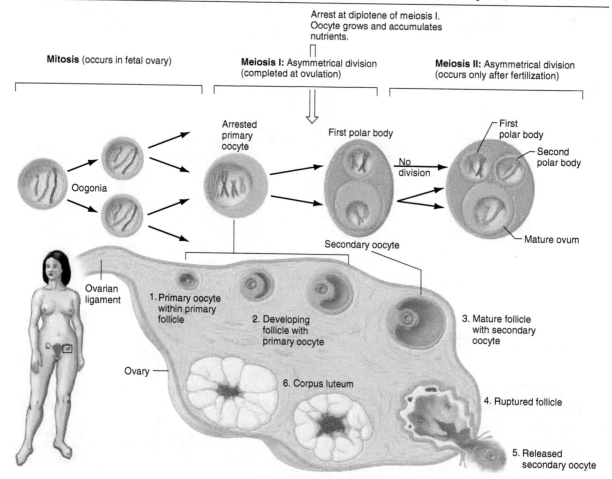

secondary oocyte, receives over 95% of the cytoplasm. The other small sister cell is known as the first **polar body.** During meiosis II, the secondary oocyte undergoes another asymmetrical division to produce a large haploid **ovum** and a small, haploid second polar body. The first polar body usually arrests its development and does not undergo the second meiotic division. However, in a small proportion of cases the first polar body does divide, producing two haploid polar bodies. The two (or rarely, three) small polar bodies apparently serve no function and disintegrate, leaving one large haploid ovum as the functional gamete. Thus, only one of the three (or rarely, four) products of a single meiosis serves as a female gamete. A normal human ovum carries 22 autosomes and an X sex chromosome.

Oogenesis begins in the fetus. By six months after conception, the fetal ovaries are fully formed and contain about half a million primary oocytes arrested in the diplotene substage of prophase I. These cells, with their homologous chromosomes locked in synapsis, are the only oocytes the female will produce, so a girl is born with all the oocytes she will ever possess. From the onset of puberty, at about age 12, until menopause, some 35–40 years later, most women release one primary oocyte each month (from alternate ovaries), amounting to roughly 480 oocytes released during the reproductive years. The remaining primary oocytes disintegrate during menopause.

At ovulation, a released oocyte completes meiosis I and proceeds as far as the metaphase of meiosis II. If the oocyte is then fertilized, that is, penetrated by a sperm nucleus, it quickly completes meiosis II. The nuclei of the sperm and ovum then fuse to form the diploid nucleus of the zygote, and the zygote divides by mitosis to produce a functional embryo. In contrast, unfertilized oocytes exit the body during the menses stage of the menstrual cycle.

The long interval before completion of meiosis in oocytes released by women in their 30s, 40s, and 50s may contribute to the observed correlation between maternal age and meiotic segregational errors, including those that produce trisomies. Women in their mid-20s, for example, run a very small risk of trisomy 21; only 0.05% of children born to women of this age have Down syndrome. During the later childbearing years, however, the risk rapidly rises; at age 35, it is 0.9% of live births, and at age 45, it is 3%. You would not expect this age-related increase in risk if meiosis were completed before the mother's birth.

Spermatogenesis in humans produces four sperm from each primary spermatocyte

The production of sperm, or **spermatogenesis** (**Fig. 4.18**), begins in the male testes in germ cells known as **spermatogonia.** Mitotic divisions of the spermatogonia produce many diploid cells, the **primary spermatocytes.** Unlike primary oocytes, primary spermatocytes undergo a symmetrical meiosis I, producing two **secondary spermatocytes,** each of which undergoes a symmetrical meiosis II. At the conclusion of meiosis, each original primary spermatocyte thus yields four equivalent haploid **spermatids.** These spermatids then mature by developing a characteristic whiplike tail and by concentrating all their chromosomal material in a head, thereby becoming functional **sperm.** A human sperm, much smaller than the ovum it will fertilize, contains 22 autosomes and *either* an X *or* a Y sex chromosome.

The timing of sperm production differs radically from that of egg formation. The meiotic divisions allowing conversion of primary spermatocytes to spermatids begin only at puberty, but meiosis then continues throughout a man's life. The entire process of spermatogenesis takes about 48–60 days: 16–20 for meiosis I, 16–20 for meiosis II, and 16–20 for the maturation of spermatids into fully functional sperm. Within each testis after puberty, millions of sperm are always in production, and a single ejaculate can contain up to 300 million. Over a lifetime, a man can produce billions of sperm, almost equally divided between those bearing an X and those bearing a Y chromosome.

Gametogenesis involves mitotic divisions of specialized germ-line cells that then undergo meiotic divisions to produce gametes. In human females, oocytes undergo asymmetrical meiosis to produce a large ovum and two or three nonfunctional polar bodies. In human males, spermatocytes undergo symmetrical meiosis to produce four sperm.

4.5 Validation of the Chromosome Theory

So far, we have presented two circumstantial lines of evidence in support of the chromosome theory of inheritance. First, the phenotype of sexual identity is associated with the inheritance of particular chromosomes. Second, the events of mitosis, meiosis, and gametogenesis ensure a constant number of chromosomes in the somatic cells of all members of a species over time; one would expect the genetic material to exhibit this kind of stability even in organisms with very different modes of reproduction. Final acceptance of the chromosome theory depended on researchers going beyond the circumstantial evidence to a rigorous demonstration of two key points: (1) that the inheritance of genes corresponds with the inheritance of chromosomes in every detail, and (2) that the transmission of particular chromosomes coincides with the transmission of specific traits other than sex determination.

Figure 4.18 Human sperm form continuously in the testes after puberty. Spermatogonia are located near the exterior of seminiferous tubules in a human testis. Once they divide to produce the primary spermatocytes, the subsequent stages of spermatogenesis—meiotic divisions in the spermatocytes and maturation of spermatids into sperm—occur successively closer to the middle of the tubule. Mature sperm are released into the central lumen of the tubule for ejaculation.

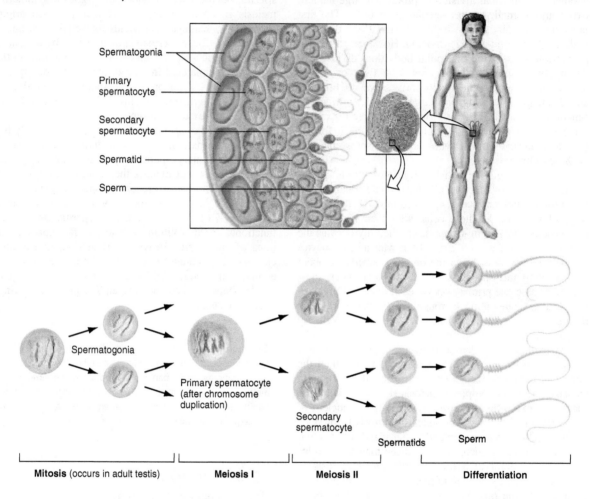

Mendel's laws correlate with chromosome behavior during meiosis

Walter Sutton first outlined the chromosome theory of inheritance in 1902–1903, building on the theoretical ideas and experimental results of Theodor Boveri in Germany, E. B. Wilson in New York, and others. In a 1902 paper, Sutton speculated that "the association of paternal and maternal chromosomes in pairs and their subsequent separation during the reducing division [that is, meiosis I] . . . may constitute the physical basis of the Mendelian law of heredity." In 1903, he suggested that chromosomes carry Mendel's hereditary units for the following reasons:

1. Every cell contains two copies of each kind of chromosome, and there are two copies of each kind of gene.

2. The chromosome complement, like Mendel's genes, appears unchanged as it is transmitted from parents to offspring through generations.

3. During meiosis, homologous chromosomes pair and then separate to different gametes, just as the alternative alleles of each gene segregate to different gametes.

4. Maternal and paternal copies of each chromosome pair move to opposite spindle poles without regard to the assortment of any other homologous chromosome pair, just as the alternative alleles of unrelated genes assort independently.

5. At fertilization, an egg's set of chromosomes unites with a randomly encountered sperm's set of chromosomes, just as alleles obtained from one parent unite at random with those from the other parent.

6. In all cells derived from the fertilized egg, one-half of the chromosomes and one-half of the genes are of maternal origin, the other half of paternal origin.

The two parts of **Table 4.4** show the intimate relationship between the chromosome theory of inheritance and Mendel's laws of segregation and independent assortment. If Mendel's genes for pea shape and pea color are assigned to different (that is, nonhomologous) chromosomes, the behavior of chromosomes can be seen to parallel the behavior of genes. Walter Sutton's observation of these parallels led him to propose that chromosomes and genes are physically connected in some manner. Meiosis ensures that each gamete will contain only a single chromatid of a bivalent and thus only a single allele of any gene on that chromatid (Table 4.4a). The independent behavior of two bivalents during meiosis means that the genes carried on different chromosomes will assort into gametes independently (Table 4.4b).

From a review of Fig. 4.16 (on p. 98), which follows two different chromosome pairs through the process of meiosis, you might wonder whether crossing-over abolishes the clear correspondence between Mendel's laws and the movement of chromosomes. The answer is no. Each chromatid of a homologous chromosome pair contains only one copy of a given gene, and only one chromatid from each pair of homologs is incorporated into each gamete. Because alternative alleles remain on different chromatids even after crossing-over has occurred, alternative alleles still segregate to different gametes as demanded by Mendel's first law. And because the orientation of nonhomologous chromosomes is completely random with respect to each other during both meiotic divisions, the genes on different chromosomes assort independently even if crossing-over occurs, as demanded by Mendel's second law.

Specific traits are transmitted with specific chromosomes

The fate of a theory depends on whether its predictions can be validated. Because genes determine traits, the prediction that chromosomes carry genes could be tested by breeding experiments that would show whether transmission of a specific chromosome coincides with transmission of a specific trait. Cytologists knew that one pair of chromosomes, the sex chromosomes, determines whether an individual is male or female. Would similar correlations exist for other traits?

A gene determining eye color on the *Drosophila* X chromosome

Thomas Hunt Morgan, an American experimental biologist with training in embryology, headed the research group whose findings eventually established a firm experimental base for the chromosome theory. Morgan chose to work with the fruit fly *Drosophila melanogaster* because it is extremely prolific and has a very short generation time, taking only 12 days to develop from a fertilized egg into a mature adult capable of producing hundreds of offspring. Morgan fed his flies mashed bananas and housed them in empty milk bottles capped with wads of cotton.

In 1910, a white-eyed male appeared among a large group of flies with brick-red eyes. A mutation had apparently altered a gene determining eye color, changing it from the normal wild-type allele specifying red to a new allele that produced white. When Morgan allowed the white-eyed male to mate with its red-eyed sisters, all the flies of the F_1 generation had red eyes; the red allele was clearly dominant to the white (**Fig. 4.19,** cross A).

Establishing a pattern of nomenclature for *Drosophila* geneticists, Morgan named the gene identified by the abnormal white eye color, the *white* gene, for the mutation that revealed its existence. The normal wild-type allele of the *white* gene, abbreviated w^+, is for brick-red eyes, while the counterpart mutant w allele results in white eye color. The superscript $+$ signifies the wild type. By writing the gene name and abbreviation in lowercase, Morgan symbolized that the mutant w allele is recessive to the wild-type w^+. (If a mutation results in a dominant non-wild-type phenotype, the first letter of the gene name or of its abbreviation is capitalized; thus the mutation known as *Bar* eyes is dominant to the wild-type Bar^+ allele. See the *Guidelines for Gene Nomenclature* on p. 731, directly following Chapter 21.)

Morgan then crossed the red-eyed males of the F_1 generation with their red-eyed sisters (Fig. 4.19, cross B) and obtained an F_2 generation with the predicted 3:1 ratio of red to white eyes. But there was something askew in the pattern: Among the red-eyed offspring, there were two females for every one male, and all the white-eyed offspring were males. This result was surprisingly different from the equal transmission to both sexes of the Mendelian traits discussed in Chapters 2 and 3. In these fruit flies, the ratio of various phenotypes was not the same in male and female progeny.

By mating F_2 red-eyed females with their white-eyed brothers (Fig. 4.19, cross C), Morgan obtained some females with white eyes, which then allowed him to mate a white-eyed female with a red-eyed wild-type male (Fig. 4.19, cross D). The result was exclusively red-eyed daughters and white-eyed sons. The pattern seen in cross D is known as **crisscross inheritance** because the males inherit their eye color from their mothers, while the daughters inherit their eye color from their fathers. Note in Fig. 4.19 that the results of the reciprocal crosses red female × white male (cross A) and white female × red male (cross D) are not identical, again in contrast with Mendel's findings.

TABLE 4.4 | How the Chromosome Theory of Inheritance Explains Mendel's Laws

(a) The Law of Segregation

(b) The Law of Independent Assortment

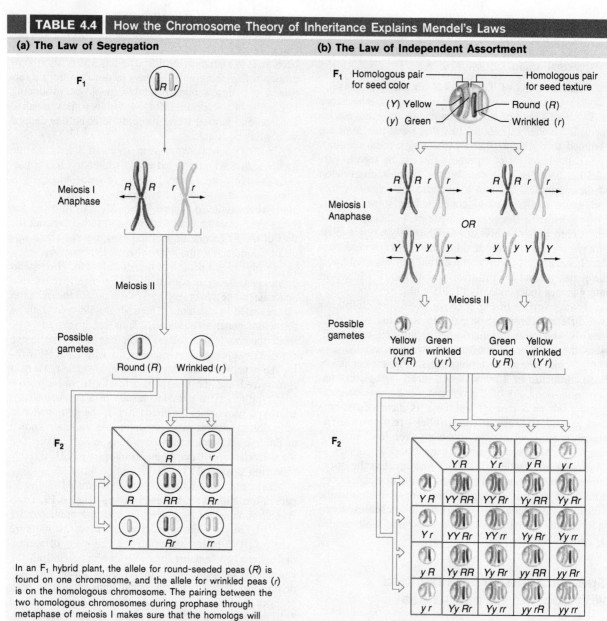

In an F_1 hybrid plant, the allele for round-seeded peas (R) is found on one chromosome, and the allele for wrinkled peas (r) is on the homologous chromosome. The pairing between the two homologous chromosomes during prophase through metaphase of meiosis I makes sure that the homologs will separate to opposite spindle poles during anaphase I. At the end of meiosis II, two types of gametes have been produced: half have R, and half have r, but no gametes have both alleles. Thus, the separation of homologous chromosomes at meiosis I corresponds to the segregation of alleles. As the Punnett square shows, fertilization of 50% R and 50% r eggs with the same proportion of R and r pollen leads to Mendel's 3:1 ratio in the F_2 generation.

One pair of homologous chromosomes carries the gene for seed texture (alleles R and r). A second pair of homologous chromosomes carries the gene for seed color (alleles Y and y). Each homologous pair aligns at random at the metaphase plate during meiosis I, independently of the other homologous pair. Thus, two equally likely configurations are possible for the migration of any two chromosome pairs toward the poles during anaphase I. As a result, a dihybrid individual will generate four equally likely types of gametes with regard to the two traits in question. As the Punnett square affirms, this independent assortment of traits carried by nonhomologous chromosomes produces Mendel's 9:3:3:1 ratio.

Figure 4.19 A *Drosophila* eye color gene is located on the X chromosome. X-linkage explains the inheritance of alleles of the *white* gene in this series of crosses performed by Thomas Hunt Morgan. The progeny of Crosses A, B, and C outlined with green dotted boxes are those used as the parents in the next cross of the series.

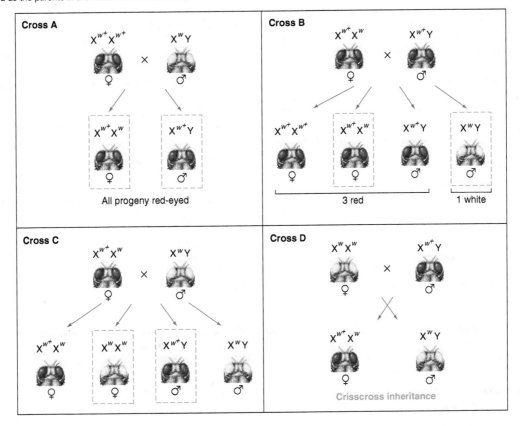

From the data, Morgan reasoned that the *white* gene for eye color is **X linked,** that is, carried by the X chromosome. (Note that while symbols for genes and alleles are italicized, symbols for chromosomes are not.) The Y chromosome carries no allele of this gene for eye color. Males, therefore, have only one copy of the gene, which they inherit from their mother along with their only X chromosome; their Y chromosome must come from their father. Thus, males are **hemizygous** for this eye color gene, because their diploid cells have half the number of alleles carried by the female on her two X chromosomes.

If the single *white* gene on the X chromosome of a male is the wild-type w^+ allele, he will have red eyes and a genotype that can be written $X^{w^+}Y$. (Here we designate the chromosome [X or Y] together with the allele it carries, to emphasize that certain genes are X linked.) In contrast to an $X^{w^+}Y$ male, a hemizygous $X^w Y$ male would have a phenotype of white eyes. Females with two X chromosomes can be one of three genotypes: $X^w X^w$ (white-eyed), $X^w X^{w^+}$ (red-eyed because w^+ is dominant to w), or $X^{w^+} X^{w^+}$ (red-eyed).

As shown in Fig. 4.19, Morgan's assumption that the gene for eye color is X linked explains the results of his breeding experiments. Crisscross inheritance, for example, occurs because the only X chromosome in sons of a white-eyed mother ($X^w X^w$) must carry the w allele, so the sons will be white-eyed. In contrast, because daughters of a red-eyed ($X^{w^+}Y$) father must receive a w^+-bearing X chromosome from their father, they will have red eyes.

Through a series of crosses, T. H. Morgan demonstrated that the inheritance of a gene controlling eye color in *Drosophila* was best explained by the hypothesis that this gene lies on the X chromosome.

Support for the chromosome theory from the analysis of nondisjunction

Although Morgan's work strongly supported the hypothesis that the gene for eye color lies on the X chromosome, he himself continued to question the validity of the chromosome theory until Calvin Bridges, one of his top students, found another key piece of evidence. Bridges repeated the cross Morgan had performed between white-eyed females and red-eyed males, but this time he did the experiment on a larger scale. As expected, the progeny of this cross consisted mostly of red-eyed females and white-eyed males. However, about 1 in every 2000 males had red eyes, and about the same small fraction of females had white eyes.

Bridges hypothesized that these exceptions arose through rare events in which the X chromosomes fail to separate during meiosis in females. He called such failures in chromosome segregation *nondisjunction*. As **Fig. 4.20a** shows, nondisjunction would result in some eggs with two X chromosomes and others with none. Fertilization of these chromosomally abnormal eggs could produce four types of zygotes: XXY (with two X chromosomes from the egg and a Y from the sperm), XXX (with two Xs from the egg and one X from the sperm), XO (with the lone sex chromosome from the sperm and no sex chromosome from the egg), and OY (with the only sex chromosome again coming from the sperm). When Bridges examined the sex chromosomes

of the rare white-eyed females produced in his large-scale cross, he found that they were indeed XXY individuals who must have received two X chromosomes and with them two *w* alleles from their white-eyed $X^w X^w$ mothers. The exceptional red-eyed males emerging from the cross were XO; their eye color showed that they must have obtained their sole sex chromosome from their $X^{w+} Y$ fathers. In this study, transmission of the *white* gene alleles followed the predicted behavior of X chromosomes during rare meiotic mistakes, indicating that the X chromosome carries the gene for eye color. These results also suggested that zygotes with the two other abnormal sex chromosome karyotypes expected from nondisjunction in females (XXX and OY) die during embryonic development and thus produce no progeny.

Because XXY white-eyed females have three sex chromosomes rather than the normal two, Bridges reasoned they would produce four kinds of eggs: XY and X, or XX and Y (**Fig. 4.20b**). You can visualize the formation of these four kinds of eggs by imagining that when the three chromosomes pair and disjoin during meiosis, two chromosomes must go to one pole and one

Figure 4.20 Nondisjunction: Rare mistakes in meiosis help confirm the chromosome theory. (a) Rare events of nondisjunction in an XX female produce XX and O eggs. The results of normal disjunction in the female are not shown. XO males are sterile because the missing Y chromosome is needed for male fertility in *Drosophila*. **(b)** In an XXY female, the three sex chromosomes can pair and segregate in two ways, producing progeny with unusual sex chromosome complements.

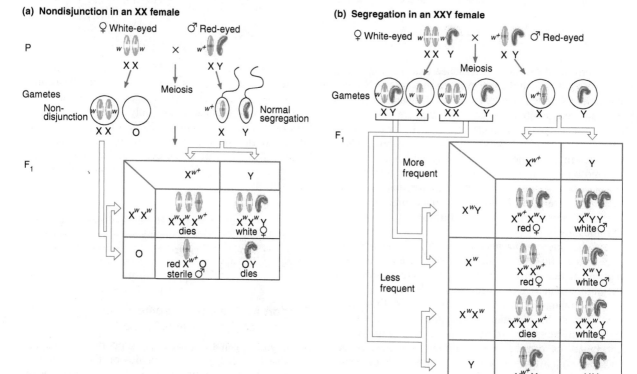

(a) Nondisjunction in an XX female

(b) Segregation in an XXY female

chromosome to the other. With this kind of segregation, only two results are possible: Either one X and the Y go to one pole and the second X to the other (yielding XY and X gametes), or the two Xs go to one pole and the Y to the other (yielding XX and Y gametes). The first of these two scenarios occurs more often because it comes about when the two similar X chromosomes pair with each other, ensuring that they will go to opposite poles during the first meiotic division. The second, less likely possibility happens only if the two X chromosomes fail to pair with each other.

Bridges next predicted that fertilization of these four kinds of eggs by normal sperm would generate an array of sex chromosome karyotypes associated with specific eye color phenotypes in the progeny. Bridges verified all his predictions when he analyzed the eye color and sex chromosomes of a large number of offspring. For instance, he showed cytologically that all of the white-eyed females emerging from the cross in Fig. 4.20b had two X chromosomes and one Y chromosome, while one-half of the white-eyed males had a single X chromosome and two Y chromosomes. Bridges' painstaking observations provided compelling evidence that specific genes do in fact reside on specific chromosomes.

X- and Y-linked traits in humans

A person unable to tell red from green would find it nearly impossible to distinguish the rose, scarlet, and magenta in the flowers of a garden bouquet from the delicately variegated greens in their foliage, or to complete a complex electrical circuit by fastening red-clad metallic wires to red ones and green to green. Such a person has most likely inherited some form of red-green colorblindness, a recessive condition that runs in families and affects mostly males. Among Caucasians in North America and Europe, 8% of men but only 0.44% of women have this vision defect. **Figure 4.21** suggests to readers with normal color vision what people with red-green colorblindness actually see.

In 1911, E. B. Wilson, a contributor to the chromosome theory of inheritance, combined familiarity with studies of colorblindness and recent knowledge of sex determination by the X and Y chromosomes to make the first assignment of a human gene to a particular chromosome. The gene for red-green colorblindness, he said, lies on the X because the condition usually passes from a maternal grandfather through an unaffected carrier mother to roughly 50% of the grandsons.

Several years after Wilson made this gene assignment, pedigree analysis established that various forms of hemophilia, or "bleeders disease" (in which the blood fails to clot properly), also result from mutations on the X chromosome that give rise to a relatively rare, recessive trait. In this context, rare means "infrequent in the population." The family histories under review, including

Figure 4.21 Red-green colorblindness is an X-linked recessive trait in humans. How the world looks to a person with either normal color vision (*top*) or a kind of red-green colorblindness known as deuteranopia (*bottom*).

one following the descendants of Queen Victoria of England (**Fig. 4.22a**), showed that relatively rare X-linked traits appear more often in males than in females and often skip generations. The clues that suggest X-linked recessive inheritance in a pedigree are summarized in **Table 4.5**.

Unlike colorblindness and hemophilia, some—although very few—of the known rare mutations on the X chromosome are dominant to the wild-type allele. With such dominant X-linked mutations, more females than males show the aberrant phenotype. This is because all the daughters of an affected male but none of the sons will have the condition, while one-half the sons and one-half the daughters of an affected female will receive the dominant allele and therefore show the phenotype (see Table 4.5). Vitamin D–resistant rickets, or hypophosphatemia, is an example of an X-linked dominant trait. **Figure 4.22b** presents the pedigree of a family affected by this disease.

Theoretically, phenotypes caused by mutations on the Y chromosome should also be identifiable by pedigree

Figure 4.22 X-linked traits may be recessive or dominant.
(a) Pedigree showing inheritance of the recessive X-linked trait hemophilia in Queen Victoria's family. **(b)** Pedigree showing the inheritance of the dominant X-linked trait hypophosphatemia, commonly referred to as vitamin D–resistant rickets.

(a) X-linked recessive: Hemophilia

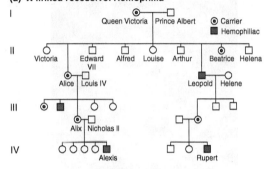

(b) X-linked dominant: Hypophosphatemia

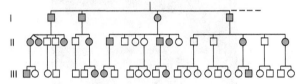

TABLE 4.5	Pedigree Patterns Suggesting Sex-Linked Inheritance

X-Linked Recessive Trait

1. The trait appears in more males than females since a female must receive two copies of the rare defective allele to display the phenotype, whereas a hemizygous male with only one copy will show it.

2. The mutation will never pass from father to son because sons receive only a Y chromosome from their father.

3. An affected male passes the X-linked mutation to all his daughters, who are thus unaffected carriers. One-half of the sons of these carrier females will inherit the defective allele and thus the trait.

4. The trait often skips a generation as the mutation passes from grandfather through a carrier daughter to grandson.

5. The trait can appear in successive generations when a sister of an affected male is a carrier. If she is, one-half her sons will be affected.

6. With the rare affected female, all her sons will be affected and all her daughters will be carriers.

X-Linked Dominant Trait

1. More females than males show the aberrant trait.

2. The trait is seen in every generation because it is dominant.

3. All the daughters but none of the sons of an affected male will be affected. This criterion is the most useful for distinguishing an X-linked dominant trait from an autosomal dominant trait.

4. One-half the sons and one-half the daughters of an affected female will be affected.

Y-Linked Trait

1. The trait is seen only in males.

2. All male descendants of an affected man will exhibit the trait.

3. Not only do females not exhibit the trait, they also cannot transmit it.

analysis. Such traits would pass from an affected father to all of his sons, and from them to all future male descendants. Females would neither exhibit nor transmit a Y-linked phenotype (see Table 4.5). However, besides the determination of maleness itself, as well as a contribution to sperm formation and thus male fertility, no clear-cut Y-linked visible traits have turned up. The paucity of known Y-linked traits in humans reflects the fact that the small Y chromosome contains very few genes. Indeed, one would expect the Y chromosome to have only a limited effect on phenotype because normal XX females do perfectly well without it.

Autosomal genes and sexual dimorphism

Not all genes that produce sexual dimorphism (differences in the two sexes) reside on the X or Y chromosomes. Some autosomal genes govern traits that appear in one sex but not the other, or traits that are expressed differently in the two sexes.

Sex-limited traits affect a structure or process that is found in one sex but not the other. Mutations in genes for sex-limited traits can influence only the phenotype of the sex that expresses those structures or processes. A curious example of a sex-limited trait occurs in *Drosophila* males homozygous for an autosomal recessive mutation known as *stuck*, which affects the ability

of mutant males to retract their penis and release the claspers by which they hold on to female genitalia during copulation. The mutant males have difficulty separating from females after mating. In extreme cases, both individuals die, forever caught in their embrace. Because females lack penises and claspers, homozygous *stuck* mutant females can mate normally.

Sex-influenced traits show up in both sexes, but expression of such traits may differ between the two sexes because of hormonal differences. Pattern baldness, a condition in which hair is lost prematurely from the top of the head but not from the sides (**Fig. 4.23**), is a sex-influenced trait in humans. Although pattern baldness is a complex trait that can be affected by many genes, an autosomal gene appears to play an important role in certain families.

Figure 4.23 Male pattern baldness, a sex-influenced trait. (a) John Adams (1735–1862), second president of the United States, at about age 60. **(b)** John Quincy Adams (1767–1848), son of John Adams and the sixth president of the United States, at about the same age. The father-to-son transmission suggests that the form of male pattern baldness in the Adams family is likely determined by an allele of an autosomal gene.

(a)   (b)

Men in these families who are heterozygous for the balding allele lose their hair while still in their 20s, whereas heterozygous women do not show any significant hair loss. In contrast, homozygotes in both sexes become bald (though the onset of baldness in homozygous women is usually much later in life than in homozygous men). This sex-influenced trait is thus dominant in men, recessive in women.

The chromosome theory integrates many aspects of gene behavior

Mendel had assumed that genes are located in cells. The chromosome theory assigned the genes to a specific structure within cells and explained alternative alleles as physically matching parts of homologous chromosomes. In so doing, the theory provided an explanation of Mendel's laws. The mechanism of meiosis ensures that the matching parts of homologous chromosomes will segregate to different gametes (except in rare instances of nondisjunction), accounting for the segregation of alleles predicted by Mendel's first law. Because each homologous chromosome pair aligns independently of all others at meiosis I, genes carried on different chromosomes will assort independently, as predicted by Mendel's second law.

The chromosome theory is also able to explain the creation of new alleles through mutation, a spontaneous change in a particular gene (that is, in a particular part of a chromosome). If a mutation occurs in the germ line, it can be transmitted to subsequent generations.

Finally, through mitotic cell division in the embryo and after birth, each cell in a multicellular organism receives the same chromosomes—and thus the same maternal and paternal alleles of each gene—as the zygote received from the egg and sperm at fertilization. In this way, an individual's genome—the chromosomes and genes he or she carries—remains constant throughout life.

The idea that genes reside on chromosomes was verified by experiments involving sex-linked genes in *Drosophila* and by the analysis of pedigrees showing X-linked patterns of inheritance in humans. The chromosome theory provides a physical basis for understanding Mendel's laws.

Connections

T. H. Morgan and his students, collectively known as the *Drosophila* group, acknowledged that Mendelian genetics could exist independently of chromosomes. "Why then, we are often asked, do you drag in the chromosomes? Our answer is that because the chromosomes furnish exactly the kind of mechanism that Mendelian laws call for, and since there is an ever-increasing body of information that points clearly to the chromosomes as the bearers of the Mendelian factors, it would be folly to close one's eyes to so patent a relation. Moreover, as biologists, we are interested in heredity not primarily as a mathematical formulation, but rather as a problem concerning the cell, the egg, and the sperm."

The *Drosophila* group went on to find several X-linked mutations in addition to white eyes. One made the body yellow instead of brown, another shortened the wings, yet another made bent instead of straight body bristles. These findings raised several compelling questions. First, if the genes for all of these traits are physically linked together on the X chromosome, does this linkage affect their ability to assort independently, and if so, how? Second, does each gene have an exact chromosomal address, and if so, does this specific location in any way affect its transmission? In Chapter 5 we describe how the *Drosophila* group and others analyzed the transmission patterns of genes on the same chromosome in terms of known chromosome movements during meiosis, and then used the information obtained to localize genes at specific chromosomal positions.

110   **Chapter 4**   The Chromosome Theory of Inheritance

ESSENTIAL CONCEPTS

1. Chromosomes are cellular structures specialized for the storage and transmission of genetic material. Genes are located on chromosomes and travel with them during cell division and gamete formation.

2. In sexually reproducing organisms, somatic cells carry a precise number of homologous pairs of chromosomes, which is characteristic of the species. One chromosome of each pair is of maternal origin; the other, paternal.

3. Mitosis underlies the growth and development of the individual. Through mitosis, diploid cells produce identical diploid progeny cells. During mitosis, the sister chromatids of every chromosome separate to each of two daughter cells. Before the next cell division, the chromosomes again duplicate to form sister chromatids.

4. During the first division of meiosis, homologous chromosomes in germ cells segregate from each other. As a result, each gamete receives one member of each matching pair, as predicted by Mendel's first law.

5. Also during the first meiotic division, the independent alignment of each pair of homologous chromosomes at the cellular midplane results in the independent assortment of genes carried on different chromosomes, as predicted by Mendel's second law.

6. Crossing-over and the independent alignment of homologs during the first meiotic division generate diversity.

7. The second meiotic division generates gametes with a haploid number of chromosomes (n).

8. Fertilization—the union of egg and sperm—restores the diploid number of chromosomes ($2n$) to the zygote.

9. The discovery of sex linkage, by which specific genes could be assigned to the X chromosome, provided important support for the chromosome theory of inheritance. Later, the analysis of rare mistakes in meiotic chromosome segregation (nondisjunction) yielded more detailed proof that specific genes are carried on specific chromosomes.

On Our Website   www.mhhe.com/hartwell4

Annotated Suggested Readings and Links to Other Websites

- More on the history of the chromosome theory of inheritance
- Mechanisms of sex determination in various organisms

- Recent research into the biochemical mechanisms underlying mitosis and meiosis
- Further examples of sex-linked inheritance in humans

Specialized Topics

- Chromosome behavior during mitosis and meiosis

Solved Problems

I. In humans, chromosome 16 sometimes has a heavily stained area in the long arm near the centromere. This feature can be seen through the microscope but has no effect on the phenotype of the person carrying it. When such a "blob" exists on a particular copy of chromosome 16, it is a constant feature of that chromosome and is inherited. A couple conceived a child, but the fetus had multiple abnormalities and was miscarried. When the chromosomes of the fetus were studied, it was discovered that it was trisomic for chromosome 16, and that two of the three chromosome 16s had large blobs. Both chromosome 16 homologs in the mother

lacked blobs, but the father was heterozygous for blobs. Which parent experienced nondisjunction, and in which meiotic division did it occur?

Answer

This problem requires an understanding of nondisjunction during meiosis. When individual chromosomes contain some distinguishing feature that allows one homolog to be distinguished from another, it is possible to follow the path of the two homologs through meiosis. In this case, because the fetus had two chromosome 16s with the blob, we can conclude that the extra chromosome came from the father (the only parent with a blobbed chromosome). In which meiotic division did the nondisjunction occur? When nondisjunction occurs during meiosis I, homologs fail to segregate to opposite poles. If this occurred in the father, the chromosome with the blob and the normal chromosome 16 would segregate into the same cell (a secondary spermatocyte). After meiosis II, the gametes resulting from this cell would carry both types of chromosomes. If such sperm fertilized a normal egg, the zygote would have two copies of the normal chromosome 16 and one of the chromosome with a blob. On the other hand, if nondisjunction occurred during meiosis II in the father in a secondary spermatocyte containing the blobbed chromosome 16, sperm with two copies of the blob-marked chromosome would be produced. After fertilization with a normal egg, the result would be a zygote of the type seen in this spontaneous abortion. *Therefore, the nondisjunction occurred in meiosis II in the father.*

II. (a) What sex ratio would you expect among the offspring of a cross between a normal male mouse and a female mouse heterozygous for a recessive X-linked lethal gene? (b) What would be the expected sex ratio among the offspring of a cross between a normal hen and a rooster heterozygous for a recessive Z-linked lethal allele?

Answer

This problem deals with sex-linked inheritance and sex determination.

a. Mice have a sex determination system of XX = female and XY = male. A normal male mouse ($X^R Y$) × a heterozygous female mouse ($X^R X^r$)

would result in $X^R X^R$, $X^R X^r$, $X^R Y$, and $X^r Y$ mice. The $X^r Y$ mice would die, so there would be a 2:1 ratio of females to males.

b. The sex determination system in birds is ZZ = male and ZW = female. A normal hen ($Z^R W$) × a heterozygous rooster ($Z^R Z^r$) would result in $Z^R Z^R$, $Z^R Z^r$, $Z^R W$, and $Z^r W$ chickens. Because the $Z^r W$ offspring do not live, the ratio of females to males would be 1:2.

III. A woman with normal color vision whose father was color-blind mates with a man with normal color vision.

a. What do you expect to see among their offspring?

b. What would you expect if it was the normal man's father who was color-blind?

Answer

This problem involves sex-linked inheritance.

a. The woman's father has a genotype of $X^{cb} Y$. Because the woman had to inherit an X from her father, she must have an X^{cb} chromosome, but because she has normal color vision, her other X chromosome must be X^{CB}. The man she mates with has normal color vision and therefore has an $X^{CB} Y$ genotype. Their children could with equal probability be $X^{CB} X^{CB}$ (normal female), $X^{CB} X^{cb}$ (carrier female), $X^{CB} Y$ (normal male), or $X^{cb} Y$ (color-blind male).

b. If the man with normal color vision had a color-blind father, the X^{cb} chromosome would not have been passed on to him, because a male does not inherit an X chromosome from his father. The man has the genotype $X^{CB} Y$ and cannot pass on the color-blind allele.

Problems

Vocabulary

1. Choose the best matching phrase in the right column for each of the terms in the left column.

a. meiosis

b. gametes

c. karyotype

d. mitosis

e. interphase

f. syncytium

g. synapsis

h. sex chromosomes

i. cytokinesis

j. anaphase

k. chromatid

l. autosomes

m. centromere

1. X and Y

2. chromosomes that do not differ between the sexes

3. one of the two identical halves of a replicated chromosome

4. microtubule organizing centers at the spindle poles

5. cells in the testes that undergo meiosis

6. division of the cytoplasm

7. haploid germ cells that unite at fertilization

8. an animal cell containing more than one nucleus

9. pairing of homologous chromosomes

10. one diploid cell gives rise to two diploid cells

11. the array of chromosomes in a given cell

12. the part of the cell cycle during which the chromosomes are not visible

13. one diploid cell gives rise to four haploid cells

n. centrosomes

o. polar body

p. spermatocytes

14. cell produced by meiosis that does not become a gamete

15. the time during mitosis when sister chromatids separate

16. connection between sister chromatids

c. metaphase

d. G$_2$

e. telophase/cytokinesis

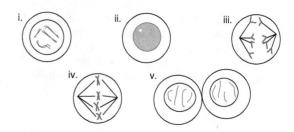

Section 4.1

2. Humans have 46 chromosomes in each somatic cell.
   a. How many chromosomes does a child receive from its father?
   b. How many autosomes and how many sex chromosomes are present in each somatic cell?
   c. How many chromosomes are present in a human ovum?
   d. How many sex chromosomes are present in a human ovum?

3. The figure that follows shows the metaphase chromosomes of a male of a particular species. These chromosomes are prepared as they would be for a karyotype, but they have not yet been ordered in pairs of decreasing size.
   a. How many centromeres are shown?
   b. How many chromosomes are shown?
   c. How many chromatids are shown?
   d. How many pairs of homologous chromosomes are shown?
   e. How many chromosomes on the figure are metacentric? Acrocentric?
   f. What is the likely mode of sex determination in this species? What would you predict to be different about the karyotype of a female in this species?

Section 4.2

4. One oak tree cell with 14 chromosomes undergoes mitosis. How many daughter cells are formed, and what is the chromosome number in each cell?

5. Indicate which of the cells numbered i–v matches each of the following stages of mitosis:
   a. anaphase
   b. prophase

6. a. What are the four major stages of the cell cycle?
   b. Which stages are included in interphase?
   c. What events distinguish G$_1$, S, and G$_2$?

7. Answer the questions that follow for each stage of the cell cycle (G$_1$, S, G$_2$, prophase, metaphase, anaphase, telophase). If necessary, use an arrow to indicate a change that occurs during a particular cell cycle stage (for example, 1 → 2 or yes → no).
   a. How many chromatids comprise each chromosome during this stage?
   b. Is the nucleolus present?
   c. Is the mitotic spindle organized?
   d. Is the nuclear membrane present?

8. Is there any reason that mitosis could not occur in a cell whose genome is haploid?

Section 4.3

9. One oak tree cell with 14 chromosomes undergoes meiosis. How many cells will result from this process, and what is the chromosome number in each cell?

10. Which type(s) of cell division (mitosis, meiosis I, meiosis II) reduce(s) the chromosome number by half? Which type(s) of cell division can be classified as reductional? Which type(s) of cell division can be classified as equational?

11. Complete the following statements using as many of the following terms as are appropriate: mitosis, meiosis I (first meiotic division), meiosis II (second meiotic division), and none (not mitosis nor meiosis I nor meiosis II).
    a. The spindle apparatus is present in cells undergoing _____ .
    b. Chromosome replication occurs just prior to _____ .
    c. The cells resulting from _____ in a haploid cell have a ploidy of *n*.

d. The cells resulting from _____ in a diploid cell have a ploidy of *n*.

e. Homologous chromosome pairing regularly occurs during _____.

f. Nonhomologous chromosome pairing regularly occurs during _____.

g. Physical recombination leading to the production of recombinant progeny classes occurs during _____.

h. Centromere division occurs during _____.

i. Nonsister chromatids are found in the same cell during _____.

12. The five cells shown in figures a–e below are all from the same individual. For each cell, indicate whether it is in mitosis, meiosis I, or meiosis II. What stage of cell division is represented in each case? What is *n* in this organism?

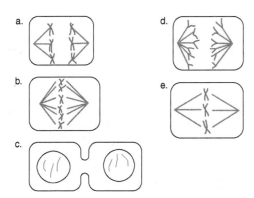

13. One of the first microscopic observations of chromosomes in cell division was published in 1905 by Nettie Stevens. Because it was hard to reproduce photographs at the time, she recorded these observations as *camera lucida* sketches. One such drawing, of a completely normal cell division in the mealworm *Tenebrio molitor,* is shown here. The techniques of the time were relatively unsophisticated by today's standards, and they did not allow her to resolve chromosomal structures that must have been present.

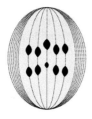

a. Describe in as much detail as possible the kind of cell division and the stage of division depicted in the drawing.

b. What chromosomal structure(s) cannot be resolved in the drawing?

c. How many chromosomes are present in normal *Tenebrio molitor* gametes?

14. A person is simultaneously heterozygous for two autosomal genetic traits. One is a recessive condition for albinism (alleles *A* and *a*); this albinism gene is found near the centromere on the long arm of an acrocentric autosome. The other trait is the dominantly inherited Huntington disease (alleles *HD* and HD^+). The Huntington gene is located near the telomere of one of the arms of a metacentric autosome. Draw all copies of the two relevant chromosomes in this person as they would appear during metaphase of (a) mitosis, (b) meiosis I, and (c) meiosis II. In each figure, label the location on every chromatid of the alleles for these two genes, assuming that no recombination takes place.

15. Assuming (i) that the two chromosomes in a homologous pair carry different alleles of some genes, and (ii) that no crossing-over takes place, how many genetically different offspring could any one human couple potentially produce? Which of these two assumptions (i or ii) is more realistic?

16. In the moss *Polytrichum commune,* the haploid chromosome number is 7. A haploid male gamete fuses with a haploid female gamete to form a diploid cell that divides and develops into the multicellular sporophyte. Cells of the sporophyte then undergo meiosis to produce haploid cells called spores. What is the probability that an individual spore will contain a set of chromosomes all of which came from the male gamete? Assume no recombination.

17. Is there any reason that meiosis could not occur in an organism whose genome is always haploid?

18. Sister chromatids are held together through metaphase of mitosis by complexes of *cohesin* proteins that form rubber band–like rings bundling the two sister chromatids. Cohesin rings are found both at centromeres and at many locations scattered along the length of the chromosomes. The rings are destroyed by protease enzymes at the beginning of anaphase, allowing the sister chromatids to separate.

a. Cohesin complexes between sister chromatids are also responsible for keeping homologous chromosomes together until anaphase of meiosis I. With this point in mind, which of the two diagrams that follow (i or ii) properly represents the arrangement of chromatids during prophase through metaphase of meiosis I? Explain.

b. What does your answer to part (a) allow you to infer about the nature of cohesin complexes at the centromere versus those along the chromosome arms? Suggest a molecular hypothesis to explain your inference.

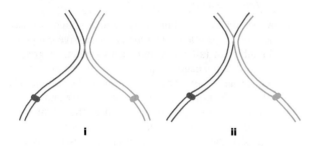

i   ii

Section 4.4

19. In humans,
    a. How many sperm develop from 100 primary spermatocytes?
    b. How many sperm develop from 100 secondary spermatocytes?
    c. How many sperm develop from 100 spermatids?
    d. How many ova develop from 100 primary oocytes?
    e. How many ova develop from 100 secondary oocytes?
    f. How many ova develop from 100 polar bodies?

20. Somatic cells of chimpanzees contain 48 chromosomes.
    How many chromatids and chromosomes are present at (a) anaphase of mitosis, (b) anaphase I of meiosis, (c) anaphase II of meiosis, (d) G_1 prior to mitosis, (e) G_2 prior to mitosis, (f) G_1 prior to meiosis I, and (g) prophase of meiosis I?
    How many chromatids or chromosomes are present in (h) an oogonial cell prior to S phase, (i) a spermatid, (j) a primary oocyte arrested prior to ovulation, (k) a secondary oocyte arrested prior to fertilization, (l) a second polar body, and (m) a chimpanzee sperm?

21. In a certain strain of turkeys, unfertilized eggs sometimes develop parthenogenetically to produce diploid offspring. (Females have ZW and males have ZZ sex chromosomes. Assume that WW cells are inviable.) What distribution of sexes would you expect to see among the parthenogenetic offspring according to each of the following models for how parthenogenesis occurs?
    a. The eggs develop without ever going through meiosis.
    b. The eggs go all the way through meiosis and then duplicate their chromosomes to become diploid.
    c. The eggs go through meiosis I, and the chromatids separate to create diploidy.
    d. The egg goes all the way through meiosis and then fuses at random with one of its three polar bodies (this assumes the first polar body goes through meiosis II).

22. Female mammals, including women, sometimes develop benign tumors called "ovarian teratomas" or "dermoid cysts" in their ovaries. Such a tumor begins when a primary oocyte escapes from its prophase I arrest and finishes meiosis I within the ovary. (Normally meiosis I does not finish until the primary oocyte is expelled from the ovary upon ovulation.) The secondary oocyte then develops as if it were an embryo, and it implants and develops within the follicle. Development is disorganized, however, and results in a tumor containing a wide variety of differentiated tissues, including teeth, hair, bone, muscle, nerve, and many others. If a dermoid cyst forms in a woman whose genotype is *Aa,* what are the possible genotypes of the cyst?

Section 4.5

23. A system of sex determination known as haplodiploidy is found in honeybees. Females are diploid, and males (drones) are haploid. Male offspring result from the development of unfertilized eggs. Sperm are produced by mitosis in males and fertilize eggs in the females. Ivory eye is a recessive characteristic in honeybees; wild-type eyes are brown.
    a. What progeny would result from an ivory-eyed queen and a brown-eyed drone? Give both genotype and phenotype for progeny produced from fertilized and nonfertilized eggs.
    b. What would result from crossing a daughter from the mating in part *a* with a brown-eyed drone?

24. Imagine you have two pure-breeding lines of canaries, one with yellow feathers and the other with brown feathers. In crosses between these two strains, yellow female × brown male gives only brown sons and daughters, while brown female × yellow male gives only brown sons and yellow daughters. Propose a hypothesis to explain these results.

25. Barred feather pattern is a Z-linked dominant trait in chickens. What offspring would you expect from (a) the cross of a barred hen to a nonbarred rooster? (b) the cross of an F_1 rooster from part (a) to one of his sisters?

26. Each of the four pedigrees that follow represents a human family within which a genetic disease is segregating. Affected individuals are indicated by filled-in symbols. One of the diseases is transmitted as an autosomal recessive condition, one as an X-linked recessive, one as an autosomal dominant, and one as an X-linked dominant. Assume all four traits are rare in the population.
    a. Indicate which pedigree represents which mode of inheritance, and explain how you know.
    b. For each pedigree, how would you advise the parents of the chance that their child (indicated by the hexagon shape) will have the condition?

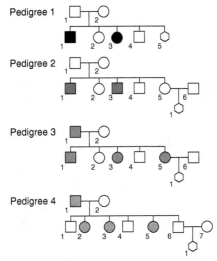

Pedigree 1

Pedigree 2

Pedigree 3

Pedigree 4

27. In a vial of *Drosophila,* a research student noticed several female flies (but no male flies) with "bag" wings each consisting of a large, liquid-filled blister instead of the usual smooth wing blade. When bag-winged females were crossed with wild-type males, 1/3 of the progeny were bag-winged females, 1/3 were normal-winged females, and 1/3 were normal-winged males. Explain these results.

28. Duchenne muscular dystrophy (DMD) is caused by a relatively rare X-linked recessive allele. It results in progressive muscular wasting and usually leads to death before age 20.
  a. What is the probability that the first son of a woman whose brother is affected will be affected?
  b. What is the probability that the second son of a woman whose brother is affected will be affected, if her first son was affected?
  c. What is the probability that a child of an unaffected man whose brother is affected will be affected?
  d. An affected man mates with his unaffected first cousin; there is otherwise no history of DMD in this family. If the mothers of this man and his mate were sisters, what is the probability that the couple's first child will be an affected boy? An affected girl? An unaffected child?
  e. If two of the parents of the couple in part (d) were brother and sister, what is the probability that the couple's first child will be an affected boy? An affected girl? An unaffected child?

29. The following is a pedigree of a family in which a rare form of colorblindness is found (filled-in symbols). Indicate as much as you can about the genotypes of all the individuals in the pedigree.

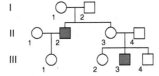

30. In 1995, doctors reported a Chinese family in which retinitis pigmentosa (progressive degeneration of the retina leading to blindness) affected only males. All six sons of affected males were affected, but all of the five daughters of affected males (and all of the children of these daughters) were unaffected.
  a. What is the likelihood that this form of retinitis pigmentosa is due to an autosomal mutation showing complete dominance?
  b. What other possibilities could explain the inheritance of retinitis pigmentosa in this family? Which of these possibilities do you think is most likely?

31. The pedigree that follows indicates the occurrence of albinism in a group of Hopi Indians, among whom the trait is unusually frequent. Assume that the trait is fully penetrant (all individuals with a genotype that could give rise to albinism will display this condition).
  a. Is albinism in this population caused by a recessive or a dominant allele?
  b. Is the gene sex-linked or autosomal?

What are the genotypes of the following individuals?
  c. individual I-1
  d. individual I-8
  e. individual I-9
  f. individual II-6
  g. individual II-8
  h. individual III-4

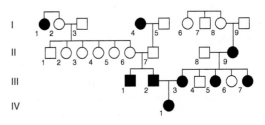

32. When Calvin Bridges observed a large number of offspring from a cross of white-eyed female *Drosophila* to red-eyed males, he observed very rare white-eyed females and red-eyed males among the offspring. He was able to show that these exceptions resulted from nondisjunction, such that the white-eyed females had received two Xs from the egg and a Y from the sperm, while the red-eyed males had received no sex chromosome from the egg and an X from the sperm. What progeny would have arisen from these same kinds of nondisjunctional events if they had occurred in the male parent? What would their eye colors have been?

33. In *Drosophila,* a cross was made between a yellow-bodied male with vestigial (not fully developed) wings and a wild-type female (brown body). The F_1 generation consisted of wild-type males and wild-type females. F_1 males and females were crossed, and the F_2 progeny consisted of 16 yellow-bodied males with vestigial wings, 48 yellow-bodied males with normal wings, 15 males with brown bodies and vestigial wings, 49 wild-type males, 31 brown-bodied females with vestigial wings, and 97 wild-type females. Explain the inheritance of the two genes in question based on these results.

34. Consider the following pedigrees from human families containing a male with Klinefelter syndrome (a set of abnormalities seen in XXY individuals; indicated with shaded boxes). In each, *A* and *B* refer to codominant alleles of the X-linked *G6PD* gene. The *phenotypes* of each individual (A, B, or AB) are shown on the pedigree. Indicate if nondisjunction occurred in the mother or father of the son with Klinefelter syndrome for each of the three examples. Can you tell if the nondisjunction was in the first or second meiotic division?

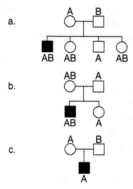

35. The pedigree at the bottom of the page shows five generations of a family that exhibits congenital hypertrichosis, a rare condition in which affected individuals are born with unusually abundant amounts of hair on their faces and upper bodies. The two small black dots in the pedigree indicate miscarriages.
   a. What can you conclude about the inheritance of hypertrichosis in this family, assuming complete penetrance of the trait?
   b. On what basis can you exclude other modes of inheritance?
   c. With how many fathers did III-2 and III-9 have children?

36. In *Drosophila*, the autosomal recessive *brown* eye color mutation displays interactions with both the X-linked recessive *vermilion* mutation and the autosomal recessive *scarlet* mutation. Flies homozygous for *brown* and simultaneously hemizygous or homozygous for *vermilion* have white eyes. Flies simultaneously homozygous for both the *brown* and *scarlet* mutations also have white eyes. Predict the F_1 and F_2 progeny of crossing the following true-breeding parents:
   a. vermilion females × brown males
   b. brown females × vermilion males
   c. scarlet females × brown males
   d. brown females × scarlet males

37. Several different antigens can be detected in blood tests. The following four traits were tested for each individual shown:

ABO type	(I^A and I^B codominant, *i* recessive)
Rh type	(Rh^+ dominant to Rh^-)
MN type	(*M* and *N* codominant)
$Xg^{(a)}$ type	($Xg^{(a+)}$ dominant to $Xg^{(a-)}$)

All of these blood type genes are autosomal, except for $Xg^{(a)}$, which is X linked.

	ABO	Rh	MN	Xg
Mother	AB	Rh^-	MN	$Xg^{(a+)}$
Daughter	A	Rh^+	MN	$Xg^{(a-)}$
Alleged father 1	AB	Rh^+	M	$Xg^{(a+)}$
Alleged father 2	A	Rh^-	N	$Xg^{(a-)}$
Alleged father 3	B	Rh^+	N	$Xg^{(a-)}$
Alleged father 4	O	Rh^-	MN	$Xg^{(a-)}$

   a. Which, if any, of the alleged fathers could be the real father?
   b. Would your answer to part *a* change if the daughter had Turner syndrome (the abnormal phenotype seen in XO individuals)? If so, how?

38. In 1919, Calvin Bridges began studying an X-linked recessive mutation causing eosin-colored eyes in *Drosophila*. Within an otherwise true-breeding culture of eosin-eyed flies, he noticed rare variants that had much lighter cream-colored eyes. By intercrossing these variants, he was able to make a true-breeding cream-eyed stock. Bridges now crossed males from

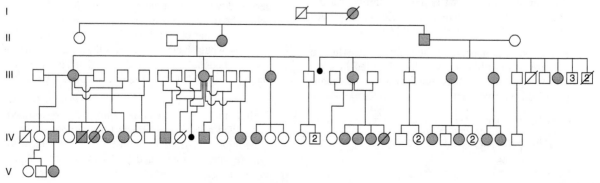

this cream-eyed stock with true-breeding wild-type females. All the F_1 progeny had red (wild-type) eyes. When F_1 flies were intercrossed, the F_2 progeny were 104 females with red eyes, 52 males with red eyes, 44 males with eosin eyes, and 14 males with cream eyes. Assume this represents an 8:4:3:1 ratio.

a. Formulate a hypothesis to explain the F_1 and F_2 results, assigning phenotypes to all possible genotypes.

b. What do you predict in the F_1 and F_2 generations if the parental cross is between true-breeding eosin-eyed males and true-breeding cream-eyed females?

c. What do you predict in the F_1 and F_2 generations if the parental cross is between true-breeding eosin-eyed females and true-breeding cream-eyed males?

39. As we learned in this chapter, the *white* mutation of *Drosophila* studied by Thomas Hunt Morgan is X linked and recessive to wild type. When true-breeding white-eyed males carrying this mutation were crossed with true-breeding purple-eyed females, all the F_1 progeny had wild-type (red) eyes. When the F_1 progeny were intercrossed, the F_2 progeny emerged in the ratio 3/8 wild-type females: 1/4 white-eyed males: 3/16 wild-type males: 1/8 purple-eyed females: 1/16 purple-eyed males.

a. Formulate a hypothesis to explain the inheritance of these eye colors.

b. Predict the F_1 and F_2 progeny if the parental cross was reversed (that is, if the parental cross was between true-breeding white-eyed females and true-breeding purple-eyed males).

40. The ancestry of a white female tiger bred in a city zoo is depicted in the pedigree following part (e) of this problem. White tigers are indicated with unshaded symbols. (As you can see, there was considerable inbreeding in this lineage. For example, the white tiger Mohan was mated with his daughter.) In answering the following questions, assume that "white" is determined by allelic differences at a single gene and that the trait is fully penetrant. Explain your answers by citing the relevant information in the pedigree.

a. Could white coat color be caused by a Y-linked allele?

b. Could white coat color be caused by a dominant X-linked allele?

c. Could white coat color be caused by a dominant autosomal allele?

d. Could white coat color be caused by a recessive X-linked allele?

e. Could white coat color be caused by a recessive autosomal allele?

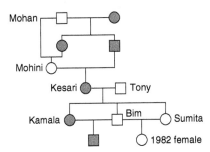

41. The pedigree at the bottom of the page shows the inheritance of various types of cancer in a particular family. Molecular analyses (described in subsequent chapters) indicate that with one exception, the cancers occurring in the patients in this pedigree are associated with a rare mutation in a gene called *BRCA2*.

a. Which individual is the exceptional cancer patient whose disease is not associated with a *BRCA2* mutation?

b. Is the *BRCA2* mutation dominant or recessive to the normal *BRCA2* allele in terms of its cancer-causing effects?

c. Is the *BRCA2* gene likely to reside on the X chromosome, the Y chromosome, or an autosome? How definitive is your assignment of the chromosome carrying *BRCA2*?

d. Is the penetrance of the cancer phenotype complete or incomplete?

e. Is the expressivity of the cancer phenotype unvarying or variable?

f. Are any of the cancer phenotypes associated with the *BRCA2* mutation sex-limited or sex-influenced?

g. How can you explain the absence of individuals diagnosed with cancer in generations I and II?

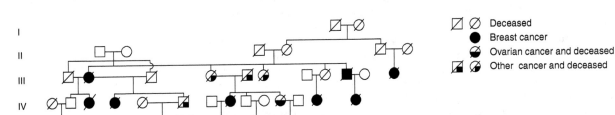

Linkage, Recombination, and the Mapping of Genes on Chromosomes

Maps illustrate the spatial relationships of objects, such as the locations of subway stations along subway lines. Genetic maps portray the positions of genes along chromosomes.

In 1928, doctors completed a four-generation pedigree tracing two known X-linked traits: red-green colorblindness and hemophilia A (the more serious X-linked form of "bleeders disease"). The maternal grandfather of the family exhibited both traits, which means that his single X chromosome carried mutant alleles of the two corresponding genes. As expected, neither colorblindness nor hemophilia showed up in his sons and daughters, but two grandsons and one great-grandson inherited both of the X-linked conditions (**Fig. 5.1a**). The fact that none of the descendants manifested one of the traits without the other suggests that the mutant alleles did not assort independently during meiosis. Instead they traveled together in the gametes forming one generation and then into the gametes forming the next generation, producing grandsons and great-grandsons with an X chromosome specifying both colorblindness and hemophilia. Genes that travel together more often than not exhibit **genetic linkage.**

In contrast, another pedigree following colorblindness and the slightly different B form of hemophilia, which also arises from a mutation on the X chromosome, revealed a different inheritance pattern. A grandfather with hemophilia B and colorblindness had four grandsons, but only one of them exhibited both conditions. In this family, the genes for colorblindness and hemophilia appeared to assort independently, producing in the male progeny all four possible combinations of the two traits—normal vision and normal blood clotting, colorblindness and hemophilia, colorblindness and normal clotting, and normal vision and hemophilia—in approximately equal frequencies (**Fig. 5.1b**). Thus, even though the mutant alleles of the two genes were on the same X chromosome in the grandfather, they had to separate to give rise to grandsons III-2 and III-3. This separation of genes on the same chromosome is the result of **recombination,** the occurrence in progeny of new gene combinations not seen in previous generations. (Note that *recombinant progeny* can result in either of two ways: from the recombination of genes on the same chromosome during gamete formation, discussed in this chapter, or from the independent assortment of genes on nonhomologous chromosomes, previously described in Chapter 4.)

Two important themes emerge as we follow the transmission of genes linked on the same chromosome. The first is that the farther apart two genes are, the greater is the probability of separation through recombination. Extrapolating from this general rule, you can see that the gene for hemophilia A must be very close to the gene

CHAPTER OUTLINE

- 5.1 Gene Linkage and Recombination
- 5.2 The Chi-Square Test and Linkage Analysis
- 5.3 Recombination: A Result of Crossing-Over During Meiosis
- 5.4 Mapping: Locating Genes Along a Chromosome
- 5.5 Tetrad Analysis in Fungi
- 5.6 Mitotic Recombination and Genetic Mosaics

Figure 5.1 Pedigrees indicate that colorblindness and two forms of hemophilia are X-linked traits. **(a)** Transmission of red-green colorblindness and hemophilia A. The traits travel together through the pedigree, indicating their genetic linkage. **(b)** Transmission of red-green colorblindness and hemophilia B. Even though both genes are X linked, the mutant alleles are inherited together in only one of four grandsons in generation III. These two pedigrees indicate that the gene for colorblindness is close to the hemophilia A gene but far away from the hemophilia B gene.

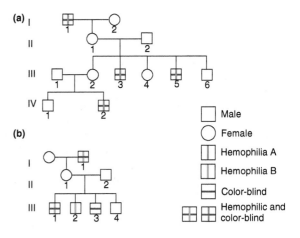

for red-green colorblindness, because, as Fig. 5.1a shows, the two rarely separate. By comparison, the gene for hemophilia B must lie far away from the colorblindness gene, because, as Fig. 5.1b indicates, new combinations of alleles of the two genes occur quite often. A second crucial theme arising from these considerations is that geneticists can use data about how often genes separate during transmission to map the genes' relative locations on a chromosome. Such mapping is a key to sorting out and tracking down the components of complex genetic networks; it is also crucial to geneticists' ability to isolate and characterize genes at the molecular level.

5.1 Gene Linkage and Recombination

If people have roughly 20,000 genes but only 23 pairs of chromosomes, most human chromosomes must carry hundreds, if not thousands, of genes. This is certainly true of the human X chromosome: In 2005, a group of bioinformatics specialists reported that they found 739 protein-encoding genes on this chromosome. This number is likely to grow, at least slightly, as geneticists develop new techniques to analyze the X chromosome's DNA sequence. Moreover, this number does not account for the many genes that do not encode proteins. Recognition that many genes reside on each chromosome raises an important question. If genes on *different* chromosomes assort independently because nonhomologous chromosomes align independently on the spindle during meiosis I, how do genes on the *same* chromosome assort?

Some genes on the same chromosome do not assort independently

We begin our analysis with X-linked *Drosophila* genes because they were the first to be assigned to a specific chromosome. As we outline various crosses, remember that females carry two X chromosomes, and thus two alleles for each X-linked gene. Males, in contrast, have only a single X chromosome (from the female parent), and thus only a single allele for each of these genes.

We look first at two X-linked genes that determine a fruit fly's eye color and body color. These two genes are said to be **syntenic** because they are located on the same chromosome. The *white* gene was previously introduced in Chapter 4; you will recall that the dominant wild-type allele w^+ specifies red eyes, while the recessive mutant allele w confers white eyes. The alleles of the *yellow* body color gene are y^+ (the dominant wild-type allele for brown bodies) and y (the recessive mutant allele for yellow bodies). To avoid confusion, note that lowercase y and y^+ refer to alleles of the *yellow* gene, while capital Y refers to the Y chromosome (which does not carry genes for either eye or body color). You should also pay attention to the slash symbol (/), which is used to separate genes found on chromosomes of a pair (either the X and Y chromosomes as in this case, or a pair of X chromosomes or homologous autosomes). Thus $w\ y\ /\ Y$ represents the genotype of a male with an X chromosome bearing w and y, as well as a Y chromosome; phenotypically this male has white eyes and a yellow body.

Detecting linkage by analyzing the gametes produced by a dihybrid

In a cross between a female with mutant white eyes and a wild-type brown body ($w\ y^+/w\ y^+$) and a male with wild-type red eyes and a mutant yellow body (w^+ y/Y), the F_1 offspring are evenly divided between brown-bodied females with normal red eyes (w y^+/w^+ y) and brown-bodied males with mutant white eyes (w y^+/Y) (**Fig. 5.2**). Note that the male progeny look like their mother because their phenotype directly reflects the genotype of the single X chromosome they received from her. The same is not true for the F_1 females, who received w and y^+ on the X from their mother and w^+ y on the X from their father. These F_1 females are thus dihybrids: With two alleles for each X-linked gene, one derived from each parent, the dominance relations of each pair of alleles determine the female phenotype.

Now comes the significant cross for answering our question about the assortment of genes on the same chromosome. If these two *Drosophila* genes for eye and body color assort independently, as predicted by Mendel's second law, the dihybrid F_1 females should make four kinds of gametes, with four different combinations of genes on the

X chromosome—w y^+, w^+ y, w^+ y^+, and w y. These four types of gametes should occur with equal frequency, that is, in a ratio of 1:1:1:1. If it happens this way, approximately half of the gametes will be of the two **parental types,** carrying either the w y^+ allele combination seen in the original female of the P generation or the w^+y allele combination seen in the original male of the P generation. The remaining half of the gametes will be of two **recombinant types,** in which reshuffling has produced either w^+y^+ or w y allele combinations not seen in the P generation parents of the F_1 females.

We can see whether the 1:1:1:1 ratio of the four kinds of gametes actually materializes by counting the different types of male progeny in the F_2 generation, as these sons receive their only X-linked genes from their maternal gamete. The bottom part of Fig. 5.2 depicts the results of a breeding study that produced 9026 F_2 males. The relative numbers of the four X-linked gene combinations passed on by the dihybrid F_1 females' gametes reflect a significant departure from the 1:1:1:1 ratio expected of independent assortment. By far, the largest numbers of gametes carry the parental combinations w y^+ and w^+y. Of the total 9026 male flies counted, 8897, or almost 99%, had these genotypes. In contrast, the new combinations w^+y^+ and w y made up little more than 1% of the total.

We can explain why the two genes fail to assort independently in one of two ways. Either the w y^+ and w^+ y combinations are preferred because of some intrinsic chemical affinity between these particular alleles, or it is the parental combination of alleles the F_1 female receives from one or the other of her P generation parents that shows up most frequently.

Linkage: A preponderance of parental classes of gametes

A second set of crosses involving the same genes but with a different arrangement of alleles explains why the dihybrid F_1 females do not produce a 1:1:1:1 ratio of the four possible types of gametes (see Cross Series B in **Fig. 5.3**). In this second set of crosses, the original parental generation consists of red-eyed, brown-bodied females (w^+ y^+/w^+ y^+) and white-eyed, yellow-bodied males (w y/Y), and the resultant F_1 females are all w^+ y^+/w y dihybrids. To find out what kinds and ratios of gametes these F_1 females produce, we need to look at the telltale F_2 males.

This time, as Cross B in Fig. 5.3 shows, w^+ y/Y and w y^+/Y are the recombinants that account for little more than 1% of the total, while w y/Y and w^+ y^+/Y are the parental combinations, which again add up to almost 99%. You can see that there is no preferred association of w^+ and y or of y^+ and w in this cross. Instead, a comparison of the two experiments with these particular X chromosome genes demonstrates that the observed

Figure 5.2 When genes are linked, parental combinations outnumber recombinant types. Doubly heterozygous w y^+/w^+ y F_1 females produce four types of male offspring. Sons that look like the father (w^+ y / Y) or mother (w y^+ / Y) of the F_1 females are parental types. Other sons (w^+y^+ / Y or w y / Y) are recombinant types. For these closely linked genes, many more parental types are produced than recombinant types.

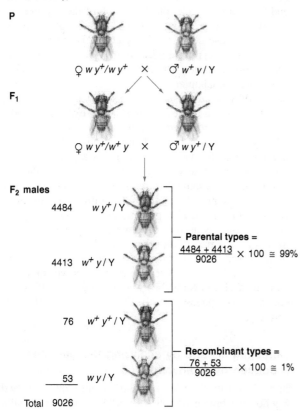

P

♀ w y^+/w y^+ ×   ♂ w^+ y/Y

F_1

♀ w y^+/w^+ y ×   ♂ w y^+/Y

F_2 males

4484 w y^+/Y

4413 w^+ y/Y

— Parental types = $\dfrac{4484 + 4413}{9026} \times 100 \cong 99\%$

76   w^+ y^+/Y

53   w y/Y

— Recombinant types = $\dfrac{76 + 53}{9026} \times 100 \cong 1\%$

Total   9026

Figure 5.3 Designations of "parental" and "recombinant" relate to past history. Figure 5.2 has been redrawn here as **Cross Series A** for easier comparison with **Cross Series B,** in which the dihybrid F₁ females received different allelic combinations of the *white* and *yellow* genes. Note that the parental and recombinant classes in the two cross series are the opposite of each other. The percentages of recombinant and parental types are nonetheless similar in both experiments, showing that the frequency of recombination is independent of the arrangement of alleles.

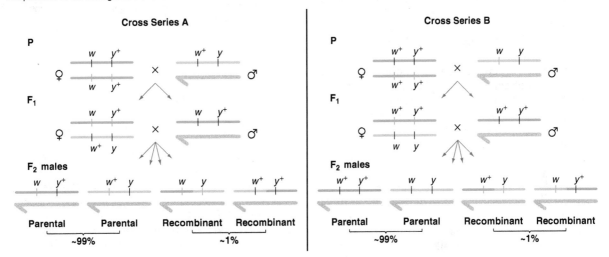

frequencies of the various types of progeny depend on how the arrangement of alleles in the F₁ females originated. We have redrawn Fig. 5.2 as Cross Series A in Fig. 5.3 so that you can make this comparison more directly. Note that in both experiments, it is the **parental classes**—the combinations originally present in the P generation—that show up most frequently in the F₂ generation. The reshuffled **recombinant classes** occur less frequently. It is important to appreciate that the designation of "parental" and "recombinant" gametes or progeny of a doubly heterozygous F₁ female is operational, that is, determined by the particular set of alleles she receives from each of her parents.

When genes assort independently, the numbers of parental and recombinant F₂ progeny are equal, because a doubly heterozygous F₁ individual produces an equal number of all four types of gametes. By comparison, two genes are considered **linked** when the number of F₂ progeny with parental genotypes exceeds the number of F₂ progeny with recombinant genotypes. Instead of assorting independently, the genes behave as if they are connected to each other much of the time. The genes for eye and body color that reside on the X chromosome in *Drosophila* are an extreme illustration of the linkage concept. The two genes are so tightly coupled that the parental combinations of alleles—w^+ y and w y^+ (in Cross Series A of Fig. 5.3) or w^+ y^+ and w y (in Cross Series B)—are reshuffled to form recombinants in only 1 out of every 100 gametes formed. In other words, the two parental allele combinations of these tightly linked genes are inherited together 99 times out of 100.

Gene-pair-specific variation in the degree of linkage

Linkage is not always this tight. In *Drosophila,* a mutation for miniature wings (*m*) is also found on the X chromosome. A cross of red-eyed females with normal wings (w^+ m^+/w^+ m^+) and white-eyed males with miniature wings (w m/Y) yields an F₁ generation containing all red-eyed, normal-winged flies. The genotype of the dihybrid F₁ females is w^+ m^+/w m. Of the F₂ males, 67.2% are parental types (w^+ m^+ and w m), while the remaining 32.8% are recombinants (w m^+ and w^+ m).

This preponderance of parental combinations among the F₂ genotypes reveals that the two genes are linked: The parental combinations of alleles travel together more often than not. But compared to the 99% linkage between the *w* and *y* genes for eye color and body color, the linkage of *w* to *m* is not that tight. The parental combinations for color and wing size are reshuffled in roughly 33 (instead of 1) out of every 100 gametes.

Autosomal traits can also exhibit linkage

Linked autosomal genes are not inherited according to the 9:3:3:1 Mendelian ratio expected for two independently assorting genes. Early twentieth-century geneticists were puzzled by the many experimentally observed departures from this ratio, which they could not explain in terms of the gene interactions discussed in Chapter 3.

They found it difficult to interpret these unexpected results because although they knew that individuals receive two copies of each autosomal gene, one from each parent, it was hard to trace which alleles came from which parent. However, by setting up testcrosses in which one parent was homozygous for the recessive alleles of both genes, they were able to analyze the gene combinations received from the gametes of the other, doubly heterozygous parent.

Fruit flies, for example, carry an autosomal gene for body color (in addition to the X-linked y gene); the wild type is once again brown, but a recessive mutation in this gene gives rise to black (b). A second gene on the same autosome helps determine the shape of a fruit fly's wing, with the wild type having straight edges and a recessive mutation (c) producing curves. **Figure 5.4** depicts a cross between black-bodied females with straight wings ($b\ c^+/\ b\ c^+$) and brown-bodied males with curved wings ($b^+\ c/\ b^+\ c$). All the F_1 progeny are double heterozygotes ($b\ c^+/\ b^+\ c$) that are phenotypically wild type. In a testcross of the F_1 females with $b\ c/\ b\ c$ males, all of the offspring receive the recessive b and c alleles from their father. The phenotypes of the offspring thus indicate the kinds of gametes received from the mother. For example, a black fly with normal wings would be genotype $b\ c^+/\ b\ c$; because we know it received the $b\ c$ combination from its father, it must have received $b\ c^+$ from its mother. As Fig. 5.4 shows, roughly 77% of the testcross progeny in one experiment received parental gene combinations (that is, allelic combinations transmitted into the F_1 females by the gametes of each of her parents), while the remaining 23% were recombinants. Because the parental classes outnumbered the recombinant classes, we can conclude that the autosomal genes for black body and curved wings are linked.

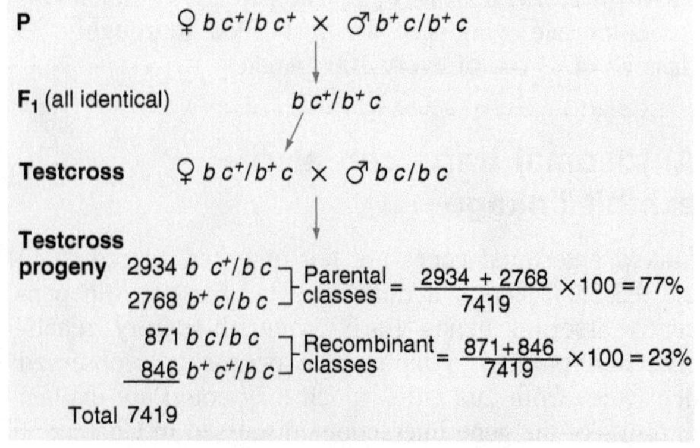

> Linkage between two genes can be detected in the proportion of gametes that a doubly heterozygous individual produces. If the numbers of parental-type and recombinant-type gametes are equal, then the two genes are assorting independently. If the parental-type gametes exceed the recombinant form, then the genes are linked.

5.2 The Chi-Square Test and Linkage Analysis

How do you know from a particular experiment whether two genes assort independently or are genetically linked? At first glance, this question should pose no problem. Discriminating between the two possibilities involves straightforward calculations based on assumptions well supported by observations. For independently assorting genes, a dihybrid F_1 female produces four types of gametes in equal numbers, so one-half of the F_2 progeny are of the parental classes and the other half of the recombinant classes. In contrast, for linked genes, the two types of parental classes by definition always outnumber the two types of recombinant classes in the F_2 generation.

The problem is that because real-world genetic transmission is based on chance events, in a particular study even unlinked, independently assorting genes can produce deviations from the 1:1:1:1 ratio, just as in 10 tosses of a coin, you may easily get 6 heads and 4 tails (rather than the predicted 5 and 5). Thus, if a breeding experiment analyzing the transmission of two genes shows a deviation from the equal ratios of parentals and recombinants expected of independent assortment, can we necessarily conclude the two genes are linked? Is it instead possible that the results represent a statistically acceptable chance fluctuation from the mean values expected of unlinked genes that assort independently? Such questions become more pressing in cases where linkage is not all that tight, so that even though the genes are linked, the percentage of recombinant classes approaches 50%.

Figure 5.4 Autosomal genes can also exhibit linkage.
A testcross shows that the recombination frequency for the body color (b) and wing shape (c) pair of *Drosophila* genes is 23%. Because parentals outnumber recombinants, the b and c genes are genetically linked and must be on the same autosome.

P	$♀\ b\ c^+/b\ c^+$ × $♂\ b^+\ c/b^+\ c$
F_1 (all identical)	$b\ c^+/b^+\ c$
Testcross	$♀\ b\ c^+/b^+\ c$ × $♂\ b\ c/b\ c$

Testcross progeny

$$\left.\begin{array}{l} 2934\ b\ c^+/b\ c \\ 2768\ b^+\ c/b\ c \end{array}\right\} \text{Parental classes} = \frac{2934+2768}{7419} \times 100 = 77\%$$

$$\left.\begin{array}{l} 871\ b\ c/b\ c \\ 846\ b^+\ c^+/b\ c \end{array}\right\} \text{Recombinant classes} = \frac{871+846}{7419} \times 100 = 23\%$$

Total 7419

The chi-square test evaluates the significance of differences between predicted and observed values

To answer these kinds of questions, statisticians have devised a quantitative measure of the likelihood that an experimentally observed deviation from the predictions of a particular hypothesis could have occurred solely by chance. This measure of the "goodness of fit" between observed and predicted results is a probability test known as the **chi-square test.** The test is designed to account for the fact that the size of an experimental population (the "sample size") is an important component of statistical significance. To appreciate the role of sample size, let's return to the proverbial coin toss before examining the details of the chi-square test.

In 10 tosses of a coin, an outcome of 6 heads (60%) and 4 tails (40%) is not unexpected because of the effects of chance. However, with 1000 tosses of the coin, a result of 600 heads (60%) and 400 tails (40%) would intuitively be highly unlikely. In the first case, a change in the results of one coin toss would alter the expected 5:5 ratio to the observed 6:4 ratio. In the second case, 100 tosses would have to change from tails to heads to generate the stated deviation from the predicted 500:500 ratio. Chance events could reasonably, and even likely, cause 1 deviation from the predicted number, but not 100.

Two important concepts emerge from this simple example. First, a comparison of percentages or ratios alone will never allow you to determine whether or not *observed* data are significantly different from *predicted* values. Second, the absolute numbers obtained are important because they reflect the size of the experiment. The larger the sample size, the closer the observed percentages can be expected to match the values predicted by the experimental hypothesis, *if the hypothesis is correct*. The chi-square test is therefore always calculated with numbers—actual data—and not percentages or proportions.

The chi-square test cannot prove a hypothesis, but it can allow researchers to reject a hypothesis. For this reason, a critical prerequisite of the chi-square test is the framing of a **null hypothesis:** a model that might possibly be refuted by the test and that leads to clear-cut numerical predictions. Although contemporary geneticists use the chi-square test to interpret many kinds of genetic experiments, they use it most often to discover whether data obtained from breeding experiments provide evidence for or against the hypothesis that two genes are linked. But the problem with the general hypothesis that "genes *A* and *B* are linked" is that there is no precise prediction of what to expect in terms of breeding data. The reason is that the frequency of recombinations, as we have seen, varies with each linked gene pair.

In contrast, the alternative hypothesis "that genes *A* and *B* are *not* linked" gives rise to a precise prediction: that alleles at different genes will assort independently and produce 50% parental and 50% recombinant progeny. So, whenever a geneticist wants to determine whether two genes are linked, he or she actually tests whether the observed data are consistent with the null hypothesis of no linkage. If the chi-square test shows that the observed data differ significantly from those expected with independent assortment—that is, they differ enough not to be reasonably attributable to chance alone—then the researcher can reject the null hypothesis of no linkage and accept the alternative of linkage between the two genes.

The Tools of Genetics box on p. 124 presents the general protocol of the chi-square test. The final result of the calculations is the determination of the numerical probability—the *p* value—that a particular set of observed experimental results represents a chance deviation from the values predicted by a particular hypothesis. If the probability is high, it is likely that the hypothesis being tested explains the data, and the observed deviation from expected results is considered *insignificant*. If the probability is very low, the observed deviation from expected results becomes *significant*. When this happens, it is unlikely that the hypothesis under consideration explains the data, and the hypothesis can be rejected.

Applying the chi-square test to linkage analysis: An example

Figure 5.5 depicts two sets of data obtained from testcross experiments asking whether genes *A* and *B* are linked. We first apply the chi-square analysis to data accumulated in the first experiment. The total number of offspring is 50, of which 31 (that is, 17 + 14) are observed to be parental types and 19 (8 + 11) recombinant types. Dividing 50 by 2, you get 25, the number of parental or recombinant offspring expected according to the null hypothesis of independent assortment (which predicts that parentals = recombinants).

Now, considering first the parental types alone, you square the observed deviation from the expected value, and divide the result by the expected value. After doing the same for the recombinant types, you add the two quotients to obtain the value of chi square.

$$\chi^2 = \frac{(31 + 25)^2}{25} + \frac{(19 - 25)^2}{25} = 1.44 + 1.44 = 2.88$$

Figure 5.5 Applying the chi-square test to see if genes *A* and *B* are linked. The null hypothesis is that the two genes are unlinked. For Experiment 1, $p > 0.05$, so it is not possible to reject the null hypothesis. For Experiment 2, with a data set twice the size, $p < 0.05$. Based on this latter result, most geneticists would reject the null hypothesis and conclude with greater than 95% confidence that the genes are linked.

Progeny	Experiment 1	Experiment 2
A B	17	34
a b	14	28
A b	8	16
a B	11	22
Total	50	100

Class	**Observed**	**Expected**	**Observed**	**Expected**
Parentals	31	25	62	50
Recombinants	19	25	38	50

TOOLS OF GENETICS

The Chi-Square Test

The general protocol for using the chi-square test and evaluating its results can be stated in a series of steps. Two preparatory steps precede the actual chi-square calculation.

1. Use the data obtained from a breeding experiment to answer the following questions:
   a. What is the *total number* of offspring (events) analyzed?
   b. How many different *classes* of offspring (events) are there?
   c. In each class, what is the *number* of offspring (events) *observed*?
2. Calculate how many offspring (events) would be expected for each class if the null hypothesis (here, no linkage) were correct: Multiply the percentage predicted by the null hypothesis (here, 50% parentals and 50% recombinants) by the total number of offspring. You are now ready for the chi-square calculation.
3. To calculate chi square, begin with one class of offspring. Subtract the expected number from the observed number to obtain the deviation from the predicted value for the class. Square the result, and divide this value by the expected number.

   Do this for all classes and then sum the individual results. The final result is the chi-square (χ^2) value. This step is summarized by the equation

$$\chi^2 = \Sigma \; \frac{(\textit{Number observed} - \textit{Number expected})^2}{\textit{Number expected}}$$

where Σ means "sum of all classes."

4. Next, you consider the **degrees of freedom (df).** The df is a measure of the number of independently varying parameters in the experiment (see text). The value of degrees of freedom is one less than the number of classes. Thus, if N is the number of classes, then the degrees of freedom (df) $= N - 1$. If there are 4 classes, then there are 3 df.
5. Use the chi-square value together with the df to determine a **p value:** the probability that a deviation from the predicted numbers at least as large as that observed in the experiment would occur by chance. Although the p value is arrived at through a numerical analysis, geneticists routinely determine the value by a quick search through a table of critical χ^2 values for different degrees of freedom, such as **Table 5.1.**
6. Evaluate the significance of the p value. You can think of the p value as the probability that the null hypothesis is true. A value greater than 0.05 indicates that in more than 1 in 20 (or more than 5%) repetitions of an experiment of the same size, the observed deviation from predicted values could have been obtained by chance, even if the null hypothesis is actually true; the data are therefore *not significant* for rejecting the null hypothesis. Statisticians have arbitrarily selected the 0.05 p value as the boundary between accepting and rejecting the null hypothesis. A p value of less than 0.05 means that you can consider the deviation to be *significant*, and you can reject the null hypothesis.

TABLE 5.1	**Critical Chi-Square Values**						
	p Values						
	Cannot Reject the Null Hypothesis				**Null Hypothesis Rejected**		
Degrees of Freedom	**0.99**	**0.90**	**0.50**	**0.10**	**0.05**	**0.01**	**0.001**
	χ^2 **Values**						
1	—	0.02	0.45	2.71	3.84	6.64	10.83
2	0.02	0.21	1.39	4.61	5.99	9.21	13.82
3	0.11	0.58	2.37	6.25	7.81	11.35	16.27
4	0.30	1.06	3.36	7.78	9.49	13.28	18.47
5	0.55	1.61	4.35	9.24	11.07	15.09	20.52

Note: χ^2 values that lie in the *yellow* region of this table allow you to reject the null hypothesis with > 95% confidence, and for recombination experiments, to postulate linkage.

You next determine the **degrees of freedom (df)** for this experiment. Degrees of freedom is a mathematical concept that takes into consideration the number of independently varying parameters. For example, if the offspring in an experiment fall into four classes, and you know the total number of offspring as well as the numbers present in three of the classes, then you can directly calculate the number present in the fourth class. Therefore, the df with four classes is one less than the number of classes, or three. Because with two classes (parentals and recombinants), the number of degrees of freedom is 1, you scan the chi-square table (see Table 5.1 on p. 124) for $\chi^2 = 2.88$ and df $= 1$. You find by extrapolation that the corresponding p value is greater than 0.05 (roughly 0.09). From this p value you can conclude that it is not possible to reject the null hypothesis on the basis of this experiment, which means that this data set is not sufficient to demonstrate linkage between A and B.

If you use the same strategy to calculate a p value for the data observed in the second experiment, where there are a total of 100 offspring and thus an expected number of 50 parentals and 50 recombinants, you get

$$\chi^2 = \frac{(62 - 50)^2}{50} + \frac{(38 - 50)^2}{50} = 2.88 + 2.88 = 5.76$$

The number of degrees of freedom (df) remains 1, so Table 5.1 arrives at a p value greater than 0.01 but less than 0.05. In this case, you can consider the difference between the observed and expected values to be significant. As a result, you can reject the null hypothesis of independent assortment and conclude it is likely that genes A and B are linked.

Statisticians have arbitrarily selected a p value of 0.05 as the boundary between significance and nonsignificance. Values lower than this indicate there would be less than 5 chances in 100 of obtaining the same results by random sampling if the null hypothesis were true. A p value of less than 0.05 thus suggests that the data shows major deviations from predicted values significant enough to reject the null hypothesis with greater than 95% confidence. More conservative scientists often set the boundary of significance at $p = 0.01$, and they would therefore reject the null hypothesis only if their confidence was greater than 99%.

In contrast, p values greater than 0.01 or 0.05 do not necessarily mean that two genes are unlinked; it may mean only that the sample size is not large enough to provide an answer. With more data, the p value normally rises if the null hypothesis of no linkage is correct and falls if there is, in fact, linkage.

Note that in Fig. 5.5 all of the numbers in the second set of data are simply double the numbers in the first set, with the percentages remaining the same. Thus, just by doubling the sample size from 50 to 100 individuals, it was possible to go from no significant difference to a significant difference between the observed and the

expected values. In other words, the larger the sample size, the less the likelihood that a certain percentage deviation from expected results happened simply by chance. Bearing this in mind, you can see that it is not appropriate to use the chi-square test when analyzing very small samples of less than 10. This creates a problem for human geneticists, because human families produce only a small number of children. To achieve a reasonable sample size for linkage studies in humans, scientists must instead pool data from a large number of family pedigrees.

The chi-square test *does not* prove linkage or its absence. What it *does* do is provide a quantitative measure of the likelihood that the data from an experiment can be explained by a particular hypothesis. The chi-square analysis is thus a general statistical test for significance; it can be used with many different experimental designs and with hypotheses other than the absence of linkage. As long as it is possible to propose a null hypothesis that leads to a predicted set of values for a defined set of data classes, you can readily determine whether or not the observed data are consistent with the hypothesis.

When experiments lead to rejection of a null hypothesis, you may need to confirm an alternative. For instance, if you are testing whether two opposing traits result from the segregation of two alleles of a single gene, you would expect a testcross between an F_1 heterozygote and a recessive homozygote to produce a 1:1 ratio of the two traits in the offspring. If instead, you observe a ratio of 6:4 and the chi-square test produces a p value of 0.009, you can reject the null hypothesis. But you are still left with the question of what the absence of a 1:1 ratio means. There are actually two alternatives: (1) Individuals with the two possible genotypes are not equally viable, *or* (2) more than one gene encodes the trait. The chi-square test cannot tell you which possibility is correct, and you would have to study the matter further. The problems at the end of this chapter illustrate several applications of the chi-square test pertinent to genetics.

> Geneticists use the chi-square test to evaluate the probability that differences between predicted results and observed results are due to random sampling error. For linkage analysis, p values of less than 0.05 allow rejection of the null hypothesis that the two genes are unlinked.

5.3 Recombination: A Result of Crossing-Over During Meiosis

It is easy to understand how genes that are physically connected on the same chromosome can be transmitted together and thus show genetic linkage. It is not as obvious why all linked genes always show some recombination in a sample population of sufficient size. Do the chromosomes participate in a physical process that gives rise to the reshuffling of linked genes that we call recombination? The answer to this question is of more than passing interest as it provides a basis for gauging relative distances between pairs of genes on a chromosome.

In 1909, the Belgian cytologist Frans Janssens described structures he had observed in the light microscope during prophase of the first meiotic division. He called these structures *chiasmata;* as described in Chapter 4, they seemed to represent regions in which nonsister chromatids of homologous chromosomes cross over each other (review Fig. 4.14 on p. 96). Making inferences from a combination of genetic and cytological data, Thomas Hunt Morgan suggested that the chiasmata observed through the light microscope were sites of chromosome breakage and exchange resulting in genetic recombination.

Reciprocal exchanges between homologs are the physical basis of recombination

Morgan's idea that the physical breaking and rejoining of chromosomes during meiosis was the basis of genetic recombination seemed reasonable. But although Janssens's chiasmata could be interpreted as signs of the process, before 1930 no one had produced visible evidence that crossing-over between homologous chromosomes actu-

ally occurs. The identification of **physical markers,** or cytologically visible abnormalities that make it possible to keep track of specific chromosome parts from one generation to the next, enabled researchers to turn the logical deductions about recombination into facts derived from experimental evidence. In 1931, Harriet Creighton and Barbara McClintock, who studied corn, and Curt Stern, who worked with *Drosophila,* published the results of experiments showing that genetic recombination indeed depends on the reciprocal exchange of parts between maternal and paternal chromosomes. Stern, for example, bred female flies with two different X chromosomes, each containing a distinct physical marker near one of the ends. These same females were also doubly heterozygous for two X-linked **genetic markers**—genes that could serve as points of reference in determining whether particular progeny were the result of recombination.

Figure 5.6 diagrams the chromosomes of these heterozygous females. One X chromosome carried mutations producing carnation eyes (a dark ruby color, abbreviated *car*) that were kidney-shaped (*Bar*); in addition, this chromosome was marked physically by a visible discontinuity, which resulted when the end of the X chromosome was broken off and attached to an autosome. The other X chromosome had wild-type alleles (+) for both the *car* and the *Bar* genes, and its physical

Figure 5.6 Evidence that recombination results from reciprocal exchanges between homologous chromosomes. Genetic recombination between the *car* and *Bar* genes on the *Drosophila* X chromosome is accompanied by the exchange of physical markers observable in the microscope. Note that this depiction of crossing-over is a simplification, as genetic recombination actually occurs after each chromosome has replicated into sister chromatids. Note also that the piece of the X chromosome to the right of the discontinuity is actually attached to an autosome.

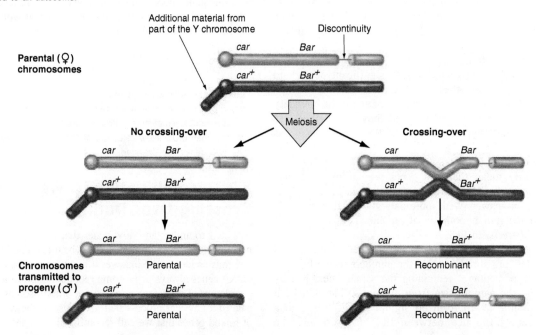

marker consisted of part of the Y chromosome that had become connected to the X-chromosome centromere.

Figure 5.6 illustrates how the chromosomes in these *car Bar* / *car⁺ Bar⁺* females were transmitted to male progeny. According to the experimental results, all sons showing a phenotype determined by one or the other parental combination of genes (either *car Bar* or *car⁺ Bar⁺*) had an X chromosome that was structurally indistinguishable from one of the original X chromosomes in the mother. In recombinant sons, however, such as those that manifested carnation eye color and normal eye shape (*car Bar⁺* / Y), an identifiable exchange of the abnormal features marking the ends of the homologous X chromosomes accompanied the recombination of genes. The evidence thus tied an instance of phenotypic recombination to the crossing-over of particular genes located in specifically marked parts of particular chromosomes. This experiment elegantly demonstrated that genetic recombination is associated with the actual reciprocal exchange of segments between homologous chromosomes during meiosis.

Chiasmata mark the sites of recombination

Figure 5.7 outlines what is currently known about the steps of recombination as they appear in chromosomes viewed through the light microscope. Although this low-resolution view may not represent certain details of recombination with complete accuracy, it nonetheless provides a useful frame of reference. In Fig. 5.7a, the two homologs of each chromosome pair have already replicated, so there are now two pairs of sister chromatids or a total of four chromatids within each bivalent. In Fig. 5.7b, the synaptonemal complex zips together homologous chromosome pairs along their length. The synaptonemal zipper aligns homologous regions of all four chromatids such that allelic DNA sequences are physically near each other (see Fig. 4.14b on p. 96 for a detailed depiction). This proximity facilitates crossing-over between homologous sequences; as we will see in Chapter 6, the biochemical mechanism of recombination requires a close interaction of DNAs on homologous chromosomes that have identical, or nearly identical, nucleotide sequences.

In Fig. 5.7c, the synaptonemal complex begins to disassemble. Although at least some steps of the recombination process occurred while the chromatids were zipped in synapsis, it is only now that the recombination event becomes apparent. As the zipper dissolves, homologous chromosomes remain attached at chiasmata, the actual sites of crossing-over. Visible in the light microscope, chiasmata indicate where chromatid sections have switched from one molecule to another. In Fig. 5.7d, during anaphase I, as the two homologs separate, starting at their centromeres, the ends of the two recombined

Figure 5.7 Recombination through the light microscope.
(a) A pair of duplicated homologous chromosomes very early in prophase of meiosis I. **(b)** During leptotene and zygotene of prophase I, the synaptonemal complex helps align corresponding regions of homologous chromosomes, allowing recombination. **(c)** As the synaptonemal complex disassembles during diplotene, homologous chromosomes remain attached at chiasmata. **(d)** and **(e)** The chiasmata terminalize (move toward the chromosome ends), allowing the recombined chromosomes to separate during anaphase and telophase. **(f)** The result of the process is recombinant gametes.

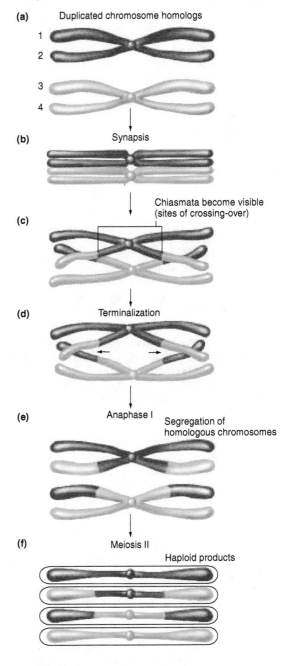

chromatids pull free of their respective sister chromatids, and the chiasmata shift from their original positions toward a chromosome end, or telomere. This movement of chiasmata is known as **terminalization.** When the chiasmata reach the telomeres, the homologous chromosomes can separate from each other (Fig. 5.7e). Meiosis continues and eventually produces four haploid cells that contain one chromatid—now a chromosome—apiece (Fig. 5.7f). Homologous chromosomes have exchanged parts.

Recombination can also take place apart from meiosis. As explained near the end of this chapter, recombination sometimes, though rarely, occurs during mitosis. It also occurs with the circular chromosomes of prokaryotic organisms and cellular organelles such as mitochondria and chloroplasts, which do not undergo meiosis and do not form chiasmata (see Chapter 14).

Recombination frequencies reflect the distances between two genes

Thomas Hunt Morgan's belief that chiasmata represent sites of physical crossing-over between chromosomes and that such crossing-over may result in recombination, led him to the following logical deduction: Different gene pairs exhibit different linkage rates because genes are arranged in a line along a chromosome. The closer together two genes are on the chromosome, the less their chance of being separated by an event that cuts and recombines the line of genes. To look at it another way, if we assume for the moment that chiasmata can form anywhere along a chromosome with equal likelihood, then the probability of a crossover occurring between two genes increases with the distance separating them. If this is so, the frequency of genetic recombination also must increase with the distance between genes. To illustrate the point, imagine pinning to a wall 10 inches of ribbon with a line of tiny black dots along its length and then repeatedly throwing a dart to see where you will cut the ribbon. You would find that practically every throw of the dart separates a dot at one end of the ribbon from a dot at the other end, while few if any throws separate any two particular dots positioned right next to each other.

Alfred H. Sturtevant, one of Morgan's students, took this idea one step further. He proposed that the percentage of total progeny that were recombinant types, the **recombination frequency (RF),** could be used as a gauge of the physical distance separating any two genes on the same chromosome. Sturtevant arbitrarily defined one RF percentage point as the unit of measure along a chromosome; later, another geneticist named the unit a **centimorgan (cM)** after T. H. Morgan. Mappers often refer to a centimorgan as a **map unit (m.u.).** Although the two terms are interchangeable, researchers prefer

Figure 5.8 Recombination frequencies are the basis of genetic maps. (a) 1.1% of the gametes produced by a female doubly heterozygous for the genes *w* and *y* are recombinant. The recombination frequency (RF) is thus 1.1%, and the genes are approximately 1.1 map units (m.u.) or 1.1 centimorgans (cM) apart. **(b)** The distance between the *w* and *m* genes is longer: 32.8 m.u. (or 32.8 cM).

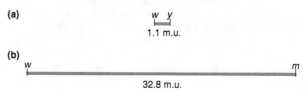

one or the other, depending on their experimental organism. *Drosophila* geneticists, for example, use map units while human geneticists use centimorgans. In Sturtevant's system, 1% RF = 1 cM = 1 m.u. A review of the two pairs of X-linked *Drosophila* genes we analyzed earlier shows how his proposal works. Because the X-linked genes for eye color (*w*) and body color (*y*) recombine in 1.1% of F_2 progeny, they are 1.1 m.u. apart (**Fig. 5.8a**). In contrast, the X-linked genes for eye color (*w*) and wing size (*m*) have a recombination frequency of 32.8 and are therefore 32.8 m.u. apart (**Fig. 5.8b**).

As a unit of measure, the map unit is simply an index of recombination probabilities assumed to reflect distances between genes. According to this index, the *y* and *w* genes are much closer together than the *m* and *w* genes. Geneticists have used this logic to map thousands of genetic markers to the chromosomes of *Drosophila*, building recombination maps step-by-step with closely linked markers. And as we see next, they have learned that genes very far apart on the same chromosome may appear unlinked, even though their recombination distances relative to closely linked intervening markers confirm that the genes are indeed on the same chromosome.

Recombination frequencies between two genes never exceed 50%

If the definition of linkage is that the proportion of recombinant classes is less than that of parental classes, a recombination frequency of less than 50% indicates linkage. But what can we conclude about the relative location of genes if there are roughly equal numbers of parental and recombinant progeny? And does it ever happen that recombinants are in the majority?

We already know one situation that can give rise to a recombination frequency of 50%. Genes located on different (that is, nonhomologous) chromosomes will obey Mendel's law of independent assortment because the two chromosomes can line up on the spindle during meiosis I in either of two equally likely configurations (review Fig. 4.16a on p. 98). A dihybrid for these two genes will thus produce all four possible types of gametes (*AB, Ab, aB,* and *ab*) with approximately equal frequency. Importantly, experiments have established that genes located very far apart on the same chromosome also show recombination frequencies of approximately 50%.

Researchers have never observed statistically significant recombination frequencies between two genes greater than 50%, which means that in any cross following two genes, recombinant types are never in the majority. As we explain in more detail later in the chapter, this upper limit of 50% on the recombination frequency between two genes results from two aspects of chromosome behavior during meiosis I. First, multiple crossovers can occur between two genes if they are far apart on the same chromosome, and second, recombination takes place after the chromosomes have replicated into sister chromatids.

For now, simply note that recombination frequencies near 50% suggest either that two genes are on different chromosomes or that they lie far apart on the same chromosome. The only way to tell whether the two genes are syntenic (that is, on the same chromosome) is through a series of matings showing definite linkage with other genes that lie between them. In short, even though crosses between two genes lying very far apart on a chromosome may show no linkage at all (because recombinant and parental classes are equal), you can demonstrate they are on the same chromosome if you can tie each of the widely separated genes to one or more common intermediaries. **Table 5.2** summarizes the relationship between the relative locations of two genes and the presence or absence of linkage as measured by recombination frequencies.

> Recombination results from crossing-over of homologs during meiosis I. If two syntenic genes are close together, little chance exists for crossing-over, so the recombination frequency is low. As the distance between syntenic genes increases, the RF increases to a maximum of 50%. Thus, genes far enough apart on a single chromosome assort independently, just as do genes on nonhomologous chromosomes.

TABLE 5.2	Properties of Linked Versus Unlinked Genes

Linked Genes

Parentals > recombinants (RF < 50%)

Linked genes must be syntenic and sufficiently close together on the same chromosome so that they do not assort independently.

Unlinked Genes

Parentals = recombinants (RF = 50%)

Occurs either when genes are on different chromosomes or when they are sufficiently far apart on the same chromosome.

5.4 Mapping: Locating Genes Along a Chromosome

Maps are images of the relative positions of objects in space. Whether depicting the floor plan of New York's Metropolitan Museum of Art, the layout of the Roman Forum, or the location of cities served by the railways of Europe, maps turn measurements into patterns of spatial relationships that add a new level of meaning to the original data of distances. Maps that assign genes to locations on particular chromosomes called *loci* (singular **locus**) are no exception. By transforming genetic data into spatial arrangements, maps sharpen our ability to predict the inheritance patterns of specific traits.

We have seen that recombination frequency (RF) is a measure of the distance separating two genes along a chromosome. We now examine how data from many crosses following two and three genes at a time can be compiled and compared to generate accurate, comprehensive gene/chromosome maps.

Comparisons of two-point crosses establish relative gene positions

In his senior undergraduate thesis, Morgan's student A. H. Sturtevant asked whether data obtained from a large number of two-point crosses (crosses tracing two genes at a time) would support the idea that genes form a definite linear series along a chromosome. Sturtevant began by looking at X-linked genes in *Drosophila*. **Figure 5.9a** lists his recombination data for several two-point crosses. Recall that the distance between two

Figure 5.9 Mapping genes by comparisons of two-point crosses. (a) Sturtevant's data for the distances between pairs of X-linked genes in *Drosophila*. **(b)** Because the distance between *y* and *m* is greater than the distance between *w* and *m*, the order of genes must be *y-w-m*. **(c)** and **(d)** Maps for five genes on the *Drosophila* X chromosome. The left-to-right orientation is arbitrary. Note that the numerical position of the *r* gene depends on how it is calculated. The best genetic maps are obtained by summing many small intervening distances as in (d).

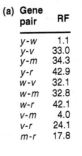

(a)

Gene pair	RF
y-w	1.1
y-v	33.0
y-m	34.3
y-r	42.9
w-v	32.1
w-m	32.8
w-r	42.1
v-m	4.0
v-r	24.1
m-r	17.8

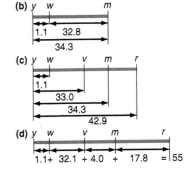

130   Chapter 5   Linkage, Recombination, and the Mapping of Genes on Chromosomes

genes that yields 1% recombinant progeny—an RF of 1%—is 1 m.u.

As an example of Sturtevant's reasoning, consider the three genes *w, y,* and *m.* If these genes are arranged in a line (instead of a more complicated branched structure, for example), then one of them must be in the middle, flanked on either side by the other two. The greatest genetic distance should separate the two genes on the outside, and this value should roughly equal the sum of the distances separating the middle gene from each outside gene. The data Sturtevant obtained are consistent with this idea, implying that *w* lies between *y* and *m* (**Fig. 5.9b**). Note that the left-to-right orientation of this map was selected at random; the map in Fig. 5.9b would be equally correct if it portrayed *y* on the right and *m* on the left.

By following exactly the same procedure for each set of three genes, Sturtevant established a self-consistent order for all the genes he investigated on *Drosophila*'s X chromosome (**Fig. 5.9c;** once again, the left-to-right arrangement is an arbitrary choice). By checking the data for every combination of three genes, you can assure yourself that this ordering makes sense. The fact that the recombination data yield a simple linear map of gene position supports the idea that genes reside in a unique linear order along a chromosome.

Limitations of two-point crosses

Though of great importance, the pairwise mapping of genes has several shortcomings that limit its usefulness. First, in crosses involving only two genes at a time, it may be difficult to determine gene order if some gene pairs lie very close together. For example, in mapping *y, w,* and *m,* 34.3 m.u. separate the outside genes *y* and *m,* while nearly as great a distance (32.8 m.u.) separates the middle *w* from the outside *m* (Fig. 5.9b). Before being able to conclude with any confidence that *y* and *m* are truly farther apart, that is, that the small difference between the values of 34.3 and 32.8 is not the result of sampling error, you would have to examine a very large number of flies and subject the data to a statistical test, such as the chi-square test.

A second problem with Sturtevant's mapping procedure is that the actual distances in his map do not always add up, even approximately. As an example, suppose that the locus of the *y* gene at the far left of the map is regarded as position 0 (Fig. 5.9c). The *w* gene would then lie near position 1, and *m* would be located in the vicinity of 34 m.u. But what about the *r* gene, named for a mutation that produces rudimentary (very small) wings? Based solely on its distance from *y,* as inferred from the *y* ↔ *r* data in Fig. 5.9a, we would place it at position 42.9 (Fig. 5.9c). However, if we calculate its position as the sum of all intervening distances inferred from the data in Fig. 5.9a, that is, as the sum of *y* ↔ *w* plus *w* ↔ *v* plus *v* ↔ *m* plus *m* ↔ *r,* the locus of *r* becomes 1.1 + 32.1 + 4.0 + 17.8 = 55.0 (**Fig. 5.9d**). What can explain this

difference, and which of these two values is closer to the truth? Three-point crosses help provide some of the answers.

Three-point crosses provide faster and more accurate mapping

The simultaneous analysis of three markers makes it possible to obtain enough information to position the three genes in relation to each other from just one set of crosses. To describe this procedure, we look at three genes linked on one of *Drosophila*'s autosomes.

A homozygous female with mutations for vestigial wings (*vg*), black body (*b*), and purple eye color (*pr*) was mated to a wild-type male (**Fig. 5.10a**). All the triply heterozygous F₁ progeny, both male and female, had normal phenotypes for the three characteristics, indicating that the mutations are autosomal recessive. In a testcross of the F₁ females with males having vestigial wings, black body, and purple eyes, the progeny were of eight different phenotypes reflecting eight different genotypes. The order in which the genes in each phenotypic class are listed in Fig. 5.10a is completely arbitrary. Thus, instead

Figure 5.10 Analyzing the results of a three-point cross.
(a) Results from a three-point testcross of F₁ females simultaneously heterozygous for *vg, b,* and *pr.* **(b)** The gene in the middle must be *pr* because the longest distance is between the other two genes: *vg* and *b.* The most accurate map distances are calculated by summing shorter intervening distances, so 18.7 m.u. is a more accurate estimate of the genetic distance between *vg* and *b* than 17.7 m.u.

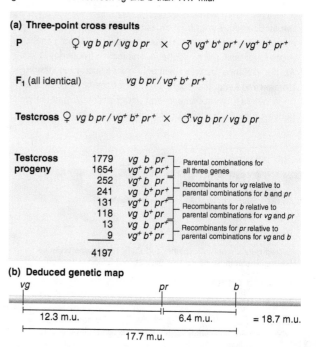

(a) Three-point cross results

P   ♀ *vg b pr / vg b pr*   ×   ♂ *vg⁺ b⁺ pr⁺ / vg⁺ b⁺ pr⁺*

F₁ (all identical)   *vg b pr / vg⁺ b⁺ pr⁺*

Testcross ♀ *vg b pr / vg⁺ b⁺ pr⁺* × ♂ *vg b pr / vg b pr*

Testcross progeny		
1779	*vg b pr*	Parental combinations for all three genes
1654	*vg⁺ b⁺ pr⁺*	
252	*vg⁺ b pr*	Recombinants for *vg* relative to parental combinations for *b* and *pr*
241	*vg b⁺ pr⁺*	
131	*vg⁺ b pr⁺*	Recombinants for *b* relative to parental combinations for *vg* and *pr*
118	*vg b⁺ pr*	
13	*vg b pr⁺*	Recombinants for *pr* relative to parental combinations for *vg* and *b*
9	*vg⁺ b⁺ pr*	
4197		

(b) Deduced genetic map

vg   pr   b

|← 12.3 m.u. →|← 6.4 m.u. →| = 18.7 m.u.

|←   17.7 m.u.   →|

of *vg b pr,* one could write *b vg pr* or *vg pr b* to indicate the same genotype. Remember that at the outset we do not know the gene order; deducing it is the goal of the mapping study.

In analyzing the data, we look at two genes at a time (recall that the recombination frequency is always a function of a pair of genes). For the pair *vg* and *b,* the parental combinations are *vg b* and $vg^+ b^+$; the nonparental recombinants are *vg b^+* and $vg^+ b$. To determine whether a particular class of progeny is parental or recombinant for *vg* and *b,* we do not care whether the flies are *pr* or pr^+. Thus, to the nearest tenth of a map unit, the *vg ↔ b* distance, calculated as the percentage of recombinants in the total number of progeny, is

$$\frac{252 + 241 + 131 + 118}{4197} \times 100$$

$$= 17.7 \text{ m.u. } (vg \leftrightarrow b \text{ distance})$$

Similarly, because recombinants for the *vg–pr* gene pair are *vg pr^+* and vg^+ *pr,* the interval between these two genes is

$$\frac{252 + 241 + 13 + 9}{4197} \times 100$$

$$= 12.3 \text{ m.u. } (vg \leftrightarrow pr \text{ distance})$$

while the distance separating the *b–pr* pair is

$$\frac{131 + 118 + 13 + 9}{4197} \times 100$$

$$= 6.4 \text{ m.u. } (b \leftrightarrow pr \text{ distance})$$

These recombination frequencies show that *vg* and *b* are separated by the largest distance (17.7 m.u., as compared with 12.3 and 6.4) and must therefore be the outside genes, flanking *pr* in the middle (**Fig. 5.10b**). But as with the X-linked *y* and *r* genes analyzed by Sturtevant, the distance separating the outside *vg* and *b* genes (17.7) does not equal the sum of the two intervening distances (12.3 + 6.4 = 18.7). In the next section, we learn that the reason for this discrepancy is the rare occurrence of double crossovers.

Correction for double crossovers

Figure 5.11 depicts the homologous autosomes of the F_1 females that are heterozygous for the three genes *vg, pr,* and *b.* A close examination of the chromosomes reveals the kinds of crossovers that must have occurred to generate the classes and numbers of progeny observed. In this and subsequent figures, the chromosomes depicted are in late prophase/early metaphase of meiosis I, when there are

Figure 5.11 Inferring the location of a crossover event. Once you establish the order of genes involved in a three-point cross, it is easy to determine which crossover events gave rise to particular recombinant gametes. Note that double crossovers are needed to generate gametes in which the gene in the middle has recombined relative to the parental combinations for the genes at the ends.

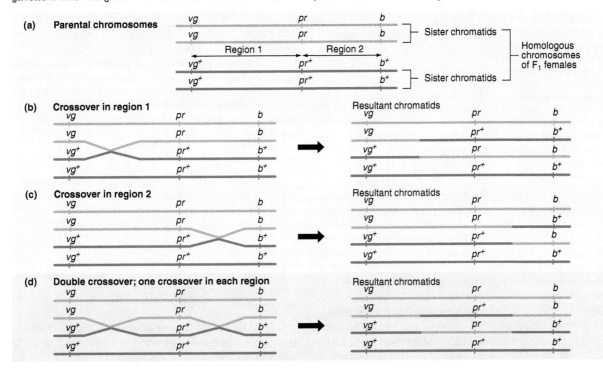

four chromatids for each pair of homologous chromosomes. As we have suggested previously and demonstrate more rigorously later, prophase I is the stage at which recombination takes place. Note that we call the space between *vg* and *pr* "region 1" and the space between *pr* and *b* "region 2."

Recall that the progeny from the testcross performed earlier fall into eight groups (review Fig. 5.10). Flies in the two largest groups carry the same configurations of genes as did their grandparents of the P generation: *vg b pr* and *vg⁺ b⁺ pr⁺*; they thus represent the parental classes (Fig. 5.11a). The next two groups—*vg⁺b pr* and *vg b⁺pr⁺*—are composed of recombinants that must be the reciprocal products of a crossover in region 1 between *vg* and *pr* (Fig. 5.11b). Similarly the two groups containing *vg⁺ b pr⁺* and *vg b⁺ pr* flies must have resulted from recombination in region 2 between *pr* and *b* (Fig. 5.11c).

But what about the two smallest groups made up of rare *vg b pr⁺* and *vg⁺ b⁺ pr* recombinants? What kinds of chromosome exchange could account for them? Most likely, they result from two different crossover events occurring simultaneously, one in region 1, the other in region 2 (Fig. 5.11d). The gametes produced by such double crossovers still have the parental configuration for the outside genes *vg* and *b,* even though not one but two exchanges must have occurred.

Because of the existence of double crossovers, the *vg* ↔ *b* distance of 17.7 m.u. calculated in the previous section does not reflect all of the recombination events producing the gametes that gave rise to the observed progeny. To correct for this oversight, it is necessary to adjust the recombination frequency by adding the double crossovers twice, because each individual in the double crossover groups is the result of two exchanges between *vg* and *b*. The corrected distance is

$$\frac{252 + 241 + 131 + 118 + 13 + 13 + 9 + 9}{4197} \times 100$$

$$= 18.7 \text{ m.u.}$$

This value makes sense because you have accounted for all of the crossovers that occur in region 1 as well as all of the crossovers in region 2. As a result, the corrected value of 18.7 m.u. for the distance between *vg* and *b* is now exactly the same as the sum of the distances between *vg* and *pr* (region 1) and between *pr* and *b* (region 2).

As previously discussed, when Sturtevant originally mapped several X-linked genes in *Drosophila* by two-point crosses, the locus of the rudimentary wings (*r*) gene was ambiguous. A two-point cross involving *y* and *r* gave a recombination frequency of 42.9, but the sum of all the intervening distances was 55.0 (review Fig. 5.9 on p. 129). This discrepancy occurred because the two-point cross ignored double crossovers that might have occurred in the large interval between the *y* and *r* genes. The data summing

the smaller intervening distances accounted for at least some of these double crossovers by catching recombinations of gene pairs between *y* and *r*. Moreover, each smaller distance is less likely to encompass a double crossover than a larger distance, so each number for a smaller distance is inherently more accurate.

Note that even a three-point cross like the one for *vg*, *pr*, and *b* ignores the possibility of two recombination events taking place in, say, region 1. For greatest accuracy, it is always best to construct a map using many genes separated by relatively short distances.

Interference: Fewer double crossovers than expected

In a three-point cross following three linked genes, of the eight possible genotypic classes, the two parental classes contain the largest number of progeny, while the two double recombinant classes, resulting from double crossovers, are always the smallest (see Fig. 5.10). We can understand why double-crossover progeny are the rarest by looking at the probability of their occurrence. If an exchange in region 1 of a chromosome does not affect the probability of an exchange in region 2, the probability that both will occur simultaneously is the product of their separate probabilities (recall the product rule in Chapter 2, p. 23). For example, if progeny resulting from recombination in region 1 alone account for 10% of the total progeny (that is, if region 1 is 10 m.u.) and progeny resulting from recombination in region 2 alone account for 20%, then the probability of a double crossover (one event in region 1, the second in region 2) is 0.10 × 0.20 = 0.02, or 2%. This makes sense because the likelihood of two rare events occurring simultaneously is even less than that of either rare event occurring alone.

If there are eight classes of progeny in a three-point cross, the two classes containing the fewest progeny must have arisen from double crossovers. The numerical frequencies of observed double crossovers, however, almost never coincide with expectations derived from the product rule. Let's look at the actual numbers from the cross we have been discussing. The probability of a single crossover between *vg* and *pr* is 0.123 (corresponding to 12.3 m.u.), and the probability of a single crossover between *pr* and *b* is 0.064 (6.4 m.u.). The product of these probabilities is

$$0.123 \times 0.064 = 0.0079 = 0.79\%$$

But the observed proportion of double crossovers (see Fig. 5.10) was

$$\frac{13 + 9}{4197} \times 100 = 0.52\%$$

The fact that the number of observed double crossovers is less than the number expected if the two exchanges are independent events suggests that the occurrence of one crossover reduces the likelihood that another crossover will occur in an adjacent part of the chromosome. This phenomenon—of crossovers not occurring independently—is called **chromosomal interference.**

Interference may exist to ensure that every pair of homologous chromosomes undergoes at least one crossover event. It is critical that every pair of homologous chromosomes sustain one or more crossover events because such events help the chromosomes orient properly at the metaphase plate during the first meiotic division. Indeed, homologous chromosome pairs without crossovers often segregate improperly. If only a limited number of crossovers can occur during each meiosis and interference lowers the number of crossovers on large chromosomes, then the remaining possible crossovers are more likely to occur on small chromosomes. This increases the probability that at least one crossover will take place on every homologous pair. Though the molecular mechanism underlying interference is not yet clear, recent experiments suggest that interference is mediated by the synaptonemal complex.

Interference is not uniform and may vary even for different regions of the same chromosome. Investigators can obtain a quantitative measure of the amount of interference in different chromosomal intervals by first calculating a **coefficient of coincidence,** defined as the ratio between the actual frequency of double crossovers observed in an experiment and the number of double crossovers expected on the basis of independent probabilities.

$$\text{Coefficient of coincidence} = \frac{\text{frequency observed}}{\text{frequency expected}}$$

For the three-point cross involving *vg, pr,* and *b*, the coefficient of coincidence is

$$\frac{0.52}{0.79} = 0.66$$

The definition of interference itself is

$$\text{Interference} = 1 - \text{coefficient of coincidence}$$

In this case, it is

$$1 - 0.66 = 0.34$$

To understand the meaning of interference, it is helpful to contrast what happens when there is no interference with what happens when it is complete. If interference is 0, the frequency of observed double crossovers equals expectations, and crossovers in adjacent regions of a chromosome occur independently of each other. If interference is complete (that is, if interference = 1), no double crossovers occur in the experimental progeny because one exchange effectively prevents another. As an example, in a particular three-point cross in mice, the recombination frequency for the pair of genes on the left (region 1) is 20, and for the pair of genes on the right (region 2), it is

also 20. Without interference, the expected rate of double crossovers in this chromosomal interval is

$$0.20 \times 0.20 = 0.04, \text{ or } 4\%$$

but when investigators observed 1000 progeny of this cross, they found 0 double recombinants instead of the expected 40.

A method to determine the gene in the middle

The smallest of the eight possible classes of progeny in a three-point cross are the two that contain double recombinants generated by double crossovers. It is possible to use the composition of alleles in these double crossover classes to determine which of the three genes lies in the middle, even without calculating any recombination frequencies. Consider again the progeny of a three-point testcross looking at the *vg, pr,* and *b* genes. The F_1 females are *vg pr b / vg⁺ pr⁺ b⁺*. As Fig. 5.11d demonstrated, testcross progeny resulting from double crossovers in the trihybrid females of the F_1 generation received gametes from their mothers carrying the allelic combinations *vg pr⁺ b* and *vg⁺ pr b⁺*. In these individuals, the alleles of the *vg* and *b* genes retain their parental associations (*vg b* and *vg⁺ b⁺*), while the *pr* gene has recombined with respect to both the other genes (*pr b⁺* and *pr⁺ b; vg pr⁺* and *vg⁺ pr*). The same is true in all three-point crosses: In those gametes formed by double crossovers, the gene whose alleles have recombined relative to the parental configurations of the other two genes must be the one in the middle.

> Genetic maps of genes along chromosomes can be approximated using data from two-point crosses. Three-point crosses yield more accurate maps because they allow correction for double crossovers as well as estimates of interference (fewer double crossovers than expected). The most accurate maps are constructed with many closely linked genetic markers.

Three-point crosses: A comprehensive example

The technique of looking at double recombinants to discover which gene has recombined with respect to both other genes allows immediate clarification of gene order even in otherwise difficult cases. Consider the three X-linked genes *y, w,* and *m* that Sturtevant located in his original mapping experiment (see Fig. 5.9 on p. 129). Because the distance between *y* and *m* (34.3 m.u.) appeared slightly larger than the distance separating *w* and *m* (32.8 m.u.), he concluded that *w* was the gene in the middle. But because of the small difference between the two numbers, his conclusion was subject to questions of statistical significance. If, however, we look at a

Figure 5.12 How three-point crosses verify Sturtevant's map. The parental classes correspond to the two X chromosomes in the F_1 female. The genotype of the double recombinant classes shows that w must be the gene in the middle.

$$\female\, w^+\, w\, y^+\, y\, m^+\, m \quad \times \quad \male\, X/Y$$

Before data analysis, you do not know the gene order or allele combination on each chromosome.

Male progeny		
2278	$w^+ y^+ m$ /Y	Parental class
2157	$w\, y\, m^+$ /Y	(noncrossover)
1203	$w\, y\, m$ /Y	Crossover in region 2
1092	$w^+ y^+ m^+$ /Y	(between w and m)
49	$w^+ y\, m$ /Y	Crossover in region 1
41	$w\, y^+ m^+$ /Y	(between y and w)
2	$w^+ y\, m^+$ /Y	Double
1	$w\, y^+ m$ /Y	crossovers
6823		

After data analysis, you can conclude that the gene order and allele combinations on the X chromosomes of the F_1 females were $y\, w\, m^+ / y^+ w^+ m$.

three-point cross following y, w, and m, these questions disappear.

Figure 5.12 tabulates the classes and numbers of male progeny arising from females heterozygous for the y, w, and m genes. Because these male progeny receive their only X chromosome from their mothers, their phenotypes directly indicate the gametes produced by the heterozygous females. In each row of the figure's table, the genes appear in an arbitrary order that does not presuppose knowledge of the actual map. As you can see, the two classes of progeny listed at the top of the table outnumber the remaining six classes, which indicates that all three genes are linked to each other. Moreover, these largest groups, which are the parental classes, show that the two X chromosomes of the heterozygous females were $w^+\, y^+\, m$ and $w\, y\, m^+$.

Among the male progeny in Fig. 5.12, the two smallest classes, representing the double crossovers, have X chromosomes carrying $w^+\, y\, m^+$ and $w\, y^+\, m$ combinations, in which the w alleles are recombined relative to those of y and m. The w gene must therefore lie between y and m, verifying Sturtevant's original assessment.

To complete a map based on the $w\, y\, m$ three-point cross, you can calculate the interval between y and w (region 1)

$$\frac{49 + 41 + 1 + 2}{6823} \times 100 = 1.3 \text{ m.u.}$$

as well as the interval between w and m (region 2)

$$\frac{1203 + 1092 + 2 + 1}{6823} \times 100 = 33.7 \text{ m.u.}$$

The genetic distance separating y and m is the sum of

$$1.3 + 33.7 = 35.0 \text{ m.u.}$$

Note that you could also calculate the distance between y and m directly by including double crossovers twice, to account for the total number of recombination events detected between these two genes.

$$\text{RF} = (1203 + 1092 + 49 + 41 + 2 + 2$$
$$+ 1 + 1)/6823 \times 100 = 35.0 \text{ m.u.}$$

This method yields the same value as the sum of the two intervening distances (region 1 + region 2).

Further calculations show that interference is considerable in this portion of the *Drosophila* X chromosome, at least as inferred from the set of data tabulated in Fig. 5.12. The percentage of observed double recombinants was

$$3/6823 = 0.00044, \text{ or } 0.044\%$$

(rounding to the nearest thousandth of a percent), while the percentage of double recombinants expected on the basis of independent probabilities by the law of the product is

$$0.013 \times 0.337 = 0.0044, \text{ or } 0.44\%$$

Thus, the coefficient of coincidence is

$$0.044/0.44 = 0.1$$

and the interference is

$$1 - 0.1 = 0.9$$

Do genetic maps correlate with physical reality?

Many types of experiments presented later in this book clearly show that the *order of genes* revealed by recombination mapping corresponds to the order of those same genes along the DNA molecule of a chromosome. In contrast, the *actual physical distances between genes*—that is, the amount of DNA separating them—does not always show a direct correspondence to genetic map distances.

The relationship between recombination frequency and physical distance along a chromosome is not simple. One complicating factor is the existence of double, triple, and even more crossovers. When genes are separated by 1 m.u. or less, double crossovers are not significant because the probability of their occurring is so small ($0.01 \times 0.01 = 0.0001$). But for genes separated by 20, 30, or 40 m.u., the probability of double crossovers skewing the data takes on greater significance. A second confounding factor is the 50% limit on the recombination frequency observable in a cross. This limit reduces the precision of RF as a measure of chromosomal distances. No matter how far apart two genes are on a long chromosome, they will never recombine more than 50% of the time. Yet a third problem is that recombination is not uniform even over the length of a single chromosome: Certain "hotspots" are favored sites of recombination, while other areas—often in the vicinity of centromeres—are "recombination deserts" in which few crossovers ever take place.

Ever since Morgan, Sturtevant, and others began mapping, geneticists have generated mathematical equations called **mapping functions** to compensate for the inaccuracies inherent in relating recombination frequencies to physical distances. These equations generally make large corrections for RF values of widely separated genes, while barely changing the map distances separating genes that lie close together. This reflects the fact that multiple recombination events and the 50% limit on recombination do not confound the calculation of distances between closely linked genes. However, the corrections for large distances are at best imprecise, because mapping functions are based on simplifying assumptions (such as no interference) that are only rarely justified. Thus, the best way to create an accurate map is still by summing many smaller intervals, locating widely separated genes through linkage to common intermediaries. Maps are subject to continual refinement as more and more newly discovered genes are included.

Rates of recombination may differ from species to species. We know this because recent elucidation of the complete DNA sequences of several organisms' genomes has allowed investigators to compare the actual physical distances between genes (in base pairs of DNA) with genetic map distances. They found that in humans, a map unit corresponds on average to about 1 million base pairs. In yeast, however, where the rate of recombination per length of DNA is much higher than in humans, one map unit is approximately 2500 base pairs. Thus, although map units are useful for estimating distances between the genes of an organism, 1% RF can reflect very different expanses of DNA in different organisms.

Recombination rates sometimes vary even between the two sexes of a single species. *Drosophila* provides an extreme example: No recombination occurs during meiosis in males. If you review the examples already discussed in this chapter, you will discover that they all measure recombination among the progeny of doubly heterozygous *Drosophila* females. Problem 19 at the end of this chapter shows how geneticists can exploit the absence of recombination in *Drosophila* males to establish rapidly that genes far apart on the same chromosome are indeed syntenic.

Multiple-factor crosses help establish linkage groups

Genes chained together by linkage relationships are known collectively as a **linkage group.** When enough genes have been assigned to a particular chromosome, the terms *chromosome* and *linkage group* become synonymous. If you

can demonstrate that gene *A* is linked to gene *B*, *B* to *C*, *C* to *D*, and *D* to *E*, you can conclude that all of these genes are syntenic. When the genetic map of a genome becomes so dense that it is possible to show that any gene on a chromosome is linked to another gene on the same chromosome, the number of linkage groups equals the number of pairs of homologous chromosomes in the species. Humans have 23 linkage groups, mice have 20, and fruit flies have 4 (**Fig. 5.13**).

The total genetic distance along a chromosome, which is obtained by adding many short distances between genes, may be much more than 50 m.u. For example, the two long *Drosophila* autosomes are both slightly more than 100 m.u. in length (Fig. 5.13), while the longest human chromosome is approximately 270 m.u. Recall, however, that even with the longest chromosomes, *pairwise* crosses between genes located at the two ends will not produce more than 50% recombinant progeny.

Linkage mapping has practical applications of great importance. For example, the Fast Forward box "Gene Mapping May Lead to a Cure for Cystic Fibrosis" on p. 137 describes how researchers used linkage information to locate the gene for this important human hereditary disease.

> When sufficient genes have been mapped, all the genes on a single chromosome will form a single linkage group. The order of the genes determined by mapping corresponds to their actual sequence along the chromosome; however, the map distance between the genes is not simply correlated with the actual physical distance along the chromosome's DNA.

5.5 Tetrad Analysis in Fungi

With *Drosophila*, mice, peas, people, and other diploid organisms, each individual represents only one of the four potential gametes generated by each parent in a single meiotic event. Thus, until now, our presentation of linkage, recombination, and mapping has depended on inferences derived from examining the phenotypes of diploid progeny resulting from random unions of random products of meiosis. For such diploid organisms, we do not know which, if any, of the parents' other progeny arose from gametes created in the same meiosis. Because of this limitation, the analysis of random products of meiosis in diploid organisms must be based on statistical samplings of large populations.

In contrast, various species of fungi provide a unique opportunity for genetic analysis because they house all four haploid products of each meiosis in a sac called an **ascus** (plural, *asci*). These haploid cells, or **ascospores** (also known as *haplospores*), can germinate and survive as viable haploid individuals that grow and perpetuate themselves by mitosis. The phenotype of such haploid fungi is a direct representation of their genotype, without complications of

Figure 5.13 *Drosophila melanogaster* **has four linkage groups.** A genetic map of the fruit fly, showing the position of many genes affecting body morphology, including those used as examples in this chapter (*highlighted in bold*). Because so many *Drosophila* genes have been mapped, each of the four chromosomes can be represented as a single linkage group.

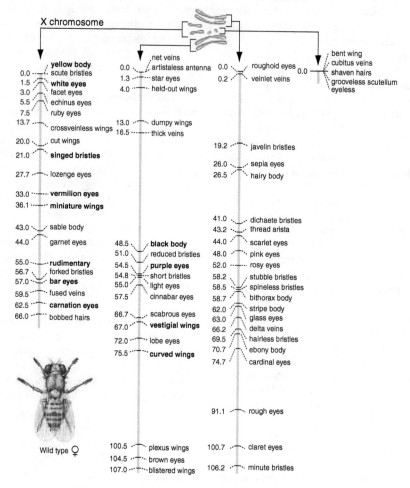

dominance. **Figure 5.14** illustrates the life cycles of two fungal species that preserve their meiotic products in a sac. One, the normally unicellular baker's yeast (*Saccharomyces cerevisiae*), is sold in supermarkets and contributes to the texture, shape, and flavor of bread; it generates four ascospores with each meiosis. The other, *Neurospora crassa,* is a bread mold that renders the bread on which it grows inedible; it too generates four ascospores with each meiosis, but at the completion of meiosis, each of the four haploid ascospores immediately divides once by mitosis to yield four pairs, for a total of eight haploid cells. The two cells in each pair of *Neurospora* ascospores have the same genotype, because they arose from mitosis.

Haploid cells of both yeast and *Neurospora* normally reproduce vegetatively (that is, asexually) by mitosis. However, sexual reproduction is possible because the haploid cells come in two mating types, and cells of opposite mating types can fuse to form a diploid zygote (Fig. 5.14).

In baker's yeast, these diploid cells are stable and can reproduce through successive mitotic cycles. Stress, such as that caused by a scarcity or lack of essential nutrients, induces the diploid cells of yeast to enter meiosis. In bread mold, the diploid zygote instead immediately undergoes meiosis, so the diploid state is only transient.

Mutations in haploid yeast and mold affect many different traits, including the appearance of the cells and their ability to grow under particular conditions. For instance, yeast cells with the *his4* mutation are unable to grow in the absence of the amino acid histidine, while yeast with the *trp1* mutation cannot grow without an external source of the amino acid tryptophan. Geneticists who specialize in the study of yeast have devised a system of representing genes that is slightly different from the ones for *Drosophila* and mice. They use capital letters (*HIS4*) to designate dominant alleles and lowercase letters (*his4*) to represent recessives. For most of the

FAST FORWARD

Gene Mapping May Lead to a Cure for Cystic Fibrosis

For 40 years after the symptoms of cystic fibrosis were first described in 1938, no molecular clue—no visible chromosomal abnormality transmitted with the disease, no identifiable protein defect carried by affected individuals—suggested the genetic cause of the disorder. As a result, there was no effective treatment for the 1 in 2000 Caucasian Americans born with the disease, most of whom died before they were 30. In the 1980s, however, geneticists were able to combine recently invented techniques for looking directly at DNA with maps constructed by linkage analysis to pinpoint a precise chromosomal position, or locus, for the cystic fibrosis gene.

The mappers of the cystic fibrosis gene faced an overwhelming task. They were searching for a gene that encoded an unknown protein, a gene that had not yet even been assigned to a chromosome. It could lie anywhere among the 23 pairs of chromosomes in a human cell. Imagine looking for a close friend you lost track of years ago, who might now be anywhere in the world. You would first have to find ways to narrow the search to a particular continent (the equivalent of a specific chromosome in the gene mappers' search); then to a country (the long or short arm of the chromosome); next to the state or province, county, city, or town, and street (all increasingly narrow bands of the chromosome); and finally, to a house address (the locus itself). Here, we briefly summarize how researchers applied some of these steps in mapping the cystic fibrosis gene.

- A review of many family pedigrees containing first-cousin marriages confirmed that cystic fibrosis is most likely determined by a single gene (*CF*). Investigators collected white blood cells from 47 families with two or more affected children, obtaining genetic data from 106 patients, 94 parents, and 44 unaffected siblings.
- They next tried to discover if any other trait is reliably transmitted with cystic fibrosis. Analyses of the easily obtainable serum enzyme paroxonase showed that its gene (*PON*) is indeed linked to *CF*. At first, this knowledge was not that helpful, because *PON* had not yet been assigned to a chromosome.
- Then, in the early 1980s, geneticists developed a large series of DNA markers, based on new techniques that enabled them to recognize variations in the genetic material. A **DNA marker** is a piece of DNA of known size, representing a specific locus, that comes in identifiable variations. These allelic variations segregate according to Mendel's laws, which means it is possible to follow their transmission as you would any gene's. Chapter 11 explains the discovery and use of DNA markers in greater detail; for now, it is only important to know that they exist and can be identified.

By 1986, linkage analyses of hundreds of DNA markers had shown that one marker, known as *D7S15*, is linked with both *PON* and *CF*. Researchers computed recombination frequencies and found that the distance from the DNA marker to *CF* was 15 cM; from the DNA marker to *PON*, 5 cM; and from *PON* to *CF*, 10 cM. They concluded that the order of the three loci was

Figure A How molecular markers helped locate the gene for cystic fibrosis (*CF*).

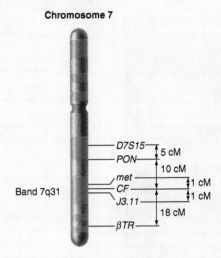

D7S15-PON-CF (**Fig. A**). Because *CF* could lie 15 cM in either of two directions from the DNA marker, the area under investigation was approximately 30 cM. And because the human genome consists of roughly 3000 cM, this step of linkage analysis narrowed the search to 1% of the human genome.

- Next, the DNA marker *D7S15* was localized to the long arm of chromosome 7, which meant that the gene for cystic fibrosis also resides in that chromosome arm. Researchers had now placed the *CF* gene in a certain country on a particular genetic continent.
- Finally, investigators discovered linkage with several other markers on the long arm of chromosome 7, called *J3.11*, *βTR*, and *met*. Two of the markers turned out to be separated from *CF* by a distance of only 1 cM. It now became possible to place *CF* in band 31 of chromosome 7's long arm (band 7q31, Fig. A). For families with at least one child who has cystic fibrosis, geneticists using DNA analyses of these closely linked markers could now identify carriers of an abnormal copy of the *CF* gene with substantial confidence.

By 1989, researchers had used this mapping information to identify and clone the *CF* gene on the basis of its location. And by 1992, they had shown it encodes a cell membrane protein that regulates the flow of chloride ions into and out of cells (review the Fast Forward box "Genes Encode Proteins" in Chapter 2). This knowledge has become the basis of new therapies to open up ion flow, as well as gene therapies to introduce normal copies of the *CF* gene into the cells of CF patients. Although only in the early stages of development, such gene therapy holds out hope of an eventual cure for cystic fibrosis.

Figure 5.14 The life cycles of the yeast *Saccharomyces cerevisiae* and the bread mold *Neurospora crassa*. Both *S. cerevisiae* and *N. crassa* have two mating types that can fuse to form diploid cells that undergo meiosis. **(a)** Yeast cells can grow vegetatively either as haploids or diploids. The products of meiosis in a diploid cell are four haploid ascospores that are arranged randomly in unordered yeast asci. **(b)** The diploid state in *Neurospora* exists only for a short period. Meiosis in *Neurospora* is followed by mitosis, to give eight haploid ascospores in the ascus. The ordered arrangement of spores in *Neurospora* asci reflects the geometry of the meiotic and mitotic spindles. The photographs showing a budding (mitotically dividing) yeast cell and a yeast tetrad in part (a) are at much higher magnification than the photograph displaying *Neurospora* asci in part (b).

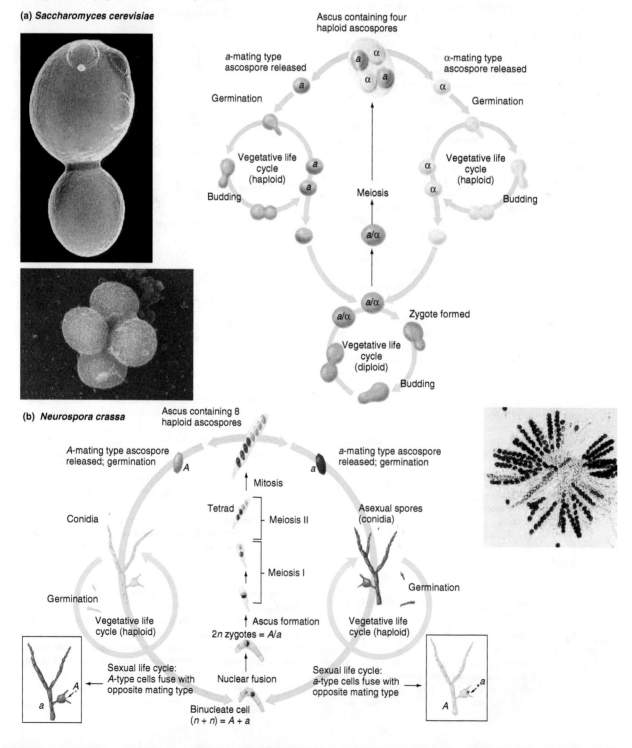

(a) *Saccharomyces cerevisiae*

Ascus containing four haploid ascospores

a-mating type ascospore released

α-mating type ascospore released

Germination

Germination

Vegetative life cycle (haploid)

Vegetative life cycle (haploid)

Budding

Meiosis

Budding

a/α

a/α

a/α

Zygote formed

Vegetative life cycle (diploid)

Budding

(b) *Neurospora crassa*

Ascus containing 8 haploid ascospores

A-mating type ascospore released; germination

a-mating type ascospore released; germination

Conidia

Mitosis

Tetrad

Meiosis II

Asexual spores (conidia)

Meiosis I

Germination

Germination

Vegetative life cycle (haploid)

Ascus formation

Vegetative life cycle (haploid)

2*n* zygotes = *A*/*a*

Sexual life cycle: *A*-type cells fuse with opposite mating type

Nuclear fusion

Sexual life cycle: *a*-type cells fuse with opposite mating type

Binucleate cell (*n* + *n*) = *A* + *a*

yeast genes we will discuss, the wild-type alleles are dominant and may be represented by the alternative shorthand "+", while the symbol for the recessive alleles remains the lowercase abbreviation (*his4*). Remember, however, that dominance or recessiveness is relevant only for diploid yeast cells, not for haploid cells that carry only one allele.

An ascus contains all four products of a single meiosis

After meiosis, the assemblage of four ascospores (or four pairs of ascospores) in a single ascus is called a **tetrad.** Note that this is a second meaning for the term *tetrad.* In Chapter 4, a tetrad was the four homologous chromatids—two in each chromosome of a bivalent—synapsed during the prophase and metaphase of meiosis I. Here, it is the four products of a single meiosis held together in a sac. Because the four chromatids of a bivalent give rise to the four products of meiosis, the two meanings of tetrad refer to almost the same things. In yeast, each tetrad is **unordered;** that is, the four meiotic products, known as spores, are arranged at random within the ascus. In *Neurospora crassa,* each tetrad is **ordered,** with the four pairs, or eight haplospores, arranged in a line.

To analyze both unordered and ordered tetrads, researchers can release the spores of each ascus, induce the haploid cells to germinate under appropriate conditions, and then analyze the genetic makeup of the resulting haploid cultures. The data they collect in this way enable them to identify the four products of a single meiosis and compare them with the four products of many other distinct meioses. Ordered tetrads offer another possibility. With the aid of a dissecting microscope, investigators can recover the ascospores in the order in which they occur within the ascus and thereby obtain additional information that is useful for mapping. We look first at the analysis of randomly arranged spores, using the unordered tetrads of yeast as an example. We then describe the additional information that can be gleaned from the microanalysis of ordered tetrads, using *Neurospora* as our model organism.

Tetrads can be characterized as parental ditypes (PDs), nonparental ditypes (NPDs), or tetratypes (Ts)

What kinds of tetrads arise when diploid yeast cells heterozygous for two genes on different chromosomes are induced to undergo meiosis? Consider a mating between a haploid strain of yeast of mating type *a,* carrying the *his4* mutation and the wild-type allele of the *TRP1* gene, and a strain of the opposite mating type α that has the genotype *HIS4 trp1.* The resulting *a*/α

diploid cells are *his4/HIS4; trp1/TRP1,* as shown in **Fig. 5.15a.** (In genetic nomenclature, a semicolon [;] is usually employed to separate genes on nonhomologous chromosomes.) When conditions promote meiosis, the two unlinked genes will assort independently to produce equal frequencies of two different kinds of tetrads. In one kind, all the spores are parental in that the genotype of each spore is the same as one of the parents: *his4 TRP1* or *HIS4 trp1* (**Fig. 5.15b**). A tetrad that contains four parental class haploid cells is known as a **parental ditype (PD).** Note that *di-,* meaning two, indicates there are two possible parental combinations of alleles; the PD tetrad contains two of each combination. The second kind of tetrad, arising from the equally likely alternative distribution of chromosomes during meiosis, contains four recombinant spores: two *his4 trp1* and two *HIS4 TRP1* (**Fig. 5.15c**). This kind of tetrad is termed a **nonparental ditype (NPD),** because the two parental classes have recombined to form two reciprocal nonparental combinations of alleles.

A third kind of tetrad also appears when *his4/HIS4; trp1/TRP1* cells undergo meiosis. Called a **tetratype (T)** from the Greek word for "four," it carries four kinds of haploid cells: two different parental class spores (one *his4 TRP1* and one *HIS4 trp1*) and two different recombinants (one *his4 trp1* and one *HIS4 TRP1*). Tetratypes result from a crossover between one of the two genes and the centromere of the chromosome on which it is located (**Fig. 5.15d**).

Figure 5.15e displays the data from one experiment. Bear in mind that the column headings of PD, NPD, and T refer to tetrads (the group of four cells produced in meiosis) and not to individual haploid cells. Because the spores released from a yeast ascus are not arranged in any particular order, the order in which the spores are listed does not matter. The classification of a tetrad as PD, NPD, or T is based solely on the number of parental and recombinant spores found in the ascus.

When PDs equal NPDs, the two genes are unlinked

A cross following two unlinked genes must give equal numbers of individual parental and recombinant spores. This is simply another way of stating Mendel's second law of independent assortment, which predicts a 50% recombination frequency in such cases. Because T tetrads, regardless of their number, contain two recombinant and two nonrecombinant spores and because all four spores in PD tetrads are parental, the only way 50% of the total progeny spores could be recombinant (as demanded by independent assortment) is if the number of NPDs (with four recombinant spores apiece) is the same as the number of PDs. For this reason, if PD = NPD (as in Fig. 5.15e), the two genes must be unlinked, either because they reside

Figure 5.15 How meiosis can generate three kinds of tetrads when two genes are on different chromosomes.
(a) Parental cross. **(b)** and **(c)** In the absence of recombination, the two equally likely alternative arrangements of two pairs of chromosomes yield either PD or NPD tetrads. T tetrads are made only if either gene recombines with respect to its corresponding centromere, as in **(d)**. Numerical data in **(e)** show that the number of PD tetrads ≈ the number of NPD tetrads when the two genes are unlinked.

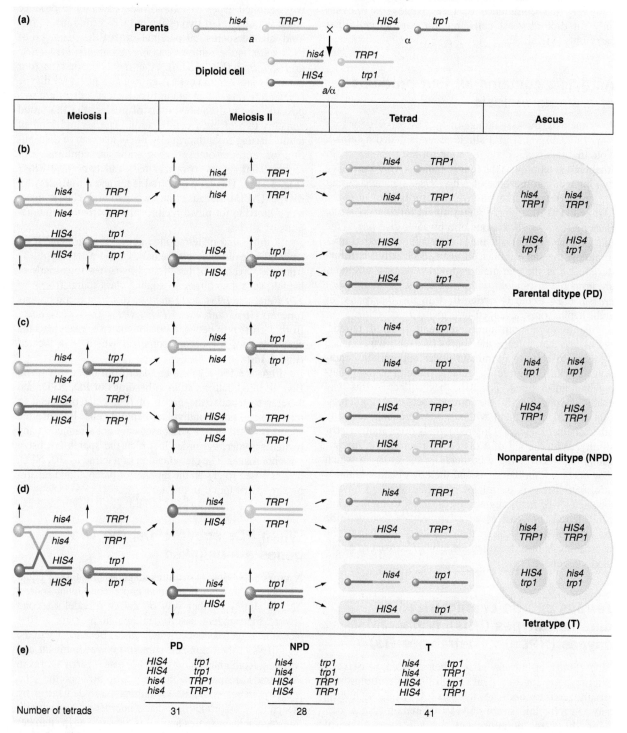

Figure 5.16 When genes are linked, PDs exceed NPDs.

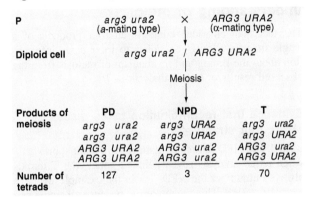

P	arg3 ura2 (*a*-mating type)	×	ARG3 URA2 (α-mating type)	
Diploid cell		arg3 ura2 / ARG3 URA2		
		Meiosis		

Products of meiosis	**PD**	**NPD**	**T**
	arg3 ura2	arg3 URA2	arg3 ura2
	arg3 ura2	arg3 URA2	arg3 URA2
	ARG3 URA2	ARG3 ura2	ARG3 ura2
	ARG3 URA2	ARG3 ura2	ARG3 URA2
Number of tetrads	127	3	70

on different chromosomes or because they lie very far apart on the same chromosome.

When PDs greatly outnumber NPDs, the two genes are linked

The genetic definition of linkage is the emergence of more parental types than recombinants among the progeny of a doubly heterozygous parent. In the preceding section, we saw that tetratypes always contribute an equal number of parental and recombinant spores. Thus, with tetrads, linkage exists only when PD >> NPD; that is, when the number of PD tetrads (carrying only parental-type spores) substantially exceeds the number of NPD tetrads (containing only recombinants). By analyzing an actual cross involving linked genes, we can see how this follows from the events occurring during meiosis.

A haploid yeast strain containing the *arg3* and *ura2* mutations was mated to a wild-type *ARG3 URA2* haploid strain (**Fig. 5.16**). When the resultant *a*/α diploid was induced to sporulate (that is, undergo meiosis), the 200 tetrads produced had the distribution shown in Fig. 5.16. As you can see, the 127 PD tetrads far outnumber the 3 NPD tetrads, suggesting that the two genes are linked.

Figure 5.17 shows how we can explain the particular kinds of tetrads observed in terms of the various types of crossovers that could occur between the linked genes. If no crossing-over occurs between the two genes, the resulting tetrad must be PD; Because none of the four chromatids participates in an exchange, all of the products are of parental configuration (Fig. 5.17a). A single crossover between *ARG3* and *URA2* will generate a tetratype, containing four genetically different spores (Fig. 5.17b). But what about double crossovers? There are actually four different possibilities, depending on which chromatids participate, and each of the four should occur with equal frequency. A double crossover involving only two chromatids (that is, one where both crossovers affect the same two chromatids) produces only parental-type progeny,

Figure 5.17 How crossovers between linked genes generate different tetrads. (a) PDs arise when there is no crossing-over. **(b)** Single crossovers between the two genes yield tetratypes. **(c)** to **(f)** Double crossovers between linked genes can generate PD, T, or NPD tetrads, depending on which chromatids participate in the crossovers.

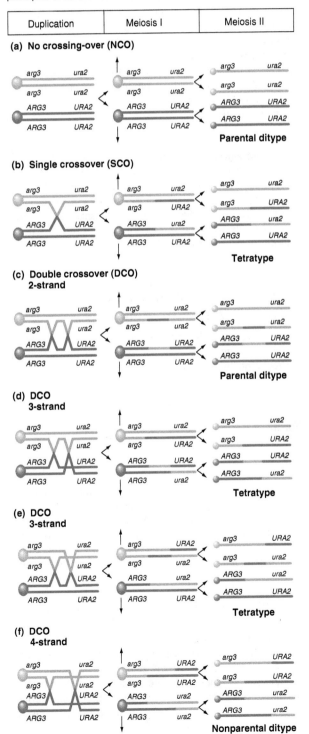

Duplication	Meiosis I	Meiosis II

(a) No crossing-over (NCO)

Parental ditype

(b) Single crossover (SCO)

Tetratype

**(c) Double crossover (DCO)
2-strand**

Parental ditype

**(d) DCO
3-strand**

Tetratype

**(e) DCO
3-strand**

Tetratype

**(f) DCO
4-strand**

Nonparental ditype

generating a PD tetrad (Fig. 5.17c). Three-strand double crossovers can occur in the two ways depicted in Fig. 5.17d and e; either way, a tetratype results. Finally, if all four strands take part in the two crossovers (one crossover involves two strands and the other crossover, the other two strands), all four progeny spores will be recombinant, and the resulting tetrad is NPD (Fig. 5.17f). Therefore, if two genes are linked, the only way to generate an NPD tetrad is through a four-strand double exchange. Meioses with crossovers generating such a specific kind of double recombination must be a lot rarer than no crossing-over or single crossovers, which produce PD and T tetrads, respectively. This explains why, if two genes are linked, PD must greatly exceed NPD.

> In certain fungi, all four products of a single meiosis are contained together in one ascus (tetrad). The asci produced by a diploid yeast cell heterozygous for two genes can be characterized by the fraction of the four ascospores that are recombinants. Tetrads are either PD (0/4 recombinants), NPD (4/4), or T (2/4). The two genes are unlinked if PD = NPD; the two genes are linked if PD >> NPD.

How to calculate recombinant frequencies in tetrad analysis

Because we know that all of the spores in an NPD tetrad are recombinant and half of the four spores in a tetratype are recombinant, we can say that

$$RF = \frac{NPD + 1/2T}{Total\ tetrads} \times 100$$

For the *ARG3 URA2* example in Fig. 5.16,

$$RF = \frac{3 + (1/2)(70)}{200} \times 100 = 19\ m.u.$$

It is reassuring that this formula gives exactly the same result as calculating the RF as the percentage of individual recombinant spores. For example, the 200 tetrads analyzed in this experiment contain 800 (that is, 200 × 4) individual spores; each NPD ascus holds 4 recombinant ascospores, and each T tetrad contains 2 recombinants. Thus,

$$RF = \frac{(4 \times 3) + (2 \times 70)}{800} \times 100 = 19\ m.u.$$

The formula used here for calculating the RF is very accurate for genes separated by small distances, but it is less reliable for more distant genes because it does not account for all types of double crossovers. Problem 39 at the end of this chapter will allow you to derive an alternative equation that yeast geneticists often use to measure large distances more accurately.

Tetrad analysis deepens our understanding of meiosis

The fact than an ascus contains all four products of a single meiosis allows geneticists to infer basic information about the timing and mechanism of meiosis from the observed results of tetrad analysis.

Evidence that recombination takes place at the four-strand stage

Both T and NPD tetrads contain recombinant spores, and when tetrad analysis reveals linked genes, the T tetrads always outnumber the NPDs, as in the example we have been discussing. This makes sense, because all single and some double crossovers yield tetratypes, while only 1/4 of the rare double crossovers produce NPDs.

The very low number of NPDs establishes that recombination occurs after the chromosomes have replicated, when there are four chromatids for each pair of homologs. If recombination took place before chromosome duplication, every single crossover event would yield four recombinant chromatids and generate an NPD tetrad (**Fig. 5.18**). A model assuming that recombination occurs when there are two rather than four chromatids per pair of homologous chromosomes would thus not allow the generation of T tetrads. Even if Ts could rarely be produced by some mechanism other than meiotic recombination (for example, errors like nondisjunction), the two-strand model would predict more NPD than T tetrads. However, experimental observations show just the opposite; Ts are always more numerous than NPDs (see Figs. 5.15e and 5.16).

The fact that recombination takes place after the chromosomes have replicated explains the 50% limit on recombination for genes on the same chromosome. Single crossovers between two genes generate T tetrads containing two out of four spores that are recombinant. Thus,

Figure 5.18 A disproven model: Recombination before chromosome replication. If recombination occurred before the chromosomes duplicated and if two genes were linked, most tetrads containing recombinant spores would be NPDs instead of Ts. Actual results show that the opposite is true.

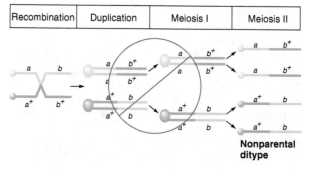

Recombination	Duplication	Meiosis I	Meiosis II

Nonparental ditype

even if one crossover occurred between two such genes in every meiosis, the observed recombination frequency would be 50%. The four kinds of double crossovers yield either

- PD tetrads with 0/4 recombinants (Fig. 5.17c),
- T tetrads with 2/4 recombinants (Fig. 5.17d),
- Other T tetrads also with 2/4 recombinants (Fig. 5.17e), or
- NPD tetrads with 4/4 recombinants (Fig. 5.17f).

Because these four kinds of double crossovers almost always occur with equal frequency, no more than 50% of the progeny resulting from double (or, in fact, triple or more) crossovers can be recombinant.

Evidence that recombination is usually reciprocal

Suppose you are following linked genes *A* and *B* in a cross between *A B* and *a b* strains of yeast. If the recombination that occurs during meiosis is reciprocal, every tetrad with recombinant progeny should contain equal numbers of both classes of recombinants. Observations have in general confirmed this prediction: Every T tetrad carries one *A b* and one *a B* spore, while every NPD tetrad contains two of each type of recombinant. We can thus conclude that meiotic recombination is almost always reciprocal, generating two homologous chromosomes that are inverted images of each other.

There are, however, exceptions. Very rarely, a particular cross produces tetrads containing unequal numbers of reciprocal classes, and such tetrads cannot be classified as PD, NPD, or T. In these exceptional tetrads, the two input alleles of one of the genes, instead of segregating at a ratio of 2*A* : 2*a,* produce ratios of 1*A* : 3*a* or 3*A* : 1*a,* or even 0*A* : 4*a* or 4*A* : 0*a* (**Fig. 5.19**). In these same tetrads, markers such as *B/b* and *C/c* that flank the *A* or *a* allele on the same chromosome still segregate 2*B* : 2*b* and 2*C* : 2*c.* Moreover, careful phenotypic and genetic tests show that even when alleles do not segregate 2:2, only the original two input alleles occur in the progeny. Thus, recombination, no matter what ratios it generates, does not create new alleles. Geneticists believe that the unusual non-2:2 segregation ratios observed in rare instances result from molecular events at the site of recombination. We discuss these events at the molecular level in Chapter 6. For now, it is simply necessary to know that the unusual ratios exist but are quite rare.

Tetrad analysis has confirmed two essential characteristics of recombination: (1) Crossing-over occurs at the four-strand stage of meiosis, after the chromosomes have duplicated, and (2) recombination is usually reciprocal, with rare exceptions.

Figure 5.19 In rare tetrads, the two alleles of a gene do not segregate 2:2. Researchers sporulated a *HIS4 / his4* diploid yeast strain and dissected the four haploid spores from three different tetrads. They then plated these spores on petri plates containing medium without histidine. Each row on the petri plate presents the four spores of a single tetrad. The top two rows show the normal 2:2 segregation of the two alleles of a single gene: two of the spores are *HIS4* and form colonies, whereas the other two spores are *his4* and cannot grow into colonies. The bottom row displays a rare tetrad with an unusual segregation of 3 *HIS4* : 1 *his4*.

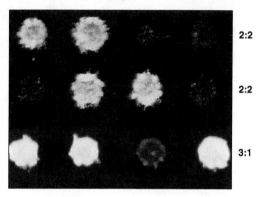

2:2

2:2

3:1

Ordered tetrads help locate genes in relation to the centromere

Analyses of ordered tetrads, such as those produced by the bread mold *Neurospora crassa*, allow you to map the centromere of a chromosome relative to other genetic markers, information that you cannot normally obtain from unordered yeast tetrads. As described earlier, immediately after specialized haploid *Neurospora* cells of different mating types fuse at fertilization, the diploid zygote undergoes meiosis within the confines of a narrow ascus (review Fig. 5.14b on p. 138). At the completion of meiosis, each of the four haploid meiotic products divides once by mitosis, yielding an **octad** of eight haploid ascospores. Dissection of the ascus at this point allows one to determine the phenotype of each of the eight haploid cells.

The cross-sectional diameter of the ascus is so small that cells cannot slip past each other. Moreover, during each division after fertilization, the microtubule fibers of the spindle extend outward from the centrosomes parallel to the long axis of the ascus. These facts have two important repercussions. First, when each of the four products of meiosis divides once by mitosis, the two genetically identical cells that result lie adjacent to each other (**Fig. 5.20**). Because of this feature, starting from either end of the ascus, you can count the octad of ascospores as four cell pairs and analyze it as a tetrad. Second, from the precise positioning of the four ascospore pairs within the ascus, you can infer the arrangement of the four chromatids of each homologous chromosome pair during the two meiotic divisions.

Figure 5.20 How ordered tetrads form. Spindles form parallel to the long axis of the growing *Neurospora* ascus, and the cells cannot slide around each other. The order of ascospores thus reflects meiotic spindle geometry. After meiosis, each haploid cell undergoes mitosis, producing an eight-cell ascus (an octad). The octad consists of four pairs of cells; the two cells of each pair are genetically identical.

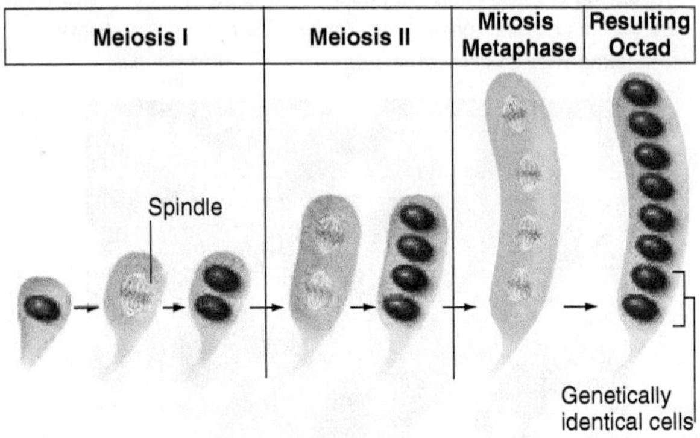

symbols similar to those used for *Drosophila,* as detailed in the nomenclature guide on p. 731 of the Appendix.) The mutant *white-spore* allele (*ws*) alters ascospore color from wild-type black to white. In the absence of recombination, the two alleles (ws^+ and *ws*) separate from each other at the first meiotic division because the centromeres to which they are attached separate at that stage. The second meiotic division and subsequent mitosis create asci in which the top four ascospores are of one genotype (for instance ws^+) and the bottom four of the other (*ws*). Whether the top four are ws^+ and the bottom four *ws*, or vice versa, depends on the random metaphase I orientation of the homologs that carry the gene relative to the long axis of the developing ascus.

The segregation of two alleles of a single gene at the first meiotic division is thus indicated by an ascus in which an imaginary line drawn between the fourth and the fifth ascospores of the octad cleanly separates haploid products bearing the two alleles. Such an ascus displays a **first-division segregation pattern** (Fig. 5.21a).

Suppose now that during meiosis I, a crossover occurs in a heterozygote between the *white-spore* gene and the centromere of the chromosome on which it travels. As **Fig. 5.21b** illustrates, this can lead to four equally possible ascospore arrangements, each one depending on a particular orientation of the four chromatids during the two meiotic divisions. In all four cases, both ws^+ and *ws* spores

To understand the genetic consequences of the geometry of the ascospores, it is helpful to consider what kinds of tetrads you would expect from the segregation of two alleles of a single gene. (In the following discussion, you will see that *Neurospora* geneticists denote alleles with

Figure 5.21 Two segregation patterns in ordered asci. (a) In the absence of a crossover between a gene and its centromere, the two alleles of a gene will separate at the first meiotic division. The result is a first-division segregation pattern in which each allele appears in spores located on only one side of an imaginary line through the middle of the ascus. **(b)** A crossover between a gene and its centromere produces a second-division segregation pattern in which both alleles appear on the same side of the middle line.

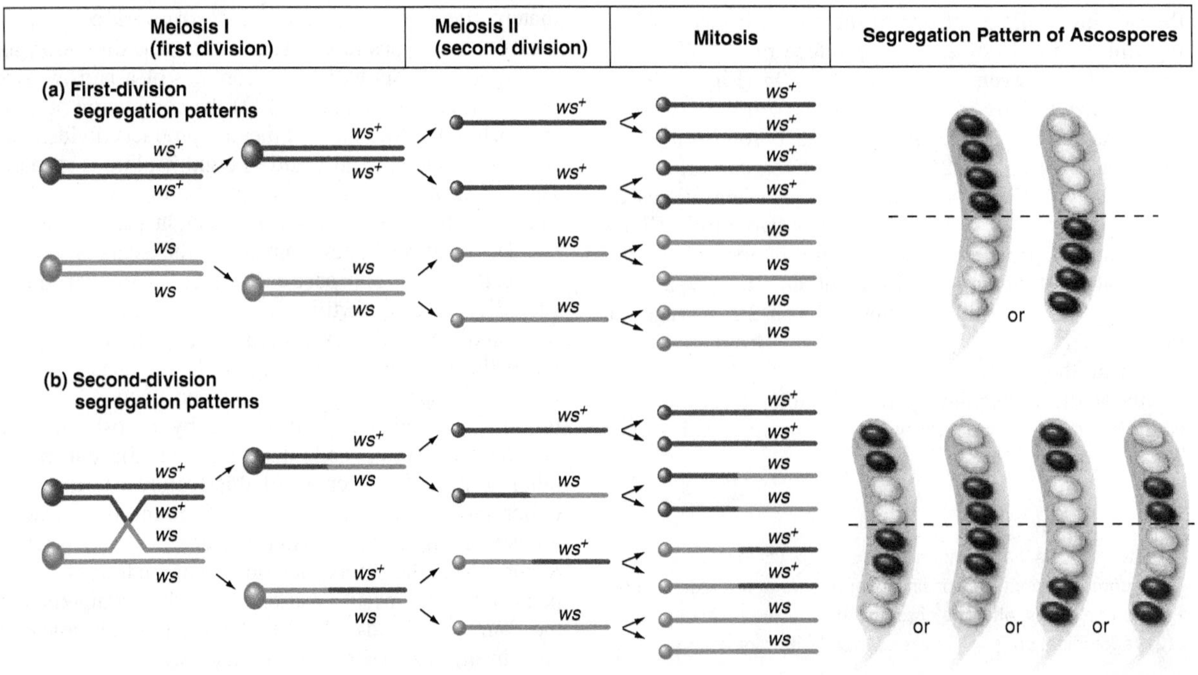

are found on both sides of the imaginary line drawn between ascospores 4 and 5, because cells with only one kind of allele do not arise until the end of the second meiotic division. Octads carrying this configuration of spores display a **second-division segregation pattern.**

Because second-division segregation patterns result from meioses in which there has been a crossover between a gene and its centromere, the relative number of asci with this pattern can be used to determine the gene ↔ centromere distance. In an ascus showing second-division segregation, one-half of the ascospores are derived from chromatids that have exchanged parts, while the remaining half arise from chromatids that have not participated in crossovers leading to recombination. To calculate the distance between a gene and its centromere, you therefore simply divide the percentage of second-division segregation octads by 2. Geneticists use information about the location of centromeres to make more accurate genetic maps as well as to study the structure and function of centromeres.

> Because meiosis in *Neurospora* occurs in a narrow ascus, the octet ascospores are generated in predictable sequence. Analysis of an ordered ascus allows researchers to deduce whether in that particular meiosis, a crossover took place between a gene and the centromere of the chromosome carrying that gene. This information can be used to calculate gene-to-centromere distances.

Tetrad analysis: A numerical example

In one experiment, a *thr⁺ arg⁺* wild-type strain of *Neurospora* was crossed with a *thr arg* double mutant. The *thr* mutants cannot grow in the absence of the amino acid threonine, while *arg* mutants cannot grow without a source of the amino acid arginine; cells carrying the wild-type alleles of both genes can grow in medium that contains neither amino acid. From this cross, 105 octads, considered here as tetrads, were obtained. These tetrads were classified in seven different groups—A, B, C, D, E, F, and G—as shown in **Fig. 5.22a.** For each of the two genes, we can now find the distance between the gene and the centromere of the chromosome on which it is located.

To do this for the *thr* gene, we count the number of tetrads with a second-division segregation pattern for that gene. Drawing an imaginary line through the middle of the tetrads, we see that those in groups B, D, E, and G are the result of second-division segregations for *thr,* while the remainder show first-division patterns. The centromere ↔ *thr* distance is thus

Percentage of second-division patterns =

$$\frac{(1/2)(16 + 2 + 2 + 1)}{105} \times 100 = 10 \text{ m.u.}$$

Figure 5.22 Genetic mapping by ordered-tetrad analysis: An example. (a) In ordered-tetrad analysis, tetrad classes are defined not only as PD, NPD, or T but also according to whether they show a first- or second-division segregation pattern. Each entry in this table represents a pair of adjacent, identical spores in the actual *Neurospora* octad. Red dots indicate the middle of the asci. **(b)** Genetic map derived from the data in part (a). Ordered-tetrad analysis allows determination of the centromere's position as well as distances between genes.

(a) A *Neurospora* cross

Tetrad group	A	B	C	D	E	F	G
Segregation pattern	*thr arg*	*thr arg*	*thr arg*	*thr arg⁺*	*thr arg⁺*	*thr arg⁺*	*thr arg*
	thr arg	*thr⁺arg*	*thr arg⁺*	*thr⁺arg*	*thr⁺arg*	*thr arg⁺*	*thr⁺arg⁺*
	thr⁺arg⁺	*thr⁺arg⁺*	*thr⁺arg*	*thr⁺arg⁺*	*thr⁺arg*	*thr arg*	*thr⁺arg⁺*
	thr⁺arg⁺	*thr arg⁺*	*thr⁺arg⁺*	*thr arg*	*thr arg⁺*	*thr⁺arg*	*thr arg*
Total in group	72	16	11	2	2	1	1

(b) Corresponding genetic map

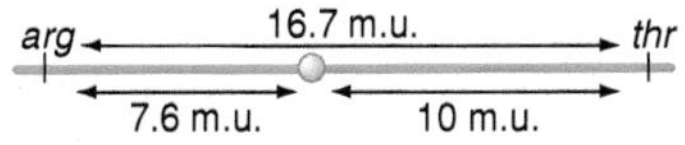

arg ←——— 16.7 m.u. ———→ thr
       ←— 7.6 m.u. —→○←— 10 m.u. —→

Similarly, the second-division tetrads for the *arg* gene are in groups C, D, E, and G, so the distance between *arg* and its centromere is

$$\frac{(1/2)(11 + 2 + 2 + 1)}{105} \times 100 = 7.6 \text{ m.u.}$$

To ascertain whether the *thr* and *arg* genes are linked, we need to evaluate the seven tetrad groups in a different way, looking at the combinations of alleles for the two genes to see if the tetrads in that group are PD, NPD, or T. We can then ask whether PD >> NPD. Referring again to Fig. 5.22a, we find that groups A and G are PD, because all the ascospores show parental combinations, while groups E and F, with four recombinant spores, are NPD. PD is thus 72 + 1 = 73, while NPD is 1 + 2 = 3. From these data, we can conclude that the two genes are linked.

What is the map distance between *thr* and *arg?* For this calculation, we need to find the numbers of T and NPD tetrads. Tetratypes are found in groups B, C, and D, and we already know that groups E and F carry NPDs. Using the same formula for map distances as the one previously used for yeast,

$$RF = \frac{NPD + 1/2T}{\text{Total tetrads}} \times 100$$

we get

$$RF = \frac{3 + (1/2)(16 + 11 + 2)}{105} \times 100 = 16.7 \text{ m.u.}$$

TABLE 5.3	Rules for Tetrad Analysis

For Ordered and Unordered Tetrads

Considering genes two at a time, assign tetrads as PD, NPD, or T.

If PD >> NPD, the two genes are genetically linked.

If PD = NPD, the two genes are genetically independent (unlinked).

The map distance between two genes if they are genetically linked

$$= \frac{NDP + (1/2)T}{\text{Total tetrads}} \times 100$$

For Ordered Tetrads Only

The map distance between a gene and its centromere

$$= \frac{(1/2) \times (\text{\# of tetrads showing second-division segregation for this gene})}{\text{Total tetrads}} \times 100$$

Because the distance between *thr* and *arg* is larger than that separating either gene from the centromere, the centromere must lie between *thr* and *arg,* yielding the map in **Fig. 5.22b.** The distance between the two genes calculated by the formula above (16.7 m.u.) is smaller than the sum of the two gene ↔ centromere distances (10.0 + 7.6 = 17.6 m.u.) because the formula does not account for all of the double crossovers. As always, calculating map positions for more genes with shorter distances between them produces the most accurate picture.

Table 5.3 summarizes the procedures for mapping genes in fungi producing ordered and unordered tetrads.

5.6 Mitotic Recombination and Genetic Mosaics

The recombination of genetic material is a critical feature of meiosis. It is thus not surprising that eukaryotic organisms express a variety of enzymes (described in Chapter 6) that specifically initiate meiotic recombination. Recombination can also occur during mitosis. Unlike what happens in meiosis, however, mitotic crossovers are initiated by mistakes in chromosome replication or by chance exposures to radiation that break DNA molecules, rather than by a well-defined cellular program. As a result, mitotic recombination is a rare event, occurring no more frequently than once in a million somatic cell divisions. Nonetheless, the growth of a colony of yeast cells or the development of a complex multicellular organism involves so many cell divisions that geneticists can routinely detect these rare mitotic events.

"Twin spots" indicate mosaicism caused by mitotic recombination

In 1936, the *Drosophila* geneticist Curt Stern originally inferred the existence of mitotic recombination from observations of "twin spots" in a few fruit flies. **Twin spots** are adjacent islands of tissue that differ both from each other and from the tissue surrounding them. The distinctive patches arise from homozygous cells with a recessive phenotype growing amid a generally heterozygous cell population displaying the dominant phenotype. In *Drosophila,* the *yellow* (*y*) mutation changes body color from normal brown to yellow, while the *singed bristles* (*sn*) mutation causes body bristles to be short and curled rather than long and straight. Both of these genes are on the X chromosome.

In his experiments, Stern examined *Drosophila* females of genotype *y sn+ / y+ sn.* These double heterozygotes were generally wild type in appearance, but Stern noticed that some flies carried patches of yellow body color, others had small areas of singed bristles, and still others displayed twin spots: adjacent patches of yellow cells and cells with singed bristles (**Fig. 5.23**). He assumed that mistakes in the mitotic divisions accompanying fly development could have led to these **mosaic** animals containing tissues of different genotypes. Individual yellow or singed patches could arise from chromosome loss or by mitotic nondisjunction. These errors in mitosis would yield XO cells containing only *y* (but not *y+*) or *sn* (but not *sn+*) alleles; such cells would show one of the recessive phenotypes.

The twin spots must have a different origin. Stern reasoned that they represented the reciprocal products of mitotic crossing-over between the *sn* gene and the centromere. The mechanism is as follows. During mitosis in a diploid cell, after chromosome duplication, homologous chromosomes occasionally—very occasionally—pair up with each other. While the chromosomes are paired,

Figure 5.23 Twin spots: A form of genetic mosaicism. In a *y sn+ / y+ sn Drosophila* female, most of the body is wild type, but aberrant patches showing either yellow color or singed bristles sometimes occur. In some cases, yellow and singed patches are adjacent to each other, a configuration known as *twin spots.*

Single yellow spot   **Twin spot**   **Single singed spot**

Figure 5.24 Mitotic crossing-over. (a) In a $y\ sn^+\ /\ y^+sn$ *Drosophila* female, a mitotic crossover between the centromere and *sn* can produce two daughter cells, one homozygous for *y* and the other homozygous for *sn,* that can develop into adjacent aberrant patches (twin spots). This outcome depends on a particular distribution of chromatids at anaphase (*top*). If the chromatids are arranged in the equally likely opposite orientation, only phenotypically normal cells will result (*bottom*). **(b)** Crossovers between *sn* and *y* can generate single yellow patches. However, a single mitotic crossover in these females cannot produce a single singed spot if the *sn* gene is closer to the centromere than the *y* gene.

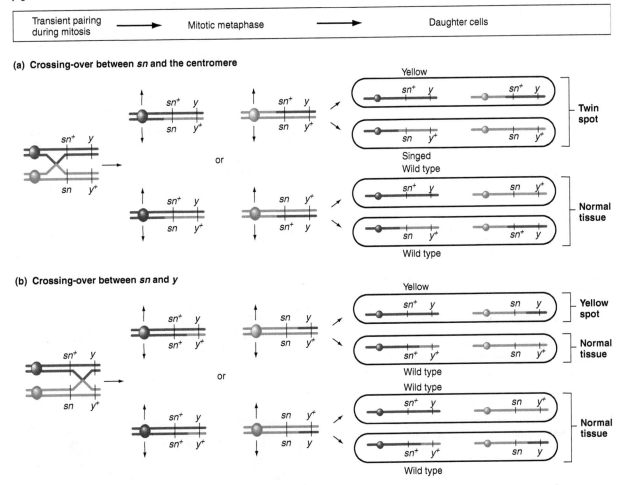

nonsister chromatids (that is, one chromatid from each of the two homologous chromosomes) can exchange parts by crossing-over. The pairing is transient, and the homologous chromosomes soon resume their independent positions on the mitotic metaphase plate. There, the two chromosomes can line up relative to each other in either of two ways (**Fig. 5.24a**). One of these orientations would yield two daughter cells that remain heterozygous for both genes and thus be indistinguishable from the surrounding wild-type cells. The other orientation, however, will generate two homozygous daughter cells, one $y\ sn^+/y\ sn^+$, the other y^+sn/y^+sn. Because the two daughter cells would lie next to each other, subsequent mitotic divisions would produce adjacent patches of *y* and *sn* tissue (that

is, twin spots). Note that if crossing-over occurs between *sn* and *y*, single spots of yellow tissue can form, but a reciprocal singed spot cannot be generated in this fashion (**Fig. 5.24b**).

Sectored yeast colonies can arise from mitotic recombination

Diploid yeast cells that are heterozygous for one or more genes exhibit mitotic recombination in the form of **sectors:** portions of a growing colony that have a different genotype than the remainder of the colony. If a diploid yeast cell of genotype *ADE2 / ade2* is placed on a petri

G E N E T I C S   A N D   S O C I E T Y

Mitotic Recombination and Cancer Formation

In humans, some tumors, such as those found in retinoblastoma, may arise as a result of mitotic recombination. Recall from the discussion of penetrance and expressivity in Chapter 3 that retinoblastoma is the most malignant form of eye cancer. The retinoblastoma gene (*RB*) resides on chromosome 13, where the normal wild-type allele (*RB*⁺) encodes a protein that regulates retinal growth and differentiation. Cells in the eye need at least one copy of the normal wild-type allele to maintain control over cell division. The normal, wild-type *RB*⁺ allele is thus known as a tumor-suppressor gene.

People with a genetic predisposition to retinoblastoma are born with only one functional copy of the normal *RB*⁺ allele; their second chromosome 13 carries either a nonfunctional *RB*⁻ allele or no *RB* gene at all. If a mutagen (such as radiation) or a mistake in gene replication or segregation destroys or removes the single remaining normal copy of the gene in a retinal cell in either eye, a retinoblastoma tumor will develop at that site. In one study of people with a genetic predisposition to retinoblastoma, cells taken from eye tumors were *RB*⁻ homozygotes, while white blood cells from the same people were *RB*⁺/*RB*⁻ heterozygotes. As **Fig. A** shows, mitotic recombination between the *RB* gene and the centromere of the chromosome carrying the gene provides one mechanism by which a cell in an *RB*⁺/*RB*⁻ individual could become *RB*⁻/*RB*⁻. Once a homozygous *RB*⁻ cell is generated, it will divide uncontrollably, leading to tumor formation.

Only 40% of retinoblastoma cases follow the preceding scenario. The other 60% occur in people who are born with two normal copies of the *RB* gene. In such people, it takes two mutational events to cause the cancer. The first of these must convert an *RB*⁺ allele to *RB*⁻, while the second could be a mitotic recombination

producing daughter cells that become cancerous because they are homozygous for the newly mutant, nonfunctional allele.

Interestingly, the role of mitotic recombination in the formation of retinoblastoma helps explain the incomplete penetrance and variable expressivity of the disease. People born as *RB*⁺/*RB*⁻ heterozygotes may or may not develop the condition (incomplete penetrance). If, as usually happens, they do, they may have it in one or both eyes (variable expressivity). It all depends on whether and in what cells of the body mitotic recombination (or some other "homozygosing" event that affects chromosome 13) occurs.

Figure A How mitotic crossing-over can contribute to cancer. Mitotic recombination during retinal growth in an *RB*⁻/*RB*⁺ heterozygote may produce an *RB*⁻/*RB*⁻ daughter cell that lacks a functional retinoblastoma gene and thus divides out of control. The crossover must occur between the *RB* gene and its centromere. Only the arrangement of chromatids yielding this result is shown.

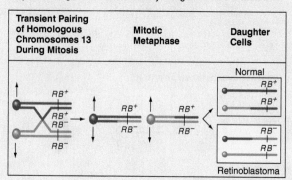

Figure A diagram: Transient Pairing of Homologous Chromosomes 13 During Mitosis | Mitotic Metaphase | Daughter Cells (Normal: *RB*⁺/*RB*⁺; Retinoblastoma: *RB*⁻/*RB*⁻)

Figure 5.25 Mitotic recombination during the growth of diploid yeast colonies can create sectors. Arrows point to large, red *ade2 / ade2* sectors formed from *ADE2 / ade2* heterozygotes.

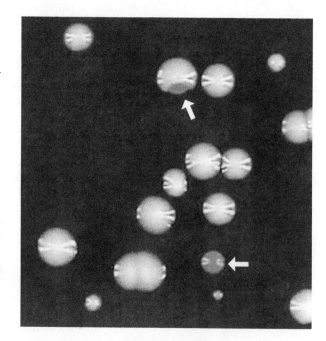

plate, its mitotic descendents will grow into a colony. Usually, such colonies will appear white because the dominant wild-type *ADE2* allele specifies that color. However, many colonies will contain red sectors of diploid *ade2 / ade2* cells, which arose as a result of mitotic recombination events between the *ADE2* gene and its centromere (**Fig. 5.25**). (Homozygous *ADE2 / ADE2* cells will also be produced by the same event, but they cannot be distinguished from heterozygotes because both types of cells are white.) The size of the red sectors indicates when mitotic recombination took place. If they are large, it happened early in the growth of the colony, giving the resulting daughter cells a long time to proliferate; if they are small, the recombination happened later.

Mitotic recombination is significant both as an experimental tool and because of the phenotypic consequences of particular mitotic crossovers. Problem 44 at the end of this chapter illustrates how geneticists use mitotic recombination to obtain information for mapping genes relative to each other and to the centromere. Mitotic crossing-over has also been of great value in the study of development because it can generate animals in which different cells have different genotypes (see Chapter 18). Finally, as the Genetics and Society box "Mitotic Recombination and Cancer Formation" explains, mitotic recombination can have major repercussions for human health.

> Crossing-over can occur in rare instances during mitosis, so that a diploid heterozygous cell can produce diploid homozygous daughter cells. The consequences of mitotic recombination include genetic mosaicism in multicellular organisms and sectoring during the growth of yeast colonies.

Connections

Medical geneticists have used their understanding of linkage, recombination, and mapping to make sense of the pedigrees presented at the beginning of this chapter (see Fig. 5.1 on p. 119). The X-linked gene for red-green colorblindness must lie very close to the gene for hemophilia A because the two are tightly coupled. In fact, the genetic distance between the two genes is only 3 m.u. The sample size in Fig. 5.1a was so small that none of the individuals in the pedigree were recombinant types. In contrast, even though hemophilia B is also on the X chromosome, it lies far enough away from the red-green colorblindness locus that the two genes recombine relatively freely. The colorblindness and hemophilia B genes may appear to be genetically unlinked in a small sample (as in Fig. 5.1b), but the actual recombination distance separating the two genes is about 36 m.u. Pedigrees pointing to two different forms of hemophilia, one very closely linked to colorblindness, the other almost not linked at all, provided one of several indications that hemophilia is determined by more than one gene (**Fig. 5.26**).

Refining the human chromosome map poses a continuous challenge for medical geneticists. The newfound potential for finding and fitting more and more DNA markers into the map (review the Fast Forward box in this chapter) enormously improves the ability to identify genes that cause disease, as discussed in Chapter 11.

Linkage and recombination are universal among life-forms and must therefore confer important advantages to living organisms. Geneticists believe that linkage provides the potential for transmitting favorable combinations of genes intact to successive generations, while recombination produces great flexibility in generating new combinations of alleles. Some new combinations may help a species adapt to changing environmental conditions, whereas the inheritance of successfully tested combinations can preserve what has worked in the past.

Thus far, this book has examined how genes and chromosomes are transmitted. As important and useful as this knowledge is, it tells us very little about the structure and mode of action of the genetic material. In the next section (Chapters 6–8), we carry our analysis to the level of DNA, the actual molecule of heredity. In Chapter 6, we look at DNA structure and learn how the DNA molecule carries genetic information. In Chapter 7, we describe how geneticists defined the gene as a localized region of DNA containing many nucleotides that together encode the information to make a protein. In Chapter 8, we examine how the cellular machinery interprets the genetic information in genes to produce the multitude of phenotypes that make up an organism.

Figure 5.26 A genetic map of part of the human X chromosome.

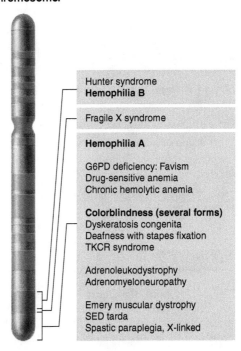

Hunter syndrome
Hemophilia B

Fragile X syndrome

Hemophilia A

G6PD deficiency: Favism
Drug-sensitive anemia
Chronic hemolytic anemia

Colorblindness (several forms)
Dyskeratosis congenita
Deafness with stapes fixation
TKCR syndrome

Adrenoleukodystrophy
Adrenomyeloneuropathy

Emery muscular dystrophy
SED tarda
Spastic paraplegia, X-linked

ESSENTIAL CONCEPTS

1. Gene pairs that are close together on the same chromosome are genetically linked because they are transmitted together more often than not. The hallmark of linkage is that the number of parental types is greater than the number of recombinant types among the progeny of double heterozygotes.

2. The recombination frequencies of pairs of genes indicate how often two genes are transmitted together. For linked genes, the recombination frequency is less than 50%.

3. Gene pairs that assort independently exhibit a recombination frequency of 50%, because the number of parental types equals the number of recombinants. Genes may assort independently either because they are on different chromosomes or because they are far apart on the same chromosome.

4. Statistical analysis helps determine whether or not two genes assort independently. The probability value (p) calculated by the chi-square test measures the likelihood that a particular set of data supports the null hypothesis of independent assortment, or no linkage. The lower the p value, the less likely is the null hypothesis, and the more likely the linkage. The chi-square test can also be used to determine how well the outcomes of crosses fit other genetic hypotheses (see www.mhhe.com/hartwell4: **Chapter 3** for examples).

5. The greater the physical distance between linked genes, the higher the recombination frequency. However, recombination frequencies become more and more inaccurate as the distance between genes increases.

6. Recombination occurs because chromatids of homologous chromosomes exchange parts (that is, cross over) during the prophase of meiosis I, after the chromosomes have replicated.

7. Genetic maps are a visual representation of relative recombination frequencies. The greater the density of genes on the map (and thus the smaller the distance between the genes), the more accurate and useful the map becomes in predicting inheritance.

8. Organisms that retain all the products of one meiosis within an ascus reveal the relation between genetic recombination and the segregation of chromosomes during the two meiotic divisions. Organisms like *Neurospora* that produce ordered octads make it possible to locate a chromosome's centromere on the genetic map.

9. In diploid organisms heterozygous for two alleles of a gene, rare mitotic recombination between the gene and its centromere can produce genetic mosaics in which some cells are homozygous for one allele or the other.

On Our Website | www.mhhe.com/hartwell4

Annotated Suggested Readings and Links to Other Websites

- The early history of genetic mapping
- Construction of a linkage map of the human genome
- New ideas about the significance of chromosomal interference
- Using mitotic recombination to trace cells during development

Specialized Topics

- The derivation and use of mapping functions
- Determining the linkage of human genes using likelihood ratios and LOD scores.

Solved Problems

I. The *Xg* locus on the human X chromosome has two alleles, a^+ and a. The a^+ allele causes the presence of the Xg surface antigen on red blood cells, while the recessive a allele does not allow antigen to appear. The *Xg* locus is 10 m.u. from the *Sts* locus. The *Sts* allele produces normal activity of the enzyme steroid sulfatase, while the recessive *sts* allele results in the lack of steroid sulfatase activity and the disease ichthyosis (scaly skin).

A man with ichthyosis and no Xg antigen has a normal daughter with Xg antigen, who is expecting a child.

a. If the child is a son, what is the probability he will lack antigen and have ichthyosis?

b. What is the probability that a son would have both the antigen and ichthyosis?

c. If the child is a son with ichthyosis, what is the probability he will have Xg antigen?

Answer

a. This problem requires an understanding of how linkage affects the proportions of gametes. First designate the genotype of the individual in which recombination during meiosis affects the transmission of alleles: in this problem, the daughter. The X chromosome she inherited from her father (who had icthyosis and no Xg antigen) must be *sts a*. (No recombination could have separated the genes during meiosis in her father since he has only one X chromosome.) Because the daughter is normal and has the Xg antigen, her other X chromosome (inherited from her mother) must contain the *Sts* and *a+* alleles. Her X chromosomes can be diagrammed as:

$$
\begin{array}{cc}
\underline{sts} & \underline{a} \\[4pt]
\overline{Sts} & \overline{a^+}
\end{array}
$$

Because the *Sts* and *Xg* loci are 10 m.u. apart on the chromosome, there is a 10% recombination frequency. Ninety percent of the gametes will be parental: *sts a* or *Sts a+* (45% of each type) and 10% will be recombinant: *sts a+* or *Sts a* (5% of each type). The phenotype of a son directly reflects the genotype of the X chromosome from his mother. *Therefore, the probability that he will lack the Xg antigen and have icthyosis (genotype: sts a/Y) is 45/100.*

b. *The probability that he will have the antigen and ichthyosis (genotype: sts a+/Y) is 5/100.*

c. There are two classes of gametes containing the ichthyosis allele: *sts a* (45%) and *sts a+* (5%). If the total number of gametes is 100, then 50 will have the *sts* allele. Of those gametes, 5 (or 10%) will have the *a+* allele. *Therefore there is a 1/10 probability that a son with the sts allele will have the Xg antigen.*

II. *Drosophila* females of wild-type appearance but heterozygous for three autosomal genes are mated with males showing three autosomal recessive traits: glassy eyes, coal-colored bodies, and striped thoraxes. One thousand (1000) progeny of this cross are distributed in the following phenotypic classes:

Wild type	27
Striped thorax	11
Coal body	484
Glassy eyes, coal body	8
Glassy eyes, striped thorax	441
Glassy eyes, coal body, striped thorax	29

a. Draw a genetic map based on this data.

b. Show the arrangement of alleles on the two homologous chromosomes in the parent females.

c. Normal-appearing males containing the same chromosomes as the parent females in the preceding cross are mated with females showing glassy eyes, coal-colored bodies, and striped thoraxes. Of 1000 progeny produced, indicate the numbers of the various phenotypic classes you would expect.

Answer

A logical, methodical way to approach a three-point cross is described here.

a. Designate the alleles:

t^+ = wild-type thorax	t = striped thorax
g^+ = wild-type eyes	g = glassy eyes
c^+ = wild-type body	c = coal-colored body

In solving a three-point cross, designate the types of events that gave rise to each group of individuals and the genotypes of the gametes obtained from their mother. (The paternal gametes contain only the recessive alleles of these genes [*t g c*]. They do not change the phenotype and can be ignored.)

Progeny	Number	Type of event	Genotype
1. wild type	27	single crossover	t^+ g^+ c^+
2. striped thorax	11	single crossover	t g^+ c^+
3. coal body	484	parental	t^+ g^+ c
4. glassy eyes, coal body	8	single crossover	t^+ g c
5. glassy eyes, striped thorax	441	parental	t g c^+
6. glassy eyes, coal body, striped thorax	29	single crossover	t g c

Picking out the parental classes is easy. If all the other classes are rare, the two most abundant categories are those gene combinations that have not undergone recombination. Then there should be two sets of two phenotypes that correspond to a single crossover event between the first and second genes, or between the second and third genes. Finally, there should be a pair of classes containing small numbers that result from double crossovers. In this example, there are no flies in the double crossover classes, which would have been in the two missing phenotypic combinations: glassy eyes, coal body, and striped thorax.

Look at the most abundant classes to determine which alleles were on each chromosome in the female heterozygous parent. One parental class had the phenotype of coal body (484 flies), so one chromosome in the female must have contained the t^+, g^+, and c alleles. (Notice that we cannot yet say in what order these alleles are located on the chromosome.) The other parental class was glassy eyes and striped thorax, corresponding to a chromosome with the t, g, and c^+ alleles.

To determine the order of the genes, compare the $t^+ g c^+$ double crossover class (not seen in the data) with the most similar parental class ($t g c^+$). The alleles of g and c retain their parental associations ($g c^+$), while the t gene has recombined with respect to both other genes in the double recombinant class. Thus, the t gene is between g and c.

In order to complete the map, calculate the recombination frequencies between the center gene and each of the genes on the ends. For g and t, the nonparental combinations of alleles are in classes 2 and 4, so RF = (11 + 8)/1000 = 19/1000, or 1.9%. For t and c, classes 1 and 6 are nonparental, so RF = (27 + 29)/1000 = 56/1000, or 5.6%.

The genetic map is

c^+ ———————————————— t^+ ———— g^+

5.6 m.u.   1.9 m.u.

b. The alleles on each chromosome were already determined (c, g^+, t^+ and c^+, g, t). Now that the order of loci has also been determined, the arrangement of the alleles can be indicated.

c ———— t^+ ———— g^+

c^+ ———— t ———— g

c. Males of the same genotype as the starting female ($c\ t^+\ g^+/c^+\ t\ g$) could produce only two types of gametes: parental types $c\ t^+\ g^+$ and $c^+\ t\ g$ because there is no recombination in male *Drosophila*. The progeny expected from the mating with a homozygous recessive female are thus 500 coal body and 500 glassy eyed, striped thorax flies.

III. The following asci were obtained in *Neurospora* when a wild-type strain ($ad^+ leu^+$) was crossed to a double mutant strain that cannot grow in the absence of adenine or leucine ($ad^- leu^-$). Only one member of each spore pair produced by the final mitosis is shown, because the two cells in a pair have the same genotype. Total asci = 120.

a. What genetic event causes the alleles of two genes to segregate to different cells at the second meiotic division, and when does this event occur?
b. Provide the best possible map for the two genes and their centromere(s).

Answer

This problem requires an understanding of tetrad analysis and the process (meiosis) that produces the patterns seen in ordered asci.

a. *A crossover between a gene and its centromere causes the segregation of alleles at the second meiotic division. The crossover event occurs during prophase of meiosis I.*

b. Using ordered tetrads you can determine whether two genes are linked, the distance between two genes, and the distance between each gene and its centromere. First designate the five classes of asci shown. The first class is a parental ditype (spores contain the same combinations of alleles as their parents); the second is a nonparental ditype; the last three are tetratypes. Next determine if these genes are linked. The number of PD = number of NPD, so the genes are not linked. When genes are unlinked, the tetratype asci are generated by a crossing-over event between a gene and its centromere. Looking at the *leu* gene, there is a second-division segregation pattern of that gene in the third and fourth asci types. Therefore, the percent of second-division segregation is

$$\frac{40 + 2}{120} \times 100 = 35\%$$

Because only half of the chromatids in the meioses that generated these tetratype asci were involved in the crossover, the map distance between *leu* and its centromere is 35/2, or 17.5 m.u. Asci of the fourth and fifth types show a second-division segregation pattern for the *ad* gene

$$\frac{2 + 18}{120} \times 100 = 16.6\%$$

Dividing 16.6% by 2 gives the recombination frequency and map distance of 8.3 m.u. *The map of these two genes is the following:*

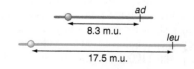

Spore pair	Ascus type				
1–2	$ad^+ leu^+$	$ad^+ leu^-$	$ad^+ leu^+$	$ad^+ leu^-$	$ad^- leu^+$
3–4	$ad^+ leu^+$	$ad^+ leu^-$	$ad^+ leu^-$	$ad^- leu^+$	$ad^+ leu^+$
5–6	$ad^- leu^-$	$ad^- leu^+$	$ad^- leu^+$	$ad^- leu^-$	$ad^- leu^-$
7–8	$ad^- leu^-$	$ad^- leu^+$	$ad^- leu^-$	$ad^+ leu^+$	$ad^+ leu^-$
# of asci	30	30	40	2	18

Problems

Vocabulary

1. Choose the phrase from the right column that best fits the term in the left column.

a. recombination	1. a statistical method for testing the fit between observed and expected results
b. linkage	2. an ascus containing spores of four different genotypes
c. chi-square test	3. one crossover along a chromosome makes a second nearby crossover less likely
d. chiasma	4. when two loci recombine in less than 50% of gametes
e. tetratype	5. the relative chromosomal location of a gene
f. locus	6. the ratio of observed double crossovers to expected double crossovers
g. coefficient of coincidence	7. individual composed of cells with different genotypes
h. interference	8. formation of new genetic combinations by exchange of parts between homologs
i. parental ditype	9. when the two alleles of a gene are segregated into different cells at the first meiotic division
j. ascospores	10. an ascus containing only two nonrecombinant kinds of spores
k. first-division segregation	11. structure formed at the spot where crossing-over occurs between homologs
l. mosaic	12. fungal spores contained in a sac

Section 5.1

2. a. A *Drosophila* male from a true-breeding stock with scabrous eyes was mated with a female from a true-breeding stock with javelin bristles. Both scabrous eyes and javelin bristles are autosomal traits. The F_1 progeny all had normal eyes and bristles. F_1 females from this cross were mated with males with both scabrous eyes and javelin bristles. Write all the possible phenotypic classes of the progeny that could be produced from the cross of the F_1 females with the scabrous, javelin males, and indicate for each class whether it is a recombinant or parental type.

   b. The cross above yielded the following progeny: 77 scabrous eyes and normal bristles; 76 wild type (normal eyes and bristles); 74 normal eyes and javelin bristles; and 73 scabrous eyes and javelin bristles. Are the genes governing these traits likely to be linked, or do they instead assort independently? Why?

   c. Suppose you mated the F_1 females from the cross in part (a) to wild-type males. Why would this cross fail to inform you whether the two genes are linked?

   d. Suppose you mated females from the true-breeding stock with javelin bristles to males with scabrous eyes and javelin bristles. Why would this cross fail to inform you whether the two genes are linked?

3. With modern molecular methods it is now possible to examine variants in DNA sequence from a very small amount of tissue like a hair follicle or even a single sperm. You can consider these variants to be "alleles" of a particular site on a chromosome (a "locus"; "loci" in plural). For example, AAAAAAA, AAACAAA, AAAGAAA, and AAATAAA at the same location (call it B) on homologous autosomes in different sperm might be called alleles *1*, *2*, *3*, and *4* of locus B (B_1, B_2, etc.). John's genotype for two loci B and D is B_1B_3 and D_1D_3. John's father was B_1B_2 and D_1D_4, while his mother was B_3B_3 and D_2D_3.

   a. What is (are) the genotype(s) of the parental type sperm John could produce?

   b. What is (are) the genotype(s) of the recombinant type sperm John could produce?

   c. In a sample of 100 sperm, 51 of John's sperm were found to be B_1 and D_1, while the remaining 49 sperm were B_3D_3. Can you conclude whether the *B* and *D* loci are linked, or whether they instead assort independently?

Section 5.2

4. Do the data that Mendel obtained fit his hypotheses? For example, Mendel obtained 315 yellow round, 101 yellow wrinkled, 108 green round, and 32 green wrinkled seeds from the selfing of *Yy Rr* individuals (a total of 556). His hypotheses of segregation and independent assortment predict a 9:3:3:1 ratio in this case. Use the chi-square test to determine whether Mendel's data are significantly different from what he predicted. (The chi-square test did not exist in Mendel's day, so he was not able to test his own data for goodness of fit to his hypotheses.)

5. Two genes control color in corn snakes as follows:

   O– B– snakes are brown, *O– bb* are orange, *oo B–* are black, and *oo bb* are albino. An orange snake was mated to a black snake, and a large number of F_1 progeny were obtained, all of which were brown. When the F_1 snakes were mated to one another, they produced 100 brown offspring, 25 orange, 22 black, and 13 albino.

a. What are the genotypes of the F_1 snakes?

b. What proportions of the different colors would have been expected among the F_2 snakes if the two loci assort independently?

c. Do the observed results differ significantly from what was expected, assuming independent assortment is occurring?

d. What is the probability that differences this great between observed and expected values would happen by chance?

6. A mouse from a true-breeding population with normal gait was crossed to a mouse displaying an odd gait called "dancing." The F_1 animals all showed normal gait.

a. If dancing is caused by homozygosity for the recessive allele of a single gene, what proportion of the F_2 mice should be dancers?

b. If mice must be homozygous for recessive alleles of both of two different genes to have the dancing phenotype, what proportion of the F_2 should be dancers if the two genes are unlinked?

c. When the F_2 mice were obtained, 42 normal and 8 dancers were seen. Use the chi-square test to determine if these results better fit the one-gene model from part a or the two-gene model from part b.

7. Figure 5.5 on p. 123 applied the chi-square method to test linkage between two genes by asking whether the observed numbers of parental and recombinant classes differed significantly from the expectation of independent assortment that parentals = recombinants. Another possible way to analyze the results from these same experiments is to ask whether the observed frequencies of the four genotypic classes ($A\ B$, $a\ b$, $A\ b$, and $a\ B$) can be explained by a null hypothesis predicting that they should appear in a 1:1:1:1 ratio. In order to consider the relative advantages and disadvantages of analyzing the data in these two different ways answer the following:

a. What is the null hypothesis in each case?

b. Which is a more sensitive test of linkage? (Analyze the data in Fig. 5.5 by the second method.)

c. How would both methods respond to a situation in which one allele of one of the genes causes reduced viability?

Section 5.3

8. In *Drosophila,* males from a true-breeding stock with raspberry-colored eyes were mated to females from a true-breeding stock with sable-colored bodies. In the F_1 generation, all the females had wild-type eye and body color, while all the males had wild-type eye color but sable-colored bodies. When F_1 males and females were mated, the F_2 generation was composed of 216 females with wild-type eyes and bodies, 223 females with wild-type eyes and sable bodies, 191 males with wild-type eyes and sable bodies, 188 males with raspberry eyes and wild-type bodies, 23 males with wild-type eyes and bodies, and 27 males with raspberry eyes and sable bodies. Explain these results by diagramming the crosses, and calculate any relevant map distances.

9. In mice, the dominant allele Gs of the X-linked gene *Greasy* produces shiny fur, while the recessive wild-type Gs^+ allele determines normal fur. The dominant allele Bhd of the X-linked *Broadhead* gene causes skeletal abnormalities including broad heads and snouts, while the recessive wild-type Bhd^+ allele yields normal skeletons. Female mice heterozygous for the two alleles of both genes were mated with wild-type males. Among 100 male progeny of this cross, 49 had shiny fur, 48 had skeletal abnormalities, 2 had shiny fur and skeletal abnormalities, and 1 was wild type.

a. Diagram the cross described, and calculate the distance between the two genes.

b. What would have been the results if you had counted 100 female progeny of the cross?

10. $CC\ DD$ and $cc\ dd$ individuals were crossed to each other, and the F_1 generation was backcrossed to the $cc\ dd$ parent. 903 $Cc\ Dd$, 897 $cc\ dd$, 98 $Cc\ dd$, and 102 $cc\ Dd$ offspring resulted.

a. How far apart are the c and d loci?

b. What progeny and in what frequencies would you expect to result from testcrossing the F_1 generation from a $CC\ dd \times cc\ DD$ cross to $cc\ dd$?

11. If the a and b loci are 20 m.u. apart in humans and an $A\ B\,/\,a\ b$ woman mates with an $a\ b\,/\,a\ b$ man, what is the probability that their first child will be $A\ b\,/\,a\ b$?

12. In a particular human family, John and his mother both have brachydactyly (a rare autosomal dominant causing short fingers). John's father has Huntington disease (another rare autosomal dominant). John's wife is phenotypically normal and is pregnant. Two-thirds of people who inherit the Huntington (HD) allele show symptoms by age 50, and John is 50 and has no symptoms. Brachydactyly is 90% penetrant.

a. What are the genotypes of John's parents?

b. What are the possible genotypes for John?

c. What is the probability the child will express both brachydactyly and Huntington disease by age 50 if the two genes are unlinked?

d. If these two loci are 20 m.u. apart, how will it change your answer to part c?

13. In mice, the autosomal locus coding for the β-globin chain of hemoglobin is 1 m.u. from the albino locus. Assume for the moment that the same is true in humans. The disease sickle-cell anemia is the result of homozygosity for a particular mutation in the β-globin gene.
  a. A son is born to an albino man and a woman with sickle-cell anemia. What kinds of gametes will the son form, and in what proportions?
  b. A daughter is born to a normal man and a woman who has both albinism and sickle-cell anemia. What kinds of gametes will the daughter form, and in what proportions?
  c. If the son in part *a* grows up and marries the daughter in part *b,* what is the probability that a child of theirs will be an albino with sickle-cell anemia?

14. In corn, the allele *A* allows the deposition of anthocyanin (blue) pigment in the kernels (seeds), while *aa* plants have yellow kernels. At a second gene, *W–* produces smooth kernels, while *ww* kernels are wrinkled. A plant with blue smooth kernels was crossed to a plant with yellow wrinkled kernels. The progeny consisted of 1447 blue smooth, 169 blue wrinkled, 186 yellow smooth, and 1510 yellow wrinkled.
  a. Are the *a* and *w* loci linked? If so, how far apart are they?
  b. What was the genotype of the blue smooth parent? Include the chromosome arrangement of alleles.
  c. If a plant grown from a blue wrinkled progeny seed is crossed to a plant grown from a yellow smooth F_1 seed, what kinds of kernels would be expected, and in what proportions?

15. Albino rabbits (lacking pigment) are homozygous for the recessive *c* allele (*C* allows pigment formation). Rabbits homozygous for the recessive *b* allele make brown pigment, while those with at least one copy of *B* make black pigment. True-breeding brown rabbits were crossed to albinos, which were *BB*. F_1 rabbits, which were all black, were crossed to the double recessive (*bb cc*). The progeny obtained were 34 black, 66 brown, and 100 albino.
  a. What phenotypic proportions would have been expected if the *b* and *c* loci were unlinked?
  b. How far apart are the two loci?

16. Write the number of *different kinds* of phenotypes, excluding gender, you would see among a large number of progeny from an F_1 mating between individuals of identical genotype that are heterozygous for one or two genes (that is, *Aa* or *Aa Bb*) as indicated. No gene interactions means that the phenotype determined by one gene is not influenced by the genotype of the other gene.
  a. One gene; *A* completely dominant to *a.*
  b. One gene; *A* and *a* codominant.
  c. One gene; *A* incompletely dominant to *a.*

  d. Two unlinked genes; no gene interactions; *A* completely dominant to *a,* and *B* completely dominant to *b.*
  e. Two genes, 10 m.u. apart; no gene interactions; *A* completely dominant to *a,* and *B* completely dominant to *b.*
  f. Two unlinked genes; no gene interactions; *A* and *a* codominant, and *B* incompletely dominant to *b.*
  g. Two genes, 10 m.u. apart; *A* completely dominant to *a,* and *B* completely dominant to *b;* and with recessive epistasis between the genes.
  h. Two unlinked duplicated genes (that is, *A* and *B* perform the same function); *A* and *B* completely dominant to *a* and *b,* respectively.
  i. Two genes, 0 m.u. apart; no gene interactions; *A* completely dominant to *a,* and *B* completely dominant to *b.* (There are two possible answers.)

17. If the *a* and *b* loci are 40 cM apart and an *AA BB* individual and an *aa bb* individual mate:
  a. What gametes will the F_1 individuals produce, and in what proportions? What phenotypic classes in what proportions are expected in the F_2 generation (assuming complete dominance for both genes)?
  b. If the original cross was *AA bb × aa BB,* what gametic proportions would emerge from the F_1? What would be the result in the F_2 generation?

18. A DNA variant has been found linked to a rare autosomal dominant disease in humans and can thus be used as a marker to follow inheritance of the disease allele. In an informative family (in which one parent is heterozygous for both the disease allele and the DNA marker in a known chromosomal arrangement of alleles, and his or her mate does not have the same alleles of the DNA variant), the reliability of such a marker as a predictor of the disease in a fetus is related to the map distance between the DNA marker and the gene causing the disease. Imagine that a man affected with the disease (genotype *Dd*) is heterozygous for the V^1 and V^2 forms of the DNA variant, with form V^1 on the same chromosome as the *D* allele and form V^2 on the same chromosome as *d.* His wife is V^3V^3 *dd,* where V^3 is another allele of the DNA marker. Typing of the fetus by amniocentesis reveals that the fetus has the V^2 and V^3 variants of the DNA marker. How likely is it that the fetus has inherited the disease allele *D* if the distance between the *D* locus and the marker locus is (a) 0 m.u., (b) 1 m.u., (c) 5 m.u., (d) 10 m.u., (e) 50 m.u.?

Section 5.4

19. In *Drosophila,* the recessive *dp* allele of the *dumpy* gene produces short, curved wings, while the recessive allele *bw* of the *brown* gene causes brown eyes.

In a testcross using females heterozygous for both of these genes, the following results were obtained:

wild-type wings, wild-type eyes	178
wild-type wings, brown eyes	185
dumpy wings, wild-type eyes	172
dumpy wings, brown eyes	181

In a testcross using males heterozygous for both of these genes, a different set of results was obtained:

| wild-type wings, wild-type eyes | 247 |
| dumpy wings, brown eyes | 242 |

a. What can you conclude from the first testcross?
b. What can you conclude from the second testcross?
c. How can you reconcile the data shown in parts *a* and *b?* Can you exploit the difference between these two sets of data to devise a general test for synteny in *Drosophila?*
d. The genetic distance between *dumpy* and *brown* is 91.5 m.u. How could this value be measured?

20. Cinnabar eyes (*cn*) and reduced bristles (*rd*) are autosomal recessive characters in *Drosophila*. A homozygous wild-type female was crossed to a reduced, cinnabar male, and the F$_1$ males were then crossed to the F$_1$ females to obtain the F$_2$. Of the 400 F$_2$ offspring obtained, 292 were wild type, 9 were cinnabar, 7 were reduced, and 92 were reduced, cinnabar. Explain these results and estimate the distance between the *cn* and *rd* loci.

21. Map distances were determined for four different genes (*MAT, HIS4, THR4,* and *LEU2*) on chromosome III of the yeast *Saccharomyces cerevisiae*:

HIS4 ↔ MAT	37 cM
THR4 ↔ LEU2	35 cM
LEU2 ↔ HIS4	23 cM
MAT ↔ LEU2	16 cM
MAT ↔ THR4	16 cM

What is the order of genes on the chromosome?

22. From a series of two-point crosses, the following map distances were obtained for the syntenic genes *A, B, C, D,* and *E* in peas:

B ↔ C	23 m.u.
A ↔ C	15 m.u.
C ↔ D	14 m.u.
A ↔ B	12 m.u.
B ↔ D	11 m.u.
A ↔ D	1 m.u.

Chi-square analysis cannot reject the null hypothesis of no linkage for gene *E* with any of the other four genes.
a. Draw a cross scheme that would allow you to determine the *B ↔ C* map distance.

b. Diagram the best genetic map that can be assembled from this dataset.
c. Explain any inconsistencies or unknown features in your map.
d. What additional experiments would allow you to resolve these inconsistencies or ambiguities?

23. In *Drosophila,* the recessive allele *mb* of one gene causes missing bristles, the recessive allele *e* of a second gene causes ebony body color, and the recessive allele *k* of a third gene causes kidney-shaped eyes. (Dominant wild-type alleles of all three genes are indicated with a + superscript.) The three different P generation crosses in the table that follows were conducted, and then the resultant F$_1$ females from each cross were testcrossed to males that were homozygous for the recessive alleles of both genes in question. The phenotypes of the testcross offspring are tabulated as follows. Determine the best genetic map explaining all the data.

Parental cross	Testcross offspring of F$_1$ females	
$mb^+\ mb^+,\ e^+\ e^+ \times$ $mb\ mb,\ e\ e$	normal bristles, normal body	117
	normal bristles, ebony body	11
	missing bristles, normal body	15
	missing bristles, ebony body	107
$k^+\ k^+,\ e\ e \times k\ k,\ e^+\ e^+$	normal eyes, normal body	11
	normal eyes, ebony body	150
	kidney eyes, normal body	144
	kidney eyes, ebony body	7
$mb^+\ mb^+,\ k^+\ k^+ \times$ $mb\ mb,\ k\ k$	normal bristles, normal eyes	203
	normal bristles, kidney eyes	11
	missing bristles, normal eyes	15
	missing bristles, kidney eyes	193

24. In the tubular flowers of foxgloves, wild-type coloration is red while a mutation called *white* produces white flowers. Another mutation, called *peloria*, causes the flowers at the apex of the stem to be huge. Yet another mutation, called *dwarf*, affects stem length. You cross a white-flowered plant (otherwise phenotypically wild type) to a plant that is dwarf and peloria but has wild-type red flower color. All of the F$_1$ plants are tall with white, normal-sized flowers. You cross an F$_1$ plant back to the dwarf and peloria parent, and you see the 543 progeny shown in the chart. (Only mutant traits are noted.)

dwarf, peloria	172
white	162
dwarf, peloria, white	56
wild type	48
dwarf, white	51
peloria	43
dwarf	6
peloria, white	5

a. Which alleles are dominant?

b. What were the genotypes of the parents in the original cross?

c. Draw a map showing the linkage relationships of these three loci.

d. Is there interference? If so, calculate the coefficient of coincidence and the interference value.

25. In *Drosophila*, three autosomal genes have the following map:

a. Provide the data, in terms of the expected number of flies in the following phenotypic classes, when $a^+ b^+ c^+ / a b c$ females are crossed to $a b c / a b c$ males. Assume 1000 flies were counted and that there is no interference in this region.

a^+	b^+	c^+
a	b	c
a^+	b	c
a	b^+	c^+
a^+	b^+	c
a	b	c^+
a^+	b	c^+
a	b^+	c

b. If the cross were reversed, such that $a^+ b^+ c^+ / a b c$ males are crossed to $a b c / a b c$ females, how many flies would you expect in the same phenotypic classes?

26. A snapdragon with pink petals, black anthers, and long stems was allowed to self-fertilize. From the resulting seeds, 650 adult plants were obtained. The phenotypes of these offspring are listed here.

78	red	long	tan
26	red	short	tan
44	red	long	black
15	red	short	black
39	pink	long	tan
13	pink	short	tan
204	pink	long	black
68	pink	short	black
5	white	long	tan
2	white	short	tan
117	white	long	black
39	white	short	black

a. Using *P* for one allele and *p* for the other, indicate how flower color is inherited.

b. What numbers of red : pink : white would have been expected among these 650 plants?

c. How are anther color and stem length inherited?

d. What was the genotype of the original plant?

e. Do any of the three genes show independent assortment?

f. For any genes that are linked, indicate the arrangements of the alleles on the homologous chromosomes in the original snapdragon, and estimate the distance between the genes.

27. Male *Drosophila* expressing the recessive mutations *sc* (*scute*), *ec* (*echinus*), *cv* (*crossveinless*), and *b* (*black*) were crossed to phenotypically wild-type females, and the 3288 progeny listed were obtained. (Only mutant traits are noted.)

653	black, scute, echinus, crossveinless
670	scute, echinus, crossveinless
675	wild type
655	black
71	black, scute
73	scute
73	black, echinus, crossveinless
74	echinus, crossveinless
87	black, scute, echinus
84	scute, echinus
86	black, crossveinless
83	crossveinless
1	black, scute, crossveinless
1	scute, crossveinless
1	black, echinus
1	echinus

a. Diagram the genotype of the female parent.

b. Map these loci.

c. Is there evidence of interference? Justify your answer with numbers.

28. *Drosophila* females heterozygous for each of three recessive autosome mutations with independent phenotypic effects (thread antennae [*th*], hairy body [*h*], and scarlet eyes [*st*]) were testcrossed to males showing all three mutant phenotypes. The 1000 progeny of this testcross were

thread, hairy, scarlet	432
wild type	429
thread, hairy	37
thread, scarlet	35
hairy	34
scarlet	33

a. Show the arrangement of alleles on the relevant chromosomes in the triply heterozygous females.

b. Draw the best genetic map that explains these data.

c. Calculate any relevant interference values.

29. A true-breeding strain of Virginia tobacco has dominant alleles determining leaf morphology (*M*), leaf color (*C*), and leaf size (*S*). A Carolina strain is

homozygous for the recessive alleles of these three genes. These genes are found on the same chromosome as follows:

An F₁ hybrid between the two strains is now backcrossed to the Carolina strain. Assuming no interference:

a. What proportion of the backcross progeny will resemble the Virginia strain for all three traits?

b. What proportion of the backcross progeny will resemble the Carolina strain for all three traits?

c. What proportion of the backcross progeny will have the leaf morphology and leaf size of the Virginia strain but the leaf color of the Carolina strain?

d. What proportion of the backcross progeny will have the leaf morphology and leaf color of the Virginia strain but the leaf size of the Carolina strain?

30. a. In *Drosophila,* crosses between F₁ heterozygotes of the form *A b / a B* always yield the same ratio of phenotypes in the F₂ progeny regardless of the distance between the two genes (assuming complete dominance for both autosomal genes). What is this ratio? Would this also be the case if the F₁ heterozygotes were *A B / a b?*

b. If you intercrossed F₁ heterozygotes of the form *A b / a B* in mice, the phenotypic ratio among the F₂ progeny would vary with the map distance between the two genes. Is there a simple way to estimate the map distance based on the frequencies of the F₂ phenotypes, assuming rates of recombination are equal in males and females? Could you estimate map distances in the same way if the mouse F₁ heterozygotes were *A B / a b?*

31. The following list of four *Drosophila* mutations indicates the symbol for the mutation, the name of the gene, and the mutant phenotype:

Allele symbol	Gene name	Mutant phenotype
dwp	*dwarp*	small body, warped wings
rmp	*rumpled*	deranged bristles
pld	*pallid*	pale wings
rv	*raven*	dark eyes and bodies

You perform the following crosses with the indicated results:

Cross #1: dwarp, rumpled females × pallid, raven males
→ dwarp, rumpled males and wild-type females

Cross #2: pallid, raven females × dwarp, rumpled males
→ pallid, raven males and wild-type females

F₁ females from cross #1 were crossed to males from a true-breeding *dwarp rumpled pallid raven* stock. The 1000 progeny obtained were as follows:

pallid	3
pallid, raven	428
pallid, raven, rumpled	48
pallid, rumpled	23
dwarp, raven	22
dwarp, raven, rumpled	2
dwarp, rumpled	427
dwarp	47

Indicate the best map for these four genes, including all relevant data. Calculate interference values where appropriate.

Section 5.5

32. A cross was performed between one haploid strain of yeast with the genotype *a f g* and another haploid strain with the genotype α *f⁺ g⁺* (*a* and α are mating types). The resulting diploid was sporulated, and a random sample of 101 of the resulting haploid spores was analyzed. The following genotypic frequencies were seen:

α	*f⁺*	*g⁺*	31
a	*f*	*g*	29
a	*f*	*g⁺*	14
α	*f⁺*	*g*	13
a	*f⁺*	*g*	6
α	*f*	*g⁺*	6
a	*f⁺*	*g⁺*	1
α	*f*	*g*	1

a. Map the loci involved in the cross.

b. Assuming all three genes are on the same chromosome arm, is it possible that a particular ascus could contain an α *f g* spore but not an *a f⁺ g⁺* spore? If so, draw a meiosis that could generate such an ascus.

33. *Neurospora* of genotype *a + c* are crossed with *Neurospora* of genotype *+ b +*. The following tetrads are obtained (note that the genotype of the four spore pairs in an ascus are listed, rather than listing all eight spores):

a + c	*a b c*	*+ + c*	*+ b c*	*a b +*	*a + c*
a + c	*a b c*	*a + c*	*a b c*	*a b +*	*a b c*
+ b +	*+ + +*	*+ b +*	*+ + +*	*+ + c*	*+ + +*
+ b +	*+ + +*	*a b +*	*a + +*	*+ + c*	*+ b +*
137	141	26	25	2	3

a. In how many cells has meiosis occurred to yield these data?

b. Give the best genetic map to explain these results. Indicate all relevant genetic distances, both between genes and between each gene and its respective centromere.

c. Diagram a meiosis that could give rise to one of the three tetrads in the class at the far right in the list.

34. Two crosses were made in *Neurospora* involving the mating type locus and either the *ad* or *p* genes. In both cases, the mating type locus (*A* or *a*) was one of the loci whose segregation was scored. One cross was *ad A* × *ad+ a* (cross a), and the other was *p A* × *p+ a* (cross b). From cross a, 10 parental ditype, 9 nonparental ditype, and 1 tetratype asci were seen. From cross b, the results were 24 parental ditype, 3 nonparental ditype, and 27 tetratype asci.

a. What are the linkage relationships between the mating type locus and the other two loci?

b. Although these two crosses were performed in *Neurospora,* you cannot use the data given to calculate centromere-to-gene distances for any of these genes. Why not?

35. A cross was performed between a yeast strain that requires methionine and lysine for growth (*met− lys−*) and another yeast strain, which is *met+ lys+*. One hundred asci were dissected, and colonies were grown from the four spores in each ascus. Cells from these colonies were tested for their ability to grow on petri plates containing either minimal medium (min), min + lysine (lys), min + methionine (met), or min + lys + met. The asci could be divided into two groups based on this analysis:

Group 1: In 89 asci, cells from two of the four spore colonies could grow on all four kinds of media, while the other two spore colonies could grow only on min + lys + met.

Group 2: In 11 asci, cells from one of the four spore colonies could grow on all four kinds of petri plates. Cells from a second one of the four spore colonies could grow only on min + lys plates and on min + lys + met plates. Cells from a third of the four spore colonies could only grow on min + met plates and on min + lys + met. Cells from the remaining colony could only grow on min + lys + met.

a. What are the genotypes of each of the spores within the two groups of asci?

b. Are the *lys* and *met* genes linked? If so, what is the map distance between them?

c. If you could extend this analysis to many more asci, you would eventually find some asci with a different pattern. For these asci, describe the phenotypes of the four spores. List these phenotypes as the ability of dissected spores to form colonies on the four kinds of petri plates.

36. The *a, b,* and *c* loci are all on different chromosomes in yeast. When *a b+* yeast were crossed to *a+ b* yeast and the resultant tetrads analyzed, it was found that

the number of nonparental ditype tetrads was equal to the number of parental ditypes, but there were no tetratype asci at all. On the other hand, many tetratype asci were seen in the tetrads formed after *a c+* was crossed with *a+ c,* and after *b c+* was crossed with *b+ c.* Explain these results.

37. Indicate the percentage of tetrads that would have 0, 1, 2, 3, or 4 viable spores after *Saccharomyces cerevisiae a / α* diploids of the following genotypes are sporulated:

a. A true-breeding wild-type strain (with no mutations in any gene essential for viability).

b. A strain heterozygous for a null (completely inactivating) mutation in a single essential gene.

For the remaining parts of this problem, consider crosses between yeast strains of the form *a* × *b,* where *a* and *b* are both temperature-sensitive mutations in different essential genes. The cross is conducted under permissive (low-temperature) conditions. Indicate the percentage of tetrads that would have 0, 1, 2, 3, or 4 viable spores subsequently measured under restrictive (high-temperature) conditions.

c. *a* and *b* are unlinked, and both are 0 m.u. from their respective centromeres.

d. *a* and *b* are unlinked; *a* is 0 m.u. from its centromere, while *b* is 10 m.u. from its centromere.

e. *a* and *b* are 0 m.u. apart.

f. *a* and *b* are 10 m.u. apart. Assume all crossovers between *a* and *b* are SCOs (single crossovers).

g. In part (*f*), if a four-strand DCO (double crossover) occurred between *a* and *b,* how many of the spores in the resulting tetrad would be viable at high temperature?

38. Two genes are located on the same chromosome as follows:

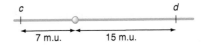

A haploid cross of the form *C D* × *c d* is made.

a. What proportions of PD, NPD, and T tetrads would you expect if this cross was made between strains of *Saccharomyces cerevisiae* and the interference in this region = 1?

b. If the interference in this region = 0?

c. What kinds of tetrads, and in what proportions, would you expect if this cross was made between strains of *Neurospora crassa* and the interference in this region = 1? (Consider not only whether a tetrad is PD, NPD, or T but also whether the tetrad shows first or second division segregation for each gene.)

d. If the interference in this region = 0?

39. A yeast strain that cannot grow in the absence of the amino acid histidine (*his⁻*) is mated with a yeast strain that cannot grow in the absence of the amino acid lysine (*lys⁻*). Among the 400 unordered tetrads resulting from this mating, 233 were PD, 11 were NPD, and 156 were T.

a. What types of spores are in the PD, NPD, and T tetrads?

b. What is the distance in map units between the *his* and *lys* genes?

c. Assuming that none of these tetrads was caused by more than two crossovers between the genes, how can you estimate the number of meioses that generated these 400 tetrads in which zero, one, or two crossovers took place?

d. Based on your answer to part *c*, what is the mean number of crossovers per meiosis in the region between the two genes?

e. The equation RF = 100 × (NPD + 1/2T) / total tetrads accounts for some, but not all, double crossovers between two genes. Which double crossovers are missed? Can you extrapolate from your answer to part *d* to obtain a more accurate equation for calculating map distances between two genes from the results of tetrad analysis?

f. Using your corrected equation from part *e*, what is a more accurate measurement of the distance in map units between the *his* and *lys* genes?

40. A research group has selected three independent *trp⁻* haploid strains of *Neurospora*, each of which cannot grow in the absence of the amino acid tryptophan. They first mated these three strains with a wild-type strain of opposite mating type, and then they analyzed the resultant octads. For all three matings, two of the four spore pairs in every octad could grow on minimal medium (that is, in the absence of tryptophan), while the other two spore pairs were unable to grow on this minimal medium.

a. What can you conclude from this result?

In the matings of mutant strains 1 and 2 with wild type, one of the two topmost pairs in some octads had spores that could grow on minimal medium while the other of the two topmost pairs in the same octads had spores that could not grow on minimal medium. In the mating of mutant strain 3 with wild type, either all the spores in the two topmost pairs could grow on minimal medium or all could not grow on minimal medium.

b. What can you conclude from this result?

The researchers next prepared two separate cultures of each mutant strain; one of these cultures was of mating type *A* and the other of mating type *a*. They mated these strains in pairwise fashion, dissected the resultant octads, and determined how many of the individual spores could grow on minimal medium. The results are shown here.

Mating	% of octads with *x* number of spores viable on minimal medium				
	x = 0	2	4	6	8
1 × 2	78	22	0	0	0
1 × 3	46	6	48	0	0
2 × 3	42	16	42	0	0

c. For each of the three matings in the table, how many of the 100 octads are PD? NPD? T?

d. Draw a genetic map explaining all of the preceding data. Assume that the sample sizes are sufficiently small that none of the octads are the result of double crossovers.

e. Although this problem describes crosses in *Neurospora*, it does not help in this particular case to present the matings in the table as ordered octads. Why not?

f. Why in this particular problem can you obtain gene ↔ centromere distances from the crosses in the table, even though the data are not presented as ordered octads?

Section 5.6

41. A single yeast cell placed on a solid agar will divide mitotically to produce a colony of about 10⁷ cells. A haploid yeast cell that has a mutation in the *ade2* gene will produce a red colony; an *ade2⁺* colony will be white. Some of the colonies formed from diploid yeast cells with a genotype of *ade2⁺/ ade2⁻* will contain sectors of red within a white colony.

a. How would you explain these sectors?

b. Although the white colonies are roughly the same size, the red sectors within some of the white colonies vary markedly in size. Why? Do you expect the majority of the red sectors to be relatively large or relatively small?

42. A diploid strain of yeast has a wild-type phenotype but the following genotype:

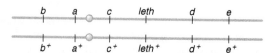

a, *b*, *c*, *d*, and *e* all represent recessive alleles that yield a visible phenotype, and *leth* represents a recessive lethal mutation. All genes are on the same chromosome, and *a* is very tightly linked to its centromere (indicated by a small circle). Which of the following phenotypes could be found in sectors resulting from mitotic recombination in this cell? (1) *a*; (2) *b*; (3) *c*; (4) *d*; (5) *e*; (6) *b e*; (7) *c d*; (8) *c d e*; (9) *d e*; (10) *a b*. Assume that double mitotic crossovers are too rare to be observed.

43. In *Drosophila,* the *yellow* (*y*) gene is near the end of the acrocentric X chromosome, while the *singed* (*sn*) gene is located near the middle of the X chromosome. On the wings of female flies of genotype *y sn*/*y*⁺ *sn*⁺, you can very rarely find patches of yellow tissue within which a small subset of cells also have singed bristles.

a. How can you explain this phenomenon?

b. Would you find similar patches on the wings of females having the genotype *y*⁺ *sn* / *y sn*⁺ ?

44. Neurofibromas are tumors of the skin that can arise when a skin cell that is originally *NF1*⁺/ *NF1*⁻ loses the *NF1*⁺ allele. This wild-type allele encodes a functional tumor suppressor protein, while the *NF1*⁻ allele encodes a nonfunctional protein.

A patient of genotype *NF1*⁺/ *NF1*⁻ has 20 independent tumors in different areas of the skin. Samples are taken of normal, noncancerous cells from this patient, as well as of cells from each of the 20 tumors. Extracts of these samples are analyzed by a technique called gel electrophoresis that can detect variant forms of four different proteins (A, B, C, and D) all encoded by genes that lie on the same autosome as *NF1*. Each protein has a slow (S) and a fast (F) form that are encoded by different alleles (for example, A^S and A^F). In the extract of normal tissue, slow and fast variants of all four proteins are found. In the extracts of the

tumors, 12 had only the fast variants of proteins A and D but both the fast and slow variants of proteins B and C; 6 had only the fast variant of protein A but both the fast and slow variants of proteins B, C, and D; and the remaining 2 tumor extracts had only the fast variant of protein A, only the slow variant of protein B, the fast and slow variants of protein C, and only the fast variant of protein D.

a. What kind of genetic event described in this chapter could cause all 20 tumors, assuming that all the tumors are produced by the same mechanism?

b. Draw a genetic map describing these data, assuming that this small sample represents all the types of tumors that could be formed by the same mechanism in this patient. Show which alleles of which genes lie on the two homologous chromosomes. Indicate all relative distances that can be estimated.

c. Another mechanism that can lead to neurofibromas in this patient is a mitotic error producing cells with 45 rather than the normal 46 chromosomes. How can this mechanism cause tumors? How do you know, just from the results described, that none of these 20 tumors is formed by such mitotic errors?

d. Can you think of any other type of error that could produce the results described?

Chromosomal Rearrangements and Changes in Chromosome Number

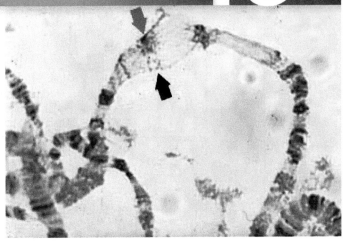

Chromosomal rearrangements can be mapped with high precision on Drosophila *polytene chromosomes. The* red arrow *points to a very large transposable element that has inserted into one chromosome but is not present in the paired homologous wild-type chromosome* (black arrow).

During the early days of genome sequencing in the 1990s, studies comparing the human genome with that of the laboratory mouse (*Mus musculus*) revealed a surprising evolutionary paradox: At the DNA level, there is a close similarity of nucleotide sequence across hundreds of thousands of base pairs; but at the chromosomal level, mouse and human karyotypes bear little resemblance to each other. These early genomic analyses focused considerable effort on the sequencing of regions encompassing more than 2000 kb of mouse and human DNA containing a complex of genes that encode immune response proteins known as T-cell receptors. Comparisons of the corresponding mouse and human regions show that the nucleotide sequences of the T-cell receptor genes are similar (though not identical) in the two species, as are the order of the genes and the relative positions of a variety of noncoding sequences (of unknown function) along the chromosome. Comparisons of mouse and human Giemsa-stained karyotypes, however, reveal no conservation of banding patterns between the 20 mouse and 23 human chromosomes.

Data for resolving this apparent paradox emerged with the 2002 publication of the nearly complete mouse genome sequence, which researchers could compare with the human genome sequence completed a year earlier. The data showed that each mouse chromosome consists of pieces of different human chromosomes, and vice versa. For example, mouse chromosome 1 contains large blocks of sequences found on human chromosomes 1, 2, 5, 6, 8, 13, and 18 (portrayed in different colors in **Fig. 13.1**). These blocks represent **syntenic segments** in which the identity, order, and transcriptional direction of the genes are almost exactly the same in the two genomes. In principle, scientists could "reconstruct" the mouse genome by breaking the human genome into 342 fragments, each an average length of about 16 Mb, and pasting these fragments together in a different order. Figure 13.1 illustrates this process in detail for mouse chromosome 1; Fig. 10.8 on p. 343 shows the syntenic relationships between the entire mouse and human genomes at lower resolution. Because a 16 Mb fragment would occupy no more than one or two bands

CHAPTER OUTLINE

- 13.1 Rearrangements of DNA Sequences
- 13.2 Transposable Genetic Elements
- 13.3 Rearrangements and Evolution: A Speculative Comprehensive Example
- 13.4 Changes in Chromosome Number
- 13.5 Emergent Technologies: Beyond the Karyotype

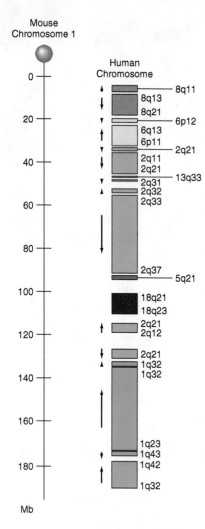

Figure 13.1 Comparing the mouse and human genomes. Mouse chromosome 1 contains large blocks of sequences found on human chromosomes 1, 2, 5, 6, 8, 13, and 18 (portrayed in different colors). *Arrows* indicate the relative orientations of sequence blocks from the same human chromosome.

of a stained chromosome, this level of conservation is not visible in karyotypes. It does, however, show up in the sequence of a smaller genomic region, such as that encoding the T-cell receptors.

These findings contribute to our understanding of how complex life-forms evolved. Although mice and humans diverged from a common ancestor about 65 million years ago, the DNA sequence in many regions of the two genomes is very similar. It is thus possible to hypothesize that the mouse and human genomes evolved through a series of approximately 300 reshaping events during which the chromosomes broke apart and the resulting fragments resealed end to end in novel ways. After each event, the newly rearranged chromosomes somehow became fixed in the genome of the emerging species. Both nucleotide sequence differences and differences in genome organization thus contribute to dissimilarities between the species.

In this chapter, we examine two types of events that reshape genomes: (1) **rearrangements,** which reorganize the DNA sequences within one or more chromosomes, and (2) changes in chromosome number involving losses or gains of entire chromosomes or sets of chromosomes (**Table 13.1**). Rearrangements and changes in chromosome number may affect gene activity or gene transmission by altering the position, order, or number of genes in a cell. Such alterations often, but not always, lead to a genetic imbalance that is harmful to the organism or its progeny.

We can identify two main themes underlying the observations of chromosomal changes. First, karyotypes generally remain constant within a species, not because rearrangements and changes in chromosome number occur infrequently (they are, in fact, quite common), but because the genetic instabilities and imbalances produced by such changes usually place individual cells or organisms and their progeny at a selective disadvantage. Second, despite selection against chromosomal variations, related species almost always have different karyotypes, with closely related species (such as chimpanzees and humans) diverging by only a few rearrangements and more distantly related species (such as mice and humans) diverging by a larger number of rearrangements. These observations suggest there is significant correlation between karyotypic rearrangements and the evolution of new species.

13.1 Rearrangements of DNA Sequences

All chromosomal rearrangements alter DNA sequence. Some do so by removing or adding base pairs. Others relocate chromosomal regions without changing the number of base pairs they contain. This chapter focuses on heritable rearrangements that can be transmitted through the germ line from one generation to the next, but it also explains that the genomes of somatic cells can undergo changes in nucleotide number or order. For example, the Fast Forward box "Programmed DNA Rearrangements and the Immune System" (pp. 432–433) describes how the normal development of the human immune system depends on noninherited, programmed rearrangements of the genome in somatic cells.

TABLE 13.1	Chromosomal Rearrangements and Changes in Chromosome Number

Chromosomal Rearrangements

Before   After

Deletion: Removal of a segment of DNA

1 | 2 | 3 | 4 | 5 | 6 | 7 | 8 ⟶ 1 | 2 | 3 | 5 | 6 | 7 | 8

Duplication: Increase in the number of copies of a chromosomal region

1 | 2 | 3 | 4 | 5 | 6 | 7 | 8 ⟶ 1 | 2 | 3 | 2 | 3 | 4 | 5 | 6 | 7 | 8

Inversion: Half-circle rotation of a chromosomal region

1 | 2 | 3 | 4 | 5 | 6 | 7 | 8 ⟶ 1 | 4 | 3 | 2 | 5 | 6 | 7 | 8

180 rotation

Translocations:

Nonreciprocal: Unequal exchanges between non-homologous chromosomes

1 | 2 | 3 | 4 | 5 | 6 | 7 | 8 ⟶ 12 | 13 | 4 | 5 | 6 | 7 | 8
12 | 13 | 14 | 15 | 16 | 17 | 18 ⟶ 14 | 15 | 16 | 17 | 18

Reciprocal: Parts of two nonhomologous chromosomes trade places

1 | 2 | 3 | 4 | 5 | 6 | 7 | 8 ⟶ 12 | 13 | 14 | 15 | 5 | 6 | 7 | 8
12 | 13 | 14 | 15 | 16 | 17 | 18 ⟶ 1 | 2 | 3 | 4 | 16 | 17 | 18

Transposition: Movement of short DNA segments from one position in the genome to another

1 | 2 | 3 | 4 | 5 | 6 | 7 | 8 ⟶ 1 | 2 | 4 | 5 | 6 | 3 | 7 | 8

Changes in Chromosome Number

Chromosomes 1, 2, and 3 (represented in different colors) are nonhomologous.

Chromosome 1   Chromosome 2   Chromosome 3

Euploidy: Cells that contain only complete sets of chromosomes

Diploidy (2x): Two copies of each homolog

Monoploidy (x): One copy of each homolog

Polyploidy: More than the normal diploid number of chromosome sets

Triploidy (3x): Three copies of each homolog

Tetraploidy (4x): Four copies of each homolog

Aneuploidy: Loss or gain of one or more chromosomes producing a chromosome number that is not an exact multiple of the haploid number

Monosomy (2n − 1)

Trisomy (2n + 1)

Tetrasomy (2n + 2)

Deletions remove material from the genome

We saw in Chapter 7 that **deletions** remove one or more contiguous base pairs of DNA from a chromosome. They may arise from errors in replication, from faulty meiotic or mitotic recombination, and from exposure to X-rays or other chromosome-damaging agents that break the DNA backbone

(**Fig. 13.2a**). Here we use the symbol *Del* to designate a chromosome that has sustained a deletion. However, many geneticists, particularly those working on *Drosophila*, prefer the term *deficiency* (abbreviated as *Df*) to deletion.

Small deletions often affect only one gene, whereas large deletions can generate chromosomes lacking tens or even hundreds of genes. In higher organisms, geneticists usually find it difficult to distinguish small deletions

FAST FORWARD

Programmed DNA Rearrangements and the Immune System

The human immune system is a marvel of specificity and diversity. It includes close to a trillion B lymphocytes, specialized white blood cells that make more than a billion different varieties of antibodies (also called *immunoglobulins, or Igs*). Each B cell, however, makes antibodies against only a single bacterial or viral protein (called an *antigen* in the context of the immune response). The binding of antibody to antigen helps the body attack and neutralize invading pathogens.

One intriguing question about antibody responses is, How can a genome containing only 20,000–30,000 (2–3×10^4) genes encode a billion (10^9) different types of antibodies? The answer is that programmed gene rearrangements, in conjunction with somatic mutations and the diverse pairing of polypeptides of different sizes, can generate roughly a billion binding specificities from a much smaller number of genes. To understand the mechanism of this diversity, it is necessary to know how antibodies are constructed and how B cells come to express the antibody-encoding genes determining specific antigen-binding sites.

The genetics of antibody formation produce specificity and diversity

All antibody molecules consist of a single copy or multiple copies of the same basic molecular unit. Four polypeptides make up this unit: two identical light chains, and two identical heavy chains. Each light chain is paired with a heavy chain (**Fig. A**). Each light

Figure A How antibody specificity emerges from molecular structure. Two heavy chains and two light chains held together by disulfide ($-S–S–$) bonds form the basic unit of an antibody molecule. Both heavy and light chains have variable (V) domains near their N termini, which associate to form the antigen-binding site. "Hypervariable" stretches of amino acids within the V domains vary extensively between antibody molecules. The remainder of each chain is composed of a C (constant) domain; that of the heavy chain has several subdomains (C_{H1}, hinge, $C_{H2,}$ and C_{H3}).

and each heavy chain has a constant (C) domain and a variable (V) domain. The C domain of the heavy chain determines whether the antibody falls into one of five major classes (designated IgM, IgG, IgE, IgD, and IgA), which influence where and how an antibody functions. For example, IgM antibodies form early in an immune response and are anchored in the B-cell membrane; IgG antibodies emerge later and are secreted into the blood serum. The C domains of the light and heavy chains are not involved in determining the specificity of antibodies. Instead, the V domains of light and heavy chains come together to form the antigen-binding site, which defines an antibody's specificity.

The DNA for all domains of the heavy chain resides on chromosome 14 (**Fig. B**). This heavy-chain gene region consists of more than 100 V-encoding segments, each preceded by a promoter, several D (for diversity) segments, several J (for joining) segments, and nine C-encoding segments preceded by an enhancer (a short DNA segment that aids in the initiation of transcription by interacting with the promoter; see Chapter 16 for details). In all germ-line cells and in most somatic cells, including the cells destined to become B lymphocytes, these various gene segments lie far apart on the chromosome. During B-cell development, however, somatic rearrangements juxtapose random, individual V, D, and J segments together to form the particular variable region that will be transcribed. These rearrangements also place the newly formed variable region next to a C segment and its enhancer, and they further bring the promoter and enhancer into proximity, allowing transcription of the heavy-chain gene. RNA splicing removes the introns from the primary transcript, making a mature mRNA encoding a complete heavy-chain polypeptide.

The somatic rearrangements that shuffle the V, D, J, and C segments at random in each B cell permit expression of one, and only one, specific heavy chain. Without the rearrangements, antibody gene expression cannot occur. Random somatic rearrangements also generate the actual genes that will be expressed as light chains. The somatic rearrangements allowing the expression of antibodies thus generate enormous diversity of binding sites through the random selection and recombination of gene elements.

Several other mechanisms add to this diversity. First, each gene's DNA elements are joined imprecisely, which is perpetrated by cutting and splicing enzymes that sometimes trim DNA from or add nucleotides to the junctions of the segments they join. This imprecise joining helps create the hypervariable regions shown in Fig. A. Next, random somatic mutations in a rearranged gene's V region increase the variation of the antibody's V domain. Finally, in every B cell, two copies of a specific H chain that emerged from random DNA rearrangements combine with two copies of a specific L chain that also emerged from random DNA rearrangements to create molecules with a specific, unique binding site. The fact that any light chain can pair with any heavy chain exponentially increases the potential diversity of antibody types. For example, if there were 10^4 different light chains and 10^5 different heavy chains, there would be 10^9 possible combinations of the two.

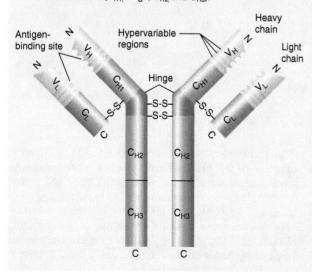

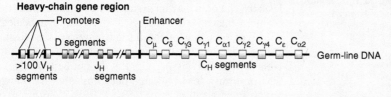

Heavy-chain gene region

Heavy-chain gene expression

Figure B The heavy-chain gene region on chromosome 14. The DNA of germ-line cells (as well as all non-antibody-producing cells) contains more than 100 V_H segments, about 20 D segments, 6 J_H segments, and 9 C_H segments (*top*). Each V_H and C_H segment is composed of two or more exons, as seen in the alternate view of the same DNA on the next line. In B cells, somatic rearrangements bring together random, individual V_H, D, and J_H segments. The primary transcript made from the newly constructed heavy-chain gene is subsequently spliced into a mature mRNA. The μ heavy chain translated from this mRNA is the type of heavy chain found in IgM antibodies. Later in B-cell development, other rearrangements (*not shown*) connect the same V-D-J variable region to other C_H segments such as C_δ, allowing the synthesis of other antibody classes.

Mistakes by the enzymes that carry out antibody gene rearrangements can lead to cancer

RagI and RagII are enzymes that interact with DNA sequences in antibody genes to help catalyze the rearrangements just discribed. In carrying out their rearrangement activities, however, the enzymes sometimes make a mistake that results in a reciprocal translocation between human chromosomes 8 and 14. After this translocation, the enhancer of the chromosome 14 heavy-chain gene lies in the vicinity of the unrelated *c-myc* gene from chromosome 8. Under normal circumstances, *c-myc* generates a transcription factor that turns on other genes active in cell division, at the appropriate time and rate in the cell cycle. However, the translocated antibody-gene enhancer accelerates expression of *c-myc*, causing B cells containing the translocation to divide out of control. This uncontrolled B-cell division leads to a cancer known as Burkitt's lymphoma (**Fig. C**).

Thus, although programmed gene rearrangements contribute to the normal development of a healthy immune system, misfiring of the rearrangement mechanism can promote disease.

Chapter 20 describes the evolution of the gene families that encode antibodies and other immune system proteins.

Figure C Misguided translocations can help cause Burkitt's lymphoma.
In DNA from this Burkitt's lymphoma patient, a translocation brings transcription of the *c-myc* gene (*green*) under the control of the enhancer adjacent to Cμ. As a result, B cells produce abnormally high levels of the c-myc protein. Apparently, the RagI and RagII enzymes have mistakenly connected a J_H segment to the *c-myc* gene from chromosome 8, instead of to a D segment.

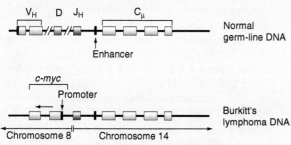

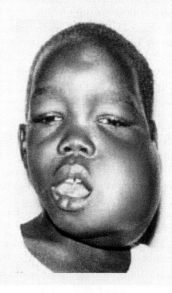

Figure 13.2 Deletions: Origin and detection. (a) When a chromosome sustains two double-strand breaks, a deletion will result if the chromosomal fragments are not properly religated. **(b)** One way to detect deletions is by PCR. The two PCR primers shown will amplify a larger PCR product from wild-type DNA than from DNA with a deletion.

(a) DNA breakage may cause deletions.

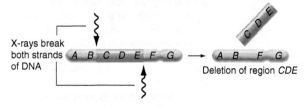

(b) Detecting deletions using PCR

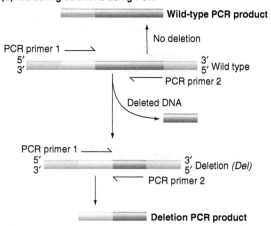

affecting only one gene from point mutations; they can resolve such distinctions only through analysis of the DNA itself. For example, deletions can result in smaller restriction fragments or polymerase chain reaction (PCR) products, whereas most point mutations would not cause such changes (**Fig. 13.2b**). Larger deletions are sometimes identifiable because they affect the expression of two or more adjacent genes. Very large deletions are visible at the relatively low resolution of a karyotype, showing up as the loss of one or more bands from a chromosome.

Lethal effects of homozygosity for a deletion

Because many of the genes in a genome are essential to an individual's survival, homozygotes (*Del/Del*) or hemizygotes (*Del/*Y) for most deletion-bearing chromosomes do not survive. In rare cases where the deleted chromosomal region is devoid of genes essential for viability, however, a deletion hemi- or homozygote may survive. For example, *Drosophila* males hemizygous for an 80 kb deletion including the *white* (*w*) gene survive perfectly well in the laboratory; lacking the *w*⁺ allele required for red eye pigmentation, they have white eyes.

Detrimental effects of heterozygosity for a deletion

Usually, the only way an organism can survive a deletion of more than a few genes is if it carries a nondeleted wild-type homolog of the deleted chromosome. Such a *Del/+* individual is known as a *deletion heterozygote*. Nonetheless, the missing segment cannot be too large, as heterozygosity for very large deletions is almost always lethal. Even small deletions can be harmful in heterozygotes. Newborn humans heterozygous for a relatively small deletion from the short arm of chromosome 5 have *cri du chat* syndrome (from the French for "cry of the cat"), so named because the symptoms include an abnormal cry reminiscent of a mewing kitten. The syndrome also leads to mental retardation.

Why should heterozygosity for a deletion have harmful consequences when the *Del/+* individual has at least one wild-type copy of all of its genes? The answer is that changes in **gene dosage**—the number of times a given gene is present in the cell nucleus—can create a **genetic imbalance.** This imbalance in gene dosage alters the amount of a particular protein relative to all other proteins, and this alteration can have a variety of phenotypic effects. For some rare genes, the normal diploid level of gene expression is essential to individual survival; fewer than two copies of such a gene results in lethality. In *Drosophila*, a single dose of the locus known as *Triplolethal* (*Tpl*⁺) is lethal in an otherwise diploid individual. For certain other genes, the phenotypic consequences of a decrease in gene dosage are noticeable but not catastrophic. For example, *Drosophila* containing only one copy of the wild-type *Notch* gene have visible wing abnormalities but otherwise seem to function normally (**Fig. 13.3**). In contrast with these unusual examples, diminishing the dosage of most genes produces no obvious change in phenotype. There is a catch, however. Although a single dose of any one gene may not cause substantial harm to the individual, the genetic imbalance resulting from a single dose of many genes at the same time can be lethal. Humans, for example, cannot survive, even as heterozygotes, with deletions that remove more than about 3% of any part of their haploid genome.

Another answer to the question of why heterozygosity for a deletion can be harmful is that with only one remaining wild-type copy of a gene, a cell is more vulnerable to subsequent mutation of that remaining copy. If the gene encodes a protein that helps control cell division, a cell without any wild-type protein may divide out of control and generate a tumor. Thus, individuals born heterozygous for certain deletions have a greatly increased risk of losing both copies of certain genes and developing cancer. One case in point is retinoblastoma (RB), the most malignant form of eye cancer, which was previously introduced in Chapter 5 (p. 148). Karyotypes of normal, noncancerous tissues from many people suffering from retinoblastoma reveal heterozygosity for deletions on chromosome 13.

Figure 13.3 Heterozygosity for deletions may have phenotypic consequences. Flies carrying only one copy of the *Notch*⁺ gene instead of the normal two copies have abnormal wings.

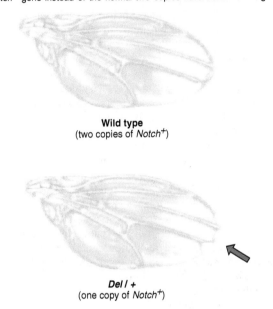

Wild type
(two copies of *Notch*⁺)

Del / +
(one copy of *Notch*⁺)

Cells from the retinal tumors of these same patients have a mutation in the remaining copy of the *RB* gene on the non-deleted chromosome 13. Chapter 17, "Somatic Mutation and the Genetics of Cancer," explains in detail how deletion of certain chromosomal regions greatly increases the risk of cancer and how researchers have used this knowledge to locate genes whose mutant forms cause cancer.

Effects of deletion heterozygosity on genetic map distances

Because recombination between maternal and paternal homologs can occur only at regions of similarity, map distances derived from genetic recombination frequencies in deletion heterozygotes will be aberrant. For example, no recombination is possible between genes *C, D,* and *E* in **Fig. 13.4** because the DNA in this region of the normal, nondeleted chromosome has nothing with which to recombine. In fact, during the pairing of homologs in prophase of meiosis I, the "orphaned" region of the nondeleted

Figure 13.4 Deletion loops form in the chromosomes of deletion heterozygotes. During prophase of meiosis I, the undeleted region of the normal chromosome has nothing with which to pair and forms a deletion loop. No recombination can occur within the deletion loop. In this simplified figure, each line represents two chromatids.

chromosome forms a **deletion loop**—an unpaired bulge of the normal chromosome that corresponds to the area deleted from the other homolog. The progeny of a *Del/+* heterozygote will always inherit the markers in a deletion loop as a unit (*C, D,* and *E* in Fig. 13.4). As a result, these genes cannot be separated by recombination, and the map distances between them, as determined by the phenotypic classes in the progeny of a *Del/+* individual, will be zero. In addition, the genetic distance between loci on either side of the deletion (such as between markers *B* and *F* in Fig. 13.4) will be shorter than expected because fewer crossovers can occur between them.

"Uncovering" genes in deletion heterozygotes

A deletion heterozygote is, in effect, a hemizygote for genes on the normal, nondeleted chromosome that are missing from the deleted chromosome. If the normal chromosome carries a mutant recessive allele of one of these genes, the individual will exhibit the mutant phenotype. This phenomenon is sometimes called **pseudodominance.** In *Drosophila,* for example, the *scarlet* (*st*) eye color mutation is recessive to wild type. However, an animal heterozygous for the *st* mutation and a deletion that removes the *scarlet* gene (*st/Del*) will have bright scarlet eyes, rather than wild-type, dark red eyes. In these circumstances, the deletion "uncovers" (that is, reveals) the phenotype of the recessive mutation (**Fig. 13.5**).

Geneticists can use pseudodominance to determine whether a deletion has removed a particular gene. If the phenotype of a recessive-allele/deletion heterozygote is mutant, the deletion has uncovered the mutated locus; the gene thus lies inside the region of deletion. In contrast, if the trait determined by the gene is wild type in these heterozygotes, the deletion has not uncovered the recessive allele, and the gene must lie outside the deleted region. You can consider this experiment as a complementation test between the mutation and the deletion: The uncovering of a mutant recessive phenotype demonstrates a lack of complementation because neither chromosome can supply wild-type gene function.

Using deletions to locate genes

Geneticists can use deletions that alter chromosomal banding patterns to map genes relative to specific regions

Figure 13.5 In deletion heterozygotes, pseudodominance shows that a deletion has removed a particular gene. A fly of genotype *st/Del* displays the recessive scarlet eye color. The deletion has thus "uncovered" the scarlet (*st*) mutation.

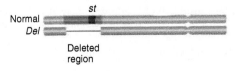

Figure 13.6 Polytene chromosomes in the salivary glands of *Drosophila* larvae. (a) A drawing of the banding pattern seen in polytene chromosomes. The inset shows the relative size of normal mitotic chromosomes. Note that the homologous polytene chromosomes are paired along their lengths. **(b)** A hypothetical model showing how the 1024 chromatids of each polytene chromosome are aligned in register, with the chromatin in the bands being more condensed than the chromatin of the interbands.

(a) Banding pattern of *Drosophila* polytene chromosomes

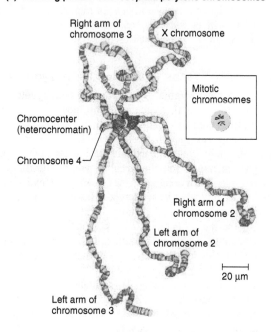

(b) Alignment of chromatids in polytene chromosomes

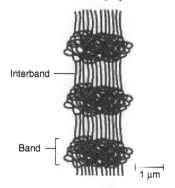

chromosomes in these cells go through 10 rounds of replication without ever entering mitosis. As a result, the sister chromatids never separate, and each chromosome consists of $2^{10} (= 1024)$ double helices. In addition, because the homologous chromosomes in the somatic cells of *Drosophila* remain tightly paired throughout interphase, pairs of homologs form a cable of double thickness containing 2048 double helices of DNA (1024 from each homolog). These giant chromosomes consisting of many identical chromatids lying in parallel register are called **polytene chromosomes (Fig. 13.6a)**.

When stained and viewed in the light microscope, *Drosophila* polytene chromosomes have an irregular fine-grain banding pattern in which denser dark bands alternate with lighter interbands. The chromatin of each dark band is roughly 10 times more condensed than the chromatin of the lighter interbands (**Fig. 13.6b**). Scientists do not yet understand the functional significance of bands and interbands. One possibility is that the bands represent units of transcriptional regulation containing genes activated at the same time. In any event, the precisely reproducible banding patterns of polytene chromosomes provide a detailed physical guide to gene mapping. *Drosophila* polytene chromosomes collectively carry about 5000 bands that range in size from 3 kb to approximately 150 kb; investigators designate these bands by numbers and letters of the alphabet.

Because homologous polytene chromosomes pair with each other, deletion loops form in the polytene chromosomes of deletion heterozygotes (**Fig. 13.7**). Scientists can pinpoint the region of the deletion by noting which bands are present in the wild-type homolog but missing in the deletion. If researchers find that a small deletion removing only a few

Figure 13.7 Deletion loops also form in the paired polytene chromosomes of *Drosophila* deletion heterozygotes. The *thick arrow* points to the wild-type chromosome; the corresponding region is missing from the *Del* homolog.

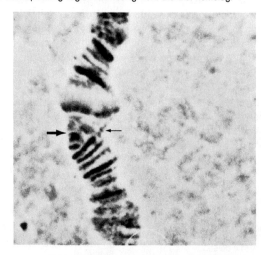

of metaphase chromosomes. A deletion that results in the loss of one or more bands from a chromosome and also uncovers the recessive mutation of a particular gene places that gene within the missing chromosomal segment.

The greater the number of distinguishable bands in a chromosome, the greater the accuracy of gene localization by this strategy. For this reason, specialized giant chromosomes found in the salivary gland cells of *Drosophila* larvae are a prized mapping resource. The interphase

Figure 13.8 Using deletions to assign genes to bands on *Drosophila* polytene chromosomes. *Red bars* show the bands removed by various deletions; for example, *Df 258-45* eliminates bands 3B3–3C3. Complementation experiments determined whether these deletions uncovered the *white* (*w*), *roughest* (*rst*), or *facet* (*fa*) genes. For instance, *w/Df 258-45* females have white eyes, so the *w* gene is removed by this deletion. The *w* gene must lie within bands 3C2–3 (*green*) because that is the region common to the deletions that uncover *w*. Similarly, *rst* must be in bands 3C5–6 (*yellow*) and *fa* in band 3C7 (*purple*).

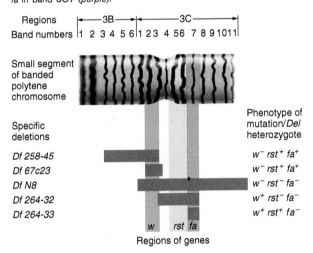

Figure 13.9 *In situ* hybridization as a tool for locating genes at the molecular level. (a) *In situ* hybridization of a probe containing the *white* gene to a single band (3C2) near the tip of the wild-type *Drosophila* X chromosome. **(b)** A particular labeled probe hybridizes to the wild-type chromosome but not to the deletion chromosome in a *Df 258-45/+* heterozygote. The *Df 258-45* deletion thus lacks DNA homologous to the probe.

(a) *In situ* hybridization of the *white* gene to wild-type polytene chromosomes

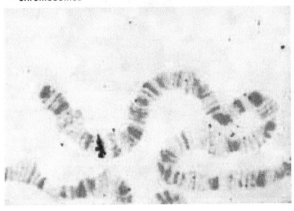

(b) Characterizing deletions with *in situ* hybridization to polytene chromosomes

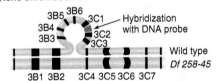

polytene chromosome bands uncovers a gene or that several overlapping larger deletions affect the same gene, they can assign the gene to one or a small number of bands, often representing less than 100 kb of DNA. **Figure 13.8** shows how geneticists used this strategy to assign three genes to regions containing only one or two polytene chromosome bands on the *Drosophila* X chromosome.

Geneticists can use deletions analyzed at even higher levels of resolution to help locate genes on cloned fragments of DNA. They must first determine whether a particular deletion uncovers a recessive allele of the gene of interest and then ascertain which DNA sequences are removed by the deletion. *In situ* hybridization provides a straightforward way to show whether a particular DNA sequence is part of a deletion. Suppose you are trying to determine whether a small segment of the *Drosophila* X chromosome in the vicinity of the *white* gene has been deleted. You could use purified DNA fragments as probes for *in situ* hybridization to polytene chromosomes prepared from female flies heterozygous for various deletions in this region of their X chromosomes. If a probe hybridizes to a *Del* chromosome, the deletion has not completely removed that particular fragment of DNA; lack of a hybridization signal on a *Del* chromosome, however, indicates that the fragment has been deleted (**Fig. 13.9**).

Geneticists can also localize deleted regions by asking whether particular bands are removed from human mitotic chromosomes, but because bands in these chromosomes that

contain less than 5 Mb of DNA cannot be detected visually, the resolution of this method is much lower than is possible with *Drosophila* polytene chromosomes. As the final section of this chapter on "Emergent Technologies: Beyond the Karyotype" illustrates, new techniques nonetheless allow human geneticists to determine the molecular extent of deletions in human chromosomes. Once this information is available, *in situ* hybridization to human mitotic chromosomes serves as a useful tool to diagnose whether individuals have genetic diseases associated with heterozygosity for particular deletions. **Figure 13.10** shows an application of this strategy to the diagnosis of DiGeorge syndrome, which accounts for approximately 5% of all congenital heart malformations.

Homozygosity or even heterozygosity for deletions can be lethal or harmful; the effects depend on the size of the deletion and the identity of the deleted genes. In deletion heterozygotes, deletions reveal or "uncover" recessive mutations on the intact homolog because the phenotype is no longer masked by the presence of a dominant wild-type allele. Geneticists can use these properties of deletions to map and identify genes.

Figure 13.10 Diagnosing DiGeorge syndrome by fluoresence *in situ* hybridization (FISH) to human metaphase chromosomes. The *green* signal is a control probe that identifies both chromosome 22's. The *red* signal is a fluorescent probe from region 22q11, which is deleted in one of the chromosome 22's in DiGeorge syndrome patients. These homologous metaphase chromosomes do not pair with each other and thus do not form a deletion loop.

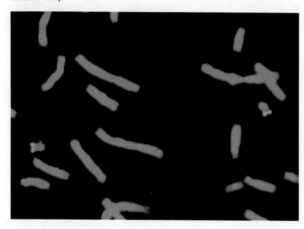

Duplications add material to the genome

Duplications increase the number of copies of a particular chromosomal region. In **tandem duplications,** repeats of a region lie adjacent to each other, either in the same order or in reverse order (**Fig. 13.11a**). In **nontandem** (or *dispersed*) **duplications,** the two or more copies of a region are not adjacent to each other and may lie far apart on the same chromosome or on different chromosomes. Duplications arise by chromosomal breakage and faulty repair, unequal crossing-over, or errors in DNA replication (**Fig. 13.11b**). In this book, we use *Dp* as the symbol for a chromosome carrying a duplication.

Most duplications have no obvious phenotypic consequences and can be detected only by cytological or molecular means. Sufficiently large duplications, for example, show up as repeated bands in metaphase or polytene chromosomes. During the prophase of meiosis I in heterozygotes for such duplications (*Dp/+*), the repeated bands form a **duplication loop**—a bulge in the *Dp*-bearing chromosome that has no similar region with which to pair in the unduplicated normal homologous chromosome. Duplication loops can occur in several alternative configurations (**Fig. 13.11c**). Such loops also form in the polytene chromosomes of *Drosophila* duplication heterozygotes, where the pattern of the bands in the duplication loops is a repeat of that seen in the other copy of the same region elsewhere on the chromosome.

Figure 13.11 Duplications: Structure, origin, and detection. (a) In tandem duplications, the repeated regions lie adjacent to each other in the same or in reverse order. In nontandem duplications, the two copies of the same region are separated. **(b)** In one scenario for duplication formation, X-rays break one chromosome twice and its homolog once. A fragment of the first chromosome inserts elsewhere on its homolog to produce a nontandem duplication. **(c)** Duplication loops form when chromosomes pair in duplication heterozygotes (*Dp/+*). During prophase I, the duplication loop can assume different configurations. A single line represents two chromatids in this simplified diagram.

(a) Types of duplications

Tandem duplications

Normal chromosome	A B C D E F G
Same order	A B C B C D E F G
Reverse order	A B C C B D E F G

Nontandem (dispersed) duplications

| Same order | A B C D E F B C G |
| Reverse order | A B C D E F C B G |

(b) Chromosome breakage can produce duplications.

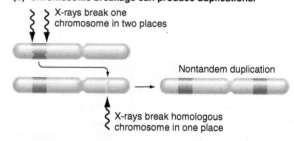

(c) Different kinds of duplication loops

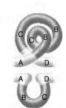

Duplicated chromosome

Normal chromosome

Phenotypic effects of duplications

Although duplications are much less likely to affect phenotype than are deletions of comparable size, some duplications do have phenotypic consequences for visible traits or for survival. Geneticists can use such phenotypes to identify individuals whose genomes contain the duplication. Duplications can produce a novel phenotype either by increasing the number of copies of a particular gene or set of genes, or by placing the genes bordering the duplication in a new chromosomal environment that alters their

Figure 13.12 The phenotypic consequences of duplications. (a) Duplication heterozygotes (*Dp/+*), have three copies of genes contained in the duplication. Flies with three copies of the *Notch⁺* gene have aberrant wing veins. This phenotype differs from that caused by only one copy of *Notch⁺* (see Fig. 13.3). **(b)** In *Drosophila*, three copies or one copy of *Tpl⁺* are lethal.

(a) Duplication heterozygosity can cause visible phenotypes.

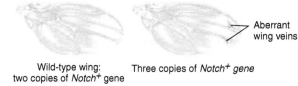

Wild-type wing: two copies of *Notch⁺* gene

Three copies of *Notch⁺* gene

Aberrant wing veins

(b) For rare genes, survival requires exactly two copies.

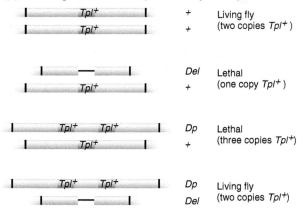

+ + Living fly (two copies *Tpl⁺*)

Del + Lethal (one copy *Tpl⁺*)

Dp + Lethal (three copies *Tpl⁺*)

Dp *Del* Living fly (two copies *Tpl⁺*)

expression. These phenotypic consequences often arise even in duplication heterozygotes (*Dp/+*). For example, *Drosophila* heterozygous for a duplication including the *Notch⁺* gene have abnormal wings that signal the three copies of *Notch⁺* (**Fig. 13.12a**); we have already seen that *Del/+* flies with only one copy of the *Notch⁺* gene have a different kind of wing abnormality (review Fig. 13.3). In another example from *Drosophila*, the locus known as *Triplolethal* (*Tpl⁺*) is lethal when present in one or three doses in an otherwise diploid individual (**Fig. 13.12b**). Thus, heterozygotes for a *Tpl* deletion (*Del/+*) or for a *Tpl⁺* duplication (*Dp/+*) do not survive. Heterozygotes carrying one homolog deleted for the locus and the other homolog duplicated for the locus (*Del/Dp*) are viable because they have two copies of *Tpl⁺*.

Organisms are usually not so sensitive to additional copies of a single gene; but just as for large deletions, imbalances for the many genes included in a very large duplication have additive deleterious effects that jeopardize survival. In humans, heterozygosity for duplications covering more than 5% of the haploid genome is most often lethal.

Unequal crossing-over between duplications

In individuals homozygous for a tandem duplication (*Dp/Dp*), homologs carrying the duplications occasionally pair out of register during meiosis. **Unequal crossing-over,** that is, recombination resulting from such out-of-register pairing, generates gametes containing increases to three and reciprocal decreases to one in the number of copies of the duplicated region. In *Drosophila*, tandem duplication of several polytene bands near the X chromosome centromere produces the Bar phenotype of kidney-shaped eyes. *Drosophila* females homozygous for the Bar eye duplication produce mostly Bar eye progeny. Some progeny, however, have wild-type eyes, whereas other progeny have double-Bar eyes that are even smaller than Bar eyes (**Fig. 13.13**). The genetic explanation is that flies with wild-type eyes carry X chromosomes containing only one copy of the region in question, flies with Bar eyes have X chromosomes containing two copies of the region, and flies with double-Bar eyes have X chromosomes carrying three copies. Unequal crossing-over in females homozygous for double-Bar chromosomes can yield progeny with even more extreme phenotypes associated with four or five copies of the duplicated region. Duplications in homozygotes thus allow for the expansion

Figure 13.13 Unequal crossing-over can increase or decrease copy number. Duplication of the X chromosome polytene region 16A causes Bar eyes. Unequal pairing and crossing-over during meiosis in females homozygous for this duplication produce chromosomes that have either one copy of region 16A (conferring normal eyes) or three copies of 16A (causing the more abnormal double-Bar eyes).

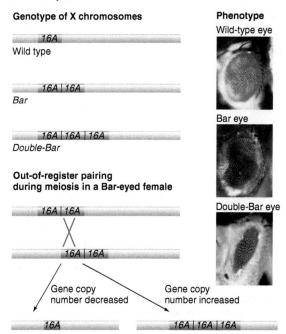

Genotype of X chromosomes

16A
Wild type

16A | 16A
Bar

16A | 16A | 16A
Double-Bar

Out-of-register pairing during meiosis in a Bar-eyed female

16A | 16A

16A | 16A

Gene copy number decreased

Gene copy number increased

16A

16A | 16A | 16A

Phenotype

Wild-type eye

Bar eye

Double-Bar eye

and contraction of the number of copies of a chromosomal region from one generation to the next.

A duplication heterozygote has three copies of a particular chromosomal region, even though the remainder of the genome is diploid. The resulting genetic imbalance can have harmful or even lethal effects, depending of the size of the duplication and the identity of the duplicated genes. Unequal crossing-over between homologous chromosomes bearing the same duplicated region can lead to increases and reciprocal decreases in the number of copies of that region.

Inversions reorganize the DNA sequence of a chromosome

The half-circle rotation of a chromosomal region known as an **inversion (*In*)** can occur when radiation produces two double-strand breaks in a chromosome's DNA. The breaks release a middle fragment, which may turn 180° before religation to the flanking chromosomal regions, resulting in an inversion (**Fig. 13.14a**). Inversions may also result from rare crossovers between related DNA sequences present in two positions on the same chromosome in inverted orientation (**Fig. 13.14b**), or they may arise by the action of transposable genetic elements (discussed later in this chapter). Inversions that include the centromere are **pericentric**, while inversions that exclude the centromere are **paracentric** (see Fig. 13.14a).

Phenotypic effects of inversions

Most inversions do not result in an abnormal phenotype, because even though they alter the order of genes along the chromosome, they do not add or remove DNA and therefore do not change the identity or number of genes. Geneticists can detect some inversions that do not affect phenotype, especially those that cause cytologically visible changes in banding patterns or those that suppress recombination in heterozygotes (as described later) and thereby change the expected results of linkage analysis. In natural populations, however, many inversions that do not affect phenotype go undetected.

If one end of an inversion lies within the DNA of a gene (**Fig. 13.14c**), a novel phenotype can occur. Inversion following an intragenic break separates the two parts of the gene, relocating one part to a distant region of the chromosome, while leaving the other part at its original site. Such a split disrupts the gene's function. If that function is essential to viability, the inversion acts as a recessive lethal mutation, and homozygotes for the inversion will not survive.

Inversions can also produce unusual phenotypes by moving genes residing near the inversion breakpoints to chromosomal environments that alter their normal expres-

Figure 13.14 Inversions: Origins, types, and phenotypic effects. (a) Inversions can arise when chromosome breakage produces a DNA segment that rotates 180° before it reattaches. When the rotated segment includes the centromere, the inversion is *pericentric;* when the rotated segment does not include the centromere, the inversion is *paracentric.* **(b)** If a chromosome has two copies of a sequence in reverse orientation, rare intrachromosomal recombination can give rise to an inversion. **(c)** An inversion can affect phenotype if it disrupts a gene. Here, the inversion *In(1)y⁴* inactivates the *y* (*yellow*) gene by dividing it in two.

(a) Chromosome breakage can produce inversions.

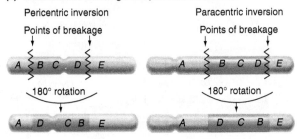

(b) Intrachromosomal recombination can also cause inversions.

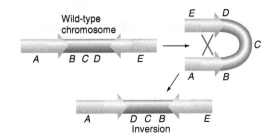

(c) Inversions can disrupt gene function.

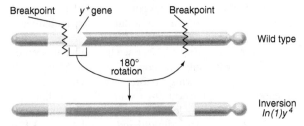

sion. For example, mutations in the *Antennapedia* gene of *Drosophila* that transform antennae into legs (review Fig. 8.31 on p. 279) are inversions that place the gene in a new regulatory environment, next to sequences that cause it to be transcribed in tissues where it would normally remain unexpressed. Inversions that reposition genes normally found in a chromosome's euchromatin to a position near a region of heterochromatin can also produce an unusual phenotype; spreading of the heterochromatin may inactivate the gene in some cells, leading to position-effect variegation, as discussed in Chapter 12 (see particularly Fig. 12.13 on p. 414).

Inversion heterozygosity and crossover suppression

Individuals heterozygous for an inversion ($In/+$) are *inversion heterozygotes*. In such individuals, when the chromosome carrying the inversion pairs with its homolog at meiosis, formation of an **inversion loop** allows the tightest possible alignment of homologous regions. In an inversion loop, one chromosomal region rotates to conform to the similar region in the other homolog (**Fig. 13.15**). Crossing-over within an inversion loop produces aberrant recombinant chromatids whether the inversion is pericentric or paracentric.

If the inversion is pericentric and a single crossover occurs within the inversion loop, each recombinant chromatid will have a single centromere—the normal number—but will carry a duplication of one region and a deletion

Figure 13.15 Inversion loops form in inversion heterozygotes. To maximize pairing during prophase of meiosis I in an inversion heterozygote ($In/+$), homologous regions form an inversion loop. (*Top*) Simplified diagram in which one line represents a pair of sister chromatids. (*Bottom*) Electron micrograph of an inversion loop during meiosis I in an $In/+$ mouse.

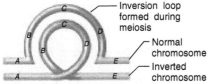

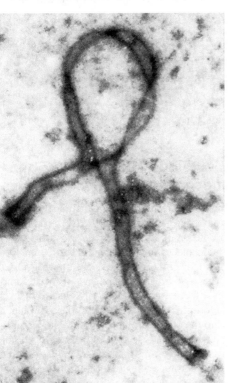

of a different region (**Fig. 13.16a**). Gametes carrying these recombinant chromatids will have an abnormal dosage of some genes. After fertilization, zygotes created by the union of these abnormal gametes with normal gametes are likely to die because of genetic imbalance.

If the inversion is paracentric and a single crossover occurs within the inversion loop, the recombinant chromatids will be unbalanced not only in gene dosage but also in centromere number (**Fig. 13.16b**). One crossover product will be an **acentric fragment** lacking a centromere; whereas the reciprocal crossover product will be a **dicentric chromatid** with two centromeres. Because the acentric fragment without a centromere cannot attach to the spindle apparatus during the first meiotic division, the cell cannot package it into either of the daughter nuclei; as a result, this chromosome is lost and will not be included in a gamete. By contrast, at anaphase of meiosis I, opposing spindle forces pull the dicentric chromatid toward both spindle poles at the same time with such strength that the dicentric chromatid breaks at random positions along the chromosome. These broken chromosome fragments are deleted for many of their genes. This loss of the acentric fragment and breakage of the dicentric chromatid results in genetically unbalanced gametes, which at fertilization will produce lethally unbalanced zygotes that cannot develop beyond the earliest stages of embryonic development. Consequently, no recombinant progeny resulting from a crossover in a paracentric inversion loop survive. Any surviving progeny are nonrecombinants.

In summary, whether an inversion is pericentric or paracentric, crossing-over within the inversion loop of an inversion heterozygote has the same effect: formation of recombinant gametes that after fertilization prevent the zygote from developing. Because only gametes containing chromosomes that did not recombine within the inversion loop can yield viable progeny, inversions act as **crossover suppressors.** This does not mean that crossovers do not occur within inversion loops, but simply that there are no recombinants among the viable progeny of an inversion heterozygote.

Geneticists use crossover suppression to create **balancer chromosomes,** which contain multiple, overlapping inversions (both pericentric and paracentric), as well as a marker mutation that produces a visible dominant phenotype (**Fig. 13.17**). The viable progeny of a *Balancer/+* heterozygote will receive either the balancer or the chromosome of normal order ($+$), but they cannot inherit a recombinant chromosome containing parts of both. Researchers can distinguish these two types of viable progeny by the presence or absence of the dominant marker phenotype. Geneticists often generate balancer heterozygotes to ensure that a chromosome of normal order, along with any mutations of interest it may carry, is transmitted to the next generation unchanged by recombination. To help create genetic stocks, the marker in

Figure 13.16 Why inversion heterozygotes produce few if any recombinant progeny. Throughout this figure, each line represents one chromatid, and different shades of *green* indicate the two homologous chromosomes. **(a)** The chromatids formed by recombination within the inversion loop of a pericentric inversion heterozygote are genetically unbalanced. **(b)** The chromatids formed by recombination within the inversion loop of a paracentric inversion heterozygote are not only genetically unbalanced but also contain two or no centromeres, instead of the normal one.

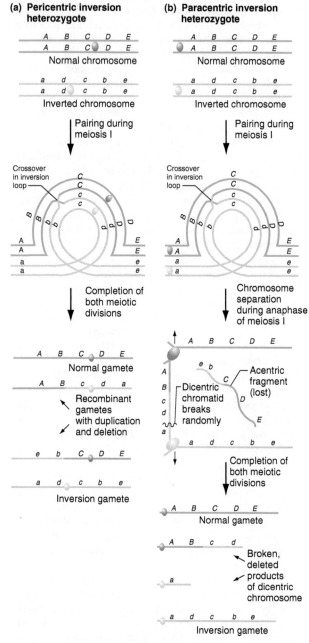

Figure 13.17 Balancer chromosomes are useful tools for genetic analysis. Balancer chromosomes carry both a dominant marker *D* as well as inversions (*brackets*) that prevent the balancer chromosome from recombining with an experimental chromosome carrying mutations of interest (m_1 and m_2). A parent heterozygous for the balancer and experimental chromosomes will transmit either the balancer or the experimental chromosome, but not a recombinant chromosome, to its surviving progeny.

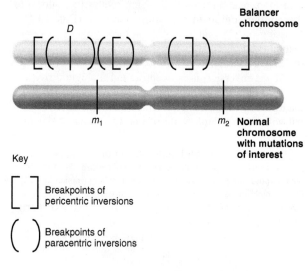

homozygotes. The *Drosophila* portrait (on our website at www.mhhe.com/hartwell4) discusses this and other significant uses of balancer chromosomes in genetic analysis.

Although inversions do not add or remove DNA, they can alter phenotype if they disrupt a gene or alter its expression. In inversion heterozygotes, recombination within the inversion loop yields genetically imbalanced gametes that produce nonviable zygotes. Geneticists can take advantage of this property to create balancer chromosomes that are useful in the production of genetic lines of known composition.

Translocations attach part of one chromosome to another chromosome

Translocations are large-scale mutations in which part of one chromosome becomes attached to a nonhomologous chromosome or in which parts of two different chromosomes trade places. This second type of translocation is known as a **reciprocal translocation** (**Fig. 13.18a**). It results when two breaks, one in each of two chromosomes, yield DNA fragments that do not religate to their chromosome of origin; rather, they switch places and become attached to the other chromosome. Depending on the positions of the breaks and the sizes of the exchanged fragments, the translocated chromosomes may be so different from the original chromosomes that the translocation is visible in a cytological examination (**Fig. 13.18b**).

most balancer chromosomes not only causes a dominant visible phenotype, but it also acts as a recessive lethal mutation that prevents the survival of balancer chromosome

Figure 13.18 Reciprocal translocations are exchanges between nonhomologous chromosomes. (a) In a reciprocal translocation, the region gained by one chromosome is the region lost by the other chromosome. **(b)** Karyotype of a human genome containing a translocation. The two translocated chromosomes are stained both red *and* green (*arrows*). Two normal, non-translocated chromosomes are stained entirely red *or* entirely green (*arrowheads*), indicating that this person is heterozygous for the translocation.

(a) Two chromosome breaks can produce a reciprocal translocation.

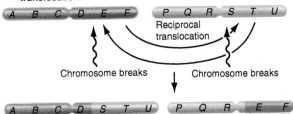

(b) Chromosome painting reveals a reciprocal translocation.

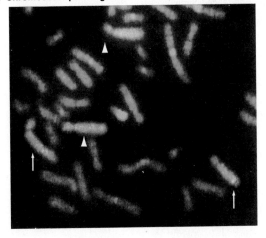

Robertsonian translocations are an important type of cytologically visible reciprocal translocations that arise from breaks at or near the centromeres of two acrocentric chromosomes (**Fig. 13.19**). The reciprocal exchange of broken parts generates one large metacentric chromosome and one very small chromosome containing few, if any, genes. This tiny chromosome may subsequently be lost from the organism. Robertsonian translocations are named after W. R. B. Robertson, who in 1911 was the first to suggest that during evolution, metacentric chromosomes may arise from the fusion of two acrocentrics.

Phenotypic effects of reciprocal translocations

Most individuals bearing reciprocal translocations are phenotypically normal because they have neither lost nor gained genetic material. As with inversions, however, if one of the translocation breakpoints occurs within a gene, that gene's function may change or be destroyed. Or if

Figure 13.19 Robertsonian translocations can reshape genomes. In a Robertsonian translocation, reciprocal exchanges between two acrocentric chromosomes generate a large metacentric chromosome and a very small chromosome. The latter may carry so few genes that it can be lost without ill effect.

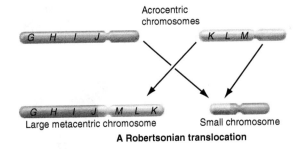

the translocation places a gene normally found in the euchromatin of one chromosome near the heterochromatin of the other chromosome, normal expression of the gene may cease in some cells, giving rise to position-effect variegation (see Fig. 12.13 on p. 414).

Several kinds of cancer are associated with translocations in somatic cells. In normal cells, genes known as *protooncogenes* help control cell division. Translocations that relocate these genes can turn them into tumor-producing *oncogenes* whose protein products have an altered structure or level of expression that leads to runaway cell division. For example, in almost all patients with chronic myelogenous leukemia, a type of cancer caused by overproduction of certain white blood cells, the leukemic cells have a reciprocal translocation between chromosomes 9 and 22 (**Fig. 13.20**). The breakpoint in chromosome 9 occurs within an intron of a protooncogene called *c-abl;* the breakpoint in chromosome 22 occurs within an intron of the *bcr* gene. After the translocation, parts of the two genes are adjacent to one another. During transcription, the RNA-producing machinery runs these two genes together, creating a long primary transcript. After splicing, the mRNA is translated into a fused protein in which 25 amino acids at the N terminus of the *c-abl*-determined protein are replaced by about 600 amino acids from the *bcr*-determined protein. The activity of this fused protein releases the normal controls on cell division, leading to leukemia. (See the Fast Forward box on pp. 432–433 of this chapter for another example of a translocation-induced cancer called Burkitt's lymphoma.)

Medical practitioners can exploit the rearrangement of DNA sequences that accompany cancer-related translocations for diagnostic and therapeutic purposes. To confirm a diagnosis of myelogenous leukemia, for example, they first obtain a blood sample from the patient, and they then use a pair of PCR primers derived from opposite sides of the breakpoint—one synthesized from the appropriate part of chromosome 22, the other from chromosome 9—to

Figure 13.20 How a reciprocal translocation helps cause one kind of leukemia. (a) Uncontrolled divisions of large, dark-staining white blood cells in a leukemia patient (*right*) produce a higher ratio of white to red blood cells than that in a normal individual (*left*). **(b)** A reciprocal translocation between chromosomes 9 and 22 contributes to chronic myelogenous leukemia. This rearrangement makes an abnormal hybrid gene composed of part of the *c-abl* gene and part of the *bcr* gene. The hybrid gene encodes an abnormal fused protein that disrupts controls on cell division. *Black arrows* indicate PCR primers that will generate a PCR product only from DNA containing the hybrid gene.

(a) Leukemia patients have too many white blood cells.

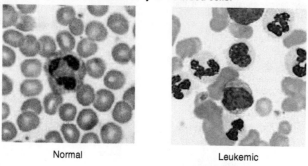

Normal   Leukemic

(b) The genetic basis for chronic myelogenous leukemia

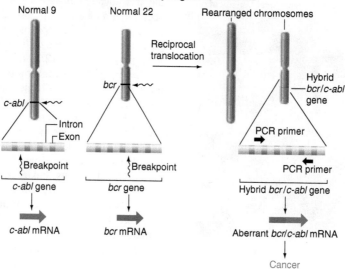

carry out a PCR on DNA from the blood cells. The PCR will amplify the region between the primers only if the DNA sample contains the translocation (**Fig. 13.20b**). To monitor the effects of chemotherapy, they again obtain a blood sample and extract genomic DNA from the white blood cells. If the sample contains even a few malignant cells, a PCR test with the same two primers will amplify the DNA translocation from those cells, indicating the need for more therapy. PCR thus becomes a sensitive assay for this type of leukemic cell.

Pharmaceutical researchers have recently exploited their understanding of the molecular nature of the translocation underlying chronic myelogenous leukemia to achieve a stunning breakthrough in the treatment of this cancer. The protein encoded by *c-abl* is a *protein tyrosine kinase,* an enzyme that adds phosphate groups to tyrosine amino acids on other proteins. This enzyme is an essential part

of the set of signals that dictate cell growth and division. Normal cells closely regulate the activity of the *c-abl* protein, blocking its function most of the time but activating it in response to stimulation by growth factors in the environment. By contrast, the fused protein encoded by *bcr/c-abl* in cells carrying the translocation is not amenable to regulation. It is always active, even in the absence of growth factor, and this leads to runaway cell division. Pharmaceutical companies have developed a drug called Gleevec® that specifically inhibits the enzymatic activity of the protein tyrosine kinase encoded by *bcr/c-abl*. In clinical trials, 98% of participants experienced a complete disappearance of leukemic blood cells and the return of normal white cells. This drug is now the standard treatment for chronic myelogenous leukemia and is a model for new types of cancer treatments that home in on cancer cells without hurting healthy ones.

Figure 13.21 The meiotic segregation of reciprocal translocations. In all parts of this figure, each bar or line represents one chromatid. **(a)** In a translocation homozygote (*T/T*), chromosomes segregate normally during meiosis I. **(b)** In a translocation heterozygote (*T/+*), the four relevant chromosomes assume a cruciform (crosslike) configuration to maximize pairing. The alleles of genes on chromosomes in the original order (*N1* and *N2*) are shown in lowercase; the alleles of these genes on the translocated chromosomes (*T1* and *T2*) are in uppercase letters. **(c)** Three segregation patterns are possible in a translocation heterozygote. Only the alternate segregation pattern gives rise to balanced gametes. **(d)** This semisterile ear of corn comes from a plant heterozygous for a reciprocal translocation. It has fewer kernels than normal because unbalanced ovules are aborted.

(a) Segregation in a translocation homozygote

(b) Chromosome pairing in a translocation heterozygote

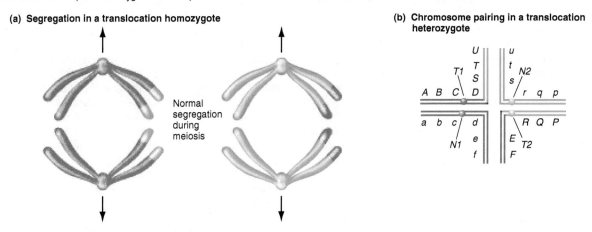

Normal segregation during meiosis

(c) Segregation in a translocation heterozygote

(d) Semisterility in corn

Segregation pattern	Alternate		Adjacent-1		Adjacent-2 (less frequent)	
	Balanced N1 + N2	Balanced T1 + T2	Unbalanced T1 + N2	Unbalanced N1 + T2	Unbalanced N1 + T1	Unbalanced N2 + T2
Gametes	a b c d e f / p q r s t u	A B C D S T U / P Q R E F	A B C D S T U / p q r s t u	a b c d e f / P Q R E F	a b c d e f / A B C D S T U	p q r s t u / P Q R E F
Type of progeny when mated with normal *abcdefpqrstu* homozygote	*abcdef pqrstu*	*ABCDEF PQRSTU*	None surviving	None surviving	None surviving	None surviving

Diminished fertility and pseudolinkage in translocation heterozygotes

Translocations, like inversions, produce no significant genetic consequences in homozygotes if the breakpoints do not interfere with gene function. During meiosis in a translocation homozygote, chromosomes segregate normally according to Mendelian principles (**Fig. 13.21a**). Even though the genes have been rearranged, both haploid sets of chromosomes in the individual have the same rearrangement. As a result, all chromosomes will find a single partner with which to pair at meiosis, and there will be no deleterious consequences for the progeny.

In translocation heterozygotes, however, certain patterns of chromosome segregation during meiosis produce genetically unbalanced gametes that at fertilization become deleterious to the zygote. In a translocation heterozygote, the two haploid sets of chromosomes do not carry the same arrangement of genetic information. As a result, during prophase of the first meiotic division, the translocated chromosomes and their normal homologs assume a crosslike configuration in which four chromosomes, rather than the normal two, pair to achieve a maximum of synapsis between similar regions (**Fig. 13.21b**). To keep track of the four chromosomes participating in this crosslike structure, we denote the chromosomes carrying translocated material with a *T* and the chromosomes with a normal order of genes with an *N*. Chromosomes *N1* and *T1* have homologous centromeres found in wild type on chromosome 1; *N2* and *T2* have centromeres found in wild type on chromosome 2.

During anaphase of meiosis I, the mechanisms that attach the spindle to the chromosomes in this crosslike configuration still usually ensure the disjunction of homologous centromeres, bringing homologous chromosomes to opposite spindle poles (that is, *T1* and *N1* go to opposite poles, as do *T2* and *N2*). Depending on the arrangement of the four chromosomes on the metaphase plate, this normal disjunction of homologs produces one of two equally likely patterns of segregation (**Fig. 13.21c**). In the **alternate segregation pattern,** the two translocation chromosomes (*T1* and *T2*) go to one pole, while the two normal chromosomes (*N1* and *N2*) move to the opposite pole. Both kinds of gametes resulting from this segregation (*T1, T2* and *N1, N2*) carry the correct haploid number of genes, and the zygotes formed by union of these gametes with a normal gamete will be viable. By contrast, in the **adjacent-1 segregation pattern,** homologous centromeres disjoin so that *T1* and *N2* go to one pole, while *N1* and *T2* go to the opposite pole. As a result, each gamete contains a large duplication (of the region found in both the normal and the translocated chromosome in that gamete) and a correspondingly large deletion (of the region found in neither of the chromosomes in that gamete), which make them genetically unbalanced. Zygotes formed by union of these gametes with a normal gamete are usually not viable.

Because of the unusual cruciform pairing configuration in translocation heterozygotes, nondisjunction of homologous centromeres occurs at a measurable but low rate. This nondisjunction produces an **adjacent-2 segregation pattern** in which the homologous centromeres *N1* and *T1* go to the same spindle pole, while the homologous centromeres *N2* and *T2* go to the other spindle pole (Fig. 13.21c). The resulting genetic imbalances are lethal after fertilization to the zygotes containing them.

Thus, of all the gametes generated by translocation heterozygotes, only those arising from alternate segregation, which account for slightly less than half the total, can produce viable progeny when crossed with individuals who do not carry the translocation. As a result, the fertility of most translocation heterozygotes, that is, their capacity for generating viable offspring, is diminished by at least 50%. This condition is known as **semisterility.** Corn plants illustrate the correlation between translocation heterozygosity and semisterility. The demise of genetically unbalanced ovules produces gaps in the ear where kernels would normally appear (**Fig. 13.21d**); in addition, genetically unbalanced pollen grains are abnormally small (not shown).

The semisterility of translocation heterozygotes undermines the potential of genes on the two translocated chromosomes to assort independently. Mendel's second law requires that all gametes resulting from both possible metaphase alignments of two chromosomal pairs produce viable progeny. But as we have seen, in a translocation heterozygote, only the alternate segregation pattern yields viable progeny in outcrosses; the equally likely adjacent-1 pattern and the rare adjacent-2 pattern do not. Because of this, genes near the translocation breakpoints on the nonhomologous chromosomes participating in a reciprocal translocation exhibit **pseudolinkage:** They behave as if they are linked.

Figure 13.21c illustrates why pseudolinkage occurs in a translocation heterozygote. In the figure, lowercase *a b c d e f* represent the alleles of genes present on normal chromosome 1 (*N1*), and *p q r s t u* are the alleles of genes on a nonhomologous normal chromosome 2 (*N2*). The alleles of these genes on the translocated chromosomes *T1* and *T2* are in uppercase. In the absence of recombination, Mendel's law of independent assortment would predict that genes on two different chromosomes will appear in four types of gametes in equal frequencies; for example, *a p, A P, a P,* and *A p*. But alternate segregation, the only pattern that can give rise to viable progeny, produces only *a p* and *A P* gametes. Thus, in translocation heterozygotes such as these, the genes on the two nonhomologous chromosomes act as if they are linked to each other.

Translocations and gene mapping

In humans, approximately 1 of every 500 individuals is heterozygous for some kind of translocation. While most such people are phenotypically normal, their fertility is diminished because many of the zygotes they produce abort spontaneously. As we have seen, this semisterility results from genetic imbalances associated with gametes formed by adjacent-1 or adjacent-2 segregation patterns. But such genetic imbalances are not inevitably lethal to the zygotes. If the duplicated or deleted regions are very small, the imbalanced gametes generated by these modes of segregation may produce children.

An important example of this phenomenon is seen among individuals heterozygous for certain reciprocal translocations involving chromosome 21, such as the Robertsonian translocation shown in **Fig. 13.22.** These people are phenotypically normal but produce some gametes from the adjacent-1 segregation pattern that have two copies of a part of chromosome 21 near the tip of its long arm. At fertilization, if a gamete with the duplication unites with a normal gamete, the resulting child will have three copies of this region of chromosome 21. A few individuals affected by Down syndrome have, in this way, inherited a third copy of only a small part of chromosome 21. These individuals with **translocation Down syndrome** provide evidence that the entirety of chromosome 21 need not be present in three copies to generate the phenotype.

Geneticists are now mapping the chromosome 21 regions duplicated in translocation Down syndrome patients to find the one or more genes responsible for the syndrome. Although chromosome 21 is the smallest human autosome, it nevertheless contains an estimated 350 genes, most of them in the 43 million base pairs of its long arm. The mapping of genes relative to the breakpoints of one or more such translocations considerably simplifies the task of identifying those genes that in triplicate produce the

Figure 13.22 How translocation Down syndrome arises. In heterozygotes for a translocation involving chromosome 21, such as 14q21q (a Robertsonian translocation between chromosomes 21 and 14), adjacent-1 segregation can produce gametes with two copies of part of chromosome 21. If such a gamete unites with a normal gamete, the resulting zygote will have three copies of part of chromosome 21. Depending on which region of chromosome 21 is present in three copies, this tripling may cause Down syndrome. (In the original translocation heterozygote, the small, reciprocally translocated chromosome [14p21p] has been lost.)

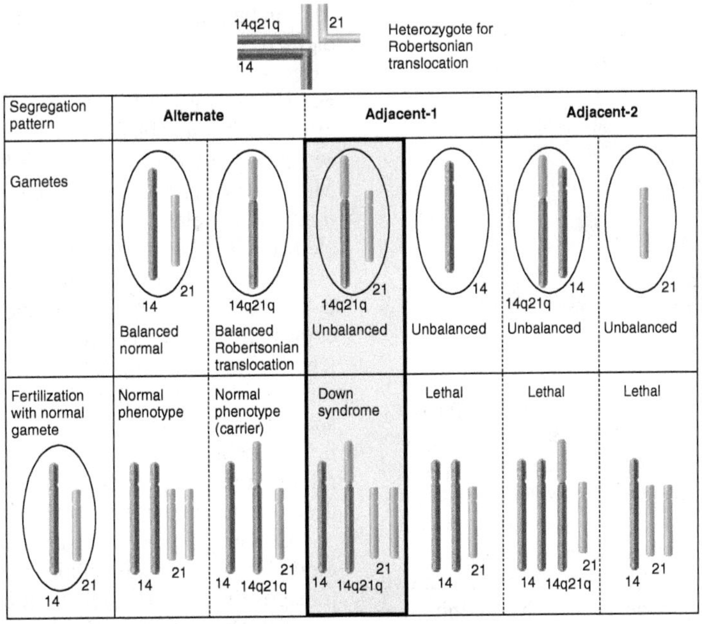

symptoms of Down syndrome. One way to locate which parts of chromosome 21 are responsible for Down syndrome is to obtain cloned chromosome 21 sequences from the Human Genome Project and then use these clones as FISH (fluorescence *in situ* hybridization) probes for the genome of the translocation Down syndrome patient. If the probe lights up the translocation chromosome as well as the two normal copies of chromosome 21, it identifies a region of the genome that is of potential importance to the syndrome.

In a reciprocal translocation, parts of two nonhomologous chromosomes trade places without any net loss or gain of DNA. As with inversions, reciprocal translocations can alter phenotype if they disrupt a gene or its expression. Translocation heterozygotes produce genetically imbalanced gametes from two of three possible meiotic segregation patterns; the result is semisterility and pseudolinkage.

13.2 Transposable Genetic Elements

Large deletions and duplications, as well as inversions and translocations, are major chromosomal reorganizations visible at the relatively low resolution of a karyotype. Small deletions and duplications are lesser chromosomal reorganizations that reshape genomes without any visible effect on karyotype. Another type of cytologically invisi-

ble sequence rearrangement with a significant genomic impact is **transposition:** the movement of small segments of DNA—entities known as **transposable elements (TEs)**—from one position in the genome to another.

Marcus Rhoades in the 1930s and Barbara McClintock in the 1950s inferred the existence of TEs from intricate genetic studies of corn. At first, the scientific community did not appreciate the importance of their work because their findings did not support the conclusion from classical recombination mapping that genes are located at fixed positions on chromosomes. Once the cloning of TEs made it possible to study them in detail, geneticists not only acknowledged their existence, but also discovered TEs in the genomes of virtually all organisms, from bacteria to humans. In 1983, Barbara McClintock received the Nobel Prize for her insightful studies on movable genetic elements (**Fig. 13.23**).

Molecular studies confirmed transposable element movement

Copia is a transposable element in *Drosophila*. If you examined the polytene chromosomes from two strains of flies isolated from different geographic locations, you would find in general that the chromosomes appear identical. A probe derived from the *white* gene for eye color, for example, would hybridize to a single site near the tip of the X chromosome in both strains (review Fig. 13.9a). However, a probe including the *copia* TE would hybridize to 30–50 sites scattered throughout the genome, and the positions of

Figure 13.23 Barbara McClintock: Discoverer of transposable elements.

in situ hybridization would not be the same in the two strains. Some sites would be identical in the two polytene sets, but others would be different (**Fig. 13.24**). These observations suggest that since the time the strains were separated geographically, the *copia* sequences have moved around (transposed) in different ways in the two genomes even though the genes have remained in fixed positions.

Any segment of DNA that evolves the ability to move from place to place within a genome is by definition a transposable element, regardless of its origin or function. TEs need not be sequences that do something for the organism; indeed, many scientists regard them primarily as "selfish" parasitic entities carrying only information that allows their self-perpetuation. Some TEs, however, appear to have evolved functions that help their host. In one interesting example, TEs maintain the length of *Drosophila* chromosomes. *Drosophila* telomeres, in contrast to those of most organisms, do not contain TTAGGG repeats that are extendable by the telomerase enzyme (see Fig. 12.19 on p. 419). Certain TEs in flies, however, combat the shortening of chromosome ends that accompanies

every cycle of replication by jumping with high frequency into DNA very near chromosome ends. As a result, chromosome size stays relatively constant.

Most transposable elements in nature range from 50 bp to approximately 10,000 bp (10 kb) in length. A particular TE can be present in a genome anywhere from one to hundreds of thousands of times. *Drosophila melanogaster,* for example, harbors approximately 80 different TEs, each an average of 5 kb in length, and each present an average of 50 times. These TEs constitute $80 \times 50 \times 5 = 20,000$ kb, or roughly 12.5% of the 160,000 kb *Drosophila* genome. Mammals carry two major classes of TEs: **LINEs,** or <u>l</u>ong <u>i</u>nterspersed <u>e</u>lements; and **SINEs,** or <u>s</u>hort <u>i</u>nterspersed <u>e</u>lements. The human genome contains approximately 20,000 copies of the main human LINE—*L1*—which is up to 6.4 kb in length. The human genome also carries 300,000 copies of the main human SINE—*Alu*—which is 0.28 kb in length (**Fig. 13.25a**). These two TEs alone thus constitute roughly 7% of the 3,000,000 kb human genome. Because some TEs exist in only one or a few closely related species, it is probable that some elements arise and then disappear rather frequently over evolutionary time. Chapter 20 describes the evolutionary origins of LINEs and SINEs.

Classification of TEs on the basis of how they move around the genome distinguishes two groups. **Retroposons** transpose via reverse transcription of an RNA intermediate. The *Drosophila copia* elements and the human SINEs and LINEs just described are retroposons. **Transposons** move their DNA directly without the requirement of an RNA intermediate. The genetic elements discovered by

Figure 13.25 TEs in human and corn genomes. (a) The human genome carries about 300,000 copies of the 0.28 kb *Alu* retroposon, the major human SINE. **(b)** Movements of a transposon mottles corn kernels when the transposon jumps into or out of genes that influence pigmentation.

(a) *Alu* **SINEs in the human genome**

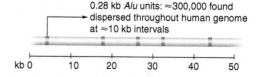

0.28 kb *Alu* units: ≈300,000 found dispersed throughout human genome at ≈10 kb intervals

(b) TEs cause mottling in corn.

Figure 13.24 Transposable elements (TEs) can move to many locations in a genome. A probe for the *copia* TE hybridizes to multiple sites (*black bands* superimposed over the *blue* chromosomes) that differ in two different fly strains.

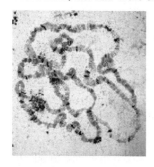
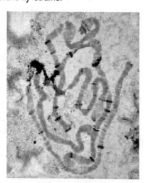

Barbara McClintock in corn responsible for mottling the kernels are transposons (**Fig. 13.25b**). Some biologists use the term "transposon" in the broader sense to refer to all TEs. In this book, we reserve it for the direct-movement class of genetic elements, and we use "transposable elements (TEs)" to indicate all DNA segments that move about in the genome, regardless of the mechanism.

> Studies in corn and *Drosophila* revealed the existence of transposable genetic elements (TEs): small segments of DNA that can move around, and accumulate in, the genome. TEs can be subdivided according to their mode of transposition. Retroposons move via RNA intermediates, whereas the DNA of transposons moves directly without first being transcribed into RNA.

Retroposons move via RNA intermediates

The transposition of a retroposon begins with its transcription by RNA polymerase into an RNA that encodes a reverse-transcriptase-like enzyme. This enzyme, like the reverse transcriptase made by the AIDS-causing HIV virus described in the Genetics and Society box on pp. 260–261 of Chapter 8, can copy RNA into a single strand of cDNA and then use that single DNA strand as a template for producing double-stranded cDNA. Many retroposons also encode polypeptides other than reverse transcriptase.

Some retroposons have a poly-A tail at the 3′ end of the RNA-like DNA strand, a configuration reminiscent of mRNA molecules (**Fig. 13.26a**). Other retroposons end

Figure 13.26 Retroposons: Structure and movement. (a) Some retroposons have a poly-A tail at the end of the RNA-like DNA strand (*top*); others are flanked on both sides by long terminal repeats (LTRs; *bottom*). (b) Researchers constructed a plasmid bearing a *Ty1* retroposon that contained an intron. When this plasmid was transformed into yeast cells, researchers could isolate new insertions of *Ty1* into yeast genomic DNA. The newly inserted *Ty1* did not have the intron, which implies that transposition involves splicing of a primary transcript to form an intronless mRNA. (c) The reverse-transcriptase-like enzyme synthesizes double-stranded retroposon cDNA in a series of steps. Insertion of this double-stranded cDNA into a new genomic location (*blue*) involves a staggered cleavage of the target site that leaves "sticky ends"; polymerization to fill in the sticky ends produces two copies of the 5 bp target site.

(a) Two kinds of retroposons

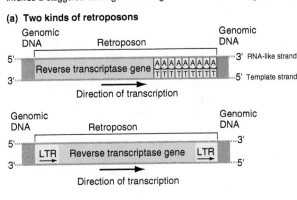

(b) Retroposons move via RNA intermediates.

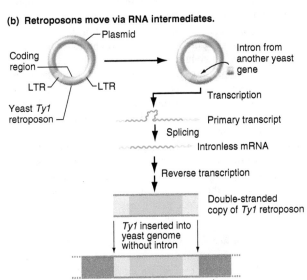

(c) How retroposons move

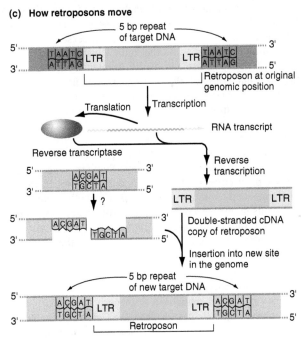

in *long terminal repeats* (*LTR*s): nucleotide sequences repeated in the same orientation at both ends of the element (Fig. 13.26a). The structure of this second type of retroposon is similar to the integrated DNA copies of RNA tumor viruses (known as retroviruses), suggesting that retroviruses evolved from this kind of retroposon, or vice versa. In support of this notion, researchers sometimes find retroposon transcripts enclosed in viruslike particles.

The structural parallels between retroposons, mRNAs, and retroviruses, as well as the fact that retroposons encode a reverse-transcriptase-like enzyme, prompted investigators to ask whether retroposons move around the genome via an RNA intermediate. Experiments in yeast helped confirm that they do. In one study, a copy of the *Ty1* retroposon found on a yeast plasmid contained an intron in one of its genes; after transposition into the yeast chromosome, however, the intron was not there (**Fig. 13.26b**). Because removal of introns occurs only during mRNA processing, researchers concluded that the *Ty1* retroposon passes through an RNA intermediate during transposition.

The mechanisms by which various retroposons move around the genome resemble each other in general outline but differ in detail. **Figure 13.26c** outlines what is known of the process for the better understood LTR-containing retroposons. As the figure illustrates, one outcome of transposition via an RNA intermediate is that the original copy of the retroposon remains in place while the new copy inserts in another location. With this mode of transmission, the number of copies can increase rapidly with time. Human LINEs and SINEs, for example, occur in tens of thousands or even hundreds of thousands of copies within the genome. Other retroposons, however, such as the *copia* elements found in *Drosophila*, do not proliferate so profusely and exist in much more moderate copy numbers of 30–50. Currently unknown mechanisms may account for these differences by regulating the rate of retroposon transcription or by limiting the number of copies through selection at the level of the whole organism.

> Retroposons encode a reverse transcriptase enzyme that copies processed retroposon RNA (without introns) into complementary DNA; this DNA can insert into a new location in the genome. Because movement of retroposons involves an RNA intermediate, the number of copies in the genome can potentially increase rapidly.

Movement of transposon DNA is catalyzed by transposase enzymes

A hallmark of transposons—TEs whose movement does not involve an RNA intermediate—is that their ends are inverted repeats of each other, that is, a sequence of base pairs at one end is present in mirror image at the other end (**Fig. 13.27a**). The inverted repeat is usually 10–200 bp long.

DNA between the transposon's inverted repeats commonly contains a gene encoding a transposase, a protein that catalyzes transposition through its recognition of those repeats. As Fig. 13.27a illustrates, the steps resulting in transposition include excision of the transposon from its original genomic position and integration into a new location. The double-stranded break at the transposon's excision site is are repaired in different ways in different cases. **Figure 13.27b** shows two of the possibilities. In *Drosophila*, after excision of a transposon known as a *P element*, DNA exonucleases first widen the resulting gap and then repair it using either a sister chromatid or a homologous chromosome as a template. If the template contains the *P* element and DNA replication is completely accurate, repair will restore a *P* element to the position from which it was excised; this will make it appear as if the *P* element remained at its original location during transposition (Fig. 13.27b, *left*). If the template does not contain a *P* element, the transposon will be lost from the original site after transposition (Fig. 13.27b, *right*).

Some strains of *D. melanogaster* are called "P strains" because they harbor many copies of the *P* element; "M strains" of the same species do not carry the *P* element at all. Virtually all commonly used laboratory flies are M strains, whereas many flies isolated from natural populations since 1950 are P strains. Because Thomas Hunt Morgan and coworkers in the early part of the twentieth century isolated the flies that have proliferated into most current laboratory strains, these observations suggest that *P* elements did not enter *D. melanogaster* genomes until around 1950. The prevalence of *P* elements in many contemporary natural populations attests to the rapidity with which transposable elements can spread once they enter a species' genome.

Interestingly, the mating of male flies from P strains with females from M strains causes a phenomenon called **hybrid dysgenesis,** which creates a series of defects including sterility of offspring, mutation, and chromosome breakage. One of the more interesting effects of hybrid dysgenesis is to promote the movement of *P* elements to new positions in the genome. Because elevated levels of transposition can foster many kinds of genetic changes (described in the following), some geneticists speculate that hybrid dysgenesis-like events involving various transposons in different species had a strong impact on evolution. The *Drosophila* portrait (on our website at www.mhhe.com/hartwell4) provides more information on the molecular mechanisms underlying hybrid dysgenesis and the ways in which fly geneticists use this phenomenon to introduce new genes into *Drosophila*.

> Transposons encode transposase enzymes that recognize the inverted repeats at the ends of the transposon DNA. These enzymes then catalyze the movement of the transposons without the involvement of an RNA intermediate.

Figure 13.27 Transposons: Structure and movement. (a) Most transposons contain inverted repeats at their ends (*light green; red arrows*) and encode a transposase enzyme that recognizes these inverted repeats. The transposase cuts at the borders between the transposon and adjacent genomic DNA, and it also helps the excised transposon integrate at a new site. **(b)** Transposase-catalyzed integration of *P* elements creates a duplication of 8 bp present at the new target site. A gap remains when transposons are excised from their original position. After exonucleases widen the gap, cells repair the gap using related DNA sequences as templates. Depending on whether the template contains or lacks a *P* element, the transposon will appear to remain or to be excised from its original location.

(a) Transposon structure

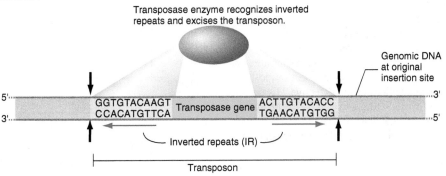

(b) How *P* element transposons move

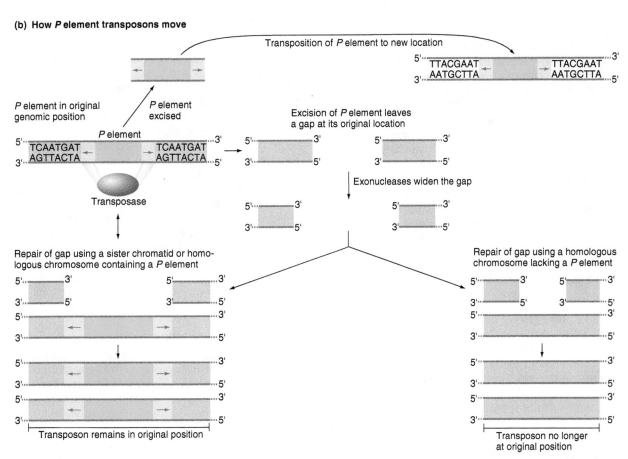

Genomes often contain defective copies of transposable elements

Many copies of TEs sustain deletions either as a result of the transposition process itself (for example, incomplete reverse transcription of a retroposon RNA) or as a result of events following transposition (for example, faulty repair of a site from which a *P* element was earlier excised). If a deletion removes the promoter needed for transcription of a retroposon, that copy of the element cannot generate the RNA intermediate for future movements. If the deletion removes one of the inverted repeats at one end of a transposon, transposase will be unable to catalyze transposition of that element. Such deletions create defective TEs unable to transpose again. Most SINEs and LINEs in the human genome are defective in this way.

Other types of deletions create defective elements that are unable to move on their own, but they can move if nondefective copies of the element elsewhere in the genome supply the deleted function. For example, a deletion inactivating the reverse transcriptase gene in a retroposon or the transposase gene in a transposon would "ground" that copy of the element at one genomic location if it is the only source of the essential enzyme in the genome. If reverse transcriptase or transposase were provided by other copies of the same element in the genome, however, the defective copy could move. Defective TEs that require the activity of nondeleted copies of the same TE for movement are called **nonautonomous elements;** the nondeleted copies that can move by themselves are **autonomous elements.**

> Deleted, defective copies of TEs that can still transpose are called nonautonomous elements. The movement of non-autonomous elements requires that the genome also contains nondefective copies (autonomous elements) that can supply reverse transcriptase or transposase enzymes.

Transposable elements can disrupt genes and alter genomes

Geneticists usually consider TEs to be segments of "selfish DNA" that exist for their own sake. However, the movement of TEs may have profound consequences for the organization and function of the genes and chromosomes of the organisms in which they are maintained.

Gene mutations caused by TEs

Insertion of a TE near or within a gene can affect gene expression and change phenotype. We now know that the wrinkled pea mutation first studied by Mendel resulted from insertion of a TE into the gene for a starch-branching enzyme. In *Drosophila,* a large percentage of spontaneous mutations, including the w^1 mutation discovered by T. H. Morgan in 1910, are caused by insertion of TEs (**Fig. 13.28**). Surprisingly, in light of the large numbers

Figure 13.28 TEs can cause mutations on insertion into a gene. Many spontaneous mutations in the *white* gene of *Drosophila* arise from insertions of TEs such as *copia, roo, pogo,* or *Doc.* The resultant eye color phenotype (indicated by the color in the *triangles*) depends on the element involved and where in the *white* gene it inserts.

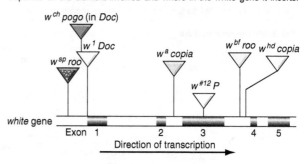

of LINEs and SINEs in human genomes, only a handful of mutant human phenotypes are known to result from insertion of TEs. Among these is a B-type hemophilia caused by *Alu* insertion into a gene encoding clotting factor IX; recall that *Alu* is the main human SINE.

A TE's effect on a gene depends on what the element is and where it inserts within or near the gene (Fig. 13.28). If an element lands within a protein-coding exon, the additional DNA may shift the reading frame or supply an in-frame stop codon that truncates the polypeptide. If the element falls in an intron, it could diminish the efficiency of splicing. Some of these inefficient splicing events might completely remove the element from the gene's primary transcript; this would still allow some—but less than normal—synthesis of functional polypeptide. TEs that land within exons or introns may also provide a transcription stop signal that prevents transcription of gene sequences downstream of the insertion site. Finally, insertions into regions that regulate transcription, such as promoters, can influence the amount of gene product made in particular tissues at particular times during development. Some transposons insert preferentially into the upstream regulatory regions of genes, and some even prefer specific types of genes, such as tRNA genes.

Chromosomal rearrangements caused by TEs

Retroposons and transposons can trigger spontaneous chromosomal rearrangements other than transpositions in several ways. Sometimes, deletion or duplication of chromosomal material adjacent to the transposon occurs as a mistake during the transposition event itself. In another mechanism, if two copies of the same TE occupy nearby but not identical sites in homologous chromosomes, the two copies of the TE in heterozygotes carrying both types of homolog may pair with each other and cross over (**Fig. 13.29a**). The recombination resulting from this unequal crossover would produce one chromosome deleted for the region between the two TEs and a reciprocal homolog with a tandem duplication of the same region. The duplication

Figure 13.29 How TEs generate chromosomal rearrangements and relocate genes. (a) If a TE (*pink*) is found in slightly different locations on homologous chromosomes (here on opposite sides of segment *B*), unequal crossing-over produces reciprocal deletions and duplications. **(b)** If two copies of a transposon are nearby on the same chromosome, transposase can recognize the outermost inverted repeats (IRs), creating a composite transposon that allows intervening genes such as w^+ (*red*) to jump to new locations.

(a) Unequal crossing-over between TEs

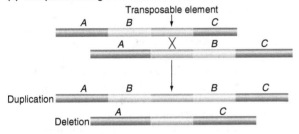

(b) Two transposons can form a large, composite transposon.

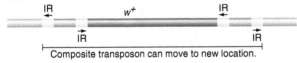

associated with the *Bar* mutation in *Drosophila* (review Fig. 13.13) probably arose in this way.

Gene relocation due to transposition

When two copies of a transposon occur in nearby but not identical locations on the same chromosome, the inverted repeats of the transposons are positioned such that an inverted version of the sequence at the 5′ end of the copy on the left will exist at the 3′ end of the copy to its right (**Fig. 13.29b**). If transposase acts on this pair of inverted repeats during transposition, it allows the entire region between them to move as one giant transposon, mobilizing and relocating any genes the region contains. Some composite transposons, such as that pictured in the figure at the beginning of this chapter on p. 429, carry as much as 400 kb of DNA. In prokaryotes, the capacity of two TEs to relocate the intervening genes helps mediate the transfer of drug resistance between different strains or species of bacteria, as will be discussed in Chapter 14.

The movement of TEs has three main genetic consequences: (1) mutation of a gene due to TE insertion within or near the gene; (2) chromosomal rearrangements either caused by unequal crossing-over between copies of the same TE, or generated as a by-product of the transposition process; and (3) relocation of genes between two nearby transposons on the same chromosome.

13.3 Rearrangements and Evolution: A Speculative Comprehensive Example

We saw at the beginning of this chapter that roughly 300 chromosomal rearrangements could reshape the human genome to a form that resembles the mouse genome. Many of these rearrangements are transpositions and translocations that could construct a new chromosome from large blocks of sequences that were on different chromosomes in an ancestral organism. Figure 13.1 provides clear evidence that these reorganizations also include inversions. For example, mouse chromosome 1 contains two adjacent syntenic segments that are found in human chromosome 6, but in a reshuffled order, with one segment turned around 180° with respect to the other segment. Direct DNA sequence comparison of the mouse and human genomes further indicates that deletions, duplications, translocations and transpositions have occurred in one or the other lineage since humans and mice began to diverge from a common ancestor 65 million years ago.

The occurrence of these various rearrangements over evolutionary time suggests two things. First, although most chromosomal variations, including single-base changes and chromosomal rearrangements, are deleterious to an organism or its progeny, a few changes are either neutral or provide an advantage for survival and manage to become fixed in a population. Second, some rearrangements almost certainly contribute to the processes underlying speciation. Although we still do not know enough to understand how any particular rearrangement that distinguishes the human from the mouse genome may have provided a survival advantage or otherwise helped guide speciation, it is nonetheless useful to consider in a general way how chromosomal rearrangements might contribute to evolution.

Deletions A small deletion that moves a coding sequence of one gene next to a promoter or other regulatory element of an adjacent gene may rarely allow expression of a protein at a novel time in development or in a novel tissue. If the new time or place of expression is advantageous to the organism, the deletion might become established in the genome.

Duplications An organism cannot normally tolerate mutations in a gene essential to its survival, but duplication would provide two copies of the gene. If one copy remained intact to perform the essential function, the other would be free to evolve a new function. The genomes of most higher plants and animals, in fact, contain many **gene families**—sets of closely related genes with slightly different functions, that most likely arose from a succession of gene duplication events. In vertebrates, some *multigene families* have hundreds of members.

Inversions Suppose one region of a chromosome has three mutations that together greatly enhance the reproductive fitness of the organism. In heterozygotes where one homolog carries the mutations and the other does not, recombination could undo the beneficial linkage. If, however, the three mutations are part of an inversion, crossover suppression will ensure that they remain together as they spread through the population.

Translocations On the tiny volcanic island of Madeira off the coast of Portugal in the Atlantic Ocean, two populations of the common house mouse (*Mus musculus*) are in the process of becoming separate species because of translocations that have led to reproductive isolation. The mice live in a few narrow valleys separated by steep mountains. Geneticists have found that populations of mice on the two sides of these mountain barriers have very different sets of chromosomes because they have accumulated different sets of Robertsonian translocations (**Fig. 13.30**). Mice in one Madeira population, for example, have a diploid

Figure 13.30 Rapid chromosomal evolution in house mice on the island of Madeira. (a) Distribution of mouse populations with different sets of Robertsonian translocations (indicated by circles of different colors). **(b)** Karyotypes of female mice from two different populations. The karyotype I at the *top* is from the population shown with *red dots* in part (a); the karyotype II at the *bottom* is from the population indicated by *green dots*. Robertsonian translocations are indicated by numbers separated by a comma (for example, 2,19 is a Robertsonian translocation between chromosomes 2 and 19 of the standard mouse karyotype).

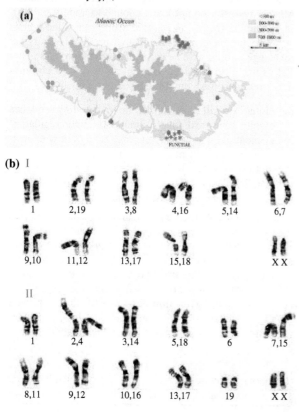

number (2n) of 22 chromosomes, whereas mice in a different population on the island have 24; for most house mice throughout the world, $2n = 40$. (Recall from Fig. 13.19 that Robertsonian translocations can reduce chromosome number if the small chromosome that results from a translocation is lost.)

The hybrid offspring of matings between individuals of these two populations are completely sterile or infertile because chromosomal complements that are so different cannot properly segregate at meiosis. Thus, reproductive isolation has reinforced the already established geographical isolation, and the two populations are close to becoming two separate species. What is remarkable about this example of speciation is that mice were introduced into Madeira by Portuguese settlers only in the fifteenth century. This means that the varied and complicated sets of Robertsonian translocations that contributed to speciation became fixed in the different populations in less than 600 years.

Transpositions Movement of TEs may cause novel mutations, a small proportion of which might be selected for because they are advantageous to the organism. TEs can also help generate potentially useful duplications and inversions.

Rearrangements and transpositions alter DNA sequences and thus provide raw material for evolutionary change. Duplicated genes can diverge by mutation to acquire different functions. The reduced fertility of heterozygotes for inversions and translocations can contribute to reproductive isolation of populations and thus promote speciation.

13.4 Changes in Chromosome Number

We have seen that in peas, *Drosophila*, and humans, normal diploid individuals carry a 2n complement of chromosomes, where n is the number of chromosomes in the gametes. All the chromosomes in the haploid gametes of these diploid organisms are different from one another. In this section, we examine two types of departure from chromosomal diploidy found in eukaryotes: (1) aberrations in usually diploid species that generate cells or individuals whose genomes contain one to a few chromosomes more or less than the normal 2n, for example, $2n + 1$ or $2n - 1$; and (2) species whose genomes contain complete but nondiploid sets of chromosomes, for example, 3n or 4n.

Aneuploidy is the loss or gain of one or more chromosomes

Individuals whose chromosome number is not an exact multiple of the haploid number (n) for the species are

aneuploids (review Table 13.1 on p. 431). Individuals lacking one chromosome from the diploid number ($2n - 1$) are **monosomic,** whereas individuals having one chromosome in addition to the normal diploid set ($2n + 1$) are **trisomic.** Organisms with four copies of a particular chromosome ($2n + 2$) are **tetrasomic.**

Deleterious effects of aneuploidy for autosomes

Monosomy, trisomy, and other forms of aneuploidy create a genetic imbalance that is usually deleterious to the organism. In humans, monosomy for any autosome is generally lethal, but medical geneticists have reported a few cases of monosomy for chromosome 21, one of the smallest human chromosomes. Although born with severe multiple abnormalities, these monosomic individuals survived for a short time beyond birth. Similarly, trisomies involving a human autosome are also highly deleterious. Individuals with trisomies for larger chromosomes, such as 1 and 2, are almost always aborted spontaneously early in pregnancy. Trisomy 18 causes Edwards syndrome, and trisomy 13 causes Patau syndrome; both phenotypes include gross developmental abnormalities that result in early death.

The most frequently observed human autosomal trisomy, trisomy 21, results in Down syndrome. As one of the shortest human autosomes, chromosome 21 contains only about 1.5% of the DNA in the human genome. Although there is considerable phenotypic variation among Down syndrome individuals, traits such as mental retardation and skeletal abnormalities are usually associated with the condition. Many Down syndrome babies die in their first year after birth from heart defects and increased susceptibility to infection. We saw earlier (in the discussion of translocations) that some people with Down syndrome have three copies of only part of, rather than the entire, chromosome 21. It is thus probable that genetic imbalance for only a few genes may be a sufficient cause of the condition. Unfortunately, as of late 2008, scientists had not yet been able to identify any of these genes unambiguously with a particular Down syndrome phenotype.

Dosage compensation through X chromosome inactivation

Although the X chromosome is one of the longest human chromosomes and contains 5% of the DNA in the genome, individuals with X chromosome aneuploidy, such as XXY males, XO females, and XXX females, survive quite well compared with aneuploids for the larger autosomes. The explanation for this tolerance of X-chromosome aneuploidy is that X-chromosome inactivation equalizes the expression of most X-linked genes in individuals with different numbers of X chromosomes.

As we saw in Chapter 12, X-chromosome inactivation represses expression of most genes on all but one X chromosome in a cell. As a result, even if the number of X chromosomes varies, the amount of protein generated by most X-linked genes remains constant. Human X-chromosome aneuploidies are nonetheless not without consequence. XXY men have *Klinefelter syndrome,* and XO women have *Turner syndrome.* The aneuploid individuals affected by these syndromes are usually infertile and display skeletal abnormalities, leading in the XXY men to unusually long limbs and in the women XO to unusually short stature.

If X inactivation were 100% effective, we would not expect to see even the relatively minor abnormalities of Klinefelter syndrome, because the number of functional X chromosomes—one—would be the same as in normal individuals. One explanation is that during X inactivation, several genes near the telomere and centromere of the short arm of the human X chromosome escape inactivation and thus remain active. As a result, XXY males make twice the amount of protein encoded by these few genes as XY males (**Fig. 13.31**).

The reverse of X inactivation is *X reactivation;* it occurs in the oogonia, the female germ-line cells that develop into the oocytes that undergo meiosis (review Fig. 4.17 on p. 100). Reactivation of the previously inactivated X chromosomes in the oogonia ensures that every mature ovum (the gamete) receives an active X. If X reactivation did not occur, half of a woman's eggs (those with inactive X chromosomes) would be incapable of supporting development after fertilization. The phenomenon of X reactivation in the oogonia might help explain the infertility of women with Turner syndrome. With X reactivation, oogonia in normal XX females have two functional doses of X chromosome genes; but the corresponding cells in XO Turner women have only one dose of the same genes and may thus undergo defective oogenesis.

Figure 13.31 Why aneuploidy for the X chromosome can have phenotypic consequences. X-chromosome inactivation does not affect all genes on the X chromosome. As a result, in XXY Klinefelter males, a few X chromosome genes are expressed inappropriately at twice their normal level.

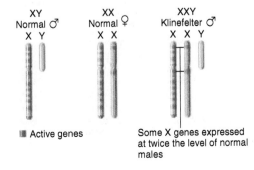

Meiotic nondisjunction

How does aneuploidy arise? Mistakes in chromosome segregation during meiosis produce aneuploids of different types, depending on when the mistakes occur. If homologous chromosomes do not separate (that is, do not disjoin) during the first meiotic division, two of the resulting haploid gametes will carry both homologs, and two will carry neither. Union of these gametes with normal gametes will produce aneuploid zygotes, half monosomic, half trisomic (**Fig. 13.32a,** *left*). By contrast, if meiotic nondisjunction occurs during meiosis II, only two of the four resulting gametes will be aneuploid (Fig. 13.32a, *right*).

Abnormal *n* + 1 gametes resulting from nondisjunction in a cell that is heterozygous for alleles on the nondisjoining chromosome will be heterozygous if the nondisjunction

happens in the first meiotic division, but they will be homozygous if the nondisjunction takes place in the second meiotic division. (We assume here that no recombination has occurred between the heterozygous gene in question and the centromere, as would be the case for genes closely linked to the centromere.) It is possible to use this distinction to determine when a particular nondisjunction occurred (Fig. 13.32a). The nondisjunction events that give rise to Down syndrome, for example, occur much more frequently in mothers (90%) than in fathers (10%). Interestingly, in women, such nondisjunction events occur more often during the first meiotic division (about 75% of the time) than during the second. By contrast, when the nondisjunction event leading to Down syndrome takes place in men, the reverse is true.

Figure 13.32 Aneuploidy is caused by problems in meiotic chromosome segregation. (a) If trisomic progeny inherit two different alleles (*A* and *a*) of a centromere-linked gene from one parent, the nondisjunction occurred in meiosis I (*left*). If the two alleles inherited from one parent are the same (*A* and *A;* or *a* and *a*), the nondisjunction occurred during meiosis II (*right*). **(b)** Because aneuploids carry chromosomes that have no homolog with which to pair, aneuploid individuals frequently produce aneuploid progeny.

(a) Nondisjunction can occur during either meiotic division.

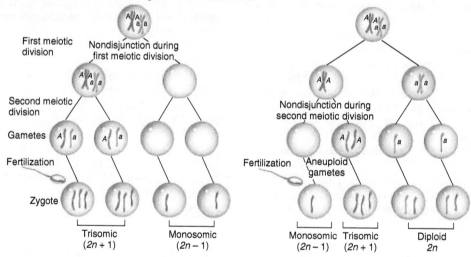

(b) Aneuploids beget aneuploid progeny.

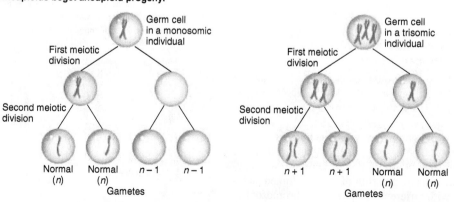

Recently obtained data show that many meiotic nondisjunction events in humans result from problems in meiotic recombination. By tracking DNA markers, clinical investigators can establish whether recombination took place anywhere along chromosome 21 during meioses that created $n + 1$ gametes. In approximately one-half of Down syndrome cases caused by nondisjunction during the first meiotic division in the mother (that is, in about 35% of all Down syndrome cases), no recombination occurred between the homologous chromosome 21's in the defective meioses. This result makes sense because chiasmata, the structures associated with crossing-over, hold the maternal and paternal homologous chromosomes together in a bivalent at the metaphase plate of the first meiotic division (review Feature Figure 4.13 on pp. 94–95). In the absence of recombination and thus of chiasmata, there is no mechanism to ensure that the maternal and paternal chromosomes will go to opposite poles at anaphase I. The increase in the frequency of Down syndrome children that is associated with increasing maternal age may therefore reflect a decline in the effectiveness of the mother's machinery for meiotic recombination.

If an aneuploid individual survives and is fertile, the incidence of aneuploidy among his or her offspring will generally be extremely high. This is because half of the gametes produced by meiosis in a monosomic individual lack the chromosome in question, while half of the gametes produced in a trisomic individual have an additional copy of the chromosome (**Fig. 13.32b**).

Mitotic nondisjunction and chromosome loss

As a zygote divides many times to become a fully formed organism, mistakes in chromosome segregation during the mitotic divisions accompanying this development may, in rare instances, augment or diminish the complement of chromosomes in certain cells. In **mitotic nondisjunction,** the failure of two sister chromatids to separate during mitotic anaphase generates reciprocal trisomic and monosomic daughter cells (**Fig. 13.33a**). Other types of mistakes, such as a lagging chromatid not pulled to either spindle pole at mitotic anaphase, result in a **chromosome loss** that produces one monosomic and one diploid daughter cell (**Fig. 13.33b**).

In a multicellular organism, aneuploid cells arising from either mitotic nondisjunction or chromosome loss may survive and undergo further rounds of cell division, producing clones of cells with an abnormal chromosome count. Nondisjunction or chromosome loss occurring

Figure 13.33 Mistakes during mitosis can generate clones of aneuploid cells. Mitotic nondisjunction **(a)** or chromosome loss during mitosis **(b)** can create monosomic or trisomic cells that can divide to produce aneuploid clones. **(c)** If an X chromosome is lost during the first mitotic division of an XX *Drosophila* zygote, one daughter cell will be XX (female), while the other will be XO (male). Such an embryo will grow into a gynandromorph. Here, the zygote was $w^+ m^+ / w m$, so the XX half of the fly (*left*) has red eyes and normal wings; loss of the $w^+ m^+$ X chromosome gives the XO half of the fly (*right*) white eyes (*w*), miniature wings (*m*), and a male-specific sex comb on the front leg.

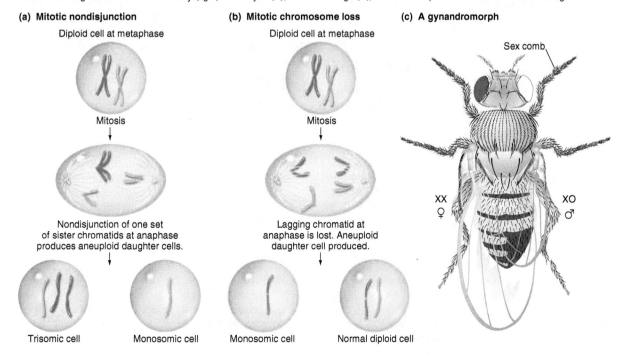

(a) Mitotic nondisjunction

Diploid cell at metaphase

Mitosis

Nondisjunction of one set of sister chromatids at anaphase produces aneuploid daughter cells.

Trisomic cell   Monosomic cell

(b) Mitotic chromosome loss

Diploid cell at metaphase

Mitosis

Lagging chromatid at anaphase is lost. Aneuploid daughter cell produced.

Monosomic cell   Normal diploid cell

(c) A gynandromorph

Sex comb

XX ♀   XO ♂

early in development will generate larger aneuploid clones than the same events occurring later in development. The side-by-side existence of aneuploid and normal tissues results in a **mosaic** organism whose phenotype depends on what tissue bears the aneuploidy, the number of aneuploid cells, and the specific genes on the aneuploid chromosome. Many examples of mosaicism involve the sex chromosomes. If an XX *Drosophila* female loses one of the X chromosomes during the first mitotic division after fertilization, the result is a **gynandromorph** composed of equal parts male and female tissue (**Fig. 13.33c**).

Interestingly, in humans, many Turner syndrome females are mosaics carrying some XX cells and some XO cells. These individuals began their development as XX zygotes, but with the loss of an X chromosome during the embryo's early mitotic divisions, they acquired a clone of XO cells. Similar mosaicism involving the autosomes also occurs. For example, physicians have recorded several cases of mild Down syndrome arising from mosaicism for trisomy 21. In people with Turner or Down mosaicism, the existence of some normal tissue appears to ameliorate the condition, with the individual's phenotype depending on the particular distribution of diploid versus aneuploid cells.

> Aneuploidy for autosomes is usually deleterious, but organisms can better tolerate aneuploidy for sex chromosomes because of dosage compensation mechanisms such as X-chromosome inactivation. Rare events of meiotic nondisjunction can produce aneuploid gametes and thus aneuploid organisms. Rare mistakes in mitosis, including mitotic nondisjunction and chromosome loss, can generate a mosaic organism that has cells with different karyotypes.

Some euploid species are not diploid

In contrast to aneuploids, **euploid** cells contain only complete sets of chromosomes. Most euploid species are diploid, but some euploid species are **polyploids** that carry three or more complete sets of chromosomes (see Table 13.1 on p. 431). When speaking of polyploids, geneticists use the symbol x to indicate the **basic chromosome number,** that is, the number of different chromosomes that make up a single complete set. Triploid species, which have three complete sets of chromosomes are then $3x;$ tetraploid species with four complete sets of chromosomes are $4x;$ and so forth. For diploid species, x is identical to n—the number of chromosomes in the gametes—because each gamete contains a single complete set of chromosomes. This identity of $x = n$ does not, however, hold for polyploid species, as the following example illustrates. Commercially grown bread wheat has a total of 42 chromosomes: 6 nearly (but not wholly) identical sets each containing 7 different chromosomes. Bread

wheat is thus a hexaploid with a basic number of $x = 7$ and $6x = 42$. But each triploid gamete has one-half the total number of chromosomes, so $n = 21$. Thus, for bread wheat, x and n are not the same. Another form of euploidy, in addition to polyploidy, exists in **monoploid** (x) organisms, which have only one set of chromosomes.

Monoploidy and polyploidy are rarely observed in animals. Among the few examples of monoploidy are some species of ants and bees in which the males are monoploid, whereas the females are diploid. Males of these species develop *parthenogenetically* from unfertilized eggs. These monoploid males produce gametes through a modified meiosis that in some unknown fashion ensures distribution of all the chromosomes to the same daughter cell during meiosis I; the sister chromatids then separate normally during meiosis II. Polyploidy in animals normally exists only in species with unusual reproductive cycles, such as hermaphroditic earthworms, which carry both male and female reproductive organs, and goldfish, which are parthenogenetically tetraploid species. In *Drosophila,* it is possible, under special circumstances, to produce triploid and tetraploid females, but never males. In humans, polyploidy is always lethal, usually resulting in spontaneous abortion during the first trimester of pregnancy.

Monoploid organisms

Botanists can produce monoploid plants experimentally by special treatment of germ cells from diploid species that have completed meiosis and would normally develop into pollen. (Note that monoploid plants obtained in this manner can also be considered haploids because $x = n$.) The treated cells divide into a mass of tissue known as an *embryoid*. Subsequent exposure to plant hormones enables the embryoid to develop into a plant (**Fig. 13.34a**). Monoploid plants may also arise from rare spontaneous events in a large natural population. Most monoploid plants, no matter how they originate, are infertile. Because the chromosomes have no homologs with which to pair during meiosis I, they are distributed at random to the two spindle poles during this division. Rarely do all chromosomes go to the same pole, and if they do not, the resulting gametes are defective as they lack one or more chromosomes. The greater the number of chromosomes in the genome, the lower the likelihood of producing a gamete containing all of them.

Despite such gamete-generating problems, monoploid plants and tissues are of great value to plant breeders. They make it possible to visualize normally recessive traits directly, without crosses to achieve homozygosity. Plant researchers can also introduce mutations into individual monoploid cells; select for desirable phenotypes, such as resistance to herbicides; and use hormone treatments to grow the selected cells into monoploid plants

Figure 13.34 The creation and use of monoploid plants. (a) Under certain conditions, haploid pollen grains can grow into haploid embryoids. When treated with plant hormones, haploid embryoids grow into monoploid plants. **(b)** Researchers select monoploid cells for recessive traits such as herbicide resistance. They then grow the selected cells into a resistant embryo, which (with hormone treatment) eventually becomes a mature, resistant monoploid plant. Treatment with colchicine doubles the chromosome number, creating diploid cells that can be grown in culture with hormones to make a homozygous herbicide-resistant diploid plant. **(c)** Colchicine treatment prevents formation of the mitotic spindle and also blocks cytokinesis, generating cells with twice the number of chromosomes. *Blue, red,* and *green* colors denote nonhomologous chromosomes.

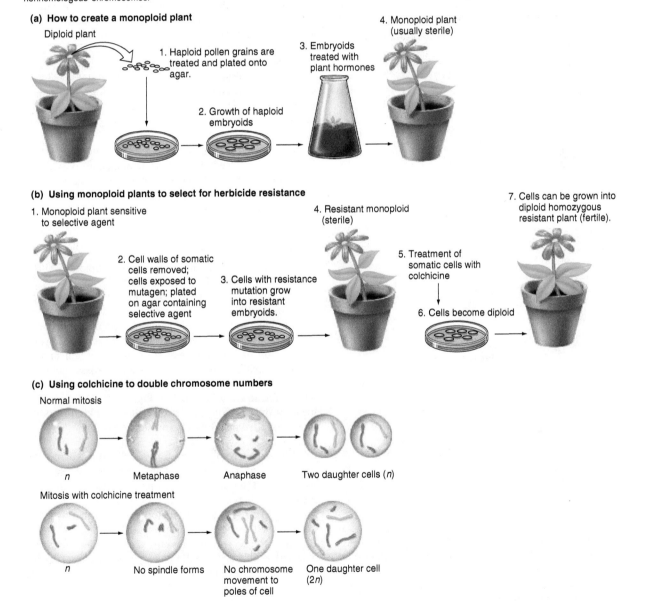

(a) How to create a monoploid plant

Diploid plant

1. Haploid pollen grains are treated and plated onto agar.

2. Growth of haploid embryoids

3. Embryoids treated with plant hormones

4. Monoploid plant (usually sterile)

(b) Using monoploid plants to select for herbicide resistance

1. Monoploid plant sensitive to selective agent

2. Cell walls of somatic cells removed; cells exposed to mutagen; plated on agar containing selective agent

3. Cells with resistance mutation grow into resistant embryoids.

4. Resistant monoploid (sterile)

5. Treatment of somatic cells with colchicine

6. Cells become diploid

7. Cells can be grown into diploid homozygous resistant plant (fertile).

(c) Using colchicine to double chromosome numbers

Normal mitosis

n   Metaphase   Anaphase   Two daughter cells (*n*)

Mitosis with colchicine treatment

n   No spindle forms   No chromosome movement to poles of cell   One daughter cell (*2n*)

(Fig. 13.34b). They can then convert monoploids of their choice into homozygous diploid plants by treating tissue with *colchicine,* an alkaloid drug obtained from the autumn crocus. By binding to tubulin—the major protein component of the spindle—colchicine prevents formation of the spindle apparatus. In cells without a spindle, the sister chromatids cannot segregate after the centromere splits, so there is often a doubling of the chromosome set following treatment with colchicine (**Fig. 13.34c**). The resulting diploid cells can be grown into diploid plants that will express the desired phenotype and produce fertile gametes.

Figure 13.35 The genetics of triploidy. (a) Production of a triploid (*x* = 3) from fertilization of a monoploid gamete by a diploid gamete. Nonhomologous chromosomes are either *blue* or *red*. **(b)** Meiosis in a triploid produces unbalanced gametes because meiosis I produces two daughter cells with unequal numbers of any one type of chromosome. If *x* is large, balanced gametes with equal numbers of all the chromosomes are very rare.

(a) Formation of a triploid organism

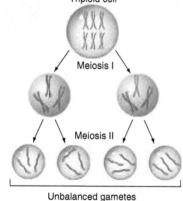

(b) Meiosis in a triploid organism

Triploid organisms

Triploids (3*x*) result from the union of monoploid (*x*) and diploid (2*x*) gametes (**Fig. 13.35a**). The diploid gametes may be the products of meiosis in tetraploid (4*x*) germ cells, or they may be the products of rare spindle or cytokinesis failures during meiosis in a diploid.

Sexual reproduction in triploid organisms is extremely inefficient because meiosis produces mostly unbalanced gametes. During the first meiotic division in a triploid germ cell, three sets of chromosomes must segregate into two daughter cells; regardless of how the chromosomes align in pairs, there is no way to ensure that the resulting

gametes obtain a complete, balanced *x* or 2*x* complement of chromosomes. In most cases, at the end of anaphase I, two chromosomes of any one type move to one pole, while the remaining chromosome of the same type moves to the opposite pole. The products of such a meiosis have two copies of some chromosomes and one copy of others (**Fig. 13.35b**). If the number of chromosomes in the basic set is large, the chance of obtaining any balanced gametes at all is remote. Thus, fertilization with gametes from triploid individuals does not produce many viable offspring.

It is possible to propagate some triploid species, such as bananas and watermelons, through asexual reproduction. The fruits of triploid plants are seedless because the unbalanced gametes do not function properly in fertilization or, if fertilization occurs, the resultant zygote is so genetically unbalanced that it cannot develop. Either way, no seeds form. Like triploids, all polyploids with odd numbers of chromosome sets (such as 5*x* or 7*x*) are sterile because they cannot reliably produce balanced gametes.

Tetraploidy and speciation

During mitosis, if the chromosomes in a diploid (2*x*) tissue fail to separate after replication, the resulting daughter cells will be tetraploid (4*x*; **Fig. 13.36a**). If such tetraploid cells arise in reproductive tissue, subsequent meioses will produce diploid gametes. Rare unions between diploid gametes produce tetraploid organisms. Self-fertilization of a newly created tetraploid organism will produce an entirely new species, because crosses between the tetraploid and the original diploid organism will produce infertile triploids (review Fig. 13.35a). Tetraploids made in this fashion are **autopolyploids,** a kind of polyploid that derives all its chromosome sets from the same species.

Maintenance of a tetraploid species depends on the production of gametes with balanced sets of chromosomes. Most successful tetraploids have evolved mechanisms ensuring that the four copies of each group of homologs pair two by two to form two **bivalents**—pairs of synapsed homologous chromosomes (**Fig. 13.36b**). Because the chromosomes in each bivalent become attached to opposite spindle poles during meiosis I, meiosis regularly produces gametes carrying two complete sets of chromosomes. The mechanism requiring that each chromosome pair with only a single homolog suppresses other pairing possibilities, such as a 3:1, which cannot guarantee equivalent chromosome segregation.

Tetraploids, with four copies of every gene, generate unusual Mendelian ratios. For example, even if there are only two alleles of a gene (say, *A* and *a*), five different genotypes are possible: *A A A A, A A A a, A A a a, A a a a,* and *a a a a.* If the phenotype depends on the dosage of *A*,

Figure 13.36 The genetics of tetraploidy. (a) Tetraploids arise from a failure of chromosomes to separate into two daughter cells during mitosis in a diploid. **(b)** In successful tetraploids, the pairing of chromosomes as bivalents generates genetically balanced gametes. **(c)** Gametes produced in an *A A a a* tetraploid heterozygous for two alleles of a centromere-linked gene, with orderly pairing of bivalents. The four chromosomes can pair to form two bivalents in three possible ways. For each pairing scheme, the chromosomes in the two pairs can assort in two different orientations. If all possibilities are equally likely, the expected genotype frequency in a population of gametes will be 1 (*A A*) : 4 (*A a*) : 1 (*a a*).

(a) Generation of tetraploid (4x) cells

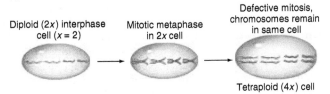

(b) Pairing of chromosomes as bivalents

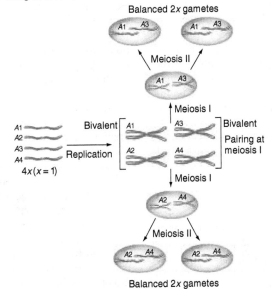

(c) Gametes formed by *A A a a* tetraploids

Chromosomes	Pairing			Gametes Produced by Random Spindle Attachment
1. *A* 2. *A* 3. *a* 4. *a*	1 ↑*A* 2 ↓*A* 3 ↓*a* 4 ↓*a* **or**	1 ↑*A* 2 ↓*A* 4 ↑*a* 3 ↓*a*		1 + 3 *A a* 1 + 4 *A a* **or** 2 + 4 *A a* 2 + 3 *A a*
	1 ↑*A* 3 ↓*a* 2 ↑*A* 4 ↓*a* **or**	1 ↑*A* 3 ↓*a* 4 ↑*a* 2 ↓*A*		1 + 2 *A A* 1 + 4 *A a* **or** 3 + 4 *a a* 2 + 3 *A a*
	1 ↑*A* 4 ↓*a* 2 ↑*A* 3 ↓*a* **or**	1 ↑*A* 4 ↓*a* 3 ↑*a* 2 ↓*A*		1 + 2 *A A* 1 + 3 *A a* **or** 3 + 4 *a a* 2 + 4 *A a*

Total:
2(*A A*) : 8(*A a*) : 2(*a a*)
= 1(*A A*) : 4(*A a*) : 1(*a a*)

then five phenotypes, each corresponding to one of the genotypes, will appear. The segregation of alleles during meiosis in a tetraploid is similarly complex. Consider an *A A a a* heterozygote in which the *A* gene is closely linked to the centromere, and the *A* allele is completely dominant. What are the chances of obtaining progeny with the recessive phenotype, generated by only the *a a a a* genotype? As **Fig. 13.36c** illustrates, if during meiosis I, the four chromosomes carrying the gene align at random in bivalents along the metaphase plate, the expected ratio of gametes is 2 (*A A*) : 8 (*A a*) : 2 (*a a*) = 1 (*A A*) : 4 (*A a*) : 1 (*a a*). The chance of obtaining *a a a a* progeny during self-fertilization is thus 1/6 × 1/6 = 1/36. In other words, because *A* is completely dominant, the ratio of dominant to recessive phenotypes, determined by the ratio of *A - - -* to *a a a a* genotypes is 35:1. The ratios will be different if the gene is not closely linked to the centromere or if the dominance relationship between the alleles is not so simple.

New levels of polyploidy can arise from the doubling of a polyploid genome. Such doubling occurs on rare occasions in nature; it also results from controlled treatment with colchicine or other drugs that disrupt the mitotic spindle. The doubling of a tetraploid genome yields an octaploid (8*x*). These higher-level polyploids created by successive rounds of genome doubling are autopolyploids because all of their chromosomes derive from a single species.

Polyploids in agriculture

Roughly one out of every three known species of flowering plants is a polyploid, and because polyploidy often increases plant size and vigor, many polyploid plants with edible parts have been selected for agricultural cultivation. Most commercially grown alfalfa, coffee, and peanuts are tetraploids (4*x*). MacIntosh apple and Bartlett pear trees that produce giant fruits are also tetraploids. Commercially grown strawberries are octaploids (8*x*) (**Fig. 13.37**). The evolutionary success of polyploid plant species may stem from the fact that polyploidy, like gene

duplication, provides additional copies of genes; while one copy continues to perform the original function, the others can evolve new functions. As you have seen, however, the fertility of polyploid species requires an even number of chromosome sets.

Polyploidy can arise not only from chromosome doubling, but also from crosses between members of two species, even if they have different numbers of chromosomes. Hybrids in which the chromosome sets come from two or more distinct, though related, species are known as **allopolyploids.** In crosses between octaploids and tetraploids, for example, fertilization unites tetraploid and diploid gametes to produce hexaploid progeny. Fertile allopolyploids arise only rarely, under special conditions, because chromosomes from the two species differ in shape, size, and number, so they cannot easily pair with each other. The resulting irregular segregation creates genetically unbalanced gametes such that the hybrid progeny will be sterile. Chromosomal doubling in germ cells, however, can restore fertility by creating a pairing partner for each chromosome. Organisms produced in this manner are termed **amphidiploids** if the two parental species were diploids; they contain two diploid genomes, each one derived from a different parent. As the following illustrations show, it is hard to predict the characteristics of an amphidiploid or other allopolyploids.

A cross between cabbages and radishes, for example, leads to the production of amphidiploids known as *Raphanobrassica*. The gametes of both parental species contain 9 chromosomes; the sterile F_1 hybrids have 18 chromosomes, none of which has a homolog. Chromosome doubling in the germ cells after treatment with colchicine, followed by union of two of the resulting gametes, produces a new species: a fertile *Raphanobrassica* amphidiploid carrying 36 chromosomes—a full complement of 18 (9 pairs) derived from cabbages and a full complement of 18 (9 pairs) derived from radishes. Unfortunately, this amphidiploid has the roots of a cabbage plant and leaves resembling those of a radish, so it is not agriculturally useful.

By contrast, crosses between tetraploid (or hexaploid) wheat and diploid rye have led to the creation of several allopolyploid hybrids with agriculturally desirable traits from both species (**Fig. 13.38**). Some of the hybrids combine the high yields of wheat with rye's ability to adapt to unfavorable environments. Others combine wheat's high level of protein with rye's high level of lysine; wheat protein does not contain very much of this amino acid, an essential ingredient in the human diet. The various hybrids between wheat and rye form a new crop known as *Triticale.* Some triticale strains produce nutritious grains that already appear in breads sold in health food stores. Plant breeders are currently assessing the usefulness of various triticale strains for large-scale agriculture.

Figure 13.37 Many polyploid plants are larger than their diploid counterparts. A comparison of octaploid (*left*) and diploid (*right*) strawberries.

Figure 13.38 Amphidiploids in agriculture. (a) Plant breeders cross wheat with rye to create allopolyploid *Triticale*. Because this strain of wheat is tetraploid, x_1 (the number of chromosomes in the basic wheat set) is one-half n_1 (the number of chromosomes in a wheat gamete). For diploid rye, $n_2 = x_2$. Note that the F_1 hybrid between wheat and rye is sterile because the rye chromosomes have no pairing partners. Doubling of chromosome numbers by colchicine treatment of the F_1 hybrid corrects this problem, allowing regular pairing. **(b)** A comparison of wheat, rye, and *Triticale* grain stalks.

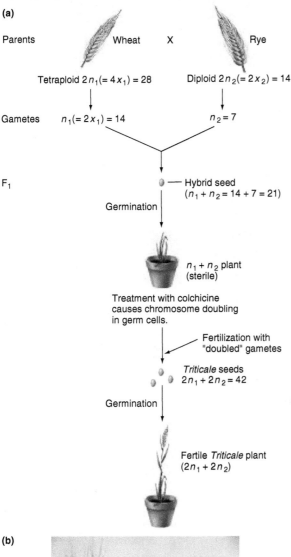

(a)

Parents   Wheat   X   Rye

Tetraploid $2n_1(= 4x_1) = 28$ Diploid $2n_2(= 2x_2) = 14$

Gametes $n_1(= 2x_1) = 14$ $n_2 = 7$

F_1

Hybrid seed
($n_1 + n_2 = 14 + 7 = 21$)

Germination

$n_1 + n_2$ plant
(sterile)

Treatment with colchicine causes chromosome doubling in germ cells.

Fertilization with "doubled" gametes

Triticale seeds
$2n_1 + 2n_2 = 42$

Germination

Fertile *Triticale* plant
($2n_1 + 2n_2$)

(b)

Wheat   Rye   *Triticale*

Organisms with odd numbers of chromosome sets are generally infertile because during meiosis, some or all of their chromosomes do not have pairing partners. Chromosome doubling can produce new, fertile polyploid species of plants with even numbers of chromosome sets. In autopolyploids, all the chromosomes originally came from a single ancestral species, but in allopolyploids, the chromosomes were derived from two different ancestral species.

13.5 Emergent Technologies: Beyond the Karyotype

Two main problems occur when searching for chromosomal rearrangements and changes in chromosome number by karyotype analysis. First, it is a tedious procedure that depends on highly trained technicians to identify chromosomal alterations under the microscope. Because of the subjective nature of the analysis, mistakes can reduce the accuracy of results. Second, even in the hands of the best technicians, there is a limit to the viewing resolution. Even under optimal circumstances, it is not possible to detect deletions or duplications of less than 5 Mb in human karyotypes. Human populations no doubt have many chromosomes with as yet undetected smaller deletions or duplications.

To overcome the limitations of karyotype analysis, researchers have developed a microarray-based hybridization protocol that can scan the genome for deletions, duplications, and aneuploidy with much greater resolution, very high accuracy, and much greater throughput and without the need for a subjective determination of the result. The technique is called *comparative genomic hybridization (CGH)* or sometimes *virtual karyotyping*.

The protocol works as follows (**Fig. 13.39**). First, a series of 20,000 BAC clones with DNA inserts averaging 150 kb that collectively represent the entire human genome are spotted onto a microarray. These BAC clones were characterized in the course of the Human Genome Project. Next, genomic DNA from a control sample with a normal genome content is labeled with a yellow fluorescent dye, while the genomic DNA from the test sample is labeled with a red fluorescent dye. The two genomic DNA samples are mixed together in equal amounts, denatured, and applied to the microarray as a probe. After hybridization is complete and unhybridized material is washed away, the fluorescence emission from each microarray dot is analyzed automatically by a machine designed for this task.

If the genomic region probed with a particular BAC clone is present in two copies in the test sample, then the ratio of red to yellow dyes on that dot will be 1 : 1. However, if a particular genomic region is duplicated or deleted from one homolog in the test sample, the ratio of red to yellow will be 1.5 : 1 or 0.5 : 1, respectively. An example of this analysis is shown in Fig. 13.39.

Figure 13.39 Comparative Genomic Hybridization detects duplications, deletions, and aneuploidy. (a) BAC clones representing the human genome are spotted in order onto a microarray. **(b)** The genomic sample to be tested is labeled with one color dye (here, *red*), and the control genome sample is labeled with a second color dye (*yellow*). **(c)** The two samples are mixed together, denatured, and then incubated on the microarray. **(d)** Automated analysis of each spot on the microarray detects the ratio of the two dyed probes that hybridize. *Orange* indicates a 1 : 1 ratio; other colors indicate deletion (0.5 : 1 ratio; *yellow*) or duplication (1.5 : 1 ratio; *red*) of BAC clone sequences in the test sample.

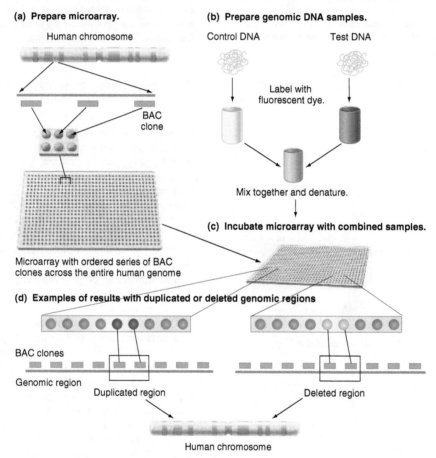

(a) Prepare microarray.

Human chromosome

BAC clone

Microarray with ordered series of BAC clones across the entire human genome

(b) Prepare genomic DNA samples.

Control DNA   Test DNA

Label with fluorescent dye.

Mix together and denature.

(c) Incubate microarray with combined samples.

(d) Examples of results with duplicated or deleted genomic regions

BAC clones

Genomic region

Duplicated region   Deleted region

Human chromosome

CGH provides a powerful clinical tool to detect any type of aneuploidy or any deletion or duplication of 50 kb or more anywhere in the genome. Clinicians can use it in conjunction with amniocentesis or preimplantation genetic analysis. They can also use CGH to screen tissue biopsies for cancerous cells that have deleted or duplicated regions containing oncogenes or tumor suppressor genes. The technique thus holds great promise for the detection of new genes that contribute to the genesis of cancer.

Connections

The detrimental consequences of most changes in chromosome organization and number cause considerable distress in humans (**Table 13.2**). Approximately 4 of every 1000 individuals has an abnormal phenotype associated with aberrant chromosome organization or number. Most of these abnormalities result from either aneuploidy for the X chromosome or trisomy 21. By comparison, about 10 people per 1000 suffer from an inherited disease caused by a single-gene mutation.

The incidence of chromosomal abnormalities among humans would be much larger were it not for the fact that many embryos or fetuses with abnormal karyotypes abort

TABLE 13.2	Aneuploidy in the Human Population	
Chromosomes	**Syndrome**	**Frequency at Birth**
Autosomes		
Trisomic 21	Down	1/700
Trisomic 13	Patau	1/5000
Trisomic 18	Edwards	1/10,000
Sex chromosomes, females		
XO, monosomic	Turner	1/5000
XXX, trisomic XXXX, tetrasomic XXXXX, pentasomic		1/700
Sex chromosomes, males		
XYY, trisomic	Normal	1/10,000
XXYY, tetrasomic XXXY, tetrasomic XXXXY, pentasomic XXXXXY, hexasomic	Klinefelter	1/500

About 0.4% of all babies born have a detectable chromosomal abnormality that generates a detrimental phenotype.

spontaneously early in pregnancy. Fully 15% to 20% of recognized pregnancies end with detectable spontaneous abortions; and half of the spontaneously aborted fetuses show chromosomal abnormalities, particularly trisomy, sex chromosome monosomy, and triploidy. These figures almost certainly underestimate the rate of spontaneous abortion caused by abnormal chromosomal variations, because embryos carrying aberrations for larger chromosomes, such as monosomy 2 or trisomy 5, may abort so early that the pregnancy goes unrecognized.

But despite all the negative effects of chromosomal rearrangements and changes in chromosome number, a few departures from normal genome organization survive to become instruments of evolution by natural selection.

As we see in the next chapter, chromosomal rearrangements occur in bacteria as well as in eukaryotic organisms. In bacteria, transposable elements catalyze many of the changes in chromosomal organization. Remarkably, the reshuffling of genes between different DNA molecules in the same cell catalyzes the transfer of genetic information from one bacterial cell to another.

ESSENTIAL CONCEPTS

1. Rearrangements reorganize the DNA sequences within genomes. The results are subject to natural selection, and thus rearrangements serve as instruments of evolution.

2. Deletions remove DNA from a chromosome. Homozygosity for a large deletion is usually lethal, but even heterozygosity for a large deletion can create a deleterious genetic imbalance. Deletions may uncover recessive mutations on the homologous chromosome and are thus useful for gene mapping.

3. Duplications add DNA to a chromosome. The additional copies of genes can be a major source of new genetic functions. Homozygosity or heterozygosity for duplications causes departures from normal gene dosage that are often harmful to the organism. Unequal crossing-over between duplicated regions expands or contracts the number of gene copies and may lead to multigene families.

4. Inversions alter the order, but not the number, of genes on a chromosome. They may produce novel phenotypes by disrupting the activity of genes near

the rearrangement breakpoints. Inversion heterozygotes exhibit crossover suppression because progeny formed from recombinant gametes are genetically imbalanced.

5. In reciprocal translocations, parts of two chromosomes trade places without the loss or gain of chromosomal material. Translocations may modify the function of genes at or near the translocation breakpoints. Heterozygosity for translocations in the germ line results in semisterility and pseudolinkage.

6. Transposable elements (TEs) are short, mobile segments of DNA that reshape genomes by generating mutations, causing chromosomal rearrangements, and relocating genes.

7. Aneuploidy, the loss or gain of one or more chromosomes, creates a genetic imbalance. Mistakes in meiosis produce aneuploid gametes, whereas mistakes in mitosis generate aneuploid clones of cells. Autosomal aneuploidy is usually lethal. Sex chromosome aneuploidy is better tolerated because of dosage compensation mechanisms.

8. Euploid organisms contain complete sets of chromosomes. Organisms with three or more sets of chromosomes are polyploids. In autopolyploidy, all chromosome sets are derived from the same species; in allopolyploidy, chromosome sets come from two or more distinct, though related, species.

9. Monoploids (with only a single complete chromosome set) as well as polyploids containing odd numbers of chromosome sets are sterile because the chromosomes cannot pair properly during meiosis I.

10. Polyploids having even numbers of chromosome sets can be fertile if proper chromosome segregation occurs. Amphidiploids, which are allopolyploids produced by chromosome doubling of genomes derived from different diploid parental species, are often fertile and are sometimes useful in agriculture.

On Our Website   www.mhhe.com/hartwell4

Annotated Suggested Readings and Links to Other Websites

- Historical articles describing early investigations on chromosomal rearrangements, transposable elements, and variations in chromosome number

- Recent reviews and research articles on these topics, with special emphasis on the use of transposable elements as tools for molecular genetic analysis

- A database cataloging human chromosomal abnormalities that have been characterized by fluorescence *in situ* hybridization (FISH) and comparative genomic hybridization (CGH)

- Online maps comparing the organization of human chromosomes with those from mice and rats

Solved Problems

I. Male *Drosophila* from a true-breeding wild-type stock were irradiated with X-rays and then mated with females from a true-breeding stock carrying the following recessive mutations on the X chromosome: yellow body (y), crossveinless wings (cv), cut wings (ct), singed bristles (sn), and miniature wings (m). These markers are known to map in the order:

$$y - cv - ct - sn - m$$

Most of the female progeny of this cross were phenotypically wild type, but one female exhibited ct and sn phenotypes. When this exceptional ct sn female was mated with a male from the true-breeding wild-type stock, there were twice as many females as males among the progeny.

a. What is the nature of the X-ray-induced mutation present in the exceptional female?

b. Draw the X chromosomes present in the exceptional ct sn female as they would appear during pairing in meiosis.

c. What phenotypic classes would you expect to see among the progeny produced by mating the exceptional ct sn female with a normal male from a true-breeding wild-type stock? List males and females separately.

Answer

To answer this problem, you need to think first about the effects of different types of chromosomal mutations in order to deduce the nature of the mutation. Then you can evaluate the consequences of the mutation on inheritance.

a. Two observations indicate that *X-rays induced a deletion mutation*. The fact that two recessive mutations are phenotypically expressed in the exceptional female suggests that a deletion was present on one of her X chromosomes that uncovered the two mutant alleles (ct and sn) on the other X chromosome. Second, the finding that there were twice as many females as males among the progeny of the exceptional female is also consistent with a deletion mutation. Males who inherit the deletion-bearing X chromosome from their exceptional mother will be inviable (because other essential genes are located in the region that is now deleted), but sons who inherit a nondeleted X chromosome will survive. On the other hand, all of the exceptional female's daughters will be viable: Even if they inherit a deleted X chromosome from their mother, they also receive a normal X chromosome from their father. As a result, there are half as many male progeny as females from the cross of the exceptional female with a wild-type male.

b. During pairing, *the DNA in the normal (nondeleted) X chromosome will loop out* because there is no homologous region in the deletion chromosome. In the simplified drawing of meiosis I that follows, each line represents both chromatids comprising each homolog.

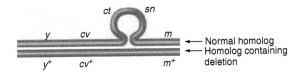

c. *All daughters of the exceptional female will be wild type* because the father contributes wild-type copies of all the genes. Each of the surviving sons must inherit a nondeleted X chromosome from the exceptional female. Some of these X chromosomes are produced from meioses in which no recombination occurred, but other X chromosomes are the products of recombination. *Males can have any of the genotypes listed here and therefore the corresponding phenotypes*. All contain the *ct sn* combination because no recombination between homologs is possible in this deleted region. Some of these genotypes require multiple crossovers during meiosis in the mother and will thus be relatively rare.

y	cv	ct	sn	m
+	+	ct	sn	+
+	cv	ct	sn	m
y	+	ct	sn	+
y	cv	ct	sn	+
+	+	ct	sn	m
+	cv	ct	sn	+
y	+	ct	sn	m

II. One of the X chromosomes in a particular *Drosophila* female had a normal order of genes but carried recessive alleles of the genes for yellow body color (*y*), vermilion eye color (*v*), and forked bristles (*f*), as well as the dominant X-linked Bar eye mutation (*B*). Her other X chromosome carried the wild-type alleles of all four genes, but the region including y^+, v^+, and f^+ (but not B^+) was inverted with respect to the normal order of genes. This female was crossed to a wild-type male in the cross diagrammed here.

The cross produced the following male offspring:

y	v	f	B	48
y^+	v^+	f^+	B^+	45
y	v	f	B^+	11
y^+	v^+	f^+	B	8
y	v^+	f	B	1
y^+	v	f^+	B^+	1

a. Why are there no male offspring with the allele combinations $y\ v\ f^+$, $y^+\ v^+\ f$, $y\ v^+\ f^+$, or $y^+\ v\ f$, (regardless of the allele of the Bar eye gene)?

b. What kinds of crossovers produced the $y\ v\ f\ B^+$ and $v^+\ y^+\ f^+\ B$ offspring? Can you determine any genetic distances from these classes of progeny?

c. What kinds of crossovers produced the $y^+\ v\ f^+\ B^+$ and $y\ v^+\ f\ B$ offspring?

Answer

To answer this question, you need to be able to draw and interpret pairing in inversion heterozygotes. Note that this inversion is paracentric.

a. During meiosis in an inversion heterozygote, a loop of the inverted region is formed when the homologous genes align. In the following simplified drawing, each line represents both chromatids comprising each homolog.

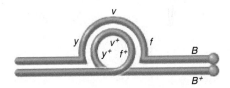

If a single crossover occurs within the inversion loop, a dicentric and an acentric chromosome are formed. Cells containing these types of chromosomes are not viable. The resulting allele combinations from such single crossovers are not recovered. The four phenotypic classes of missing male offspring would be formed by single crossovers between the y and v or between the v and f genes in the female inversion heterozygote and therefore are not recovered.

b. *The* y v f B^+ *and* y^+ v^+ f^+ B *offspring are the result of single crossover events outside of the inversion loop, between the end of the inversion (just to the right of* f *on the preceding diagram) and the B gene. This region is approximately 16.7 m.u. in length (19 recombinants out of 114 total progeny).*

c. *The* y^+ v f^+ B^+ *and* y v^+ f B *offspring would result from two crossover events within the inversion loop, one between the* y *and* v *genes and the other between the* v *and* f *genes.* You should note that these could be either two-strand or three-strand double crossovers, but they could not be four-strand double crossovers.

III. In maize trisomics, $n + 1$ pollen is not viable. If a dominant allele at the *B* locus produces purple color instead of the recessive phenotype bronze and a *B b b* trisomic plant is pollinated by a *B B b* plant, what proportion of the progeny produced will be trisomic and have a bronze phenotype?

Answer

To solve this problem, think about what is needed to produce trisomic bronze progeny: three *b* chromosomes in the zygote. The female parent would have to contribute two *b* alleles, because the $n + 1$ pollen from the male is not viable. What kinds of gametes could be generated by the trisomic *B b b* purple female parent, and in what proportion? To track all the possibilities, rewrite this genotype as $B\ b_1\ b_2$, even though b_1 and b_2 have identical effects on phenotype. In the trisomic female, there are three possible ways the chromosomes carrying these alleles could pair as bivalents during the first meiotic division so that they would segregate to opposite poles: *B* with b_1, *B* with b_2, and b_1 with b_2. In all three cases, the remaining chromosome could move to either pole. To tabulate the possibilities as a branching diagram:

Pairing possibilities

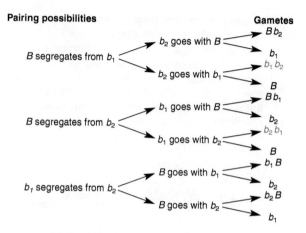

Gametes

Of the 12 gamete classes produced by these different possible segregations, only the 2 classes written in red contain the two *b* alleles needed to generate the bronze (*b b b*) trisomic zygotes. There is thus a $2/12 = 1/6$ chance of obtaining such gametes.

Although segregation in the *B B b* male parent is equally complicated, remember that males cannot produce viable $n + 1$ pollen. The only surviving gametes would thus be *B* and *b,* in a ratio (*2/3 B* and *1/3 b*) that must reflect their relative prevalence in the male parent genome. *The probability of obtaining trisomic bronze progeny from this cross is therefore the product of the individual probabilities of the appropriate* b b *gametes from the female parent (1/6) and* b *pollen from the male parent (1/3): 1/6 × 1/3 = 1/18.*

Problems

Vocabulary

1. For each of the terms in the left column, choose the best matching phrase in the right column.

a. reciprocal translocation	1. lacking one or more chromosomes or having one or more extra chromosomes
b. gynandromorph	2. movement of short DNA elements
c. pericentric	3. having more than two complete sets of chromosomes
d. paracentric	4. exact exchange of parts of two nonhomologous chromosomes
e. euploids	5. excluding the centromere
f. polyploidy	6. including the centromere
g. transposition	7. having complete sets of chromosomes
h. aneuploids	8. mosaic combination of male and female tissue

Section 13.1

2. For each of the following types of chromosomal aberrations, tell: (i) whether an organism heterozygous for the aberration will form any type of loop in the chromosomes during prophase I of meiosis; (ii) whether a chromosomal bridge can be formed during anaphase I in a heterozygote, and if so, under what condition; (iii) whether an acentric fragment can be formed during anaphase I in a heterozygote, and if so, under what condition; (iv) whether the aberration can suppress meiotic recombination; and (v) whether the two chromosomal breaks responsible for the aberration occur on the same side or on opposite sides of a single centromere, or if the two breaks occur on different chromosomes.
a. reciprocal translocation
b. paracentric inversion
c. small tandem duplication
d. Robertsonian translocation
e. paracentric inversion
f. large deletion

3. In flies that are heterozygous for either a deletion or a duplication, there will be a looped-out region in a preparation of polytene chromosomes. How could you distinguish between a deletion or a duplication using polytene chromosome analysis?

4. For the following types of chromosomal rearrangements, would it theoretically ever be possible to obtain a perfect reversion of the rearrangement? If so, would such revertants be found only rarely, or would they be relatively common?
a. a deletion of a region including five genes
b. a tandem duplication of a region including five genes
c. a pericentric inversion
d. a Robertsonian translocation
e. a mutation caused by a transposable element jumping into a protein-coding exon of a gene

5. Four strains of *Drosophila* were constructed in which one autosome contained recessive mutant alleles of the four genes *rolled eyes, thick legs, straw bristles,* and *apterous wings,* and the homologous autosome contained one of four different deletions (deletions 1–4). The phenotypes of the flies were as follows:

Deletion	Phenotype
1	rolled eyes, straw bristles
2	apterous wings, rolled eyes
3	thick legs, straw bristles
4	apterous wings

Whole-genome DNA was prepared from the flies. The DNA was digested to completion with the restriction enzyme *Bam*HI, run on an agarose gel, and transferred to nitrocellulose filters. The filters were then probed with a 20 kb cloned piece of wild-type genomic DNA obtained by partially digesting the plasmid clone with *Bam*HI (so the ends of the probe were *Bam*HI ends, but the piece was not digested into all the possible *Bam*HI fragments). The results of this whole-genome Southern blot are shown below. Dark bands indicate fragments present twice in the diploid genome; light bands indicate fragments present once in the genome.

	6.3	6.3	6.3	6.3
	5.6	5.6	5.6	5.6
	5.1			
				4.9
	4.2	4.2	4.2	4.2
	3.8			
		3.3		
	3.0	3.0	3.0	3.0
			1.7	
	0.9	0.9	0.9	0.9

Deletion   1   2   3   4

a. Make a map of the *Bam*HI restriction sites in this 20 kb part of the wild-type *Drosophila* genome, indicating distances in kilobases between adjacent *Bam*HI sites. (*Hint:* The genomic DNA fragments in wild type are 6.3, 5.6, 4.2, 3.0, and 0.9 kb long.)
b. On your map, indicate the locations of the genes.

6. A diploid strain of yeast was made by mating a haploid strain with a genotype w^-, x^-, y^-, and z^- with a haploid strain of opposite mating type that is wild type for these four genes. The diploid strain was phenotypically wild type. Four different X-ray-induced diploid mutants with the following phenotypes were produced from this diploid yeast strain. Assume there is a single new mutation in each strain.

Strain 1	w^-	x^+	y^-	z^+
Strain 2	w^+	x^-	y^-	z^-
Strain 3	w^-	x^+	y^-	z^-
Strain 4	w^-	x^+	y^+	z^+

When these mutant diploid strains of yeast go through meiosis, each ascus is found to contain only two viable haploid spores.
a. What kind of mutations were induced by X-rays to make the listed diploid strains?
b. Why did two spores in each ascus die?
c. Are any of the genes *w, x, y,* or *z* located on the same chromosome?
d. Give the order of the genes that are found on the same chromosome.

7. Human chromosome 1 is a large, metacentric chromosome. A map of a cloned region from near the telomere of chromosome 1 is shown below. Three probe DNAs (A, B, and C) from this region were used for *in situ* hybridization to human mitotic metaphase chromosome squashes made with cells obtained from individuals with various genotypes. The breakpoints of chromosomal rearrangements in this region are indicated on the map. The black bars for deletions (*Del*) 1 and 2 represent DNA that is deleted. The breakpoints of inversions (*Inv*) 1 and 2 not shown in the figure are near but not at the centromere. For each of the following genotypes, draw chromosome 1 as it would appear after *in situ* hybridization. An example is shown in the following figure for hybridization of probe A to the two copies of chromosome 1 in wild type($+/+$).

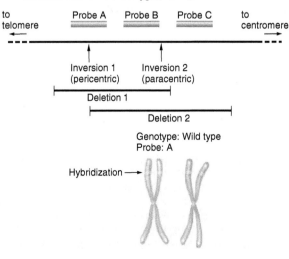

a. genotype: *Del1/Del2;* probe: B
b. genotype: *Del1/Del2;* probe: C
c. genotype: *Del1/+;* probe: A
d. genotype: *Inv1/+;* probe: A
e. genotype: *Inv2/+;* probe: B
f. genotype: *Inv2/Inv2;* probe: C

8. A series of chromosomal mutations in *Drosophila* were used to map the *javelin* gene, which affects bristle shape, and *henna,* which affects eye pigmentation. Both the *javelin* and *henna* mutations are recessive. A diagram of region 65 of the *Drosophila* polytene chromosomes is shown here.

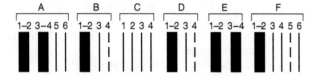

The chromosomal breakpoints for six chromosome rearrangements are indicated in the following table. (For example, deletion A has one breakpoint between bands A2 and A3 and the other between bands D2 and D3.)

Breakpoints in region 65			
Deletions	A	A2–3;	D2–3
	B	C2–3;	E4–F1
	C	D2–3;	F4–5
	D	D4–E1;	F3–4

Breakpoints			
Inversions	A	Band 65A6	Band 82A1
	B	Band 65B4	Band 98A3

Flies with a chromosome containing one of these six rearrangements (deletions or inversions) were mated to flies homozygous for both *javelin* and *henna.* The phenotypes of the heterozygous progeny (that is, *rearrangement/javelin, henna*) are shown here.

Phenotypes of F₁ flies		
Deletions	A	javelin, henna
	B	henna
	C	wild type
	D	wild type
Inversions	A	javelin
	B	wild type

Using these data, what can you conclude about the cytogenetic location for the *javelin* and *henna* genes?

9. The partially recessive, X-linked z^1 mutation of the *Drosophila* gene *zeste* (*z*) can produce a yellow (zeste) eye color only in flies that have two or more copies of the wild-type *white* (*w*) gene. Using this property, tandem duplications of the w^+ gene called w^{+R} were identified. Males with the genotype $z^1 \, w^{+R}/Y$ thus have zeste eyes. These males were crossed to females

with the genotype $y \, z^1 \, w^{+R} \, spl/y^+ \, z^1 \, w^{+R} \, spl^+$. (These four genes are closely linked on the X chromosome, in the order given in the genotype, with the centromere to the right of all these genes: y = yellow bodies; y^+ = tan bodies; spl = split bristles; spl^+ = normal bristles.) Out of 81,540 male progeny of these females, the following exceptions were found:

Class A	2430 yellow bodies, zeste eyes, wild-type bristles
Class B	2394 tan bodies, zeste eyes, split bristles
Class C	23 yellow bodies, wild-type eyes, wild-type bristles
Class D	22 tan bodies, wild-type eyes, split bristles

a. What were the phenotypes of the remainder of the 81,540 males from the first cross?
b. What events gave rise to progeny of classes A and B?
c. What events gave rise to progeny of classes C and D?
d. On the basis of these experiments, what is the genetic distance between *y* and *spl?*

10. Genes *a* and *b* are 21 m.u. apart when mapped in highly inbred strain 1 of corn and 21 m.u. apart when mapped in highly inbred strain 2. But when the distance is mapped by testcrossing the F₁ progeny of a cross between strains 1 and 2, the two genes are only 1.5 m.u. apart. What arrangement of genes *a* and *b* and any potential rearrangement breakpoints could explain these results?

11. In the following group of figures, the *pink* lines indicate an area of a chromosome that is inverted relative to the normal (*black* line) order of genes. The diploid chromosome constitution of individuals 1–4 is shown. Match the individuals with the appropriate statement(s) that follow. More than one diagram may correspond to the following statements, and a diagram may be a correct answer for more than one question.

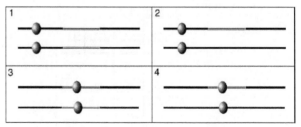

a. An inversion loop would form during meiosis I and in polytene chromosomes.
b. A single crossover involving the inverted region on one chromosome and the homologous region of the other chromosome would yield genetically imbalanced gametes.
c. A single crossover involving the inverted region on one chromosome and the homologous region of the other chromosome would yield an acentric fragment.
d. A single crossover involving the inverted region yields four viable gametes.

12. Three strains of *Drosophila* (Bravo, X-ray, and Zorro) are obtained that are homozygous for three variant forms of a particular chromosome. When examined in salivary gland polytene chromosome spreads, all chromosomes have the same number of bands in all three strains. When genetic mapping is performed in the Bravo strain, the following map is obtained (distances in map units).

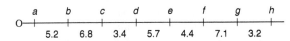

Bravo and X-ray flies are now mated to form Bravo/X-ray F_1 progeny, and Bravo flies are also mated with Zorro flies to form Bravo/Zorro F_1 progeny. In subsequent crosses, the following genetic distances were found to separate the various genes in the hybrids:

	Bravo/X-ray	Bravo/Zorro
a–b	5.2	5.2
b–c	6.8	0.7
c–d	0.2	<0.1
d–e	<0.1	<0.1
e–f	<0.1	<0.1
f–g	0.65	0.7
g–h	3.2	3.2

a. Make a map showing the relative order of genes *a* through *h* in the X-ray and Zorro strains. Do not show distances between genes.

b. In the original X-ray homozygotes, would the physical distance between genes *c* and *d* be greater than, less than, or approximately equal to the physical distance between these same genes in the original Bravo homozygotes?

c. In the original X-ray homozygotes, would the physical distance between genes *d* and *e* be greater than, less than, or approximately equal to the physical distance between these same genes in the original Bravo homozygotes?

13. Two yeast strains were mated and sporulated (allowed to carry out meiosis). One strain was a haploid with normal chromosomes and the linked genetic markers *ura3* (requires uracil for growth) and *arg9* (requires arginine for growth) surrounding their centromere. The other strain was wild type for the two markers (*URA3* and *ARG9*) but had an inversion in this region of the chromosome as shown here in *pink:*

During meiosis, several different kinds of crossover events could occur. For each of the following events, give the genotype and phenotype of the resulting four haploid spores. Assume that any chromosomal defi-ciencies are lethal in haploid yeast. Do not consider crossovers between sister chromatids.

a. a single crossover outside the inverted region

b. a single crossover between *URA3* and the centromere

c. a double crossover involving the same two chromatids each time, where one crossover occurs between *URA3* and the centromere and the other occurs between *ARG9* and the centromere

14. Suppose a haploid yeast strain carrying two recessive linked markers *his4* and *leu2* was crossed with a strain that was wild type for *HIS4* and *LEU2* but had an inversion of this region of the chromosome as shown here in *blue.*

Several different kinds of crossover events could occur during meiosis in the resulting diploid. For each of the following events, state the genotype and phenotype of the resulting four haploid spores. Do not consider crossover events between chromatids attached to the same centromere.

a. a single crossover between the markers *HIS4* and *LEU2*

b. a double crossover involving the same chromatids each time, where both crossovers occur between the markers *HIS4* and *LEU2*

c. a single crossover between the centromere and the beginning of the inverted region

15. In the mating between two haploid yeast strains depicted in Problem 14, describe a scenario that would result in a tetratype ascus in which all four spores are viable.

16. During ascus formation in *Neurospora,* any ascospore with a chromosomal deletion dies and appears white in color. How many ascospores of the eight spores in the ascus would be white if the octad came from a cross of a wild-type strain with a strain of the opposite mating type carrying

a. a paracentric inversion, and no crossovers occurred between normal and inverted chromosomes?

b. a pericentric inversion, and a single crossover occurred in the inversion loop?

c. a paracentric inversion, and a single crossover occurred outside the inversion loop?

d. a reciprocal translocation, and an adjacent-1 segregation occurred with no crossovers between translocated chromosomes?

e. a reciprocal translocation, and alternate segregation occurred with no crossovers between translocated chromosomes?

f. a reciprocal translocation, and alternate segregation occurred with one crossover between translocated chromosomes (but not between the translocation breakpoint and the centromere of any chromosome)?

17. In the following figure, *black* and *pink* lines represent nonhomologous chromosomes. Which of the figures matches the descriptions below? More than one diagram may correspond to the statements, and a diagram may be a correct answer for more than one question.

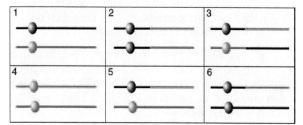

a. gametes produced by a translocation heterozygote
b. gametes that could not be produced by a translocation heterozygote
c. genetically balanced gametes produced by a translocation heterozygote
d. genetically imbalanced gametes that can be produced (at any frequency) by a translocation heterozygote

18. In *Drosophila*, the gene for cinnabar eye color is on chromosome 2, and the gene for scarlet eye color is on chromosome 3. A fly homozygous for both recessive *cinnabar* and *scarlet* alleles (*cn/cn; st/st*) is white-eyed.
a. If male flies (containing chromosomes with the normal gene order) heterozygous for *cn* and *st* alleles are crossed to white-eyed females homozygous for the *cn* and *st* alleles, what are the expected phenotypes and their frequencies in the progeny?
b. One unusual male heterozygous for *cn* and *st* alleles, when crossed to a white-eyed female, produced only wild-type and white-eyed progeny. Explain the likely chromosomal constitution of this male.
c. When the wild-type F_1 females from the cross with the unusual male were backcrossed to normal *cn/cn; st/st* males, the following results were obtained:

wild type	45%
cinnabar	5%
scarlet	5%
white	45%

Diagram a genetic event at metaphase I that could produce the rare cinnabar or scarlet flies among the progeny of the wild-type F_1 females.

19. Semisterility in corn, as seen by unfilled ears with gaps due to abortion of approximately half the ovules, is an indication that the strain is a translocation heterozygote. The chromosomes involved in the translocation can be identified by crossing the translocation heterozygote to a strain homozygous recessive for a gene on the chromosome being tested. The ratio of phenotypic classes produced from crossing semisterile F_1 progeny back to a homozygous recessive plant indicates whether the gene is on one of the chromosomes involved in the translocation. For example, a semisterile strain could be crossed to a strain homozygous for the *yg* mutation on chromosome 9. (The mutant has yellow-green leaves instead of the wild-type green leaves.) The semisterile F_1 progeny would then be backcrossed to the homozygous *yg* mutant.
a. What types of progeny (fertile or semisterile, green or yellow-green) would you predict from the backcross of the F_1 to the homozygous *yg* mutant if the gene was not on one of the two chromosomes involved in the translocation?
b. What types of progeny (fertile or semisterile, green or yellow-green) would you predict from the backcross of the F_1 to the homozygous mutant if the *yg* gene is on one of the two chromosomes involved in the translocation?
c. If the *yg* gene is located on one of the chromosomes involved in the translocation, a few fertile, green progeny and a few semisterile, yellow-green progeny are produced. How could these relatively rare progeny classes arise? What genetic distance could you determine from the frequency of these rare progeny?

20. A proposed biological method for insect control involves the release of insects that could interfere with the fertility of the normal resident insects. One approach is to introduce sterile males to compete with the resident fertile males for matings. A disadvantage of this strategy is that the irradiated sterile males are not very robust and can have problems competing with the fertile males. An alternate approach that is being tried is to release laboratory-reared insects that are homozygous for several translocations. Explain how this strategy will work. Be sure to mention which insects will be sterile.

21. A *Drosophila* male is heterozygous for a translocation between an autosome originally bearing the dominant mutation *Lyra* (shortened wings) and the Y chromosome; the other copy of the same autosome is *Lyra*$^+$. This male is now mated with a true-breeding, wild-type female. What kinds of progeny would be obtained, and in what proportions?

22. a. Among the selfed progeny of a semisterile corn plant that is heterozygous for a reciprocal translocation, what ratio do you expect for progeny plants with normal fertility versus those showing semisterility? In this problem, ignore the rare gametes produced by adjacent-2 segregation.
b. Among the selfed progeny of a particular semisterile corn plant heterozygous for a reciprocal translocation, the ratio of fertile to semisterile plants was 1:4. How can you explain this deviation from your answer to part *a?*

23. Solved problem I on p. 195 of Chapter 6 shows the genesis of a small chromosomal inversion. Assuming that 11 bp-long primers can be used for the polymerase chain reaction (even though ordinarily longer primers are needed), give the sequences of the two 11 bp primers that could be used to generate the longest PCR product that would indicate the presence of the inversion. (That is, this pair of primers would produce a PCR product from the genomic DNA of individuals with the inversion, but not from wild type genomic DNA.)

24. The figure below portrays human chromosome 21 in blue and chromosome 14 in red. The arrows represent the 5′-to-3′ orientations of various PCR primers. If primer A is one of the two primers used, what is the other primer you could employ to diagnose the presence of a Robertsonian translocation (14q21q) that might be involved in translocation Down syndrome? (That is, which numbered primer, in conjunction with primer A, would produce a PCR product from the genomic DNA of individuals with the translocation, but no PCR product from genomic DNA lacking the translocation?)

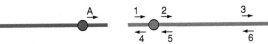

Section 13.2

25. The picture at the beginning of this chapter on p. 429 shows a polytene chromosome preparation from a fruit fly heterozygous for a chromosome carrying a very large composite transposon and a wild-type homolog. Suppose you had a probe made from wild-type DNA sequences that span the site into which the transposon is inserted. Diagram the pattern of *in situ* hybridization you would expect on the polytene chromosome preparation shown on p. 429.

26. Explain how transposable elements can cause movement of genes that are not part of the transposable element.

27. In the 1950s, Barbara McClintock found a transposable element in corn she called *Ds* (*Dissociator*). When inserted at a particular location, this element could often cause chromosomal breaks at that site, but these breaks occurred only in the presence of another unlinked genetic element she called *Ac* (*Activator*). She found further that in the presence of *Ac*, *Ds* could jump to other chromosomal locations. At some of these locations (and in the presence of *Ac*), *Ds* would now cause chromosomal breakage at the new position; at other positions, it appeared that *Ds* could cause new mutations that were unstable as shown by their patchy, variegated expression in kernels. Interestingly, the position of the *Ac* element seemed to be very different in various strains of corn. Explain these results in terms of our present-day understanding of transposons.

28. Gerasimova and colleagues in the former Soviet Union characterized a mutation in the *Drosophila* cut wing (*ct*) gene called ct^{MR2}, which is associated with the insertion of a transposable element called *gypsy*. This

allele is very unstable: approximately 1 in 100 of the progeny of flies bearing ct^{MR2} show new *ct* variants. Some of these are ct^+ revertants, whereas others appear to be more severe alleles of *ct* with stronger effects on wing shape. When the ct^+ revertants themselves are mated, some of the ct^+ alleles appear to be stable (no new *ct* mutants appear), whereas others are highly unstable (many new mutations appear). What might explain the generation of stable and unstable ct^+ revertants as well as the stronger *ct* mutant alleles?

29. In sequencing a region of the human genome, you have come across a segment of about 200 A nucleotides. You suspect that the sequence preceding the A residues may have been moved here by a transposition event mediated by reverse transcriptase. If the adjacent sequence is in fact a retroposon, you might expect to find other copies in the genome. How could you determine if other copies of this DNA exist in the genome, and whether this DNA is indeed transposable?

30. The *Eco*RI restriction map of the region in which a coat-color gene in mice is located is presented in the following. The left-most *Eco*RI site is arbitrarily labeled 0 and the other distances in kilobases are given relative to this coordinate. Genomic DNA was prepared from one wild-type mouse and 10 mice homozygous for various mutant alleles. This genomic DNA is digested with *Eco*RI, fractionated on agarose gels, and then transferred to nitrocellulose filters. The filters were probed with the radioactive DNA fragment indicated by the *purple* bar, extending from coordinate 2.6 kb to coordinate 14.5. The resultant autoradiogram is shown schematically.

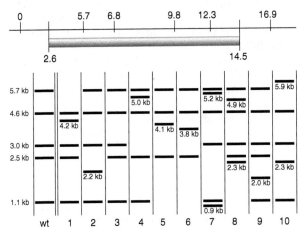

Assume that each of the mutations 1–10 is caused by one and only one of the events on the following list. Which event corresponds to which mutation?

a. a point mutation exactly at coordinate 6.8

b. a point mutation exactly at coordinate 6.9

c. a deletion between coordinates 10.1 and 10.4

d. a deletion between coordinates 6.7 and 7.0

e. insertion of a transposable element at coordinate 6.2

f. an inversion with breakpoints at coordinates 2.2 and 9.9

g. a reciprocal translocation with another chromosome with a breakpoint at coordinate 10.1

h. a reciprocal translocation with another chromosome with a breakpoint at coordinate 2.4

i. a tandem duplication of sequences between coordinates 7.2 and 9.2

j. a tandem duplication of sequences between coordinates 11.3 and 14.3

Section 13.3

31. In the figure at the bottom of the page, the top and bottom lines represent chromosomes 4 and 12 of the yeast *Saccharomyces cerevisiae* (*Scer 4* and *Scer 12*). Numbers refer to specific genes, and the red arrows represent the direction and extent of transcription. The middle line is the sequence of a region from chromosome 1 from a different, but related yeast species called *Klyuyveromyces waltii* (*Kwal 1*), with genes indicated in *light blue*. Homologies (close relationships in DNA sequence) are shown as lines joining chromosomes of the two species.

a. What is the meaning of the two *K. waltii* genes filled in *dark purple?*

b. Based on these data, formulate a hypothesis to explain the genesis of the part of the *S. cerevisiae* genome illustrated in the figure.

32. Two possible models have been proposed to explain the potential evolutionary advantage of gene duplications. In the first model, one of the two duplicated copies retains the same function as the ancestral gene, leaving the other copy to diverge through mutation to fulfill a new biochemical function. In the second model, both copies can diverge rapidly from the ancestral gene, so that both can acquire new properties. Considering your answer to Problem 31, and given that both the *S. cerevisiae* and *K. waltii* genomes have been completely sequenced, how could you determine which of these two models better represents the course of evolution?

Section 13.4

33. The number of chromosomes in the somatic cells of several oat varieties (*Avena* species) are: sand oats (*Avena strigosa*)—14; slender wild oats (*Avena barata*)—28; and cultivated oats (*Avena sativa*)—42.

a. What is the basic chromosome number (*x*) in *Avena?*

b. What is the ploidy for each of the different species?

c. What is the number of chromosomes in the gametes produced by each of these oat varieties?

d. What is the *n* number of chromosomes in each species?

34. Common red clover, *Trifolium pratense,* is a diploid with 14 chromosomes per somatic cell. What would be the somatic chromosome number of

a. a trisomic variant of this species?

b. a monosomic variant of this species?

c. a triploid variant of this species?

d. an autotetraploid variant?

35. Somatic cells in organisms of a particular diploid plant species normally have 14 chromosomes. The chromosomes in the gametes are numbered from 1 through 7. Rarely, zygotes are formed that contain more or fewer than 14 chromosomes. For each of the zygotes below, (i) state whether the chromosome complement is euploid or aneuploid; (ii) provide terms that describe the individual's genetic makeup as accurately as possible; and (iii) state whether or not the individual will likely develop through the embryonic stages to make an adult plant, and if so, whether or not this plant will be fertile.

a. 11 22 33 44 5 66 77

b. 111 22 33 44 555 66 77

c. 111 222 333 444 555 666 777

d. 1111 2222 3333 4444 5555 6666 7777

36. Genomes A, B, and C all have basic chromosome numbers (*x*) of nine. These genomes were originally derived from plant species that had diverged from each other sufficiently far back in the evolutionary past that the chromosomes from one genome can no longer pair with the chromosomes from any other genome. For plants with the following kinds of euploid chromosome complements, (i) state the number of chromosomes in the organism; (ii) provide terms that describe the individual's genetic makeup as accurately as possible; (iii) state whether or not it is likely that this plant will be fertile, and if so, give the number of chromosomes (*n*) in the gametes.

a. AABBC

b. BBBB

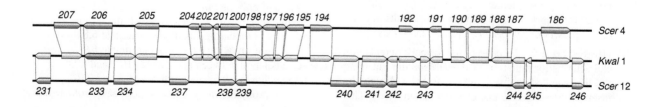

c. CCC

d. BBCC

e. ABC

f. AABBCC

37. Fred and Mary have a child with Down syndrome. A probe derived from chromosome 21 was used to identify RFLPs in Fred, Mary, and the child (darker bands indicate signals of twice the intensity). Explain what kind of nondisjunction events must have occurred to produce the child if the child's RFLP pattern looked like that in lanes A, B, C, or D of the following figure:

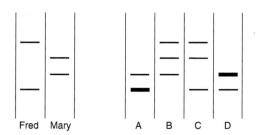

38. *Uniparental disomy* is a rare phenomenon in which only one of the parents of a child with a recessive disorder is a carrier for that trait; the other parent is homozygous normal. By analyzing DNA polymorphisms, it is clear that the child received both mutant alleles from the carrier parent but did not receive any copy of the gene from the other parent.

a. Diagram at least two ways in which uniparental disomy could arise. (*Hint:* These mechanisms all require more than one error in cell division, explaining why uniparental disomy is so rare.) Is there any way to distinguish between these mechanisms to explain any particular case of uniparental disomy?

b. How might the phenomenon of uniparental disomy explain rare cases in which girls are affected with rare X-linked recessive disorders but have unaffected fathers, or other cases in which an X-linked recessive disorder is transmitted from father to son?

c. If you were a human geneticist and believed one of your patients had a disease syndrome caused by uniparental disomy, how could you establish that the cause was not instead mitotic recombination early in the patient's development from a zygote?

39. Human geneticists interested in the effects of abnormalities in chromosome number often karyotype tissue obtained from spontaneous abortions. About 35% of these samples show autosomal trisomies, but only about 3% of the samples display autosomal monosomies. Based on the kinds of errors that can give rise to aneuploidy, would you expect that the frequencies of autosomal trisomy and autosomal monosomy should be more equal? Why or why not? If you think the frequencies should be more equal, how can you explain the large excess of trisomies as opposed to monosomies?

40. Among adults with Turner syndrome, it has been found that a very high proportion are genetic mosaics. These are of two types: In some individuals, the majority of cells are 45, XO, but a minority of cells are 46, XX. In other Turner individuals, the majority of cells are 45, XO, but a minority of cells are 46, XY. Explain how these somatic mosaics could arise.

41. The *Drosophila* chromosome 4 is extremely small; there is virtually no recombination between genes on this chromosome. You have available three differently marked chromosome 4's: one has a recessive allele of the gene *eyeless* (*ey*), causing very small eyes; one has a recessive allele of the *cubitus interruptus* (*ci*) gene, which causes disruptions in the veins on the wings; and the third carries the recessive alleles of both genes. *Drosophila* adults can survive with two or three, but not with one or four, copies of chromosome 4.

a. How could you use these three chromosomes to find *Drosophila* mutants with defective meioses causing an elevated rate of nondisjunction?

b. Would your technique allow you to discriminate nondisjunction occurring during the first meiotic division from nondisjunction occurring during the second meiotic division?

c. What progeny would you expect if a fly recognizably formed from a gamete produced by nondisjunction were testcrossed to a fly homozygous for a chromosome 4 carrying both *ey* and *ci?*

d. Geneticists have isolated so-called *compound 4th chromosomes* in which two entire chromosome 4's are attached to the same centromere. How can such chromosomes be used to identify mutations causing increased meiotic nondisjunction? Are there any advantages relative to the method you described in part *a?*

42. In *Neurospora*, *his2* mutants require the amino acid histidine for growth, and *lys4* mutants require the amino acid lysine. The two genes are on the same arm of the same chromosome, in the order

centromere - *his2* - *lys4*.

A *his2* mutant is mated with a *lys4* mutant. Draw all of the possible ordered asci that could result from meioses in which the following events occurred, accounting for the nutritional requirements for each ascospore. Ascospores without any copy of a chromosome will abort and die, turning white in the process.

a. a single crossover between the centromere and *his2*

b. a single crossover between *his2* and *lys4*

c. nondisjunction during the first meiotic division

d. nondisjunction during the second meiotic division

e. a single crossover between the centromere and *his2,* followed by nondisjunction during the first meiotic division

f. a single crossover between *his2* and *lys4,* followed by nondisjunction during the first meiotic division

43. You have haploid tobacco cells in culture and have made transgenic cells that are resistant to herbicide. What would you do to obtain a diploid cell line that could be used to generate a new fertile herbicide-resistant plant?

44. An allotetraploid species has a genome composed of two ancestral genomes, A and B, each of which have a basic chromosome number (x) of seven. In this species, the two copies of each chromosome of each ancestral genome pair only with each other during meiosis. Resistance to a pathogen that attacks the foliage of the plant is controlled by a dominant allele at the F locus. The recessive alleles F^a and F^b confer sensitivity to the pathogen, but the dominant resistance alleles present in the two genomes have slightly different effects. Plants with at least one F^A allele are resistant to races 1 and 2 of the pathogen regardless of the genotype in the B genome, and plants with at least one F^B allele are resistant to races 1 and 3 of the pathogen regardless of the genotype in the A genome. What proportion of the self-progeny of an F^A F^a F^B F^b plant will be resistant to all three races of the pathogen?

45. Using karyotype analysis, how could you distinguish between autopolyploids and allopolyploids?

46. Chromosomes normally associate during meiosis I as bivalents (a pair of synapsed homologous chromosomes) because chromosome pairing involves the synapsis of the corresponding regions of two homologous chromosomes. However, Fig. 13.21b on p. 445 shows that in a heterozygote for a reciprocal translocation, chromosomes pair as quadrivalents (that is, four chromosomes are associated with each other).

Quadrivalents can form in other ways: For example, in some autotetraploid species, chromosomes can pair as quadrivalents rather than as bivalents.

a. How could quadrivalents actually form in these autotetraploids, given that chromosomal regions synapse in pairs? To answer this question, diagram such a quadrivalent.

b. How can these autotetraploid species generate euploid gametes if the chromosomes pair as quadrivalents rather than bivalents?

c. Could quadrivalents form in an amphidiploid species? Discuss.

Section 13.5

47. The accompanying figure shows a virtual karyotype obtained from a line of tumor cells derived from a human leukemia. The left-to-right direction for each chromosome corresponds to the orientation of that chromosome from the telomere of the small arm to the telomere of the long arm. Every colored dot corresponds to a different short region of the chromosome analyzed by a microarray technique similar to that shown in Fig. 13.39 on p. 464.

a. Do the data indicate the existence of aneuploidy or any chromosomal rearrangements within the genome of the tumor cell?

b. What do you think you would see if you did a virtual karyotype of a cell line derived from normal, nonleukemic cells from the same person?

c. Are there any kinds of chromosomal rearrangements that could not be detected by this virtual karyotyping method?

d. What do these data say about genes that might be responsible for the leukemia?

e. Do these data tell us anything about the dosage of genes needed for the viability of individual cells?

Anatomy and Function of a Gene: Dissection Through Mutation

A scale played on a piano keyboard and a gene on a chromosome are both a series of simple, linear elements (keys or nucleotide pairs) that produce information. A wrong note or an altered nucleotide pair calls attention to the structure of the musical scale or the gene.

Human chromosome 3 consists of approximately 220 million base pairs and carries 1000–2000 genes (**Fig. 7.1**). Somewhere on the long arm of the chromosome resides the gene for rhodopsin, a light-sensitive protein active in the rod cells of our retinas. The rhodopsin gene determines perception of low-intensity light. People who carry the normal, wild-type allele of the gene see well in a dimly lit room and on the road at night. One simple change—a mutation—in the rhodopsin gene, however, diminishes light perception just enough to lead to night blindness. Other alterations in the gene cause the destruction of rod cells, resulting in total blindness. Medical researchers have so far identified more than 30 mutations in the rhodopsin gene that affect vision in different ways.

The case of the rhodopsin gene illustrates some very basic questions. Which of the 220 million base pairs on chromosome 3 make up the rhodopsin gene? How are the base pairs that comprise this gene arranged along the chromosome? How can a single gene sustain so many mutations that lead to such divergent phenotypic effects? In this chapter, we describe the ingenious experiments performed by geneticists during the 1950s and 1960s as they examined the relationships among mutations, genes, chromosomes, and phenotypes in an effort to understand, at the molecular level, what genes are and how they function.

We can recognize three main themes from the elegant work of these investigators. The first is that mutations are heritable changes in base sequence that affect phenotype. The second is that physically, a gene is usually a specific protein-encoding segment of DNA in a discrete region of a chromosome. (We now know that some genes encode various kinds of RNA that do not get translated into protein.) Third, a gene is not simply a bead on a string, changeable only as a whole and only in one way, as some had believed. Rather, genes are divisible, and each gene's subunits—the individual nucleotide pairs of DNA—can mutate independently and can recombine with each other.

Knowledge of what genes are and how they work deepens our understanding of Mendelian genetics by providing a biochemical explanation for how genotype influences phenotype. One mutation in the rhodopsin gene, for example, causes

CHAPTER OUTLINE

- 7.1 Mutations: Primary Tools of Genetic Analysis
- 7.2 What Mutations Tell Us About Gene Structure
- 7.3 What Mutations Tell Us About Gene Function
- 7.4 A Comprehensive Example: Mutations That Affect Vision

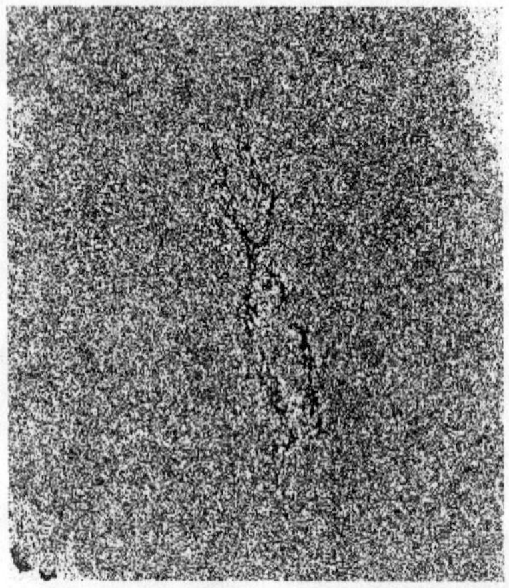

Figure 7.1 The DNA of each human chromosome contains hundreds to thousands of genes. The DNA of this human chromosome has been spread out and magnified 50,000×. No topological signs reveal where along the DNA the genes reside. The darker, chromosome-shaped structure in the middle is a scaffold of proteins to which the DNA is attached.

the substitution of one particular amino acid for another in the construction of the rhodopsin protein. This single substitution changes the three-dimensional structure of rhodopsin and thus the protein's ability to absorb photons, ultimately altering a person's ability to perceive light.

7.1 Mutations: Primary Tools of Genetic Analysis

We saw in Chapter 3 that genes with one common allele are *monomorphic,* while genes with several common alleles in natural populations are *polymorphic.* The term **wild-type allele** has a clear definition for monomorphic genes, where the allele found on the large majority of chromosomes in the population under consideration is wild-type. In the case of polymorphic genes, the definition is less straightforward. Some geneticists consider all alleles with a frequency of greater than 1% to be wild-type, while others describe the many alleles present at appreciable frequencies in the population as *common variants* and reserve "wild-type allele" for use only in connection with monomorphic genes.

Mutations are heritable changes in DNA base sequences

A mutation that changes a wild-type allele of a gene (regardless of the definition) to a different allele is called a **forward mutation.** The resulting novel mutant allele can be either recessive or dominant to the original wild type. Geneticists often diagram forward mutations as $A^+ \rightarrow a$ when the mutation is recessive and as $b^+ \rightarrow B$ when the mutation is dominant. Mutations can also cause a novel mutant allele to revert back to wild type ($a \rightarrow A^+$, or $B \rightarrow b^+$) in a process known as **reverse mutation,** or **reversion.** In this chapter, we designate wild-type alleles, whether recessive or dominant, with a plus sign (+).

Mendel originally defined genes by the visible phenotypic effects—yellow or green, round or wrinkled—of their alternative alleles. In fact, the only way he knew that genes existed at all was because alternative alleles for seven particular pea genes had arisen through for-

ward mutations. Close to a century later, knowledge of DNA structure clarified that such mutations are heritable changes in DNA base sequence. DNA thus carries the potential for genetic change in the same place it carries genetic information—the sequence of its bases.

Mutations may be classified by how they change DNA

A **substitution** occurs when a base at a certain position in one strand of the DNA molecule is replaced by one of the other three bases (**Fig. 7.2a**); after DNA replication, a new base pair will appear in the daughter double helix. Substitutions can be subdivided into *transitions,* in which one purine (A or G) replaces the other purine, or one pyrimidine (C or T) replaces the other; and *transversions,* in which a purine changes to a pyrimidine, or vice versa.

Other types of mutations produce more complicated rearrangements of DNA sequence. A **deletion** occurs when a block of one or more nucleotide pairs is lost from a DNA molecule; an **insertion** is just the reverse—the addition of one or more nucleotide pairs (**Figs. 7.2b** and **c**). Deletions and insertions can be as small as a single base pair or as large as megabases (that is, millions of base pairs). Researchers can see the larger changes under the microscope when they observe chromosomes in the context of a karyotype, such as that shown in Fig. 4.4 on p. 82.

More complex mutations include **inversions,** 180° rotations of a segment of the DNA molecule (**Fig. 7.2d**), and **reciprocal translocations,** in which parts of two nonhomologous chromosomes change places (**Fig. 7.2e**). Large-scale DNA rearrangements, including megabase deletions and insertions as well as inversions and translocations, cause major genetic reorganizations that can change either the order of genes along a chromosome or the number of chromosomes in an organism. We discuss

Figure 7.2 Mutations classified by their effect on DNA.

Starting sequence

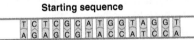

Type of mutation and effect on base sequence

(a) Substitution
Transition: Purine for purine, pyrimidine for pyrimidine

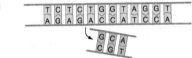

Transversion: Purine for pyrimidine, pyrimidine for purine

(b) Deletion

(c) Insertion

(d) Inversion

Site of inversion

(e) Reciprocal translocation

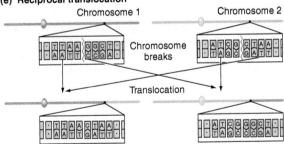

Chromosome 1   Chromosome 2

Chromosome breaks

Translocation

these **chromosomal rearrangements,** which affect many genes at a time, in Chapter 13. In this chapter, we focus on mutations that alter only one gene at a time.

Only a small fraction of the mutations in a genome actually alter the nucleotide sequences of genes in a way that affects gene function. By changing one allele to another, these mutations modify the structure or amount of a gene's protein product, and the modification in protein structure or amount influences phenotype. All other mutations either alter genes in a way that does not affect their function or change the DNA between genes. We discuss mutations

without observable phenotypic consequences in Chapter 11; such mutations are very useful for mapping genes and tracking differences between individuals. In the remainder of this chapter, we focus on those mutations that have an impact on gene function and thereby influence phenotype.

> Mutations—heritable changes in DNA base sequences—include substitutions, deletions, insertions, inversions, and translocations.

Spontaneous mutations occur at a very low rate

Mutations that modify gene function happen so infrequently that geneticists must examine a very large number of individuals from a formerly homogeneous population to detect the new phenotypes that reflect these mutations. In one ongoing study, dedicated investigators have monitored the coat colors of millions of specially bred mice and discovered that on average, a given gene mutates to a recessive allele in roughly 11 out of every 1 million gametes (**Fig. 7.3**). Studies of several other organisms have yielded similar results: an average spontaneous rate of $2-12 \times 10^{-6}$ mutations per gene per gamete.

Figure 7.3 Rates of spontaneous mutation. (a) Mutant mouse coat colors: albino (*left*), brown (*right*). **(b)** Mutation rates from wild type to recessive mutant alleles for five coat color genes. Mice from highly inbred wild-type strains were mated with homozygotes for recessive coat color alleles. Progeny with mutant coat colors indicated the presence of recessive mutations in gametes produced by the inbred mice.

(a)

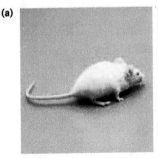

(b)

Locus[a]	Number of gametes tested	Number of mutations	Mutation rate ($\times 10^{-6}$)
a^- (albino)	67,395	3	44.5
b^- (brown)	919,699	3	3.3
c^- (nonagouti)	150,391	5	33.2
d^- (dilute)	839,447	10	11.9
ln^- (leaden)	243,444	4	16.4
	2,220,376	25	11.2 (average)

[a] Mutation is from wild type to the recessive allele shown.

Looking at the mutation rate from a different perspective, you could ask how many mutations there might be in the genes of an individual. To find out, you would simply multiply the rate of $2-12 \times 10^{-6}$ mutations per gene times 30,000, a generous current estimate of the number of genes in the human genome, to obtain an answer of between $0.06-0.36$ mutations per haploid genome. This very rough calculation would mean that, on average, 1 new mutation affecting phenotype could arise in every 4–20 human gametes.

Different genes, different mutation rates

Although the average mutation rate per gene is $2-12 \times 10^{-6}$, this number masks considerable variation in the mutation rates for different genes. Experiments with many organisms show that mutation rates range from less than 10^{-9} to more than 10^{-3} per gene per gamete. Variation in the mutation rate of different genes within the same organism reflects differences in gene size (larger genes are larger targets that sustain more mutations) as well as differences in the susceptibility of particular genes to the various mechanisms that cause mutations (described later in this chapter).

Estimates of the average mutation rates in bacteria range from 10^{-8} to 10^{-7} mutations per gene per cell division. Although the units here are slightly different than those used for multicellular eukaryotes (because bacteria do not produce gametes), the average rate of mutation in gamete-producing eukaryotes still appears to be considerably higher than that in bacteria. The main reason is that numerous cell divisions take place between the formation of a zygote and meiosis, so mutations that appear in a gamete may have actually occurred many cell generations before the gamete formed. In other words, there are more chances for mutations to accumulate. Some scientists speculate that the diploid genomes of multicellular organisms allow them to tolerate relatively high rates of mutation in their gametes because a zygote would have to receive recessive mutations in the same gene from both gametes for any deleterious effects to occur. In contrast, a bacterium would be affected by just a single mutation that disrupted its only copy of the gene.

Gene function: Easy to disrupt, hard to restore

In the mouse coat color study, when researchers allowed brother and sister mice homozygous for a recessive mutant allele of one of the five mutant coat color genes to mate with each other, they could estimate the rate of reversion by examining the F_1 offspring. Any progeny expressing the dominant wild-type phenotype for a particular coat color, of necessity, carried a gene that had sustained a reverse mutation. Calculations based on observations of several million F_1 progeny revealed a reverse mutation rate ranging from $0-2.5 \times 10^{-6}$ per gene per gamete; the rate of reversion varied somewhat from gene to gene. In this study, then, the rate of reversion was significantly lower than the rate of forward mutation, most likely because there are many ways to disrupt gene function, but there are only a few ways to restore function once it has been disrupted. The conclusion that the rate of reversion is significantly lower than the rate of forward mutation holds true for most types of mutation. In one extreme example, deletions of more than a few nucleotide pairs can never revert, because DNA information that has disappeared from the genome cannot spontaneously reappear.

> Although estimates of mutation rates are extremely rough, they nonetheless support three general conclusions: (1) Mutations affecting phenotype occur very rarely; (2) different genes mutate at different rates; and (3) the rate of forward mutation (a disruption of gene function) is almost always higher than the rate of reversion.

Spontaneous mutations arise from many kinds of random events

Because spontaneous mutations affecting a gene occur so infrequently, it is very difficult to study the events that produce them. To overcome this problem, researchers turned to bacteria as the experimental organisms of choice. It is easy to grow many millions of individuals and then rapidly search through enormous populations to find the few that carry a novel mutation. In one study, investigators spread wild-type bacteria on the surface of agar containing sufficient nutrients for growth as well as a large amount of a bacteria-killing substance, such as an antibiotic or a bacteriophage. Although most of the bacterial cells died, a few showed resistance to the bactericidal substance and continued to grow and divide. The descendants of a single resistant bacterium, produced by many rounds of binary fission, formed a mound of genetically identical cells called a **colony**.

The few bactericide-resistant colonies that appeared presented a puzzle. Had the cells in the colonies somehow altered their internal biochemistry to produce a life-saving response to the antibiotic or bacteriophage? Or did they carry heritable mutations conferring resistance to the bactericide? And if they did carry mutations, did those mutations arise by chance from random spontaneous events that take place continuously, even in the absence of a bactericidal substance, or did they only arise in response to environmental signals (in this case, the addition of the bactericide)?

The fluctuation test

In 1943, Salvador Luria and Max Delbrück devised an experiment to examine the origin of bacterial resistance (**Fig. 7.4**). According to their reasoning, if bacteriophage-resistant colonies arise in direct response to infection by

Figure 7.4 The Luria-Delbrück fluctuation experiment. (a) Hypothesis 1: If resistance arises only after exposure to a bactericide, all bacterial cultures of equal size should produce roughly the same number of resistant colonies. Hypothesis 2: If random mutations conferring resistance arise before exposure to bactericide, the number of resistant colonies in different cultures should vary (fluctuate) widely. **(b)** Actual results showing large fluctuations suggest that mutations in bacteria occur as spontaneous mistakes independent of exposure to a selective agent.

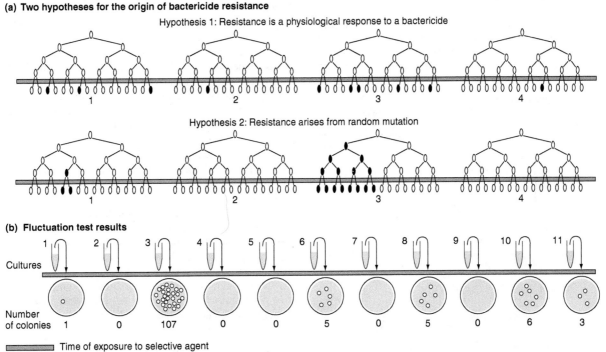

(a) Two hypotheses for the origin of bactericide resistance

Hypothesis 1: Resistance is a physiological response to a bactericide

Hypothesis 2: Resistance arises from random mutation

(b) Fluctuation test results

Cultures

Number of colonies   1   0   107   0   0   5   0   5   0   6   3

Time of exposure to selective agent

bacteriophages, separate suspensions of bacteria containing equal numbers of cells will generate similar, small numbers of resistant colonies when spread in separate petri plates on nutrient agar suffused with phages. By contrast, if resistance arises from mutations that occur spontaneously even when the phages are not present, then different liquid cultures, when spread on separate petri plates, will generate very different numbers of resistant colonies. The reason is that the mutation conferring resistance can, in theory, arise at any time during the growth of the culture. If it happens early, the cell in which it occurs will produce many mutant progeny prior to petri plating; if it happens later, there will be far fewer mutant progeny when the time for plating arrives. After plating, these numerical differences will show up as fluctuations in the numbers of resistant colonies growing in the different petri plates.

The results of this **fluctuation test** were clear: Most plates supported zero to a few resistant colonies, but a few harbored hundreds of resistant colonies. From this observation of a substantial fluctuation in the number of resistant colonies in different petri plates, Luria and Delbrück concluded that bacterial resistance arises from mutations that exist before exposure to bacteriophage. After exposure, however, the bactericide in the petri plate becomes a selective agent that kills off nonresistant cells, allowing only the preexisting resistant ones to survive.

Figure 7.5 illustrates how researchers used another technique, known as *replica plating*, to demonstrate even more directly that the mutations conferring bacterial resistance occur before the cells encounter the bactericide that selects for their resistance.

These key experiments showed that bacterial resistance to phages and other bactericides is the result of mutations, and these mutations do not arise in particular genes as a directed response to environmental change. Instead, mutations occur spontaneously as a result of random processes that can happen at any time and hit the genome at any place. Once such random changes occur, however, they usually remain stable. If the resistant mutants of the Luria-Delbrück experiment, for example, were grown for many generations in medium that did not contain bacteriophages, they would nevertheless remain resistant to this bactericidal virus.

We now describe some of the many kinds of random events that cause mutations; later, we discuss how cells cope with the damage.

Luria and Delbrück's fluctuation test showed that mutations in bacteria conferring resistance to bacteriophages occur prior to exposure to the phages and are caused by random, spontaneous events.

Figure 7.5 Replica plating verifies that bacterial resistance is the result of preexisting mutations. (a) Pressing a *master plate* onto a velvet surface transfers some cells from each bacterial colony onto the velvet. Pressing a *replica plate* onto the velvet then transfers some cells from each colony onto the replica plate. Investigators track which colonies on the master plate are able to grow on the replica plate (here, only penicillin-resistant ones). **(b)** Colonies on a master plate without penicillin are sequentially transferred to three replica plates with penicillin. Resistant colonies grow in the same positions on all three replicas, showing that some colonies on the master plate had multiple resistant cells before exposure to the antibiotic.

(a) The replica plating technique

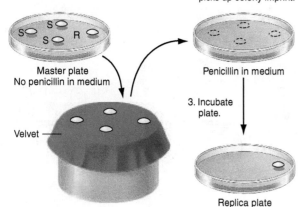

1. Invert master plate; pressing against velvet surface leaves an imprint of colonies. Save plate.

2. Invert second plate (replica plate); pressing against velvet surface picks up colony imprint.

Master plate
No penicillin in medium

Penicillin in medium

3. Incubate plate.

Velvet

Replica plate

S = penicillin-sensitive bacteria
R = penicillin-resistant bacteria

4. Only penicillin-resistant colonies grow. Compare with position of colonies on original plate.

(b) Mutations occur prior to penicillin exposure

10^7 colonies of penicillin-sensitive bacteria

Make three replica plates. Incubate to allow penicillin-resistant colonies to grow.

Master plate
No penicillin in medium

Penicillin in medium

Velvet

Penicillin in medium

Penicillin in medium

Penicillin-resistant colonies grow in the same position on all three plates.

Natural processes that alter DNA

Chemical and physical assaults on DNA are quite frequent. Geneticists estimate, for example, that the hydrolysis of a purine base, A or G, from the deoxyribose-phosphate backbone occurs 1000 times an hour in every human cell. This kind of DNA alteration is called **depurination** (**Fig. 7.6a**). Because the resulting *apurinic site* cannot specify a complementary base, the DNA replication process sometimes introduces a random base opposite the apurinic site, causing a mutation in the newly synthesized complementary strand three-quarters of the time.

Another naturally occurring process that may modify DNA's information content is **deamination:** the removal of an amino (–NH$_2$) group. Deamination can change cytosine to uracil (U), the nitrogenous base found in RNA but not in DNA. Because U pairs with A rather than G, deamination followed by replication may alter a C–G base pair to a T–A pair in future generations of DNA molecules (**Fig. 7.6b**); such a C–G to T–A change is a transition mutation.

Other assaults include naturally occurring radiation such as cosmic rays and X-rays, which break the sugar-phosphate backbone (**Fig. 7.6c**); ultraviolet light, which causes adjacent thymine residues to become chemically linked into thymine–thymine dimers (**Fig. 7.6d**); and oxidative damage to any of the four bases (**Fig. 7.6e**). All of these changes alter the information content of the DNA molecule.

Mistakes during DNA replication

If the cellular machinery for some reason incorporates an incorrect base during replication, for instance, a C opposite an A instead of the expected T, then during the next replication cycle, one of the daughter DNAs will have the normal A–T base pair, while the other will have a mutant G–C. Careful measurements of the fidelity of replication *in vivo,* in both bacteria and human cells, show that such errors are exceedingly rare, occurring less than once in every 10^9 base pairs. That is equivalent to typing this entire book 1000 times while making only one typing error. Considering the complexities of helix unwinding, base pairing, and polymerization, this level of accuracy is amazing. How do cells achieve it?

The replication machinery minimizes errors through successive stages of correction. In the test tube, DNA polymerases replicate DNA with an error rate of about one mistake in every 10^6 bases copied. This rate is about 1000-fold worse than that achieved by the cell. Even so, it is impressively low and is only attained because polymerase molecules provide, along with their polymerization function, a proofreading/editing function in the form of a nuclease that is activated whenever the polymerase makes a mistake. This nuclease portion of the polymerase molecule, called the *3'-to-5' exonuclease,* recognizes a mispaired base and excises it, allowing the polymerase to copy the nucleotide correctly on the next try (**Fig. 7.7**). Without its nuclease portion, DNA polymerase would have an error

Figure 7.6 How natural processes can change the information stored in DNA. (a) In depurination, the hydrolysis of A or G bases leaves a DNA strand with an unspecified base. **(b)** In deamination, the removal of an amino group from C initiates a process that causes a transition after DNA replication. **(c)** X-rays break the sugar-phosphate backbone and thereby split a DNA molecule into smaller pieces, which may be spliced back together improperly. **(d)** Ultraviolet (UV) radiation causes adjacent Ts to form dimers, which can disrupt the readout of genetic information. **(e)** Irradiation causes the formation of *free radicals* (such as oxygen molecules with an unpaired electron) that can alter individual bases. Here, the pairing of the altered base GO with A creates a transversion that changes a G–C base pair to T–A.

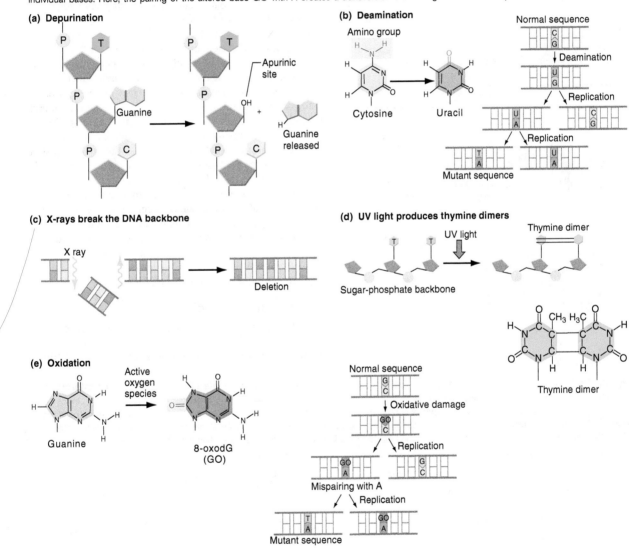

rate of one mistake in every 10^4 bases copied, so its editing function improves the fidelity of replication 100-fold. DNA polymerase *in vivo* is part of a replication system including many other proteins that collectively improve on the error rate another 10-fold, bringing it to within about 100-fold of the fidelity attained by the cell.

The 100-fold higher accuracy of the cell depends on a backup system called *methyl-directed mismatch repair* that notices and corrects residual errors in the newly replicated DNA. We present the details of this repair system later in the chapter when we describe the various ways in which cells attempt to correct mutations once they occur.

Unequal crossing-over and transposable elements

Some mutations arise from events other than chemical and physical assaults or replication errors. Erroneous recombination is one such mechanism. For example, in **unequal crossing-over,** two closely related DNA sequences that are located in different places on two homologous chromosomes can pair with each other during meiosis. If recombination takes place between the mispaired sequences, one homologous chromosome ends up with a duplication (a kind of insertion), while the other homolog sustains a

Figure 7.7 DNA polymerase's proofreading function. If DNA polymerase mistakenly adds an incorrect nucleotide at the 3'-end of the strand it is synthesizing, the enzyme's 3'-to-5' exonuclease activity removes this nucleotide, giving the enzyme a second chance to add the correct nucleotide.

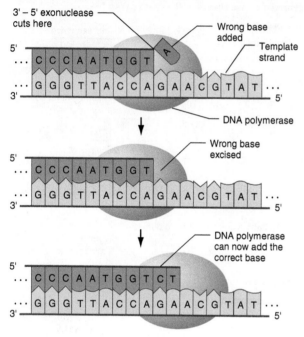

deletion. As **Fig. 7.8a** shows, some forms of red-green colorblindness arise from deletions and duplications in the genes that enable us to perceive red and green wavelengths of light; these reciprocal informational changes are the result of unequal crossing-over.

Another notable mechanism for altering DNA sequence involves the units of DNA known as **transposable elements (TEs).** TEs are DNA segments several hundred to several thousand base pairs long that move (or "transpose" or "jump") from place to place in the genome. If a TE jumps into a gene, it can disrupt the gene's function and cause a mutation. Certain TEs frequently insert themselves into particular genes and not others; this is one reason that mutation rates vary from gene to gene. Although some TEs move by making a copy that becomes inserted into a different chromosomal location while the initial version stays put, other TE types actually leave their original position when they move (**Fig. 7.8b**). Mutations caused by TEs that transpose by this second mechanism are exceptions to the general rule that the rate of reversion is lower than the rate of forward mutation. This is because TE transposition can occur relatively frequently, and when it is accompanied by excision of the TE, the original sequence and function of the gene are restored. Chapter 13 discusses additional genetic consequences of TE behavior.

Unstable trinucleotide repeats

In 1992, a group of molecular geneticists discovered an unusual and completely unexpected type of mutation in humans: the excessive amplification of a CGG base triplet

Figure 7.8 How unequal crossing-over and the movement of transposable elements (TEs) change DNA's information content. **(a)** If two nearby regions contain a similar DNA sequence, the two homologous chromosomes may pair out of register during meiosis and produce gametes with either a deletion or a reciprocal duplication. Colorblindness in humans can result from unequal crossing-over between the nearby and highly similar genes for red and green photoreceptors. **(b)** TEs move around the genome. Some TEs copy themselves before moving, while others are excised from their original positions during transposition. Insertion of a TE into a gene often has phenotypic consequences.

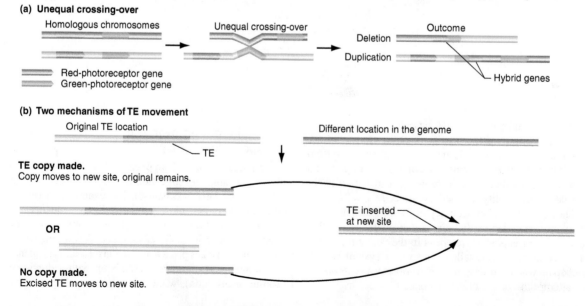

normally repeated only a few to 50 times in succession. If, for example, a normal allele of a gene carries 5 consecutive repetitions of the base triplet CGG (that is, CGGCGGCGGCGGCGG on one strand), an abnormal allele resulting from mutation could carry 200 repeats in a row. Further investigations revealed that repeats of several trinucleotides—CAG, CTG, and GAA, in addition to CGG—can be unstable such that the number of repeats often increases or decreases in different cells of a single individual. Instability can also occur during the production of gametes, resulting in changes in repeat number from one generation to the next. The expansion and contraction of trinucleotide repeats has now been found not only in humans but in many other species as well.

The rules governing trinucleotide repeat instability appear to be quite complicated, but one general feature is that the larger the number of repeats at a particular location, the higher the probability that expansion and contraction will occur. Usually, tracts with less than 30–50 repetitions of a triplet change in size only infrequently, and the mutations that do occur cause only small variations in the repeat number. Larger tracts involving hundreds of repeats change in size more frequently, and they also exhibit more variation in the number of repetitions.

Researchers have not yet determined the precise mechanism of triplet repeat amplification. One possibility is that regions with long trinucleotide repeats form unusual DNA structures that are hard to replicate because they force the copying machinery to slip off, then hop back on, slip off, then hop back on. Such stopping and starting may produce a replication "stutter" that causes synthesis of the same triplet to repeat over and over again, expanding the number of

copies. This type of mechanism could conversely shrink the size of the trinucleotide repeat tract if, after slipping off, the replication machinery restarts copying at a repeat farther down the template sequence. Whatever the cause, mutations of long trinucleotide stretches occur quite often, suggesting that the enzymes for excision or mismatch repair are not very efficient at restoring the original number of repeats.

The expansion of trinucleotide repeats is at the root of *fragile X syndrome,* one of the most common forms of human mental retardation, as well as Huntington disease and many other disorders of the nervous system. The Genetics and Society box "Unstable Trinucleotide Repeats and Fragile X Syndrome" on pp. 208–209 discusses the fascinating medical implications of this phenomenon.

> Many naturally occurring mechanisms can generate spontaneous mutations. These include chemical or radiation assaults that modify DNA bases or break DNA chains, mistakes during DNA replication or recombination, the movement of transposable elements, and the expansion or contraction of unstable trinucleotide repeats.

Mutagens induce mutations

Mutations make genetic analysis possible, but most mutations appear spontaneously at such a low rate that researchers have looked for controlled ways to increase their occurrence. H. J. Muller, an original member of Thomas Hunt Morgan's *Drosophila* group, first showed that exposure to a dose of X-rays higher than the naturally occurring level increases the mutation rate in fruit flies (**Fig. 7.9**).

Figure 7.9 Exposure to X-rays increases the mutation rate in *Drosophila*. F_1 females are constructed that have an irradiated paternal X chromosome (*red line*), and a *Bar*-marked "balancer" maternal X chromosome (*wavy blue line*). These two chromosomes cannot recombine because the balancer chromosome has multiple inversions (as explained in Chapter 13). Single F_1 females, each with a single X-ray-exposed X chromosome from their father, are then individually mated with wild-type males. If the paternal X chromosome in any one F_1 female has an X-ray-induced recessive lethal mutation (*m*), she can produce only Bar-eyed sons (*left*). If the X chromosome has no such mutation, this F_1 female will produce both Bar-eyed and non-Bar-eyed sons (*right*).

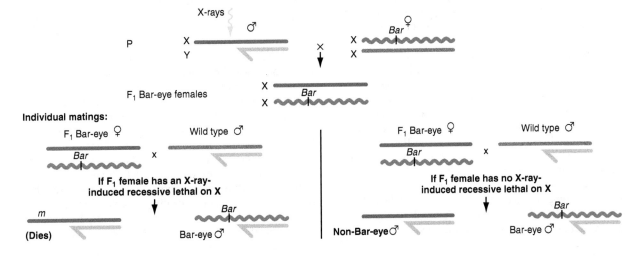

GENETICS AND SOCIETY

Unstable Trinucleotide Repeats and Fragile X Syndrome

Expansions of the base triplet CGG cause a heritable disorder known as *fragile X syndrome*. Adults affected by this syndrome manifest several physical anomalies, including an unusually large head, long face, large ears, and in men, large testicles. They also exhibit moderate to severe mental retardation. Fragile X syndrome has been found in men and women of all races and ethnic backgrounds. The fragile X mutation is, in fact, a leading genetic cause of mental retardation worldwide, second only to the trisomy 21 that results in Down syndrome.

Specially prepared karyotypes of cells from people with fragile X symptoms reveal a slightly constricted, so-called fragile site near the tip of the long arm of the X chromosome (**Fig. A**). The long tracts of CGG trinucleotides, which make up the fragile X mutation, apparently produce a localized constricted region that can even break off in some karyotype preparations. Geneticists named the fragile X disorder for this specific pinpoint of fragility more than 20 years before they identified the mutation that gives rise to it.

The gene in which the fragile X mutation occurs is called *FMR-1* (for fragile-X-associated mental retardation). Near one end of the gene, different people carry a different number of repeats of the sequence CGG, and geneticists now have the molecular tools to quantify these differences. Normal alleles contain 5–54 of these triplet repeats, while the *FMR-1* gene in people with fragile X syndrome contains 200–4000 repeats (**Fig. B.1**). The rest of the gene's base sequence is the same in both normal and abnormal alleles.

The triplet repeat mutation that underlies fragile X syndrome has a surprising transmission feature. Alleles with a full-blown mutation are foreshadowed by *premutation alleles* that carry an intermediate number of repeats—more than 50 but fewer than 200 (Fig. B.1). Premutation alleles do not themselves generate fragile X symptoms in most carriers, but they show significant instability and

Figure A A karyotype reveals a fragile X chromosome. The fragile X site is seen on the bottom of both chromatids of the X chromosome at the *right*.

thus forecast the risk of genetic disease in a carrier's progeny. The greater the number of repeats in a premutation allele, the higher the risk of disease in that person's children. For example, if a woman carries a premutation allele with 60 CGG repeats, 17% of her offspring run the risk of exhibiting fragile X syndrome. If she carries a premutation allele with 90 repeats, close to 50% of her offspring will show symptoms. Interestingly, the expansion of *FMR-1* premutation alleles has some as-yet-unexplained relation to the

---

Muller exposed male *Drosophila* to increasingly large doses of X-rays and then mated these males with females that had one X chromosome containing an easy-to-recognize dominant mutation causing Bar eyes. This X chromosome (called a *balancer*) also carried chromosomal rearrangements known as inversions that prevented it from crossing-over with other X chromosomes. (Chapter 13 explains the details of this phenomenon.) Some of the F₁ daughters of this mating were heterozygotes carrying a mutagenized X from their father and a *Bar*-marked X from their mother. If X-rays induced a recessive lethal mutation anywhere on the paternally derived X chromosome, then these F₁ females would be unable to produce non-Bar-eyed sons. Thus, simply by noting the presence or absence of non-Bar-eyed sons, Muller could establish whether a mutation had occurred in any of the more than 1000 genes on the X chromosome that are essential to *Drosophila* viability. He concluded that the greater the X-ray dose, the greater the frequency of recessive lethal mutations.

Any physical or chemical agent that raises the frequency of mutations above the spontaneous rate is called a **mutagen.** Researchers use many different mutagens to produce mutations for study. With the Watson-Crick model of DNA structure as a guide, they can understand the action of most mutagens at the molecular level. The X-rays used by Muller to induce mutations on the X chromosome, for example, can break the sugar-phosphate backbones of DNA strands, sometimes at the same position on the two strands of the double helix. Multiple double-strand breaks produce DNA fragmentation, and the improper stitching back together of the fragments can cause inversions, deletions, or other rearrangements (see Fig. 7.6c).

Another molecular mechanism of mutagenesis involves mutagens known as **base analogs,** which are so similar in chemical structure to the normal nitrogenous bases that the replication machinery can incorporate them into DNA (**Fig. 7.10a,** p. 210). Because a base analog may have pairing properties different from those of the base it replaces, it can

Figure B Amplification of CGG triplet repeats correlates with the fragile X syndrome. **(1)** *FMR-1* genes in unaffected people generally have fewer than 50 CGG repeats. Unstable premutation alleles have between 50 and 200 repeats. Disease-causing alleles have more than 200 CGG repeats. **(2)** A fragile X pedigree showing the number of CGG repeats in each chromosome. Fragile X patients are almost always the progeny of mothers with premutation alleles.

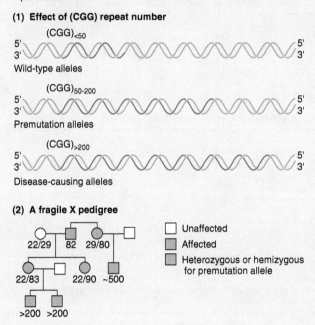

(1) Effect of (CGG) repeat number

$(CGG)_{<50}$

Wild-type alleles

$(CGG)_{50-200}$

Premutation alleles

$(CGG)_{>200}$

Disease-causing alleles

(2) A fragile X pedigree

22/29   82   29/80

22/83   22/90   ~500

>200   >200

☐ Unaffected
■ Affected
▨ Heterozygous or hemizygous for premutation allele

parental origin of the repeats. Whereas most male carriers transmit their *FMR-1* allele with only a small change in the number of repeats, many women with premutation alleles bear children with 250–4000 CGG repeats in their *FMR-1* gene (**Fig. B.2**). One possible explanation is that whatever conditions generate fragile X mutations occur most readily during oogenesis.

The CGG trinucleotide repeat expansion underlying fragile X syndrome has interesting implications for genetic counseling. Thousands of possible alleles of the *FMR-1* gene exist, ranging from the smallest normal allele isolated to date, with 5 triplet repeats, to the largest abnormal allele so far isolated, with roughly 4000 repeats. The relation between genotype and phenotype is clear at both ends of the triplet-repeat spectrum: Individuals whose alleles contain less than 55 repeats are normal, while people with an allele carrying more than 200 repeats are almost always moderately to severely retarded. With an intermediate number of repeats, however, expression of the mental retardation phenotype is highly variable, depending to an unknown degree on chance, the environment, and modifier genes.

This range of variable expressivity leads to an ethical dilemma: Where should medical geneticists draw the line in their assessment of risk? Prospective parents with a family history of mental retardation may consult with a counselor to determine their options. The counselor would first test the parents for fragile X premutation alleles. If the couple is expecting a child, the counselor would also want to analyze the fetal cells directly by amniocentesis, to determine whether the fetus carries an expanded number of CGG repeats in its *FMR-1* gene. If the results indicate the presence of an allele in the middle range of triplet repeats, the counselor will have to acknowledge the unpredictability of outcomes. The prospective parents' difficult decision of whether or not to continue the pregnancy will then rest on the very shaky ground of an inconclusive, overall evaluation of risk.

cause base substitutions on the complementary strand synthesized in the next round of DNA replication. Other chemical mutagens generate substitutions by directly altering a base's chemical structure and properties (**Fig. 7.10b**). Again, the effects of these changes become fixed in the genome when the altered base causes incorporation of an incorrect complementary base during a subsequent round of replication.

Yet another class of chemical mutagens consists of compounds known as **intercalators:** flat, planar molecules that can sandwich themselves between successive base pairs and disrupt the machinery for replication, recombination, or repair (**Fig. 7.10c**). The disruption may eventually generate deletions or insertions of a single base pair.

Scientists use mutagens such as X-rays, base analogs, and intercalators to increase the frequency of mutation as an aid to genetic research.

DNA repair mechanisms minimize mutations

Natural environments expose genomes to many kinds of chemicals or radiation that can alter DNA sequences; furthermore, the side effects of normal DNA metabolism within cells, such as inaccuracies in DNA replication or the movement of TEs, can also be mutagenic. Cells have evolved a variety of enzymatic systems that locate and repair damaged DNA and thereby dramatically diminish the high potential for mutation. The combination of these repair systems must be extremely efficient, because the rates of spontaneous mutation observed for almost all genes are very low.

Reversal of DNA base alterations

If methyl or ethyl groups were mistakenly added to guanine (as in Fig. 10.7b), *alkyltransferase* enzymes can remove them so as to recreate the original base. Other enzymes remedy other base structure alterations. For example, the

Figure 7.10 How mutagens alter DNA. (a) Base analogs incorporated into DNA may pair aberrantly, allowing the addition of incorrect nucleotides to the opposite strand during replication. **(b)** Some mutagens alter the structure of bases such that they pair inappropriately in the next round of replication. **(c)** Intercalating agents are roughly the same size and shape as a base pair of the double helix. Their incorporation into DNA produces insertions or deletions of single base pairs.

Type of Mutagen	Chemical Action of Mutagen		
(a) Replace a base: Base analogs have a chemical structure almost identical to that of a DNA base.	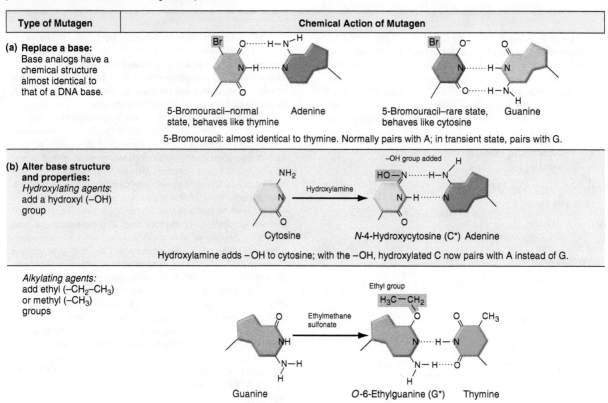 5-Bromouracil: almost identical to thymine. Normally pairs with A; in transient state, pairs with G.		
(b) Alter base structure and properties: *Hydroxylating agents:* add a hydroxyl (–OH) group			
Alkylating agents: add ethyl (–CH₂–CH₃) or methyl (–CH₃) groups			
Deaminating agents: remove amine (–NH₂) groups	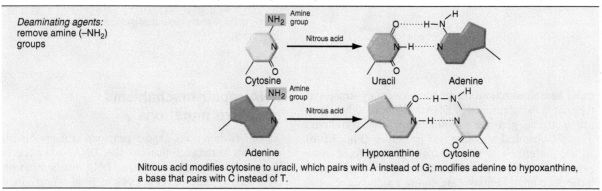		

(a) Replace a base:
Base analogs have a chemical structure almost identical to that of a DNA base.

5-Bromouracil–normal state, behaves like thymine   Adenine

5-Bromouracil–rare state, behaves like cytosine   Guanine

5-Bromouracil: almost identical to thymine. Normally pairs with A; in transient state, pairs with G.

(b) Alter base structure and properties:
Hydroxylating agents: add a hydroxyl (–OH) group

–OH group added

Cytosine   *N*-4-Hydroxycytosine (C*) Adenine

Hydroxylamine adds – OH to cytosine; with the –OH, hydroxylated C now pairs with A instead of G.

Alkylating agents: add ethyl (–CH₂–CH₃) or methyl (–CH₃) groups

Ethyl group

Guanine   *O*-6-Ethylguanine (G*)   Thymine

Ethylmethane sulfonate adds an ethyl group to guanine or thymine. Modified G pairs with T above, and modified T pairs with G (not shown).

Deaminating agents: remove amine (–NH₂) groups

Amine group

Cytosine   Uracil   Adenine

Amine group

Adenine   Hypoxanthine   Cytosine

Nitrous acid modifies cytosine to uracil, which pairs with A instead of G; modifies adenine to hypoxanthine, a base that pairs with C instead of T.

(c) Insert between bases:
Intercalating agents

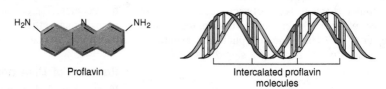

Proflavin   Intercalated proflavin molecules

Proflavin intercalates into the double helix. This disrupts DNA metabolism, eventually resulting in deletion or addition of a base pair.

(Continued)

Figure 7.10 How mutagens alter DNA. (*Continued*)

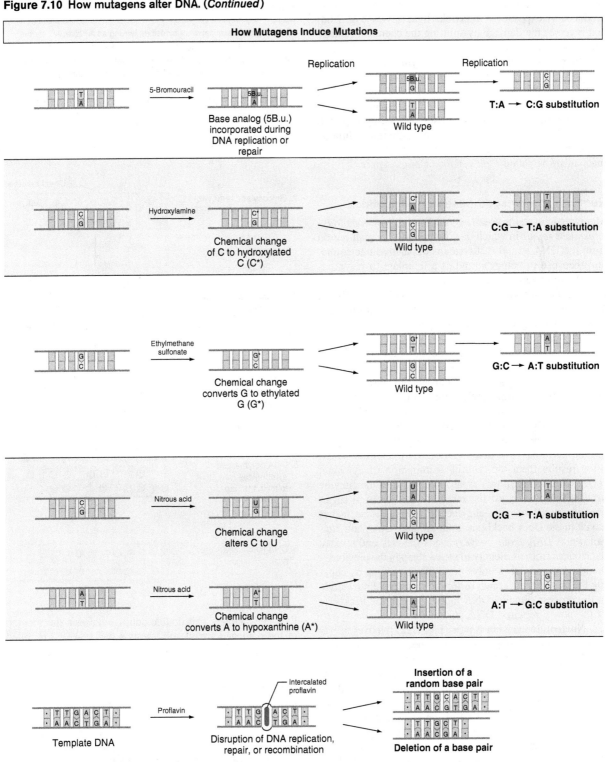

enzyme *photolyase* recognizes the thymine–thymine dimers produced by exposure to ultraviolet light (review Fig. 7.6d) and reverses the damage by splitting the chemical linkage between the thymines.

Interestingly, the photolyase enzyme works only in the presence of visible light. In carrying out its DNA repair tasks, it associates with a small molecule called a *chromophore* that absorbs light in the visible range of the spectrum; the enzyme then uses the energy captured by the chromophore to split thymine–thymine dimers. Because it does not function in the dark, the photolyase mechanism is called *light repair,* or *photorepair.*

Removal of damaged bases or nucleotides

Many repair systems use the general strategy of *homology-dependent repair* in which they first remove a small region from the DNA strand that contains the altered nucleotide, and then use the other strand as a template to resynthesize the removed region. This strategy makes use of one of the great advantages of the double-helical structure: If one strand sustains damage, cells can use complementary base pairing with the undamaged strand to re-create the original sequence.

Base excision repair is one homology-dependent mechanism. In this type of repair, enzymes called *DNA glycosylases* cleave an altered nitrogenous base from the sugar of its nucleotide, releasing the base and creating an apurinic or apyrimidinic (AP) site in the DNA chain (**Fig. 7.11**). Different glycosylase enzymes cleave specific damaged bases. Base excision repair is particularly important in the removal of uracil from DNA (recall that uracil often results from the natural deamination of cytosine; review Fig. 7.6b). In this repair process, after the enzyme *uracil-DNA glycosylase* has removed uracil from its sugar, leaving an AP site, the enzyme *AP endonuclease* makes a nick in the DNA backbone at the AP site. Other enzymes (known as *DNA exonucleases*) attack the nick and remove nucleotides from its vicinity to create a gap in the previously damaged strand. DNA polymerase fills in the gap by copying the undamaged strand, restoring the original nucleotide in the process. Finally, DNA ligase seals up the backbone of the newly repaired DNA strand.

Nucleotide excision repair (Fig. 7.12) removes alterations that base excision cannot repair because the cell lacks a DNA glycosylase that recognizes the problem base. Nucleotide excision repair depends on enzyme complexes containing more than one protein molecule. In *E. coli,* these complexes are made of two out of three possible proteins: UvrA, UvrB, and UvrC. One of the complexes (UvrA + UvrB) patrols the DNA for irregularities, detecting lesions that disrupt Watson-Crick base pairing and thus distort the double helix (such as thymine–thymine dimers that have not been corrected by photorepair). A second complex (UvrB + UvrC) cuts the damaged strand in two places that

Figure 7.11 Base excision repair removes damaged bases. Glycosylase enzymes remove aberrant bases [like uracil (*red*), formed by the deamination of cytosine], leaving an AP site. AP endonuclease cuts the sugar-phosphate backbone, creating a nick. Exonucleases extend the nick into a gap, which is filled in with the correct information (*green*) by DNA polymerase. DNA ligase reseals the corrected strand.

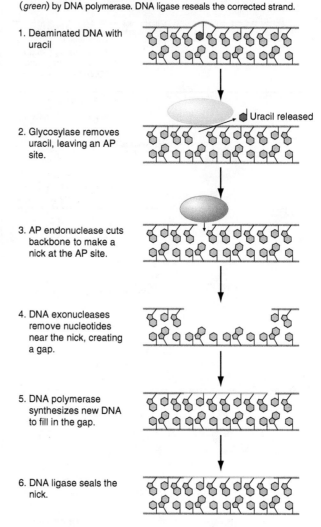

1. Deaminated DNA with uracil

2. Glycosylase removes uracil, leaving an AP site.

Uracil released

3. AP endonuclease cuts backbone to make a nick at the AP site.

4. DNA exonucleases remove nucleotides near the nick, creating a gap.

5. DNA polymerase synthesizes new DNA to fill in the gap.

6. DNA ligase seals the nick.

flank the damage. This double-cutting excises a short region of the damaged strand and leaves a gap that will be filled in by DNA polymerase and sealed with DNA ligase.

Correction of DNA replication errors

DNA polymerase is remarkably accurate in copying DNA, but the DNA replication system still makes about 100 times more mistakes than most cells can tolerate. A backup repair system called **methyl-directed mismatch repair** corrects almost all of these errors (**Fig. 7.13**). Because mismatch repair is active only *after* DNA replication, this system needs to solve a difficult problem. Suppose that a G–C pair

Figure 7.12 Nucleotide excision repair corrects damaged nucleotides. A complex of the UvrA and UvrB proteins (*not shown*) scans DNA for distortions caused by DNA damage, such as thymine–thymine dimers. At the damaged site, UvrA dissociates from UvrB, allowing UvrB (*red*) to associate with UvrC (*blue*). These enzymes nick the DNA exactly 4 nucleotides to one side of the damage and 7 nucleotides to the other side, releasing a small fragment of single-stranded DNA. DNA polymerases then resynthesize the missing information (*green*), and DNA ligase reseals the now-corrected strand.

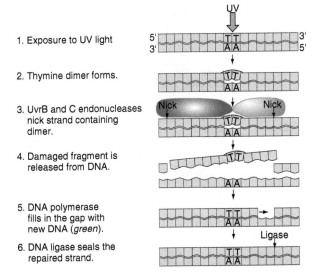

1. Exposure to UV light
2. Thymine dimer forms.
3. UvrB and C endonucleases nick strand containing dimer.
4. Damaged fragment is released from DNA.
5. DNA polymerase fills in the gap with new DNA (*green*).
6. DNA ligase seals the repaired strand.

Figure 7.13 In bacteria, methyl-directed mismatch repair corrects mistakes in replication. Parental strands are in *light blue* and newly synthesized strands are *purple*. The MutS protein is *green*, MutL is *dark blue*, and MutH is *yellow*. See text for details.

(a) Parental strands are marked with methyl groups.

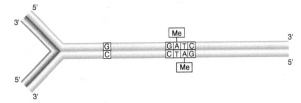

(b) MutS and MutL recognize mismatch in replicated DNA.

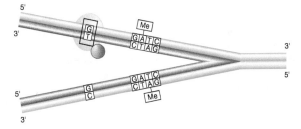

(c) MutL recruits MutH to GATC; MutH makes a nick (**short arrow**) in strand opposite methyl tag.

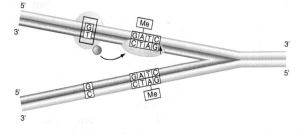

(d) DNA exonucleases (*not shown*) excise DNA from unmethylated new strand.

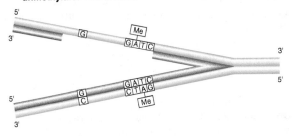

(e) Repair and methylation of newly synthesized DNA strand

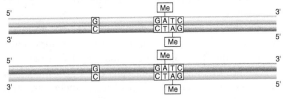

has been copied to produce two daughter molecules, one of which has the correct G–C base pair, the other an incorrect G–T. The mismatch repair system can easily recognize the incorrectly matched G–T base pair because the improper base pairing distorts the double helix, resulting in abnormal bulges and hollows. But how does the system know whether to correct the pair to a G–C or to an A–T?

Bacteria solve this problem by placing a distinguishing mark on the parental DNA strands at specific places: Everywhere the sequence GATC occurs, the enzyme *adenine methylase* puts a methyl group on the A (Fig. 7.13a). Shortly after replication, the old template strand bears the methyl mark, while the new daughter strand—which contains the wrong nucleotide—is as yet unmarked (Fig. 7.13b). A pair of proteins in *E. coli,* called MutL and MutS, detect and bind to the mismatched nucleotides. MutL and MutS direct another protein, MutH, to nick the newly synthesized strand of DNA at a position across from the nearest methylated GATC; MutH can discriminate the newly synthesized strand because its GATC is *not* methylated (Fig. 7.13c). DNA exonucleases then remove all the nucleotides between the nick and a position just beyond the mismatch, leaving a gap on the new, unmethylated strand (Fig. 7.13d). DNA polymerase can now resynthesize the information using the old, methylated strand as a template, and DNA ligase then seals up the repaired strand.

With the completion of replication and repair, enzymes mark the new strand with methyl groups so that its parental origin will be evident in the next round of replication (Fig. 7.13e).

Eukaryotic cells also have a mismatch correction system, but we do not yet know how this system distinguishes templates from newly replicated strands. Unlike prokaryotes, GATCs in eukaryotes are not tagged with methyl groups, and eukaryotes do not seem to have a protein closely related to MutH. One potentially interesting clue is that the MutS and MutL proteins in eukaryotes associate with DNA replication factors; perhaps these interactions might help MutS and MutL identify the strand to be repaired.

> Cells contain many enzymatic systems to repair DNA. The most accurate systems take advantage of complementary base pairing, using the undamaged strand as a template to correct the damaged DNA strand. Some examples are base or nucleotide excision repair systems, and mismatch repair systems.

Error-prone repair systems: A last resort

The repair systems just described are very accurate in repairing DNA damage because they are able to replace damaged nucleotides with a complementary copy of the undamaged strand. However, cells sometimes become exposed to levels or types of mutagens that they cannot handle with these high-fidelity repair systems. Strong doses of UV light, for example, might make more thymine–thymine dimers than the cell can fix. Any unrepaired damage has severe consequences for cell division: The DNA polymerases normally used in replication will stall at such lesions, so the cells cannot proliferate. Although these cells can initiate emergency responses that may allow them to survive and divide despite the stalling, their ability to proceed in such circumstances comes at the expense of introducing new mutations into the genome.

One type of emergency repair in bacteria, called the **SOS system** (after the Morse code distress signal), relies on error-prone (or "sloppy") DNA polymerases. These sloppy DNA polymerases are not available for normal DNA replication; they are produced only in the presence of DNA damage. The damage-induced, error-prone DNA polymerases are attracted to replication forks that have become stalled at sites of unrepaired, damaged nucleotides. There they add random nucleotides to the strand being synthesized opposite the damaged bases. The SOS polymerase enzymes thus allow the cell with damaged DNA to divide into two daughter cells, but because the sloppy polymerases restore the proper nucleotide only 1/4 of the time, the genomes of these daughter cells carry new mutations. In bacteria, the mutagenic effect of many mutagens either depends on, or is enhanced by, the SOS system.

Figure 7.14 Repair of double-strand breaks by nonhomologous end-joining. The proteins KU70, KU80, and PK$_{CS}$ bind to DNA ends and bring them together. Other proteins (*not shown*) trim the ends so as to remove any single-stranded regions, and then ligate the two ends together. This mechanism may result in the deletion of nucleotides and is thus potentially mutagenic.

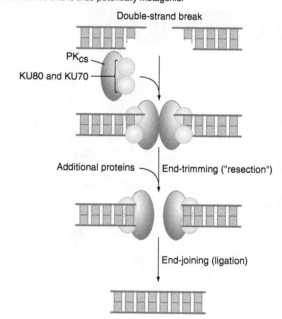

Another kind of emergency repair system deals with a particularly dangerous kind of DNA lesion: *double-strand breaks,* in which both strands of the double helix are broken at nearby sites (**Fig. 7.14**). Recall from Chapter 6 that double-strand breaks occur as the first step in meiotic recombination. We do not consider this type of double-strand break here because the mechanism of recombination repairs them with high fidelity and efficiency using complementary base pairing (review Fig. 6.24 on pp. 190–193). However, double-strand breaks can also result from exposure to high-energy radiation such as X-rays (Fig. 7.6c) or highly reactive oxygen molecules. If left unrepaired, these breaks can lead to a variety of potentially lethal chromosome aberrations, such as large deletions, inversions, or translocations.

Cells can restitch the ends formed by such double-strand breaks using a mechanism called **nonhomologous end-joining,** which relies on a group of three proteins that bind to the strand ends and bring them close together (Fig. 7.14). After binding, these proteins recruit other proteins that cut back (or "resect") any overhanging nucleotides on the ends that do not have a complementary nucleotide to pair with, and then join the two ends together. Because of the resection step, nonhomologous end-joining can result in the loss of DNA and is thus error prone. Evidently, the mutagenic effects of nonhomologous end-joining are less deleterious to the cell than genomic injuries caused by unrepaired double-strand breaks.

> Error-prone DNA repair systems, such as the SOS system and nonhomologous end-joining, do not utilize complementary base pairing. Cells use these systems only as a last resort.

Health consequences of mutations in genes encoding DNA repair proteins

Although differences of detail exist between the DNA repair systems of various organisms, DNA repair mechanisms appear in some form in virtually all species. For example, humans have six proteins with amino acid compositions that are about 25% identical with that of the *E. coli* mismatch repair protein MutS. DNA repair systems are thus very old and must have evolved soon after life emerged roughly 3.5 billion years ago. Some scientists believe DNA repair became essential when plants first started to deposit oxygen into the atmosphere, because oxygen favors the formation of free radicals that can damage DNA.

The many known human hereditary diseases associated with the defective repair of DNA damage reveal how crucial these mechanisms are for survival. In one example, the cells of patients with *Xeroderma pigmentosum* lack the ability to conduct nucleotide excision repair; these people are homozygous for mutations in one of seven genes encoding enzymes that normally function in this repair system. As a result, the thymine–thymine dimers caused by ultraviolet light cannot be removed efficiently. Unless these people avoid all exposure to sunlight, their skin cells begin to accumulate mutations that eventually lead to skin cancer (**Fig. 7.15**). In another example, researchers have recently learned that hereditary forms of colorectal cancer in humans are associated with mutations in human genes that are closely related to the *E. coli* genes encoding the mismatch-repair proteins MutS and MutL. Chapter 17 dis-

cusses the fascinating connections between DNA repair and cancer in more detail.

> Mutations in genes encoding DNA repair proteins can allow other mutations to accumulate throughout the genome, often leading toward cancer.

Mutations have consequences for species evolution as well as individual survival

"The capacity to blunder slightly is the real marvel of DNA. Without this special attribute, we would still be anaerobic bacteria and there would be no music." In these two sentences, the eminent medical scientist and self-appointed "biology watcher" Lewis Thomas acknowledges that changes in DNA are behind the phenotypic variations that are the raw material on which natural selection has acted for billions of years to drive evolution. The wide-ranging variation in the genetic makeup of the human population—and other populations as well—is, in fact, the result of a balance between: (1) the continuous introduction of new mutations; (2) the loss of deleterious mutations because of the selective disadvantage they impose on the individuals that carry them; and (3) the increase in frequency of rare mutations that either provide a selective advantage to the individuals carrying them or that spread through a population by other means.

In sexually reproducing multicellular organisms, only germline mutations that can be passed on to the next generation play a role in evolution. Nevertheless, mutations in somatic cells can still have an impact on the well-being and survival of individuals. Somatic mutations in genes that help regulate the cell cycle may, for example, lead to cancer. The U.S. Food and Drug Administration tries to identify potential cancer-causing agents (known as carcinogens) by using the **Ames test** to screen for chemicals that cause mutations in bacterial cells (**Fig. 7.16**). This test asks whether a particular chemical can induce histidine$^+$ *(his$^+$)* revertants of a special histidine$^-$ *(his$^-$)* mutant strain of the bacterium *Salmonella typhimurium*. The *his$^+$* revertants can synthesize all the histidine they need from simple compounds in their environment; whereas the original *his$^-$* mutants cannot make histidine, so they can survive only if histidine is supplied.

The advantage of the Ames test is that only revertants can grow on petri plates that do not contain histidine, so it is possible to examine large numbers of cells from an originally *his$^-$* culture to find the rare *his$^+$* revertants induced by the chemical in question. To increase the sensitivity of mutation detection, the *his$^-$* strain used in the Ames test system contains a second mutation that inactivates the nucleotide excision repair system and

Figure 7.15 Skin lesions in a xeroderma pigmentosum patient. This heritable disease is caused by the lack of a critical enzyme in the nucleotide excision repair system.

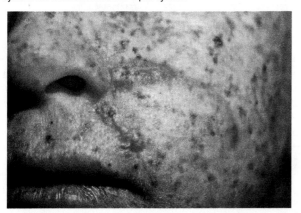

Figure 7.16 The Ames test identifies potential carcinogens. A compound to be tested is mixed with cells of a *his⁻* strain of *Salmonella typhimurium* and with a solution of rat liver enzymes (which can sometimes convert a harmless compound into a mutagen). Only *his⁺* revertants grow on a petri plate without histidine. If this plate (*left*) has more *his⁺* revertants than a control plate (also without histidine), containing unexposed cells (*right*), the compound is considered mutagenic and a potential carcinogen. The rare revertants on the control plate represent the spontaneous rate of mutation.

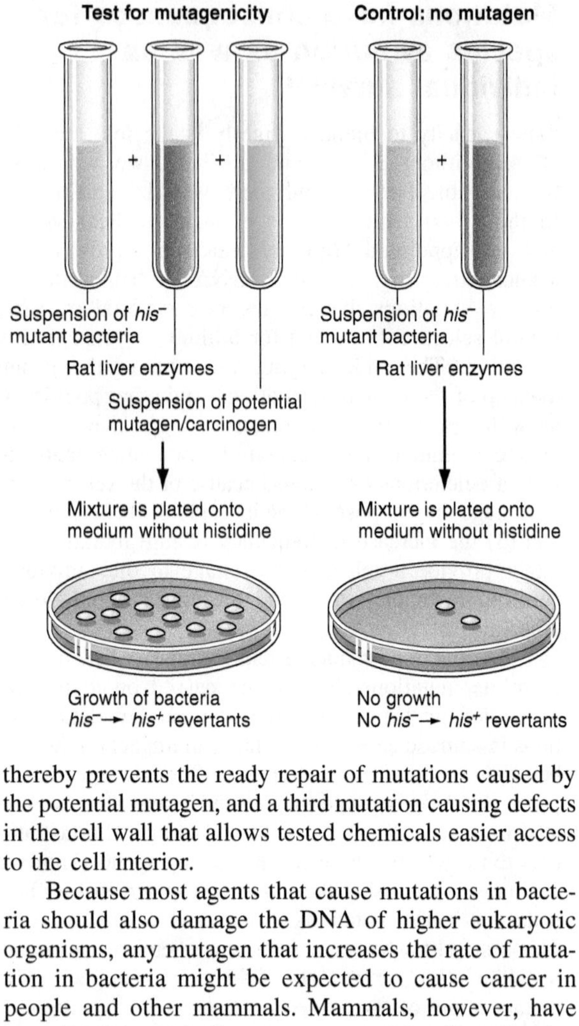

Mutations are the ultimate source of variation within and between species. Although some mutations confer a selective advantage, most are deleterious. DNA repair systems help keep mutations to a low level that balances organisms' need to evolve with their need to avoid damage to their genomes.

Test for mutagenicity

Control: no mutagen

Suspension of *his⁻* mutant bacteria

Rat liver enzymes

Suspension of potential mutagen/carcinogen

Suspension of *his⁻* mutant bacteria

Rat liver enzymes

Mixture is plated onto medium without histidine

Mixture is plated onto medium without histidine

Growth of bacteria
his⁻ → *his⁺* revertants

No growth
No *his⁻* → *his⁺* revertants

7.2 What Mutations Tell Us About Gene Structure

The science of genetics depends absolutely on mutations because we can track genes in crosses only through the phenotypic effects of their mutant variants. In the 1950s and 1960s, scientists realized they could also use mutations to learn how DNA sequences along a chromosome constitute individual genes. These investigators wanted to collect a large series of mutations in a single gene and analyze how these mutations are arranged with respect to each other. For this approach to be successful, they had to establish that various mutations were, in fact, in the same gene. This was not a trivial exercise, as illustrated by the following situation.

Early *Drosophila* geneticists identified a large number of X-linked recessive mutations affecting the normally red wild-type eye color (**Fig. 7.17**). The first of these to be discovered produced the famous white eyes studied by Morgan's group. Other mutations caused a whole palette of hues to appear in the eyes: darkened shades such as garnet and ruby; bright colors such as vermilion, cherry, and coral; and lighter pigmentations known as apricot, buff, and carnation. This wide variety of eye color phenotypes posed a puzzle: Were the mutations that caused them multiple alleles of a single gene, or did they affect more than one gene?

Complementation testing reveals whether two mutations are in a single gene or in different genes

Researchers commonly define a gene as a functional unit that directs the appearance of a molecular product that, in turn, contributes to a particular phenotype. They can use this definition to determine whether two mutations are in the same gene or in different genes. If two homologous chromosomes in an individual each carries a mutation recessive to wild type, a normal phenotype will result if the mutations are in different genes. The normal phenotype occurs because almost all recessive mutations disrupt a gene's function (as will be explained in Chapter 8). The dominant wild-type alleles on each of the two homologs can make up for, or **complement,**

thereby prevents the ready repair of mutations caused by the potential mutagen, and a third mutation causing defects in the cell wall that allows tested chemicals easier access to the cell interior.

Because most agents that cause mutations in bacteria should also damage the DNA of higher eukaryotic organisms, any mutagen that increases the rate of mutation in bacteria might be expected to cause cancer in people and other mammals. Mammals, however, have complicated metabolic processes capable of inactivating hazardous chemicals. Other biochemical events in mammals can create a mutagenic substance from nonhazardous chemicals. To simulate the action of mammalian metabolism, toxicologists often add a solution of rat liver enzymes to the chemical under analysis by the Ames test (Fig. 7.16). Because this simulation is not perfect, Food and Drug Administration agents ultimately assess whether bacterial mutagens identified by the Ames test can cause cancer in rodents by including the agents in test animals' diets.

Figure 7.17 *Drosophila* **eye color mutations produce a variety of phenotypes.** Flies carrying different X-linked eye color mutations. From the *left:* ruby, white, and apricot; a wild-type eye is at the *far right.*

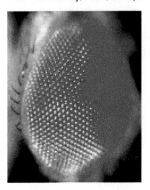  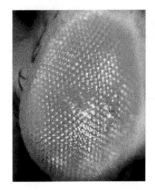 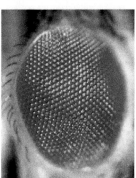

the defect in the other chromosome by generating enough of both gene products to yield a normal phenotype (**Fig. 7.18a,** *left*).

In contrast, if the recessive mutations on the two homologous chromosomes are in the same gene, no wild-type allele of that gene exists in the individual and neither mutated copy of the gene will be able to perform the normal function. As a result, no complementation will occur and no normal gene product will be made, so a mutant phenotype will appear (Fig. 7.18a, *right*). Ironically, a collection of mutations that do *not* complement each other is known as a **complementation group.** Geneticists often use "complementation group" as a synonym for "gene" because the mutations in a complementation group all affect the same unit of function, and thus, the same gene.

A simple test based on the idea of a gene as a unit of function can determine whether or not two mutations are alleles of the same gene. You simply examine the phenotype of a heterozygous individual in which one homolog of a particular chromosome carries one of the recessive mutations and the other homolog carries the other recessive mutation. If the phenotype is wild type, the mutations cannot be in the same gene. This technique is known as **complementation testing.** For example, because a female *Drosophila* heterozygous for garnet and ruby (*garnet ruby⁺* / *garnet⁺ ruby*) has wild-type brick-red eyes, it is possible to conclude that the mutations causing garnet and ruby colors complement each other and are therefore in different genes.

Complementation testing has, in fact, shown that garnet, ruby, vermilion, and carnation pigmentation are governed by separate genes. But chromosomes carrying mutations yielding white, cherry, coral, apricot, and buff phenotypes fail to complement each other. These mutations therefore make up different alleles of a single gene. *Drosophila* geneticists named this gene the *white,* or *w,* gene after the first mutation observed; they designate the

wild-type allele as w^+ and the various mutations as w^1 (the original white-eyed mutation discovered by T. H. Morgan, often simply designated as *w*), w^{cherry}, w^{coral}, $w^{apricot}$, and w^{buff}. As an example, the eyes of a w^1 / $w^{apricot}$ female are a dilute apricot color; because the phenotype of this heterozygote is not wild type, the two mutations are allelic. **Figure 7.18b** illustrates how researchers collate data from many complementation tests in a **complementation table.** Such a table helps visualize the relationships among a large group of mutants.

In *Drosophila,* mutations in the *w* gene map very close together in the same region of the X chromosome, while mutations in other eye color genes lie elsewhere on the chromosome (**Fig. 7.18c**). This result suggests that genes are not disjointed entities with parts spread out from one end of a chromosome to another; each gene, in fact, occupies only a relatively small, discrete area of a chromosome. Studies defining genes at the molecular level have shown that most genes consist of 1000–20,000 contiguous base pairs (bp). In humans, among the shortest genes are the roughly 500-bp-long genes that govern the production of histone proteins, while the longest gene so far identified is the Duchenne muscular dystrophy (*DMD*) gene, which has a length of more than 2 million nucleotide pairs. All known human genes fall somewhere between these extremes. To put these figures in perspective, an average human chromosome is approximately 130 million base pairs in length.

The complementation test looks at the phenotype of individuals simultaneously heterozygous for two different recessive mutations. A mutant phenotype indicates that the mutations fail to complement each other, that is, they are in the same gene (complementation group). A wild-type phenotype indicates the mutations complement each other, and thus are in different genes.

Figure 7.18 Complementation testing of *Drosophila* eye color mutations. (a) A heterozygote has one mutation (m₁) on one chromosome and a different mutation (m₂) on its homolog. If the mutations are in different genes, the heterozygote will be wild type; the mutations complement each other (*left*). If both mutations affect the same gene, the phenotype will be mutant; the mutations do not complement each other (*right*). Complementation testing makes sense only when both mutations are recessive to wild type. **(b)** This complementation table reveals five complementation groups (five different genes) for eye color. A "+" indicates mutant combinations with wild type eye color; these mutations complement and are thus in different genes. Several mutations fail to complement (−) and are thus alleles of one gene, *white*. **(c)** Recombination mapping shows that mutations in different genes are often far apart, while different mutations in the same gene are very close together.

(a) Complementation testing

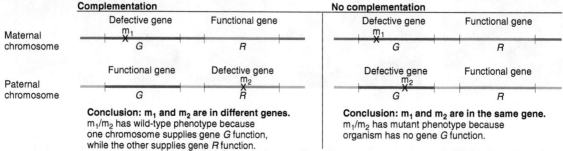

(b) A complementation table: X-linked eye color mutations in *Drosophila*

Mutation	white	garnet	ruby	vermilion	cherry	coral	apricot	buff	carnation
white	−	+	+	+	−	−	−	−	+
garnet		−	+	+	+	+	+	+	+
ruby			−	+	+	+	+	+	+
vermilion				−	+	+	+	+	+
cherry					−	−	−	−	+
coral						−	−	−	+
apricot							−	−	+
buff								−	+
carnation									−

(c) Genetic map: X-linked eye color mutations in *Drosophila*

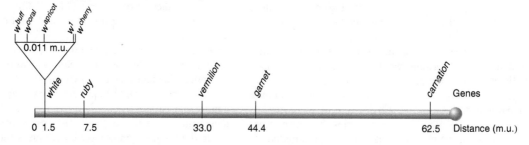

A gene is a set of nucleotide pairs that can mutate independently and recombine with each other

Although complementation testing makes it possible to distinguish mutations in different genes from mutations in the same gene, it does not clarify how the structure of a gene can accommodate different mutations and how these different mutations can alter phenotype in different ways. Does each mutation change the whole gene at a single stroke in a particular way, or does it change only a specific part of a gene, while other mutations alter other parts?

In the late 1950s, the American geneticist Seymour Benzer used recombination analysis to show that two different mutations that did not complement each other and were therefore known to be in the same gene can in fact change different parts of that gene. He reasoned that if recombination can occur not only between genes but within a gene as well, crossovers between homologous chromosomes carrying different mutations known to be in the same gene could in theory generate a wild-type allele (**Fig. 7.19**). Because mutations affecting a single gene are likely to lie very close together, it is necessary to examine a very large number of progeny to see even one crossover event between them. The resolution of the experimental system must thus be extremely high, allowing rapid detection of rare genetic events. For his experimental organism, Benzer chose bacteriophage T4, a DNA virus that infects *Escherichia coli* cells

Figure 7.19 How recombination within a gene could generate a wild-type allele. Suppose a gene, indicated by the region between brackets, is composed of many sites that can mutate independently. Recombination between mutations m₁ and m₂ at different sites in the same gene produces a wild-type allele and a reciprocal allele containing both mutations.

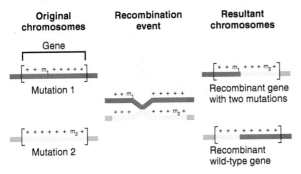

(**Fig. 7.20a**). Because each T4 phage that infects a bacterium generates 100–1000 phage progeny in less than an hour, Benzer could easily produce enough rare recombinants for his analysis (Fig. 7.20a.1 and 2). Moreover, by exploiting a peculiarity of certain T4 mutations, he devised conditions that allowed only recombinant phages, and not parental phages, to proliferate.

The experimental system: *rII⁻* mutations of bacteriophage T4

Even though bacteriophages are too small to be seen without the aid of an electron microscope, a simple technique makes it possible to detect their presence with the unaided eye (Fig. 7.20a.3). To do this, researchers mix a population of bacteriophage particles with a much larger number of bacteria and then pour this mixture onto a petri plate, where the cells are immobilized in a nutrient agar. If a single phage infects a single bacterial cell somewhere on this so-called **lawn** of bacteria, the cell produces and releases progeny viral particles that diffuse away to infect adjacent bacteria, which, in turn, produce and release yet more phage progeny. With each release of virus particles, the bacterial host cell dies. Thus, several cycles of phage infection, replication, and release produce a circular cleared area in the plate, called a **plaque,** devoid of living bacterial cells. The rest of the petri plate surface is covered by an opalescent lawn of living bacteria.

Most plaques contain from 1 million to 10 million viral progeny of the single bacteriophage that originally infected a cell in that position on the petri plate. Sequential dilution of phage-containing solutions makes it possible to measure the number of phages in a particular plaque and arrive at a countable number of viral particles (Fig. 7.20a.4).

When Benzer first looked for genetic traits associated with bacteriophage T4, he found mutants that, when added to a lawn of *E. coli* B strain bacteria, produced larger plaques with sharper, more clearly rounded edges than those produced by the wild-type bacteriophage (**Fig. 7.20b**). Because these changes in plaque morphology seemed to result from the abnormally rapid lysis of the host bacteria, Benzer named the mutations *r* for "rapid lysis." Many *r* mutations map to a region of the T4 chromosome known as the *rII* region; these are called *rII⁻* mutations.

An additional property of *rII⁻* mutations makes them ideal for the genetic **fine structure mapping** (the mapping of mutations within a gene) undertaken by Benzer. Wild-type *rII⁺* bacteriophages form plaques of normal shape and size on cells of both the *E. coli* B strain and a strain known as *E. coli* K(λ). The *rII⁻* mutants, however, have an altered host range: They cannot form plaques with *E. coli* K(λ) cells, although as we have seen, they produce large, unusually distinct plaques with *E. coli* B cells (Fig. 7.20b). The reason that *rII⁻* mutants are unable to infect cells of the K(λ) strain was not clear to Benzer, but this property allowed him to develop an extremely simple and effective test for *rII⁺* gene function.

The *rII* region has two genes

Before he could check whether two mutations in the same gene could recombine, Benzer had to be sure he was really looking at two mutations in a single gene. To verify this, he performed customized complementation tests tailored to two significant characteristics of bacteriophage T4: They are haploid (that is, each phage carries a single T4 chromosome), and they can replicate only in a host bacterium. Because T4 phages are haploid, Benzer needed to ensure that two T4 chromosomes entered the same bacterial cell in order to test for complementation between the mutations. In his complementation tests, he simultaneously infected *E. coli* K(λ) cells with two types of T4 chromosomes—one carried one *rII⁻* mutation, the other carried a different *rII⁻* mutation—and then looked for cell lysis (**Fig. 7.20c**). To ensure that the two kinds of phages would infect almost every bacterial cell, he added many more phages of each type than there were bacteria. If the two *rII⁻* mutations were in different genes, each of the mutant T4 chromosomes would supply one wild-type *rII⁺* gene function, making up for the lack of that function in the other chromosome and resulting in lysis. On the other hand, if the two *rII⁻* mutations were in the same gene, no plaques would appear, because neither mutant chromosome would be able to supply the missing function.

Benzer had to satisfy one final experimental requirement: For the complementation test to be meaningful, he had to make sure that the two *rII⁻* mutations were each recessive to wild type and did not interact with each other to produce an *rII⁻* phenotype dominant to wild type. He checked these points by a control experiment in which he placed the two *rII⁻* mutations on the same chromosome and then simultaneously infected *E. coli* K(λ) with these

FEATURE FIGURE 7.20

How Benzer Analyzed the *rII* Genes of Bacteriophage T4

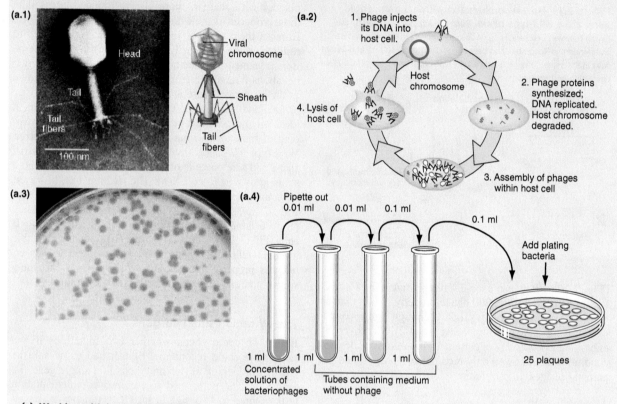

(a.1) [photo labeled: Head, Tail, Tail fibers, 100 nm; artist's rendering labeled: Viral chromosome, Sheath, Tail fibers]

(a.2)
1. Phage injects its DNA into host cell.
2. Phage proteins synthesized; DNA replicated. Host chromosome degraded.
3. Assembly of phages within host cell
4. Lysis of host cell

Host chromosome

(a.3) [photo of petri plate with plaques]

(a.4)
Pipette out
0.01 ml   0.01 ml   0.1 ml
0.1 ml
Add plating bacteria
25 plaques
1 ml   1 ml   1 ml   1 ml
Concentrated solution of bacteriophages
Tubes containing medium without phage

(a) Working with bacteriophage T4

1. Bacteriophage T4 (at a magnification of approximately 100,000×) and in an artist's rendering. The viral chromosome is contained within a protein head. Other proteinaceous parts of the phage particle include the tail fibers, which help the phage attach to host cells, and the sheath, a conduit for injecting the phage chromosome into the host cell.

2. The lytic cycle of bacteriophage T4. A single phage particle infects a host cell; the phage DNA replicates and directs the synthesis of viral protein components using the machinery of the host cell; the new DNA and protein components assemble into new bacteriophage particles. Eventual lysis of the host cell releases up to 1000 progeny bacteriophages into the environment.

3. Clear plaques of bacteriophages in a lawn of bacterial cells. A mixture of bacteriophages and a large number of bacteria are poured onto the agar surface of a petri plate. Uninfected bacterial cells grow, producing an opalescent lawn. A bacterial cell infected by even a single bacteriophage will lyse and release progeny bacteriophages, which can infect adjacent bacteria. Several cycles of infection result in a plaque: a circular cleared area containing millions of bacteriophages genetically identical to the one that originally infected the bacterial cell.

4. Counting bacteriophages by serial dilution. A small sample of a concentrated solution of bacteriophages is transferred to a test tube containing fresh medium, and a small sample of this dilution is transferred to another tube of fresh medium. Successive repeats of this process increase the degree of dilution. A sample of the final dilution, when mixed with bacteria and poured on the agar of a petri plate, yields a countable number of plaques from which it is possible to extrapolate back and calculate the number of bacteriophage particles in the starting solution. The original 1 ml of solution in this illustration contained roughly 2.5×10^7 bacteriophages.

(b) Phenotypic properties of *rII⁻* mutants of bacteriophage T4

1. *rII⁻* mutants, when plated on *E. coli* B cells, produce plaques that are larger and more distinct (with sharper edges) than plaques formed by *rII⁺* wild-type phage.

2. *rII⁻* mutants are particularly useful for looking at rare recombination events because they have an altered host range. In contrast to *rII⁺* wild-type phages, *rII⁻* mutants cannot form plaques in lawns of *E. coli* strain K(λ) host bacteria.

(b.1)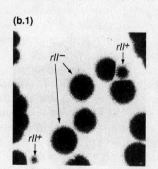
[labeled: *rII⁻*, *rII⁺*]

(b.2)

T4 strain	*E. coli* strain	
	B	K(λ)
rII⁻	Large, distinct	No plaques
rII⁺	Small, fuzzy	Small, fuzzy

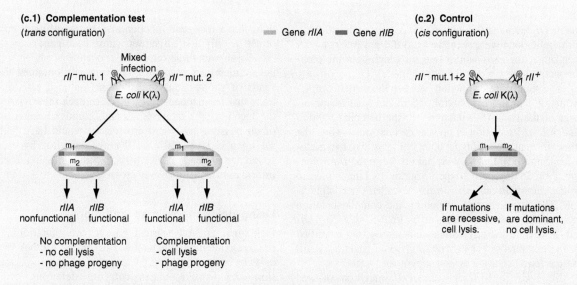

(c.1) Complementation test
(*trans* configuration)

Gene *rIIA* Gene *rIIB*

(c.2) Control
(*cis* configuration)

Mixed infection

rII⁻ mut. 1   *rII⁻* mut. 2

E. coli K(λ)

rII⁻ mut.1+2   *rII⁺*

E. coli K(λ)

m₁
m₂

m₁
m₂

m₁   m₂

rIIA
nonfunctional

rIIB
functional

rIIA
functional

rIIB
functional

If mutations are recessive, cell lysis.

If mutations are dominant, no cell lysis.

No complementation
- no cell lysis
- no phage progeny

Complementation
- cell lysis
- phage progeny

(c) A customized complementation test between *rII⁻* mutants of bacteriophage T4

1. *E. coli* K(λ) cells are simultaneously infected with an excess of two different *rII⁻* mutants (m₁ and m₂). Inside the cell, the two mutations will be in *trans;* that is, they lie on different chromosomes. If the two mutations are in the same gene, they will affect the same function and cannot complement each other, so no progeny phages will be produced. If the two mutations are in different genes (*rIIA* and *rIIB*), they will complement each other, leading to progeny phage production and cell lysis.

2. An important control for this complementation test is the simultaneous infection of *E. coli* K(λ) bacteria with a wild-type T4 strain and a T4 strain containing both m₁ and m₂. Inside the infected cells, the two mutations will be in *cis;* that is, they lie on the same chromosome. Release of phage progeny shows that both mutations are recessive to wild type and that there is no interaction between the mutations that prevents the cells from producing progeny phages. Complementation tests are meaningful only if the two mutations tested are both recessive to wild type.

(d.1) Recombination test

rIIA₁   *rIIA₂*

rIIA₁   *rIIA₂*

E. coli B

(d.2) Control

Recombination

rIIA₁   rIIA₂

rIIA₁   *rIIA₂*

E. coli B   *E. coli* B

rII⁺
wild type

rIIA₁ + rIIA₂
double mutant

rIIA₁   *rIIA₂*

Forms plaques on *E. coli* K(λ)

No plaques on *E. coli* K(λ)

No plaques on *E. coli* K(λ)

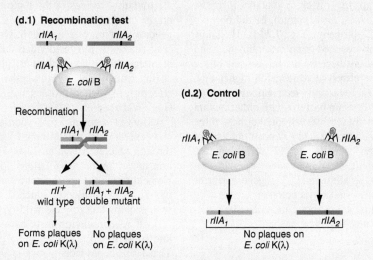

(d) Detecting recombination between two mutations in the same gene

1. *E. coli* B cells are simultaneously infected with a large excess of two different *rIIA⁻* mutants (*rIIA₁* and *rIIA₂*). If no recombination between the two *rIIA⁻* mutations takes place, progeny phages will carry either of the original mutations and will be phenotypically *rII⁻*. If recombination between the two mutations occurs, one of the products will be an *rII⁺* recombinant, while the reciprocal product will be a double mutant chromosome containing both *rIIA₁* and *rIIA₂*. When the phage progeny subsequently infect *E. coli* K(λ) bacteria, only *rII⁺* recombinants will be able to form plaques.

2. As a control, *E. coli* B cells are infected with a large amount of only one kind of mutant (*rIIA₁* or *rIIA₂*). The only *rII⁺* phages that can result are revertants of either mutation. This control experiment shows that such revertants are extremely rare and can be ignored among the *rII⁺* progeny made in the recombination experiment at the *left*. Even if the two *rIIA⁻* mutations are in adjacent base pairs, the number of *rII⁺* recombinants obtained is more than 100 times higher than the number of *rII⁺* revertants the cells infected by a single mutant could produce.

double rII^- mutants and with wild-type phages (Fig. 7.20c). If the mutations were recessive and did not interact with each other, the cells would lyse, in which case the complementation test would be interpretable.

The significant distinction between the actual complementation test and the control experiment is in the placement of the two rII^- mutations. In the complementation test, one rII^- mutation is on one chromosome, while the other rII^- mutation is on the other chromosome; two mutations arranged in this way are said to be in the *trans* configuration. In the control experiment, the two mutations are on the same chromosome, in the so-called *cis* configuration. The complete test, including the complementation test and the control experiment, is known as a *cis-trans* test. Benzer called any complementation group identified by the cis-trans test a **cistron,** and some geneticists still use the term "cistron" as a synonym for "gene."

Tests of many different pairs of rII^- mutations showed that they fall into two complementation groups: the genes *rIIA* and *rIIB*. With this knowledge, Benzer could look for two mutations in the same gene and then see if they ever recombine to produce wild-type progeny.

Recombination between different mutations in a single gene

When Benzer infected *E. coli* B strain bacteria with a mixture of phages carrying different mutations in the same gene ($rIIA_1$ and $rIIA_2$, for example), he did observe the appearance of rII^+ progeny (**Fig. 7.20d**). He knew these wild-type progeny resulted from recombination and not from reverse mutations because the frequencies of the rII^+ phage particles he observed were much higher than the frequencies of rII^+ revertants seen among progeny produced by infecting B strain bacteria with either mutant alone. On the basis of these observations, he drew three conclusions about gene structure: (1) A gene consists of different parts that can each mutate; (2) recombination between different mutable sites in the same gene can generate a normal, wild-type allele; and (3) a gene performs its normal function only if all of its components are wild type. From what we now know about the molecular structure of DNA, this all makes perfect sense.

Different nucleotide pairs within a gene are independently mutable, and recombination can occur between nucleotide pairs within a gene as well as between genes.

A gene is a discrete linear set of nucleotide pairs

How are the multiple nucleotide pairs that make up a gene arranged—in a continuous row or dispersed in precise patterns around the genome? And do the various muta-

tions that affect gene function alter many different nucleotides or only a small subset within each gene?

To answer these questions about the arrangement of nucleotides in a gene, Benzer eventually obtained thousands of spontaneous and mutagen-induced rII^- mutations that he mapped with respect to each other. To map the location of a thousand mutants through comparisons of all possible two-point crosses, he would have had to set up a million ($10^3 \times 10^3$) matings. But by taking advantage of deletion mutations, he could obtain the same information with far fewer crosses.

Using deletions to map mutations

Deletions, as you learned earlier, are mutations that remove contiguous nucleotide pairs along a DNA molecule. In crosses between bacteriophages carrying a mutation and bacteriophages carrying deletions of the corresponding region, no wild-type recombinant progeny can arise, because neither chromosome carries the proper information at the location of the mutation. However, if the mutation lies outside the region deleted from the homologous chromosome, wild-type progeny can appear (**Fig. 7.21a**). This is true whether the mutation is a **point mutation,** that is, a mutation of one nucleotide, or is itself a deletion. Crosses between any uncharacterized mutation and a known deletion thus immediately reveal whether the mutation resides in the region deleted from the other phage chromosome, providing a rapid way to find the general location of a mutation. Using a series of overlapping deletions, Benzer divided the *rII* region into a series of intervals. He could then assign any point mutation to an interval by observing whether it recombined to give rII^+ progeny when crossed with the series of deletions (**Fig. 7.21b**).

Benzer mapped 1612 spontaneous point mutations and several deletions in the *rII* locus of bacteriophage T4 through recombination analysis. He first used recombination to determine the relationship between the deletions. He next found the approximate location of individual point mutations by observing which deletions could recombine with each mutant to yield wild-type progeny. He then performed recombination tests between all point mutations known to lie in the same small region of the chromosome. These results produced a map of the "fine structure" of the region (**Fig. 7.21c**).

From the observation that the number of mutable sites in the *rII* region is very close to the number of nucleotides estimated to be in this region, Benzer inferred that a mutation can arise from the change of a single nucleotide and that recombination can occur between adjacent nucleotide pairs. From the observation that mutations within the *rII* region form a self-consistent, linear recombination map, he concluded that a gene is composed of a continuous linear sequence of nucleotide pairs within the DNA. And from observations that the positions of mutations in the

Figure 7.21 Fine structure mapping of the bacteriophage T4 *rII* genes. (a) A phage cross between a point mutation and a deletion removing the DNA at the position of the mutation cannot yield wild-type recombinants. The same is true if two different deletion mutations overlap each other. **(b)** Large deletions divide the *rII* locus into regions; finer deletions divide each region into subsections. Point mutations, such as 271 (*in red at bottom*), map to region 3 if they do not recombine with deletions PT1, PB242, or A105 but do recombine with deletion 638 (*top*). Point mutations can be mapped to subsections of region 3 using other deletions (*middle*). Recombination tests map point mutations in the same subregion (*bottom*). Point mutations 201 and 155 cannot recombine to yield wild-type recombinants because they affect the same nucleotide pair. **(c)** Benzer's fine structure map. Hot spots are locations with many independent mutations that cannot recombine with each other.

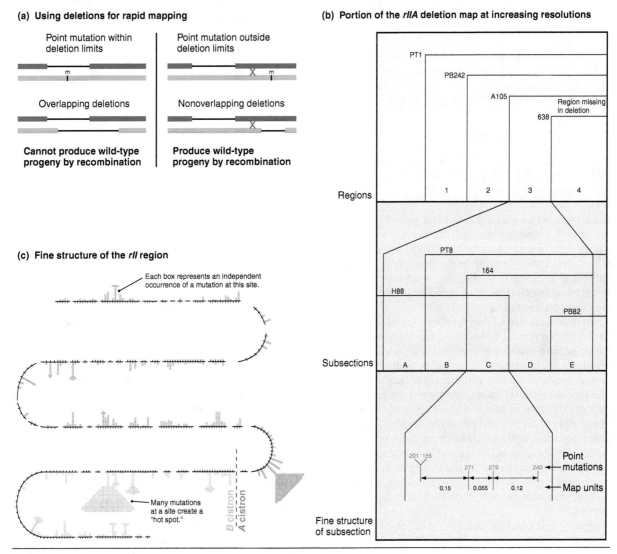

(a) Using deletions for rapid mapping

(b) Portion of the *rIIA* deletion map at increasing resolutions

(c) Fine structure of the *rII* region

rIIA gene did not overlap those of the *rIIB* gene, he inferred that the nucleotide sequences composing those two genes are separate and distinct. A *gene* is thus a linear set of nucleotide pairs, located within a discrete region of a chromosome, that serves as a unit of function.

"Hot spots" of mutation

Some sites within a gene spontaneously mutate more frequently than others and as a result are known as **hot spots**

(Fig. 7.21c). The existence of hot spots suggests that certain nucleotides can be altered more readily than others. Treatment with mutagens also turns up hot spots, but because mutagens have specificities for particular nucleotides, the highly mutable sites that turn up with various mutagens are often at different positions in a gene than the hot spots resulting from spontaneous mutation.

Nucleotides are chemically the same whether they lie within a gene or in the DNA between genes, and as Benzer's experiments show, the molecular machinery responsible for mutation and recombination does not discriminate between those nucleotides that are *intragenic* (within a gene) and those that are *intergenic* (between genes). The main distinction between DNA within and DNA outside a gene is that the array of nucleotides composing a gene has evolved a function that determines phenotype. Next, we describe how geneticists discovered what that function is.

> The mechanisms governing mutation and recombination do not discriminate between nucleotide pairs within or outside of genes; however, the nucleotide pairs within a gene together comprise a unit of function that contributes to phenotype.

7.3 What Mutations Tell Us About Gene Function

Mendel's experiments established that an individual gene can control a visible characteristic, but his laws do not explain how genes actually govern the appearance of traits. Investigators working in the first half of the twentieth century carefully studied the biochemical changes caused by mutations in an effort to understand the genotype–phenotype connection.

In one of the first of these studies, conducted in 1902, the British physician Dr. Archibald Garrod showed that a human genetic disorder known as *alkaptonuria* is determined by the recessive allele of an autosomal gene. Garrod analyzed family pedigrees and performed biochemical analyses on family members with and without the trait. The urine of people with alkaptonuria turns black on exposure to air. Garrod found that a substance known as homogentisic acid, which blackens upon contact with oxygen, accumulates in the urine of alkaptonuria patients. Alkaptonuriacs excrete all of the homogentisic acid they ingest, while people without the condition excrete no homogentisic acid in their urine even after ingesting the substance.

From these observations, Garrod concluded that people with alkaptonuria are incapable of metabolizing homogentisic acid to the breakdown products generated by normal individuals (**Fig. 7.22**). Because many biochemical reactions within the cells of organisms are catalyzed by enzymes, Garrod hypothesized that lack of the enzyme that breaks down homogentisic acid is the cause of alkaptonuria. In the absence of this enzyme, the acid accumulates and causes the urine to turn black on contact with oxygen. He called this condition an "inborn error of metabolism."

Garrod studied several other inborn errors of metabolism and suggested that all arose from mutations that prevented a particular gene from producing an enzyme

Figure 7.22 Alkaptonuria: An inborn error of metabolism. The biochemical pathway in humans that degrades phenylalanine and tyrosine via homogentisic acid (HA). In alkaptonuria patients, the enzyme HA hydroxylase is not functional so it does not catalyze the conversion of HA to maleylacetoacetic acid. As a result, HA, which oxidizes to a black compound, accumulates in the urine.

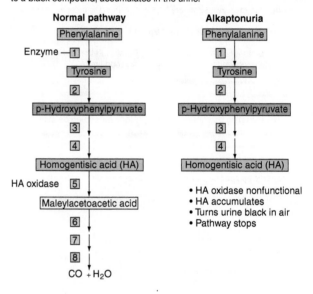

required for a specific biochemical reaction. In today's terminology, the wild-type allele of the gene would allow production of functional enzyme (in the case of alkaptonuria, the enzyme is homogentisic acid oxidase), whereas the mutant allele would not. Because the single wild-type allele in heterozygotes generates sufficient enzyme to prevent accumulation of homogentisic acid and thus the condition of alkaptonuria, the mutant allele is recessive.

A gene contains the information for producing a specific enzyme: The one gene, one enzyme hypothesis

In the 1940s, George Beadle and Edward Tatum carried out a series of experiments on the bread mold *Neurospora crassa* (whose life cycle was described in Chapter 5) that demonstrated a direct relation between genes and the enzymes that catalyze specific biochemical reactions. Their strategy was simple. They first isolated a number of mutations that disrupted synthesis of the amino acid arginine, a compound needed for *Neurospora* growth. They next hypothesized that different mutations blocked different steps in a particular **biochemical pathway:** the orderly series of reactions that allows *Neurospora* to obtain simple molecules from the environment and convert them step-by-step into successively more complicated molecules culminating in arginine.

Figure 7.23 Experimental support for the "one gene, one enzyme" hypothesis. (a) Beadle and Tatum mated an X-ray-mutagenized strain of *Neurospora* with another strain, and they isolated haploid ascospores that grew on complete medium. Cultures that failed to grow on minimal medium were nutritional mutants. Nutritional mutants that could grow on minimal medium plus arginine were *arg⁻* auxotrophs. **(b)** The ability of wild-type and mutant strains to grow on minimal medium supplemented with intermediates in the arginine pathway. **(c)** Each of the four *ARG* genes encodes an enzyme needed to convert one intermediate to the next in the pathway.

(a) Isolation of arginine auxotrophs

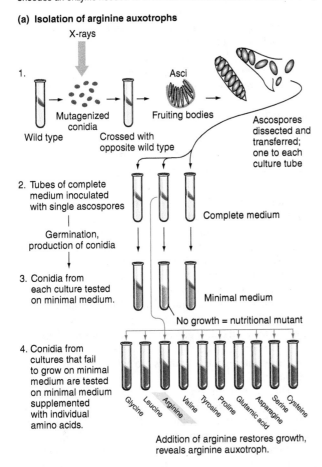

Addition of arginine restores growth,
reveals arginine auxotroph.

(b) Growth response if nutrient is added to minimal medium

Mutant strain	Nothing	Ornithine	Citrulline	Arginino-succinate	Arginine
Wildtype: *Arg⁺*	+	+	+	+	+
Arg-E⁻	−	+	+	+	+
Arg-F⁻	−	−	+	+	+
Arg-G⁻	−	−	−	+	+
Arg-H⁻	−	−	−	−	+

(c) Inferred biochemical pathway

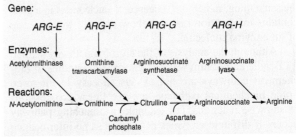

mutations in four distinct regions of the genome, and complementation tests showed that each of the four regions correlated with a different complementation group. On the basis of these results, Beadle and Tatum concluded that at least four genes support the biochemical pathway for arginine synthesis. They named the four genes *ARG-E, ARG-F, ARG-G,* and *ARG-H.*

They next asked whether any of the mutant *Neurospora* strains could grow in minimal medium supplemented with any of three known intermediates (ornithine, citrulline, and arginosuccinate) in the biochemical pathway leading to arginine, instead of with arginine itself. This test would identify *Neurospora* mutants able to convert the intermediate compound into arginine. Beadle and Tatum compiled a table describing which arginine auxotrophic mutants were able to grow on minimal medium supplemented with each of the intermediates (**Fig. 7.23b**).

Experimental evidence for "one gene, one enzyme"

Figure 7.23a illustrates the experiments Beadle and Tatum performed to test their hypothesis. They first obtained a set of mutagen-induced mutations that prevented *Neurospora* from synthesizing arginine. Cells with any one of these mutations were unable to make arginine and could therefore grow on a minimal medium containing salt and sugar only if it had been supplemented with arginine. A nutritional mutant microorganism that requires supplementation with substances not needed by wild-type strains is known as an **auxotroph.** The cells just mentioned were arginine auxotrophs. (In contrast, a cell that does not require addition of a substance is a **prototroph** for that factor. In a more general meaning, *prototroph* refers to a wild-type cell that can grow on minimal medium alone.) Recombination analyses located the auxotrophic arginine-blocking

Interpretation of results: Genes encode enzymes

On the basis of these results, Beadle and Tatum proposed a model of how *Neurospora* cells synthesize arginine (**Fig.7.23c**). In the linear progression of biochemical reactions by which a cell constructs arginine from the constituents of minimal medium, each intermediate is both the product of one step and the substrate for the next. Each reaction in the precisely ordered sequence is catalyzed by a specific enzyme, and the presence of each enzyme depends on one of the four *ARG* genes. A mutation in one gene blocks the pathway at a particular step because the cell lacks the corresponding enzyme and thus cannot make arginine on its own. Supplementing the medium with any intermediate that occurs beyond the blocked reaction restores growth because the organism has all the enzymes required to convert the intermediate to arginine. Supplementation with an intermediate that occurs before the missing enzyme does not work because the cell is unable to convert the intermediate into arginine.

Each mutation abolishes the cell's ability to make an enzyme capable of catalyzing a certain reaction. By inference, then, each gene controls the synthesis or activity of an enzyme, or as stated by Beadle and Tatum: one gene, one enzyme. Of course, the gene and the enzyme are not the same thing; rather, the sequence of nucleotides in a gene contains information that somehow encodes the structure of an enzyme molecule.

Although the analysis of the arginine pathway studied by Beadle and Tatum was straightforward, studies of biochemical pathways are not always so easy to interpret. Some biochemical pathways are not linear progressions of stepwise reactions. For example, a branching pathway occurs if different enzymes act on the same intermediate to convert it into two different end products. If the cell requires both of these end products for growth, a mutation in a gene encoding any of the enzymes required to synthesize the intermediate would make the cell dependent on supplementation with both end products. A second possibility is that a cell might employ either of two independent, parallel pathways to synthesize a needed end product. In such a case, a mutation in a gene encoding an enzyme in one of the pathways would be without effect. Only a cell with mutations affecting both pathways would display an aberrant phenotype.

Even with nonlinear progressions such as these, careful genetic analysis can reveal the nature of the biochemical pathway on the basis of Beadle and Tatum's insight that genes encode proteins.

> Beadle and Tatum found that mutations in a single complementation group (that is, a single gene) disrupted one particular enzymatic step of a known biochemical pathway, while mutations in other genes disrupted other steps. They concluded that each gene specifies a different enzyme ("one gene, one enzyme").

Genes specify the identity and order of amino acids in polypeptide chains

Although the one gene, one enzyme hypothesis was a critical advance in understanding how genes influence phenotype, it is an oversimplification. Not all genes govern the construction of enzymes active in biochemical pathways. Enzymes are only one class of the molecules known as proteins, and cells contain many other kinds of proteins. Among the other types are proteins that provide shape and rigidity to a cell, proteins that transport molecules in and out of cells, proteins that help fold DNA into chromosomes, and proteins that act as hormonal messengers. Genes direct the synthesis of all proteins, enzymes and nonenzymes alike. Moreover, as we see next, genes actually determine the construction of polypeptides, and because some proteins are composed of more than one type of polypeptide, more than one gene determines the construction of such proteins.

Proteins: Linear polymers of amino acids linked by peptide bonds

To review the basics, proteins are polymers composed of building blocks known as **amino acids.** Cells use mainly 20 different amino acids to synthesize the proteins they need. All of these amino acids have certain basic features, encapsulated by the formula $NH_2–CHR–COOH$ (**Fig. 7.24a**). The –COOH component, also known as *carboxylic acid,* is, as the name implies, acidic; the –NH_2 component, also known as an *amino group,* is basic. The R refers to side chains that distinguish each of the 20 amino acids (**Fig. 7.24b**). An R group can be as simple as a hydrogen atom (in the amino acid glycine) or as complex as a benzene ring (in phenylalanine). Some side chains are relatively neutral and nonreactive, others are acidic, and still others are basic.

During protein synthesis, a cell's protein-building machinery links amino acids by constructing covalent **peptide bonds** that join the –COOH group of one amino acid to the –NH_2 group of the next (**Fig. 7.24c**). A pair of amino acids connected in this fashion is a **dipeptide;** several amino acids linked together constitute an **oligopeptide.** The amino acid chains that make up proteins contain hundreds to thousands of amino acids joined by peptide bonds and are known as **polypeptides.** Proteins are thus linear polymers of amino acids. Like the chains of nucleotides in DNA, polypeptides have a chemical polarity. One end of a polypeptide is called the **N terminus** because it contains a free amino group that is not connected to any other amino acid. The other end of the polypeptide chain is the **C terminus,** because it contains a free carboxylic acid group.

Mutations can alter amino acid sequences

Each protein is composed of a unique sequence of amino acids. The chemical properties that enable structural proteins to give a cell its shape, or enzymes to catalyze specific reactions are a direct consequence of the identity, number, and linear order of amino acids in the protein.

(a) Generic amino acid structure

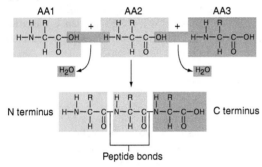

Amino (–NH₂) group

CHR group

Carboxyl (–COOH) group

(c) Peptide bond formation

(b) Amino acids with nonpolar R groups

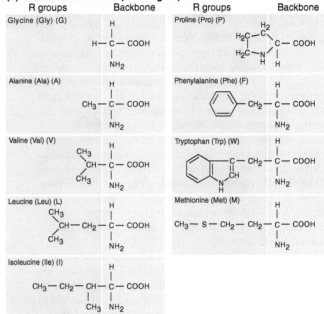

Amino acids with uncharged polar R groups

Amino acids with basic R groups

Amino acids with acidic R groups

Figure 7.24 Proteins are chains of amino acids linked by peptide bonds. (a) Amino acids contain a basic amino group (–NH₂), an acidic carboxylic acid group (–COOH), and a CHR moiety, where R stands for one of the 20 different side chains. **(b)** Amino acids commonly found in proteins, arranged according to the properties of their R groups. **(c)** One molecule of water is lost when a covalent amide linkage (a peptide bond) is formed between the –COOH of one amino acid and the –NH₂ of the next amino acid. Polypeptides such as the tripeptide shown here have polarity; they extend from an N terminus (with a free amino group) to a C terminus (with a free carboxylic acid group).

If genes encode proteins, then at least some mutations could be changes in a gene that alter the proper sequence of amino acids in the protein encoded by that gene. In the mid-1950s, Vernon Ingram began to establish what kinds of changes particular mutations cause in the corresponding protein. Using recently developed techniques for determining the sequence of amino acids in a protein, he compared the amino acid sequence of the normal adult form of hemoglobin (HbA) with that of hemoglobin in the bloodstream of people homozygous for the mutation that causes sickle-cell anemia (HbS). Remarkably, he found only a single amino acid difference between the wild-type and mutant proteins (**Fig. 7.25a**). Hemoglobin consists of two types of polypeptides: a so-called α (alpha) chain and a β (beta) chain. The sixth amino acid from the N terminus of the β chain was glutamic acid in normal individuals but valine in sickle-cell patients.

Ingram thus established that a mutation substituting one amino acid for another had the power to change the structure and function of hemoglobin and thereby alter the phenotype from normal to sickle-cell anemia (**Fig. 7.25b**). We now know that the glutamic acid–to-valine change affects the solubility of hemoglobin within the red blood cell. At low concentrations of oxygen, the less soluble sickle-cell form of hemoglobin aggregates into long chains that deform the red blood cell (Fig. 7.25a).

Because people suffering from a variety of inherited anemias also have defective hemoglobin molecules, Ingram and other geneticists were able to determine how a large number of different mutations affect the amino acid sequence of hemoglobin (**Fig. 7.25c**). Most of the altered hemoglobins have a change in only one amino acid. In various patients with anemia, the alteration is generally in different amino acids, but occasionally, two independent mutations result in different substitutions for the same amino acid. Geneticists use the term **missense mutation** to describe a genetic alteration that causes the substitution of one amino acid for another.

> Proteins are polymers of amino acids linked by peptide bonds; protein chains are polar because they have chemically distinct N and C termini. Some mutations in genes can change the identify of a single amino acid in a protein; such amino acid substitutions can disrupt the protein's function.

Figure 7.25 The molecular basis of sickle-cell and other anemias. (a) Substitution of glutamic acid with valine at the sixth amino acid from the N terminus affects the three-dimensional structure of the β chain of hemoglobin. Hemoglobins incorporating the mutant β chain form aggregates that cause red blood cells to sickle. **(b)** Red blood cell sickling has many phenotypic effects. **(c)** Other mutations in the β-chain gene also cause anemias.

(a) From mutation to phenotype

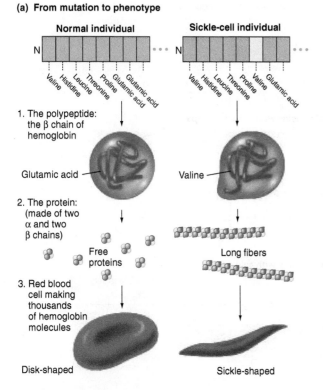

(b) Sickle-cell anemia is pleiotropic

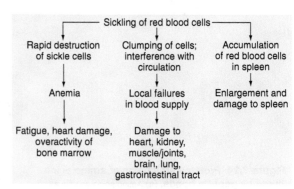

(c) β-chain substitutions/variants

| | \multicolumn{11}{c}{Amino-acid position} |
	1	2	3 ···	6	7 ···	26 ···	63 ···	67 ···	125 ···	146
Normal (HbA)	Val	His	Leu	Glu	Glu	Glu	His	Val	Glu	His
HbS	Val	His	Leu	Val	Glu	Glu	His	Val	Glu	His
HbC	Val	His	Leu	Lys	Glu	Glu	His	Val	Glu	His
HbG San Jose	Val	His	Leu	Glu	Gly	Glu	His	Val	Glu	His
HbE	Val	His	Leu	Glu	Glu	Lys	His	Val	Glu	His
HbM Saskatoon	Val	His	Leu	Glu	Glu	Glu	Tyr	Val	Glu	His
Hb Zurich	Val	His	Leu	Glu	Glu	Glu	Arg	Val	Glu	His
HbM Milwaukee 1	Val	His	Leu	Glu	Glu	Glu	His	Glu	Glu	His
HbDβ Punjab	Val	His	Leu	Glu	Glu	Glu	His	Val	Gln	His

Primary, secondary, and tertiary protein structures

Despite the uniform nature of protein construction—a line of amino acids joined by peptide bonds—each type of polypeptide folds into a unique three-dimensional shape. The linear sequence of amino acids within a polypeptide is its **primary structure.** Each unique primary structure places constraints on how a chain can arrange itself in three-dimensional space. Because the R groups distinguishing the 20 amino acids have dissimilar chemical properties, some amino acids form hydrogen bonds or electrostatic bonds when brought into proximity with other amino acids. Nonpolar amino acids, for example, may become associated with each other by interactions that "hide" them from water in localized hydrophobic regions. As another example, two cysteine amino acids can form covalent disulfide bridges (–S–S–) through the oxidation of their –SH groups.

All of these interactions (**Fig. 7.26a**) help stabilize the polypeptide in a specific three-dimensional conformation. The primary structure (**Fig. 7.26b**) determines three-dimensional shape by generating localized regions with a characteristic geometry known as **secondary structure** (**Fig. 7.26c**). Primary structure is also responsible for

other folds and twists that together with the secondary structure produce the ultimate three-dimensional **tertiary structure** of the entire polypeptide (**Fig. 7.26d**). Normal tertiary structure—the way a long chain of amino acids naturally folds in three-dimensional space under physiological conditions—is known as a polypeptide's *native configuration.* Various forces, including hydrogen bonds, electrostatic bonds, hydrophobic interactions, and disulfide bridges, help stabilize the native configuration.

It is worth repeating that primary structure—the sequence of amino acids in a polypeptide—directly determines secondary and tertiary structures. The information required for the chain to fold into its native configuration is inherent in its linear sequence of amino acids. In one example of this principle, many proteins unfold, or become **denatured,** when exposed to urea and mercaptoethanol or to increasing heat or pH. These treatments disrupt the interactions that normally stabilize the secondary and tertiary structures. When conditions return to normal, many proteins spontaneously refold into their native configuration without help from other agents. No other information beyond the primary structure is needed to achieve the proper three-dimensional shape of such proteins.

Figure 7.26 Levels of polypeptide structure. (a) Covalent and noncovalent interactions determine the structure of a polypeptide. **(b)** A polypeptide's primary (1°) structure is its amino acid sequence. **(c)** Localized regions form secondary (2°) structures such as α helices and β-pleated sheets. **(d)** The tertiary (3°) structure is the complete three-dimensional arrangement of a polypeptide. In this portrait of myoglobin, the iron-containing heme group, which carries oxygen, is *red,* while the polypeptide itself is *green.*

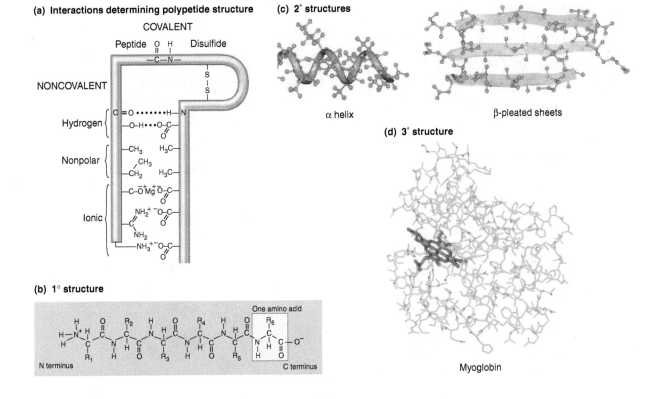

Quaternary structure: Multimeric proteins

Certain proteins, such as the rhodopsin that promotes black-and-white vision, consist of a single polypeptide. Many others, however, such as the lens crystallin protein, which provides rigidity and transparency to the lenses of our eyes, or the hemoglobin molecule described earlier, are composed of two or more polypeptide chains that associate in a specific way (**Fig. 7.27a and b**). The individual polypeptides in an aggregate are known as *subunits,* and the complex of subunits is often referred to as a *multimer.* The three-dimensional configuration of subunits in a multimer is a complex protein's **quaternary structure.**

The same forces that stabilize the native form of a polypeptide (that is, hydrogen bonds, electrostatic bonds, hydrophobic interactions, and disulfide bridges) also contribute to the maintenance of quaternary structure. As Fig. 7.27a shows, in some multimers, the two or more interacting subunits are identical polypeptides. These identical chains are encoded by one gene. In other multimers, by contrast, more than one kind of polypeptide makes up the protein (Fig. 7.27b). The different polypeptides in these multimers are encoded by different genes.

Alterations in just one kind of subunit, caused by a mutation in a single gene, can affect the function of a multimer. The adult hemoglobin molecule, for example, consists of two α and two β subunits, with each type of subunit determined by a different gene—one for the α chain and one for the β chain. A mutation in the *Hbβ* gene resulting in an amino acid switch at position 6 in the β chain causes sickle-cell anemia. Similarly, if several multimeric proteins share a common subunit, a single mutation in the gene encoding that subunit may affect all the

Figure 7.27 Multimeric proteins. (a) β2 lens crystallin contains two copies of one kind of subunit; the two subunits are the product of a single gene. The peptide backbones of the two subunits are shown in different shades of *purple.* **(b)** Hemoglobin is composed of two different kinds of subunits, each encoded by a different gene. **(c)** Three distinct protein receptors for the immune-system molecules called interleukins (ILs; *purple*). All contain a common gamma (γ) chain (*yellow*), plus other receptor-specific polypeptides (*green*). A mutant γ chain blocks the function of all three receptors, leading to XSCID. **(d)** One α-tubulin and one β-tubulin polypeptide associate to form a tubulin dimer. Many tubulin dimers form a single microtubule. The mitotic spindle is an assembly of many microtubules.

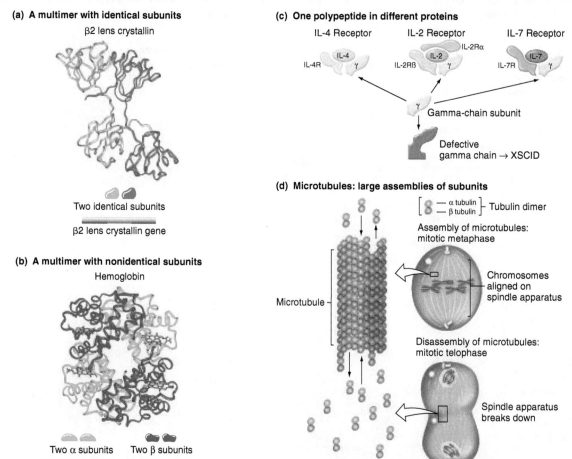

(a) A multimer with identical subunits
β2 lens crystallin
Two identical subunits
β2 lens crystallin gene

(b) A multimer with nonidentical subunits
Hemoglobin
Two α subunits   Two β subunits
Hb α gene   *Hb* β gene

(c) One polypeptide in different proteins
IL-4 Receptor   IL-2 Receptor   IL-7 Receptor
IL-4   IL-2   IL-2Rα   IL-7
IL-4R   γ   IL-2Rβ   γ   IL-7R   γ
Gamma-chain subunit
Defective gamma chain → XSCID

(d) Microtubules: large assemblies of subunits
— α tubulin
— β tubulin   Tubulin dimer
Assembly of microtubules: mitotic metaphase
Microtubule
Chromosomes aligned on spindle apparatus
Disassembly of microtubules: mitotic telophase
Spindle apparatus breaks down

proteins simultaneously. An example is an X-linked mutation in mice and humans that incapacitates several different proteins all known as interleukin (IL) receptors. Because all of these receptors are essential to the normal function of immune-system cells that fight infection and generate immunity, this one mutation causes the life-threatening condition known as X-linked severe combined immune deficiency (XSCID; **Fig. 7.27c**).

The polypeptides of complex proteins can assemble into extremely large structures capable of changing with the needs of the cell. For example, the microtubules that make up the spindle during mitosis are gigantic assemblages of mainly two polypeptides: α tubulin and β tubulin (**Fig. 7.27d**). The cell can organize these subunits into very long hollow tubes that grow or shrink as needed at different stages of the cell cycle.

One gene, one polypeptide

Because more than one gene governs the production of some multimeric proteins and because not all proteins are enzymes, the "one gene, one enzyme" hypothesis is not broad enough to define gene function. A more accurate statement is "one gene, one polypeptide": Each gene governs the construction of a particular polypeptide. As you will see in Chapter 8, even this reformulation does not encompass the function of all genes, as a few genes in all organisms do not determine the construction of proteins; instead, they encode RNAs that are not translated into polypeptides.

Beadle and Tatum's experiments were based on the concept that if each gene encodes a different polypeptide and if each polypeptide plays a specific role in the development, physiology, or behavior of an organism, then a mutation in the gene will block a biological process (like arginine synthesis in *Neurospora*) in a characteristic way. Other scientists soon realized they could use this approach to study virtually any interesting problem in biology. In the Fast Forward box "Using Mutagenesis to Look at Biological Processes" on the following page, we describe how one biologist found a large group of mutations that disrupted the assembly of bacteriophage T4 particles. By carefully studying the phenotypes caused by these mutations, he inferred the complex pathway that produces an entire bacteriophage.

Knowledge about the connection between genes and polypeptides enabled geneticists to analyze how different mutations in a single gene can produce different phenotypes. If each amino acid has a specific effect on the three-dimensional structure of a protein, then changing amino acids at different positions in a polypeptide chain can alter protein function in different ways. For example, most enzymes have an active site that carries out the enzymatic task, while other parts of the protein support the shape and position of that site. Mutations that change the identity of amino acids at the active site may have more

serious consequences than those affecting amino acids outside the active site. Some kinds of amino acid substitutions, such as replacement of an amino acid having a basic side chain with an amino acid having an acidic side chain, would be more likely to compromise protein function than would substitutions that retain the chemical characteristics of the original amino acid.

Some mutations do not affect the amino acid composition of a protein but still generate an abnormal phenotype. As discussed in the following chapter, such mutations change the amount of normal polypeptide produced by disrupting the biochemical processes responsible for decoding a gene into a polypeptide.

> Most (but not all) genes specify the amino acid sequence of a polypeptide; a protein is comprised of one or more polypeptides. The primary amino acid sequences of the constituent polypeptides determine a protein's three-dimensional structure and thus its function.

7.4 A Comprehensive Example: Mutations That Affect Vision

Researchers first described anomalies of color perception in humans close to 200 years ago. Since that time, they have discovered a large number of mutations that modify human vision. By examining the phenotype associated with each mutation and then looking directly at the DNA alterations inherited with the mutation, they have learned a great deal about the genes influencing human visual perception and the function of the proteins they encode.

Using human subjects for vision studies has several advantages. First, people can recognize and describe variations in the way they see, from trivial differences in what the color red looks like, to not seeing any difference between red and green, to not seeing any color at all. Second, the highly developed science of psychophysics provides sensitive, noninvasive tests for accurately defining and comparing phenotypes. One diagnostic test, for example, is based on the fact that people perceive each color as a mixture of three different wavelengths of light—red, green, and blue—and the human visual system can adjust ratios of red, green, and blue light of different intensities to match an arbitrarily chosen fourth wavelength such as yellow. The mixture of wavelengths does not combine to form the fourth wavelength; it just appears that way to the eye. A person with normal vision, for instance, will select a well-defined proportion of red and green lights to match a particular yellow, but a person who can't tell red from green will permit any proportion of these two color lights to make the same match. Finally, because inherited variations in the visual system rarely

▶▶ FAST FORWARD

Using Mutagenesis to Look at Biological Processes

Geneticists can use mutations to dissect complicated biological processes into their protein components. To determine the specific, dedicated role of each protein, they introduce mutations into the genes encoding the protein. The mutations knock out, or delete, functional protein either by preventing protein production altogether or by altering it such that the resulting protein is nonfunctional. The researchers then observe what happens when the cell or organism attempts to perform the biological process without the deleted protein.

In the 1960s, Robert Edgar set out to delineate the function of the proteins determined by all the genes in the T4 bacteriophage genome. After a single viral particle infects an *E. coli* bacterium, the host cell stops producing bacterial proteins and becomes a factory for making only viral proteins. Thirty minutes after infection, the bacterial cell lyses, releasing 100 new viral particles. The head of each particle carries a DNA genome 200,000 base pairs in length that encodes at least 120 genes.

Edgar's experimental design was to obtain many different mutant bacteriophages, each containing a mutation that inactivates one of the genes essential for viral reproduction. By analyzing what went wrong with each type of mutant during the infective cycle, he would learn something about the function of each of the proteins produced by the T4 genome.

There was just one barrier to implementing this plan. A mutation that prevents viral reproduction by definition makes the virus unable to reproduce and therefore unavailable for experimental study. The solution to this dilemma came with the discovery of *conditional lethal mutants:* viruses, microbes, or other organisms carrying mutations that are lethal to the organism under one condition but not another. One type of conditional lethal mutant used by Edgar was temperature-sensitive; that is, the mutant T4 phage could reproduce only at low temperatures. The mutations causing temperature sensitivity changed one amino acid in a polypeptide such that the protein was stable and functional at a low temperature but became unstable and nonfunctional at a higher temperature. Temperature-sensitive mutations can occur in almost any gene. Edgar isolated thousands of conditional lethal bacteriophage T4 mutants, and using complementation studies, he discovered that they fall into 65 complementation groups. These complementation groups defined 65 genes whose function is required for bacteriophage replication.

Edgar next studied the consequences of infecting bacterial cells under *restrictive conditions,* that is, under conditions in which the mutant protein could not function. For the temperature-sensitive mutants, the restrictive condition was high temperature. He found that mutations in 17 genes prevented viral DNA replication and concluded that these 17 genes contribute to that process. Mutations in most of the other 48 genes did not impede viral DNA replication but were necessary for the construction of complete viral particles.

Electron microscopy showed that mutations in these 48 genes caused the accumulation of partially constructed viral particles. Edgar used the incomplete particles to plot the path of viral assembly. As **Fig. A** illustrates, three subassembly lines—one for the tail, one for the head, and one for the tail fibers—come together during the assembly of the viral product. Once the heads are completed and filled with DNA, they attach to the tails, after which attachment of the fibers completes particle construction. It would have been very difficult to discern this trilateral assembly pathway by any means other than mutagenesis-driven genetic dissection.

Between 1990 and 1995, molecular geneticists determined the complete DNA sequence of the T4 genome, and then using the genetic code dictionary (described in Chapter 8), translated that sequence into coding regions for proteins. In addition to the 65 genes identified by Edgar, another 55 genes became evident from the sequence. Edgar did not find these genes because they are not essential to viral reproduction under the conditions used in the laboratory. The previously unidentified genes most likely play important roles in the T4 life cycle outside the laboratory, perhaps when the virus infects hosts other than the *E. coli* strain normally used in the laboratory, or when the virus grows under different environmental conditions and is competing with other viruses.

Figure A Steps in the assembly of bacteriophage T4.

Robert Edgar determined what kinds of phage structures formed in bacterial cells infected with mutant T4 phage at restrictive temperatures. As an example, a cell infected with a phage carrying a temperature-sensitive mutation in gene 63 filled up with normal-looking phage that lacked tail fibers, and with normal-looking tail fibers. Edgar concluded that gene 63 encodes a protein that allows tail fibers to attach to otherwise completely assembled phage particles.

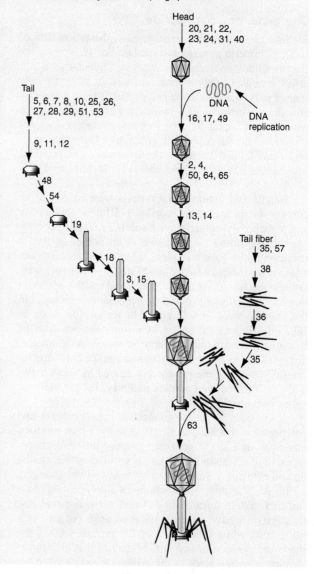

affect an individual's life span or ability to reproduce, mutations generating many of the new alleles that change visual perception remain in a population over time.

Cells of the retina carry light-sensitive proteins

People perceive light through neurons in the retina at the back of the eye (**Fig. 7.28a**). These neurons are of two types: rods and cones. The rods, which make up 95% of all light-receiving neurons, are stimulated by weak light over a range of wavelengths. At higher light intensities, the rods become saturated and no longer send meaningful information to the brain. This is when the cones take over, processing wavelengths of bright light that enable us to see color.

The cones come in three forms—one specializes in the reception of red light, a second in the reception of green, and a third in the reception of blue. For each photoreceptor cell, the act of reception consists of absorbing photons from light of a particular wavelength, transducing information about the number and energy of those photons to electrical signals, and transmitting the signals via the optic nerve to the brain.

Four related proteins with different light sensitivities

The protein that receives photons and triggers the processing of information in rod cells is **rhodopsin.** It consists of a single polypeptide chain containing 348 amino acids that snakes back and forth across the cell membrane (**Fig. 7.28b**). One lysine within the chain associates with retinal, a carotenoid pigment molecule that actually absorbs photons. The amino acids in the vicinity of the retinal constitute rhodopsin's active site; by positioning the retinal in a particular way, they determine its response to light. Each rod cell contains approximately 100 million molecules of rhodopsin in its specialized membrane. As you learned at the beginning of this chapter, the gene governing the production of rhodopsin is on chromosome 3.

The protein that receives and initiates the processing of photons in the blue cones is a relative of rhodopsin, also consisting of a single polypeptide chain containing 348 amino acids and also encompassing one molecule of retinal. Slightly less than half of the 348 amino acids in the blue-receiving protein are the same as those found in rhodopsin; the rest are different and account for the specialized light-receiving ability of the protein (Fig. 7.28b). The gene for the blue protein is on chromosome 7.

Similarly related to rhodopsin are the red- and green-receiving proteins in the red and green cones. These are also single polypeptides associated with retinal and embedded in the cell membrane, although they are both slightly larger at 364 amino acids in length (Fig. 7.28b). Like the blue protein, the red and green proteins differ from

Figure 7.28 The cellular and molecular basis of vision.
(a) Rod and cone cells in the retina carry membrane-bound photoreceptors. **(b)** The photoreceptor in rod cells is rhodopsin. The blue, green, and red receptor proteins in cone cells are related to rhodopsin. **(c)** One red photoreceptor gene and one to three green photoreceptor genes are clustered on the X chromosome. **(d)** The genes for rhodopsin and the three color receptors probably evolved from a primordial photoreceptor gene through three gene duplication events followed by divergence of the duplicated copies.

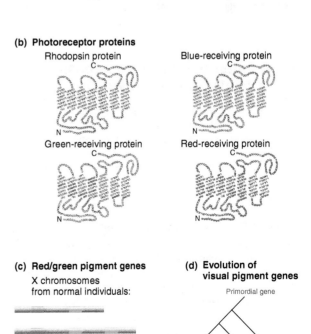

rhodopsin in nearly half of their amino acids; they differ from each other in only four amino acids out of every hundred. Even these small differences, however, are sufficient to differentiate the light sensitivities of the two types of cones and confer on them distinct spectral sensitivities. The genes for the red and green proteins both reside on the X chromosome in a tandem head-to-tail arrangement. Most individuals have one red gene and one to three green genes on their X chromosomes (**Fig. 7.28c**).

Evolution of the rhodopsin gene family

The similarity in structure and function between the four rhodopsin proteins suggests that the genes encoding these polypeptides arose by duplication of an original photoreceptor gene and then divergence through the accumulation of many mutations. Many of the mutations that promoted the ability to see color must have provided selective advantages to their bearers over the course of evolution. The red and green genes are the most similar, differing by less than five nucleotides out of every hundred. This suggests they diverged from each other only in the relatively recent evolutionary past. The less pronounced amino acid similarity of the red or green proteins with the blue protein, and the even lower relatedness between rhodopsin and any color photoreceptor, reflect earlier duplication and divergence events (**Fig. 7.28d**).

> Duplication and divergence (through mutation) of an ancestral rhodopsin-like gene have produced four specialized genes encoding rhodopsin and the blue, red, and green photoreceptor proteins.

How mutations in the rhodopsin gene family affect the way we see

Mutations in the genes encoding rhodopsin and the three color photoreceptor proteins can alter vision through many different mechanisms. These mutations range from point mutations that change the identity of a single amino acid in a single protein to larger aberrations resulting from unequal crossing-over that can increase or decrease the number of photoreceptor genes.

Mutations in the rhodopsin gene

At least 29 different single nucleotide substitutions in the rhodopsin gene cause an autosomal dominant vision disorder known as *retinitis pigmentosa* that begins with an early loss of rod function, followed by a slow progressive degeneration of the peripheral retina. **Figure 7.29a** shows the location of the amino acids affected by these mutations. These amino acid changes result in abnormal rhodopsin proteins that either do not fold properly or, once folded, are unstable. Although normal rhodopsin is an essential structural element of rod cell membranes, these nonfunctional

mutant proteins are retained in the body of the cell, where they remain unavailable for insertion into the membrane. Rod cells that cannot incorporate enough rhodopsin into their membranes eventually die. Depending on how many rod cells die, partial or complete blindness ensues.

Other mutations in the rhodopsin gene cause the far less serious condition of night blindness (Fig. 7.29a). These mutations change the protein's amino acid sequence so that the threshold of stimulation required to trigger the vision cascade increases. With the changes, very dim light is no longer enough to initiate vision.

Mutations in the cone-cell pigment genes

Vision problems caused by mutations in the cone-cell pigment genes are less severe than those caused by similar defects in the rod cells' rhodopsin genes. Most likely, this difference occurs because the rods make up 95% of a person's light-receiving neurons, while the cones comprise only about 5%. Some mutations in the blue gene on chromosome 7 cause *tritanopia,* a defect in the ability to discriminate between colors that differ only in the amount of blue light

Figure 7.29 How mutations modulate light and color perception. (a) Amino acid substitutions (*black dots*) that disrupt rhodopsin's three-dimensional structure result in retinitis pigmentosa. Other substitutions diminishing rhodopsin's sensitivity to light cause night blindness. **(b)** Substitutions in the blue pigment can produce tritanopia (blue colorblindness). **(c)** Red colorblindness can result from particular mutations that destabilize the red photoreceptor. **(d)** Unequal crossing-over between the red and green genes can change gene number and create genes encoding hybrid photoreceptor proteins.

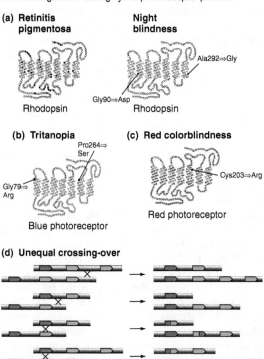

(a) Retinitis pigmentosa   **Night blindness**

Rhodopsin

Rhodopsin   Ala292⇒Gly   Gly90⇒Asp

(b) Tritanopia   **(c) Red colorblindness**

Pro264⇒Ser   Cys203⇒Arg

Gly79⇒Arg

Blue photoreceptor   Red photoreceptor

(d) Unequal crossing-over

Figure 7.30 How the world looks to a person with tritanopia. Compare with Fig. 4.21 on p. 107.

they contain (**Figs. 7.29b** and **7.30**). Mutations in the red gene on the X chromosome can modify or abolish red protein function and as a result, the red cone cells' sensitivity to light. For example, a change at position 203 in the red-receiving protein from cysteine to arginine disrupts one of the disulfide bonds required to support the protein's tertiary structure (see **Fig. 7.29c**). Without that bond, the protein cannot stably maintain its native configuration, and a person with the mutation has red colorblindness.

Unequal crossing-over between the red and green genes

People with normal color vision have a single red gene; some of these normal individuals also have a single adjacent green gene, while others have two or even three green genes. The red and green genes are 96% identical in DNA sequence; the different green genes, 99.9% identical. The proximity and high degree of homology make these genes unusually prone to unequal crossing-over. A variety of unequal recombination events produce DNA containing no red gene, no green gene, various combinations of green genes, or hybrid red-green genes (see **Fig. 7.29d**). These different DNA combinations account for the large majority of the known aberrations in red-green color perception, with the remaining abnormalities stemming from point mutations, as described earlier. Because the accurate perception of red and green depends on the differing ratios of red and green light processed, people with no red or no green gene perceive red and green as the same color (see Fig. 4.21 on p. 107).

We see the way we do in part because four genes direct the production of four photoreceptor polypeptides in the rod and cone cells of the retina. Mutations that alter those polypeptides or their amounts change our perception of light or color.

Connections

Careful studies of mutations showed that genes are linear arrays of mutable elements that direct the assembly of amino acids in a polypeptide. The mutable elements are the nucleotide building blocks of DNA.

Biologists call the parallel between the sequence of nucleotides in a gene and the order of amino acids in a polypeptide **colinearity.** In Chapter 8, we explain how colinearity arises from base pairing, a genetic code, specific enzymes, and macromolecular assemblies like ribosomes that guide the flow of information from DNA through RNA to protein.

ESSENTIAL CONCEPTS

1. Mutations are alterations in the nucleotide sequence of the DNA molecule that occur by chance and modify the genome at random. Mutations in single-celled organisms or in the germ line of multicelluar organisms can be transmitted from generation to generation when DNA replicates.

2. Mutations that affect phenotype occur naturally at a very low rate. Forward mutations usually occur more often than reversions.

3. The agents of spontaneously occurring mutations include chemical hydrolysis, radiation, and mistakes during DNA replication.

4. Mutagens raise the frequency of mutation above the spontaneous rate. The Ames test screens for mutagenic chemicals.

5. Cells have evolved a number of enzyme systems that repair DNA and thus minimize mutations.

6. Mutations are the raw material of evolution. Although some mutations may confer a selective advantage, most are harmful. Somatic mutations can cause cancer and other illnesses in individuals.

7. Mutations within a single gene usually fail to complement each other. The concept of a complementation group thus defines the gene as a unit of function. A gene is composed of a linear sequence of nucleotide pairs in a discrete, localized region of a chromosome. Recombination can occur within a gene, and even between adjacent nucleotide pairs.

8. The function of most genes is to specify the linear sequence of amino acids in a particular polypeptide

(one gene, one polypeptide). The sequence determines the polypeptide's three-dimensional structure, which, in turn, determines its function. Mutations can alter amino acid sequence and thus change protein function in many ways.

9. Each protein consists of one, two, or more polypeptides. Proteins composed of two or more different subunits are encoded by two or more genes.

10. The rhodopsin gene family provides an example of how the processes of gene duplication followed by gene divergence mutation can lead to evolution of functional refinements, such as the emergence of accurate systems for color vision.

On Our Website | www.mhhe.com/hartwell4

Annotated Suggested Readings and Links to Other Websites

- Historical monographs on the nature of mutation, the action of mutagens, DNA repair systems, fine-structure mapping, the "one gene, one polypeptide" hypothesis, and the genetics of human color vision.

- Interesting recent research articles about whether mutations are truly introduced at random, how TEs and trinucleotide repeats affect genomic stability and human health, and examples of the use of genetics to analyze complicated biological processes.

Specialized Topics

- Complications in the interpretation of complementation analysis: a document explaining rare exceptions to the rule that mutations in the same gene are unable to complement each other, as well as other rare cases in which mutations in different genes can fail to complement each other.

Solved Problems

I. Mutations can often be reverted to wild type by treatment with mutagens. The type of mutagen that will reverse a mutation gives us information about the nature of the original mutation. The mutagen EMS almost exclusively causes transitions; proflavin is an intercalating agent that causes insertion or deletion of a base; ultraviolet (UV) light causes single-base substitutions. Cultures of several *E. coli* *met⁻* mutants were treated with three mutagens separately and spread onto a plate lacking methionine to look for revertants. (In the chart, − indicates that no colonies grew, and + indicates that some *met⁺* revertant colonies grew.)

Mutant number	Mutagen treatment		
	EMS	**Proflavin**	**UV light**
1	+	−	+
2	−	+	−
3	−	−	−
4	−	−	+

a. Given the results, what can you say about the nature of the original mutation in each of the strains?

b. Experimental controls are designed to eliminate possible explanations for the results, thereby ensuring that data are interpretable. In the experiment described, we scored the presence or absence of colonies. How do we know if colonies that appear on plates are mutagen-induced revertants? What else could they be? What control would enable us to be confident of our revertant analysis?

Answer

To answer this question, you need to understand the concepts of mutation and reversion.

a. Mutation 1 is reverted by the mutagen that causes transitions, *so mutation 1 must have been a transition.* Consistent with this conclusion is the fact the UV light can also revert the mutation and the intercalating agent proflavin does not cause reversion. *Mutation 2 is reverted by proflavin and therefore must be either an insertion or a deletion of a base.* The other two mutagens do not revert mutation 2. Mutation 3 is not reverted by any of these mutagenic agents. It is therefore not a single-base substitution, a single-base insertion, or a single-base deletion. *Mutation 3 could be a deletion of several bases or an inversion.* Mutation 4 is reverted by UV light, so it is a single-base change, but it is not a transition, since EMS did not revert the mutation. *Mutation 4 must be a transversion.*

b. *The colonies on the plates could arise by spontaneous reversion of the mutation.* Spontaneous reversion should occur with lower frequency than mutagen-induced reversion. The important control here is to *spread each mutant culture without any mutagen treatment onto selective media to assess the level of spontaneous reversion.*

II. Imagine that 10 independently isolated recessive lethal mutations (l^1, l^2, l^3, etc.) map to chromosome 7 in mice. You perform complementation testing by mating all pairwise combinations of heterozygotes bearing these lethal mutations, and you score the absence of complementation by examining pregnant females for dead fetuses. A + in the chart means that the two lethals complemented, and dead embryos were not found. A − indicates that dead embryos were found, at the rate of about one in four conceptions. (The crosses between heterozygous mice would be expected to yield the homozygous recessive showing the lethal phenotype in 1/4 of the embryos.) The lethal mutation in the parental heterozygotes for each cross are listed across the top and down the left side of the chart (that is, l^1 indicates a heterozygote in which one chromosome bears the l^1 mutation and the homologous chromosome is wild type).

	l^1	l^2	l^3	l^4	l^5	l^6	l^7	l^8	l^9	l^{10}
l^1	−	+	+	+	+	−	−	+	+	+
l^2		−	+	+	+	+	+	+	+	−
l^3			−	−	−	+	+	−	−	+
l^4				−	−	+	+	−	−	+
l^5					−	+	+	−	−	+
l^6						−	−	+	+	+
l^7							−	+	+	+
l^8								−	−	+
l^9									−	+
l^{10}										−

How many genes do the 10 lethal mutations represent? What are the complementation groups?

Answer

This problem involves the application of the complementation concept to a set of data. There are two ways to analyze these results. You can focus on the mutations that do complement each other, conclude that they are in different genes, and begin to create a list of mutations in separate genes. Alternatively, you can focus on mutations that do not complement each other and therefore are alleles of the same genes. The latter approach is more efficient when several mutations are involved. For example, l^1 does not complement l^6 and l^7. These three alleles are in one complementation group. l^2 does not complement l^{10}; they are in a second complementation group. l^3 does

not complement l^4, l^5, l^8, or l^9, so they form a third complementation group. *There are three complementation groups.* (Note also that for each mutant, the cross between individuals carrying the same alleles resulted in no complementation, because the homozygous recessive lethal was generated.) *The three complementation groups consist of (1)* l^1, l^6, l^7; *(2)* l^2, l^{10}; *and (3)* l^3, l^4, l^5, l^8, l^9.

III. W, X, and Y are the intermediates (in that order) in a biochemical pathway whose product is Z. Z^- mutants are found in five different complementation groups. *Z1* mutants will grow on Y or Z but not W or X. *Z2* mutants will grow on X, Y, or Z. *Z3* mutants will only grow on Z. *Z4* mutants will grow on Y or Z. Finally, *Z5* mutants will grow on W, X, Y, or Z.
a. Order the five complementation groups in terms of the steps they block.
b. What does this genetic information reveal about the nature of the enzyme that carries out the conversion of X to Y?

Answer

This problem requires that you understand complementation and the connection between genes and enzymes in a biochemical pathway.
a. A biochemical pathway represents an ordered set of reactions that must occur to produce a product. This problem gives the order of intermediates in a pathway for producing product Z. The lack of any enzyme along the way will cause the phenotype of Z^-, but the block can occur at different places along the pathway. If the mutant grows when given an intermediate compound, the enzymatic (and hence gene) defect must be before production of that intermediate compound. The *Z1* mutants that grow on Y or Z (but not on W or X) must have a defect in the enzyme that produces Y. *Z2* mutants have a defect prior to X; *Z3* mutants have a defect prior to Z; *Z4* mutants have a defect prior to Y; *Z5* have a defect prior to W. *The five complementation groups can be placed in order of activity within the biochemical pathway as follows:*

$$\xrightarrow{\ Z5\ } W \xrightarrow{\ Z2\ } X \xrightarrow{\ Z1,\ Z4\ } Y \xrightarrow{\ Z3\ } Z$$

b. Mutants *Z1* and *Z4* affect the same step, but because they are in different complementation groups, we know they are in different genes. *Mutations Z1 and Z4 are probably in genes that encode subunits of a multisubunit enzyme that carries out the conversion of X to Y.* Alternatively, there could be a currently unknown additional intermediate step between X and Y.

Problems

Vocabulary

1. The following is a list of mutational changes. For each of the specific mutations described, indicate which of the terms in the right-hand column applies, either as a description of the mutation or as a possible cause. More than one term from the right column can apply to each statement in the left column.

1. an A–T base pair in the wild-type gene is changed to a G–C pair	a. transition
2. an A–T base pair is changed to a T–A pair	b. base substitution
3. the sequence AAGCTTATCG is changed to AAGCTATCG	c. transversion
4. the sequence AAGCTTATCG is changed to AAGCTTTATCG	d. inversion
5. the sequence AACGTTATCG is changed to AATGTTATCG	e. translocation
6. the sequence AACGTCACACACACATCG is changed to AACGTCACATCG	f. deletion
7. the gene map in a given chromosome arm is changed from *bog-rad-fox1-fox2-try-duf* (where *fox1* and *fox2* are highly homologous, recently diverged genes) to *bog-rad-fox1-fox3-fox2-try-duf* (where *fox3* is a new gene with one end similar to *fox1* and the other similar to *fox2*)	g. insertion
	h. deamination
	i. X-ray irradiation
	j. intercalator
	k. unequal crossing-over
8. the gene map in a chromosome is changed from *bog-rad-fox1-fox2-try-duf* to *bog-rad-fox2-fox1-try-duf*	
9. the gene map in a given chromosome is changed from *bog-rad-fox1-fox2-try-duf* to *bog-rad-fox1-mel-qui-txu-sqm*	

Section 7.1

2. What explanations can account for the pedigree of the very rare trait shown below? Be as specific as possible. How might you be able to distinguish between these explanations?

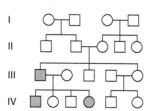

3. The DNA sequence of a gene from three independently isolated mutants is given here. Using this information, what is the sequence of the wild-type gene in this region?

```
mutant 1    ACCGTAATCGACTGGTAAACTTTGCGCG
mutant 2    ACCGTAGTCGACCGGTAAACTTTGCGCG
mutant 3    ACCGTAGTCGACTGGTTAACTTTGCGCG
```

4. Among mammals, measurements of the rate of generation of autosomal recessive mutations have been made almost exclusively in mice, while many measurements of the rate of generation of dominant mutations have been made both in mice and in humans. Why do you think there has been this difference?

5. Over a period of several years, a large hospital kept track of the number of births of babies displaying the trait achondroplasia. Achondroplasia is a very rare autosomal dominant condition resulting in dwarfism with abnormal body proportions. After 120,000 births, it was noted that there had been 27 babies born with achondroplasia. One physician was interested in determining how many of these dwarf babies result from new mutations and whether the apparent mutation rate in his area was higher than normal. He looked up the families of the 27 dwarf births and discovered that 4 of the dwarf babies had a dwarf parent. What is the apparent mutation rate of the achondroplasia gene in this population? Is it unusually high or low?

6. Suppose you wanted to study genes controlling the structure of bacterial cell surfaces. You decide to start by isolating bacterial mutants that are resistant to infection by a bacteriophage that binds to the cell surface. The selection procedure is simple: Spread cells from a culture of sensitive bacteria on a petri plate, expose them to a high concentration of phages, and pick the bacterial colonies that grow. To set up the selection you could (1) spread cells from a single liquid culture of sensitive bacteria on many different plates and pick every resistant colony *or* (2) start many different cultures, each grown from a single colony of sensitive bacteria, spread one plate from each culture, and then pick a single mutant from each plate. Which method would ensure that you are isolating many independent mutations?

7. In a genetics lab, Kim and Maria infected a sample from an *E. coli* culture with a particular virulent bacteriophage. They noticed that most of the cells were lysed, but a few survived. The survival rate in their sample was about 1×10^{-4}. Kim was sure the bacteriophage induced the resistance in the cells, while Maria thought that resistant mutants probably already existed in the sample of cells they used. Earlier, for a different experiment, they had spread a dilute suspension of *E. coli* onto solid medium in a large petri dish, and, after seeing that about 10^5 colonies were growing up, they had replica-plated that plate onto three other plates. Kim and Maria decided to use these plates to test their theories. They pipette a suspension of the bacteriophage onto each of the three replica plates. What should they see if Kim is right? What should they see if Maria is right?

8. The pedigree below shows the inheritance of a completely penetrant, dominant trait called amelogenesis imperfecta that affects the structure and integrity of the teeth. DNA analysis of blood obtained from affected individuals III-1 and III-2 shows the presence of the same mutation in one of the two copies of an autosomal gene called *ENAM* that is not seen in DNA from the blood of any of the parents in generation II. Explain this result, citing Fig. 4.18 on p. 102 and Fig. 7.4 on p. 203. Do you think this type of inheritance pattern is rare or common?

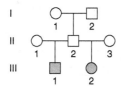

9. A wild-type male *Drosophila* was exposed to a large dose of X-rays and was then mated to an unirradiated female, one of whose X chromosomes carried both a dominant mutation for the trait *Bar* eyes and several inversions. Many F_1 females from this mating were recovered who had the *Bar*, multiply inverted X chromosome from their mother, and an irradiated X chromosome from their fathers. (The inversions ensure that viable offspring of these F_1 females will not have recombinant X chromosomes, as explained in Chapter 13.) After mating to normal males, most F_1 females produced *Bar* and wild-type sons in equal proportions. There were three exceptional F_1 females, however. Female A produced as many sons as daughters, but half of the sons had *Bar* eyes, and the other half had white eyes. Female B produced half as many sons as daughters, and all of the sons had *Bar* eyes. Female C produced 75% as many sons as daughters. Of these sons, 2/3 had *Bar* eyes, and 1/3 had wild-type eyes. Explain the results obtained with each exceptional F_1 female.

10. A wild-type *Drosophila* female was mated to a wild-type male that had been exposed to X-rays. One of the F_1 females was then mated with a male that had the following recessive markers on the X chromosome: *yellow* body (*y*), *crossveinless* wings (*cv*), *cut* wings (*ct*), *singed* bristles (*sn*), and *miniature* wings (*m*). These markers are known to map in the order *y−cv−ct−sn−m*. The progeny of this second mating were unusual in two respects. First, there were twice as many females as males. Second, while all of the males were wild type in phenotype, 1/2 of the females were wild type, and the other 1/2 exhibited the *ct* and *sn* phenotypes.
   a. What did the X-rays do to the irradiated male?
   b. Draw the X-chromosome pair present in a progeny female fly produced by the second mating that was phenotypically *ct* and *sn*.

c. If the *ct* and *sn* female fly whose chromosomes were drawn in part *b* was then crossed to a wild-type male, what phenotypic classes would you expect to find among the progeny males?

11. In the experiment shown in Fig. 7.9 on p. 207, H. J. Muller first performed a control in which the P generation males were not exposed to X-rays. He found that 99.7% of the individual F_1 Bar-eyed females produced some male progeny with Bar eyes and some with wild-type (non-Bar) eyes, but 0.3% of these females produced male progeny that were all wild type.
   a. If the average spontaneous mutation rate for *Drosophila* genes is 3.5×10^{-6} mutations/gene/gamete, how many genes on the X chromosome can be mutated to produce a recessive lethal allele?
   b. As of the year 2010, analysis of the *Drosophila* genome had revealed a total of 2283 genes on the X chromosome. Assuming the X chromosome is typical of the genome, what is the fraction of genes in the fly genome that is essential to survival?
   c. Muller now exposed male flies to a specific high dosage of X-rays and found that 12% of F_1 Bar-eyed females produced male progeny that were all wild type. What does this new information say?

12. Figure 7.10 on pp. 210–211 shows examples of base substitutions induced by the mutagens 5-bromouracil, hydroxylamine, ethylmethane sulfonate, and nitrous acid. Which of these mutagens cause transitions, and which cause transversions?

13. So-called *two-way mutagens* can induce both a particular mutation and (when added subsequently to cells whose chromosomes carry this mutation) a reversion of the mutation that restores the original DNA sequence. In contrast, *one-way mutagens* can induce mutations but not exact reversions of these mutations. Based on Fig. 7.10 (pp. 210–211), which of the following mutagens can be classified as one-way and which as two-way?
   a. 5-bromouracil
   b. hydroxylamine
   c. ethylmethane sulfonate
   d. nitrous acid
   e. proflavin

14. In 1967, J. B. Jenkins treated wild-type male *Drosophila* with the mutagen ethylmethane sulfonate (EMS) and mated them with females homozygous for a recessive mutation called *dumpy* that causes shortened wings. He found some F_1 progeny with two wild-type wings, some with two short wings, and some with one short wing and one wild-type wing. When he mated single F_1 flies with two short wings to *dumpy* homozygotes, he surprisingly found that

only about 1/3 of these matings produced any short-winged progeny.

a. Explain these results in light of the mechanism of action of EMS shown in Fig. 7.10 on pp. 210–211.

b. Should the short-winged progeny of the second cross have one or two short wings? Why?

15. Aflatoxin B_1 is a highly mutagenic and carcinogenic compound produced by certain fungi that infect crops such as peanuts. Aflatoxin is a large, bulky molecule that chemically bonds to the base guanine to form the aflatoxin-guanine "adduct" that is pictured below. (In the figure, the aflatoxin is *orange,* and the guanine base is *purple.*) This adduct distorts the DNA double helix and blocks replication.

a. What type(s) of DNA repair system is (are) most likely to be involved in repairing the damage caused by exposure of DNA to aflatoxin B_1?

b. Recent evidence suggests that the adduct of guanine and aflatoxin B_1 can attack the bond that connects it to deoxyribose; this liberates the adduced base, forming an apurinic site. How does this new information change your answer to part *a*?

Aflatoxin-guanine **adduct**

16. When a particular mutagen identified by the Ames test is injected into mice, it causes the appearance of many tumors, showing that this substance is carcinogenic. When cells from these tumors are injected into other mice not exposed to the mutagen, almost all of the new mice develop tumors. However, when mice carrying mutagen-induced tumors are mated to unexposed mice, virtually all of the progeny are tumor free. Why can the tumor be transferred horizontally (by injecting cells) but not vertically (from one generation to the next)?

17. When the *his⁻ Salmonella* strain used in the Ames test is exposed to substance X, no *his⁺* revertants are seen. If, however, rat liver supernatant is added to the cells along with substance X, revertants do occur. Is substance X a potential carcinogen for human cells? Explain.

Section 7.2

18. Imagine that you caught a female albino mouse in your kitchen and decided to keep it for a pet. A few months later, while vacationing in Guam, you caught a male albino mouse and decided to take it home for some interesting genetic experiments. You wonder

whether the two mice are both albino due to mutations in the same gene. What could you do to find out the answer to this question? Assume that both mutations are recessive.

19. Plant breeders studying genes influencing leaf shape in the plant *Arabidopsis thaliana* identified six independent recessive mutations that resulted in plants that had unusual leaves with serrated rather than smooth edges. The investigators started to perform complementation tests with these mutants, but some of the tests could not be completed because of an accident in the greenhouse. The results of the complementation tests that could be finished are shown in the table that follows.

	1	2	3	4	5	6
1	−	+	−		+	
2		−				−
3			−	−		
4				−		
5					−	+
6						−

a. Exactly what experiment was done to fill in individual boxes in the table with a + or a − ? What does + represent? What does − represent? Why are some boxes in the table filled in *green?*

b. Assuming no complications, what do you expect for the results of the complementation tests that were not performed? That is, complete the table above by placing a + or a − in each of the blank boxes.

c. How many genes are represented among this collection of mutants? Which mutations are in which genes?

20. In humans, albinism is normally inherited in an autosomal recessive fashion. Figure 3.19c on p. 63 shows a pedigree in which two albino parents have several children, none of whom is an albino.

a. Interpret this pedigree in terms of a complementation test.

b. It is very rare to find examples of human pedigrees such as Fig. 3.19c that could be interpreted as a complementation test. This is because most genetic conditions in humans are rare, so it is highly unlikely that unrelated people with the same condition would mate. In the absence of complementation testing, what kinds of experiments could be done to determine whether a particular human disease phenotype can be caused by mutations at more than one gene?

c. Complementation testing requires that the two mutations to be tested both be recessive to wild type. Suppose that two dominant mutations cause similar phenotypes. How could you establish whether these mutations affected the same gene or different genes?

21. a. Seymour Benzer's fine structure analysis of the *rII* region of bacteriophage T4 depended in large part on deletion analysis as shown in Fig. 7.21 on p. 223. But to perform such deletion analysis, Benzer had to know which *rII*⁻ bacteriophage strains were deletions and which were point mutations. How do you think he was able to distinguish *rII*⁻ deletions from point mutations?

b. Benzer concluded that recombination can occur between adjacent nucleotide pairs, even within the same gene. How was he able to make this statement? At the time, Benzer had two relevant pieces of information: (i) the total length in μm of the bacteriophage T4 chromosome (measured in the electron microscope) and (ii) many mutations in many bacteriophage T4 genes, including *rIIA* and *rIIB*.

c. Figure 7.21c on p. 223 shows Benzer's fine structure map of point mutations in the *rII* region. A key feature of this map is the existence of "hot spots," which Benzer interpreted as nucleotide pairs that were particularly susceptible to mutation. How could Benzer say that all the independent mutations in a hot spot were due to mutations of the same nucleotide pair?

22. a. You have a test tube containing 5 ml of a solution of bacteriophage, and you would like to estimate the number of bacteriophage in the tube. Assuming the tube actually contains a total of 15 billion bacteriophage, design a serial dilution experiment that would allow you to estimate this number. Ideally, the final plaque-containing plates you count should contain more than 10 and less than 1000 plaques.

b. When you count bacteriophage by the serial dilution method as in part *a*, you are assuming a *plating efficiency* of 100%; that is, the number of plaques on the petri plate exactly represents the number of bacteriophage you mixed with the plating bacteria. Is there any way to test the possibility that only a certain percentage of bacteriophage particles are able to form plaques (so that the plating efficiency would be less than 100%)? Conversely, why is it fair to assume that any plaques are initiated by one rather than multiple bacteriophage particles?

23. You found five T4 *rII*⁻ mutants that will not grow on *E. coli* K(λ). You mixed together all possible combinations of two mutants (as indicated in the following chart), added the mixtures to *E. coli* K(λ), and scored for the ability of the mixtures to grow and make plaques (indicated as a + in the chart).

	1	2	3	4	5
1	-	+	+	-	+
2		-	-	+	-
3			-	+	-
4				-	+
5					-

a. How many genes were identified by this analysis?

b. Which mutants belong to the same complementation groups?

24. The *rosy (ry)* gene of *Drosophila* encodes an enzyme called xanthine dehydrogenase. Flies homozygous for *ry* mutations exhibit a rosy eye color. Heterozygous females were made that had ry^{41} *Sb* on one homolog and *Ly* ry^{564} on the other homolog, where ry^{41} and ry^{564} are two independently isolated alleles of *ry*. *Ly* (*Lyra* [narrow] wings) and *Sb* (*Stubble* [short] bristles) are dominant markers to the left and right of *ry*, respectively. These females are now mated to males homozygous for ry^{41}. Out of 100,000 progeny, 8 have wild-type eyes, *Lyra* wings, and *Stubble* bristles, while the remainder have rosy eyes.

a. What is the order of these two *ry* mutations relative to the flanking genes *Ly* and *Sb*?

b. What is the genetic distance separating ry^{41} and ry^{564}?

25. Nine *rII*⁻ mutants of bacteriophage T4 were used in pairwise infections of *E. coli* K(λ) hosts. Six of the mutations in these phages are point mutations; the other three are deletions. The ability of the doubly infected cells to produce progeny phages in large numbers is scored in the following chart.

	1	2	3	4	5	6	7	8	9
1	-	-	+	+	-	-	-	+	+
2		-	+	+	-	-	-	+	+
3			-	-	+	-	+	-	-
4				-	+	-	+	-	-
5					-	-	-	+	+
6						-	-	-	-
7							-	+	+
8								-	-
9									-

The same nine mutants were then used in pairwise infections of *E. coli* B hosts. The production of progeny phage that can subsequently lyse *E. coli* K(λ) hosts is now scored. In the table, 0 means the progeny do not produce any plaques on *E. coli* K(λ) cells; − means that only a very few progeny phages produce plaques; and + means that many progeny produce plaques (more than 10 times as many as in the − cases).

	1	2	3	4	5	6	7	8	9
1	-	+	+	+	+	-	-	+	+
2		-	+	+	+	+	-	+	+
3			0	-	+	0	+	+	-
4				-	+	-	+	+	+
5					-	+	-	+	+
6						0	0	-	+
7							0	+	+
8								-	+
9									-

a. Which of the mutants are the three deletions? What criteria did you use to reach your conclusion?

b. If you know that mutation 9 is in the *rIIB* gene, draw the best genetic map possible to explain the data, including the positions of all point mutations and the extent of the three deletions.

c. There should be one uncertainty remaining in your answer to part *b*. How could you resolve this uncertainty?

26. In a haploid yeast strain, eight recessive mutations were found that resulted in a requirement for the amino acid lysine. All the mutations were found to revert at a frequency of about 1×10^{-6}, except mutations 5 and 6, which did not revert. Matings were made between *a* and α cells carrying these mutations. The ability of the resultant diploid strains to grow on minimal medium in the absence of lysine is shown in the following chart (+ means growth and − means no growth.)

	1	2	3	4	5	6	7	8
1	−	+	+	+	+	−	+	−
2	+	−	+	+	+	+	+	+
3	+	+	−	−	−	−	−	+
4	+	+	−	−	−	−	−	+
5	+	+	−	−	−	−	−	+
6	−	+	−	−	−	−	−	−
7	+	+	−	−	−	−	−	+
8	−	+	+	+	+	−	+	−

a. How many complementation groups were revealed by these data? Which point mutations are found within which complementation groups?

The same diploid strains are now induced to undergo sporulation. The vast majority of resultant spores are auxotrophic; that is, they cannot form colonies when plated on minimal medium minus lysine. However, particular diploids can produce rare spores that do form colonies when plated on minimal medium minus lysine (prototrophic spores). The following table shows whether (+) or not (−) any prototrophic spores are formed upon sporulation of the various diploid cells.

	1	2	3	4	5	6	7	8
1	−	+	+	+	+	−	+	+
2	+	−	+	+	+	+	+	+
3	+	+	−	+	−	+	+	+
4	+	+	+	−	−	−	+	+
5	+	+	−	−	−	−	+	+
6	−	+	+	−	−	−	+	+
7	+	+	+	+	+	+	−	+
8	+	+	+	+	+	+	+	−

b. When prototrophic spores occur during sporulation of the diploids just discussed, what ratio of auxotrophic to prototrophic spores would you generally

expect to see in any tetrad containing such a prototrophic spore? Explain the ratio you expect.

c. Using the data from all parts of this question, draw the best map of the eight lysine mutations under study. Show the extent of any deletions involved, and indicate the boundaries of the various complementation groups.

Section 7.3

27. The pathway for arginine biosynthesis in *Neurospora crassa* involves several enzymes that produce a series of intermediates.

$$\text{argE} \quad\quad \text{argF} \quad\quad \text{argG} \quad\quad \text{argH}$$
$$N\text{-acetylornithine} \rightarrow \text{ornithine} \rightarrow \text{citrulline} \rightarrow \text{argininosuccinate} \rightarrow \text{arginine}$$

a. If you did a cross between $argE^-$ and $argH^-$ *Neurospora* strains, what would be the distribution of Arg^+ and Arg^- spores within parental ditype and nonparental ditype asci? Give the spore types in the order in which they would appear in the ascus.

b. For each of the spores in your answer to part *a*, what nutrients could you supply in the media to get spore growth?

28. In corn snakes, the wild-type color is brown. One autosomal recessive mutation causes the snake to be orange, and another causes the snake to be black. An orange snake was crossed to a black one, and the F_1 offspring were all brown. Assume that all relevant genes are unlinked.

a. Indicate what phenotypes and ratios you would expect in the F_2 generation of this cross if there is one pigment pathway, with orange and black being different intermediates on the way to brown.

b. Indicate what phenotypes and ratios you would expect in the F_2 generation if orange pigment is a product of one pathway, black pigment is the product of another pathway, and brown is the effect of mixing the two pigments in the skin of the snake.

29. In a certain species of flowering plants with a diploid genome, four enzymes are involved in the generation of flower color. The genes encoding these four enzymes are on different chromosomes. The biochemical pathway involved is as follows; the figure shows that either of two different enzymes is sufficient to convert a blue pigment into a purple pigment.

$$\text{white} \rightarrow \text{green} \rightarrow \text{blue} \overset{\longrightarrow}{\underset{\longrightarrow}{}} \text{purple}$$

A true-breeding green-flowered plant is mated with a true-breeding blue-flowered plant. All of the plants in the resultant F_1 generation have purple flowers. F_1 plants are allowed to self-fertilize, yielding an F_2 generation. Show genotypes for P, F_1, and F_2 plants, and indicate which genes specify which biochemical steps.

Determine the fraction of F_2 plants with the following phenotypes: white flowers, green flowers, blue flowers, and purple flowers. Assume the green-flowered parent is mutant in only a single step of the pathway.

30. The intermediates A, B, C, D, E, and F all occur in the same biochemical pathway. G is the product of the pathway, and mutants 1 through 7 are all G^-, meaning that they cannot produce substance G. The following table shows which intermediates will promote growth in each of the mutants. Arrange the intermediates in order of their occurrence in the pathway, and indicate the step in the pathway at which each mutant strain is blocked. A + in the table indicates that the strain will grow if given that substance, an O means lack of growth.

	Supplements						
Mutant	A	B	C	D	E	F	G
1	+	+	+	+	+	O	+
2	O	O	O	O	O	O	+
3	O	+	+	O	+	O	+
4	O	+	O	O	+	O	+
5	+	+	+	O	+	O	+
6	+	+	+	+	+	+	+
7	O	O	O	O	+	O	+

31. In each of the following cross schemes, two true-breeding plant strains are crossed to make F_1 plants, all of which have purple flowers. The F_1 plants are then self-fertilized to produce F_2 progeny as shown here.

Cross	Parents	F_1	F_2
1	blue × white	all purple	9 purple: 4 white: 3 blue
2	white × white	all purple	9 purple: 7 white
3	red × blue	all purple	9 purple: 3 red: 3 blue: 1 white
4	purple × purple	all purple	15 purple: 1 white

a. For each cross, explain the inheritance of flower color.
b. For each cross, show a possible biochemical pathway that could explain the data.
c. Which of these crosses is compatible with an underlying biochemical pathway involving only a single step that is catalyzed by an enzyme with two dissimilar subunits, both of which are required for enzyme activity?
d. For each of the four crosses, what would you expect in the F_1 and F_2 generations if all relevant genes were tightly linked?

32. The pathways for the biosynthesis of the amino acids glutamine (Gln) and proline (Pro) involve one or more common intermediates. Auxotrophic yeast mutants numbered 1–7 are isolated that require either glutamine or proline or both amino acids for their growth,

as shown in the following table (+ means growth; − no growth). These mutants are also tested for their ability to grow on the intermediates A–E. What is the order of these intermediates in the glutamine and proline pathways, and at which point in the pathway is each mutant blocked?

Mutant	A	B	C	D	E	Gln	Pro	Gln + Pro
1	+	−	−	−	+	−	+	+
2	−	−	−	−	−	−	+	+
3	−	−	+	−	−	−	−	+
4	−	−	−	−	−	+	−	+
5	−	−	+	+	−	−	−	+
6	+	−	−	−	−	−	+	+
7	−	+	−	−	−	+	−	+

33. The following noncomplementing *E. coli* mutants were tested for growth on four known precursors of thymine, A–D.

	Precursor/product				
Mutant	A	B	C	D	Thymine
9	+	−	+	−	+
10	−	−	+	−	+
14	+	+	+	−	+
18	+	+	+	+	+
21	−	−	−	−	+

a. Show a simple linear biosynthetic pathway of the four precursors and the end product, thymine. Indicate which step is blocked by each of the five mutations.
b. What precursor would accumulate in the following double mutants: 9 and 10? 10 and 14?

34. In 1952, an article in the *British Medical Journal* reported interesting differences in the behavior of blood plasma obtained from several individuals who suffered from X-linked recessive hemophilia. When mixed together, the cell-free blood plasma from certain combinations of individuals could form clots in the test tube. For example, the following table shows whether (+) or not (−) clots could form in various combinations of plasma from four individuals with hemophilia:

1 and 1	−	2 and 3	+
1 and 2	−	2 and 4	+
1 and 3	+	3 and 3	−
1 and 4	+	3 and 4	−
2 and 2	−	4 and 4	−

What do these data tell you about the inheritance of hemophilia in these individuals? Do these data allow you to exclude any models for the biochemical pathway governing blood clotting?

35. Mutations in an autosomal gene in humans cause a form of hemophilia called von Willebrand disease (vWD). This gene specifies a blood plasma protein cleverly called von Willebrand factor (vWF). vWF stabilizes factor VIII, a blood plasma protein specified by the wild-type hemophilia A gene. Factor VIII is needed to form blood clots. Thus, factor VIII is rapidly destroyed in the absence of vWF.

Which of the following might successfully be employed in the treatment of bleeding episodes in hemophiliac patients? Would the treatments work immediately or only after some delay needed for protein synthesis? Would the treatments have only a short-term or a prolonged effect? Assume that all mutations are null (that is, the mutations result in the complete absence of the protein encoded by the gene) and that the plasma is cell-free.

a. transfusion of plasma from normal blood into a vWD patient

b. transfusion of plasma from a vWD patient into a different vWD patient

c. transfusion of plasma from a hemophilia A patient into a vWD patient

d. transfusion of plasma from normal blood into a hemophilia A patient

e. transfusion of plasma from a vWD patient into a hemophilia A patient

f. transfusion of plasma from a hemophilia A patient into a different hemophilia A patient

g. injection of purified vWF into a vWD patient

h. injection of purified vWF into a hemophilia A patient

i. injection of purified factor VIII into a vWD patient

j. injection of purified factor VIII into a hemophilia A patient

36. Antibodies were made that recognize six proteins that are part of a complex inside the *Caenorhabditis elegans* one-cell embryo. The mother produces proteins that are believed to assemble stepwise into a structure in the egg, beginning at the embryo's inner surface. The antibodies were used to detect the protein location in embryos produced by mutant mothers (who are homozygous recessive for the gene[s] encoding each protein). The *C. elegans* mothers are self-fertilizing hermaphrodites so no wild-type copy of a gene will be introduced during fertilization. In the following table, * means the protein was present and at the embryo surface, − means that the protein was not present, and + means that the protein was present but not at the embryo surface. Assume all mutations prevent production of the corresponding protein.

Mutant in gene for protein	Protein production and location					
	A	B	C	D	E	F
A	−	+	*	+	*	+
B	*	−	*	*	*	*
C	*	+	−	+	*	+
D	*	+	*	−	*	+
E	+	+	+	+	−	+
F	*	+	*	*	*	−

Complete the following figure, which shows the construction of the hypothetical protein complex, by writing the letter of the proper protein in each circle. The two proteins marked with arrowheads can assemble into the complex independently of each other, but both are needed for the addition of subsequent proteins to the complex.

Outside

Embryo surface —

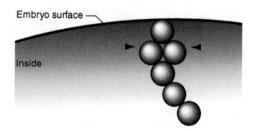

Inside

37. Adult hemoglobin is a multimeric protein with four polypeptides, two of which are α globin and two of which are β globin.

a. How many genes are needed to define the structure of the hemoglobin protein?

b. If a person is heterozygous for wild-type alleles and alleles that would yield amino acid substitution variants for both α globin and β globin, how many different kinds of hemoglobin protein would be found in the person's red blood cells and in what proportion? Assume all alleles are expressed at the same level.

38. This problem refers to Fig. A in the Fast Forward box on p. 232. For each part that follows, describe what structures Robert Edgar would have seen in the electron microscope if he examined extracts of *E. coli* cells infected with the indicated temperature-sensitive mutant strains of bacteriophage T4 under restrictive conditions.

a. A strain with a mutation in gene 19

b. A strain with a mutation in gene 16

c. Simultaneous infection with two mutant strains, one in gene 13 and the other in gene 14. The polypeptides produced by genes 13 and 14 associate with each other to form a multimeric protein that governs one step of phage head assembly (see Fig. A on p. 232).

d. A strain whose genome contains mutations in both genes 15 and 35

Section 7.4

39. In addition to the predominant adult hemoglobin, HbA, which contains two α-globin chains and two β-globin chains ($\alpha_2\beta_2$), there is a minor hemoglobin, HbA$_2$, composed of two α and two δ chains ($\alpha_2\delta_2$). The β- and δ-globin genes are arranged in tandem and are highly homologous. Draw the chromosomes that would result from an event of unequal crossing-over between the β and δ genes.

40. Most mammals, including "New World" primates such as marmosets (a kind of monkey), are *dichromats*: they have only two kinds of rhodopsin-related color receptors. "Old World" primates such as humans and gorillas are *trichromats* with three kinds of color receptors. Primates diverged from other mammals roughly 65 million years ago (Myr), while Old World and New World primates diverged from each other roughly 35 Myr.

a. Using this information, define on Fig. 7.28d (see p. 233) the time span of any events that can be dated.

b. Some New World monkeys have an autosomal color receptor gene and a single X-linked color receptor gene. The X-linked gene has three alleles, each of which encodes a photoreceptor that responds to light of a different wavelength (all three wavelengths are different from that recognized by the autosomal color receptor). How is color vision inherited in these monkeys?

c. About 95% of all light-receiving neurons in humans and other mammals are rod cells containing rhodopsin, a pigment that responds to low-level light of many wavelengths. The remaining 5% of light-receiving neurons are cone cells with pigments that respond to light of specific wavelengths of high intensity. What does this suggest about the lifestyle of the earliest mammals?

Brief Answer Section

Chapter 2

1. a. 4; b. 3; c. 6; d. 7; e. 11; f. 13; g. 10; h. 2; i. 14; j. 9; k. 12; l. 8; m. 5; n. 1.

3. For peas: (1) rapid generation time; (2) can either self-fertilize or be artificially crossed; (3) large numbers of offspring; (4) can be maintained as pure-breeding lines; (5) maintained as inbred stocks and two discrete forms of many phenotypic traits are known; (6) easy and inexpensive to grow. In contrast, for humans (1) generation time is long; (2) no self-fertilization, it is not ethical to manipulate crosses; (3) produce only a small number of offspring per mating; (4) although people that are homozygous for a trait exist, homozygosity cannot be maintained; (5) populations are not inbred so most traits show a continuum of phenotypes; (6) require a lot of expensive care to "grow" One advantage to the study of genetics in humans-a very large number of individuals with variant phenotypes can be recognized. Thus, the number of genes identified in this way is rapidly increasing.

5. Short hair is dominant to long hair.

7. The genotype can be determined by performing a testcross; that is, crossing your fly with the dominant phenotype (but unknown genotype) to a fly with the recessive (short wing) phenotype. If your fly has the homozygous dominant genotype the progeny in this case would be *Ww* and would have the dominant phenotype. If your fly had a heterozygous genotype, 1/2 of the progeny would be normal (*Ww*) and 1/2 of the progeny would be short (*ww*).

9. The dominant trait (short tail) is easier to eliminate from the population by selective breeding. You can recognize every animal that has inherited the allele, because only one dominant allele is needed to see the phenotype. Those mice that have inherited the dominant allele can be prevented from mating.

11. a. Dry is recessive, sticky is dominant; b. The 3:1 and 1:1 ratios are obscured because the offspring are then combined results of different crosses.

13. a. 1/6; b. 1/2; c. 1/3; d. 1/36; e. 1/2; f. 1/6; g. 1/9.

15. a. 2; b. 4; c. 8; d. 16.

17. a. *aa Bb Cc DD Ee*; b. *a B C D E* or *a B c D E* or *a B C D e* or *a B c D e* or *a b C D E* or *a b C D e* or *a b c D E* or *a b c D e*.

19. They must both be carriers (*Pp*); the probability that their next child will have the *pp* genotype is 1/4.

21. a. Rough and black are the dominant alleles (*R* = rough, *r* = smooth; *B* = black, *b* = white); b. a ratio of 1/4 rough black: 1/4 rough white: 1/4 smooth black: 1/4 smooth white.

23. a. 3/16; b. 1/16.

25. *P* = purple, *p* = white; *S* = spiny, *s* = smooth. a. *Pp Ss × Pp Ss;* b. *PP Ss × P– ss* or *P– Ss × PP ss;* c. *Pp S– × pp SS* or *Pp SS × pp S–;* d. *Pp Ss × pp Ss;* e. *Pp ss × Pp ss;* f. *pp Ss × pp SS.*

27. Cross 1: male: *tt Nn*, female: *tt Nn;* Cross 2: male: *Tt nn*, female: *tt Nn;* Cross 3: male: *Tt nn*, female: *Tt Nn;* Cross 4: male: *Tt nn*, female: *Tt NN*

29. a. Recessive. Two unaffected individuals have an affected child. It was a consanguineous marriage that produced the affected child. II-1 and V-2 are affected (*aa*); all unaffected individuals except II-2, II-4, III-4, III-5, and possibly V-1 are carriers (*Aa*). b. Dominant. The trait is seen in each generation and each affected child has an affected parent; if the trait were recessive it would not be possible for III-3 to be unaffected even though both his parents are affected. All affected individuals are *Aa*, though III-4, III-5, and III-6 could be *AA*; carrier, is not applicable when the mutation is dominant; c. Recessive. Unaffected parents have an affected child. I-2 and III-4 are affected (*aa*); II-4 and II-5 are carriers (*Aa*); all others could be *AA* or *Aa*, but I-1 is almost certainly *AA* if the disease is rare.

31. a. 2/3; b. 1/9; c. 4/9.

33. Recessive; common.

35. a. 1/16 = 0.0625; b. 0.067.

37. In about 40% of the families, both parents were *Mm* heterozygotes. In the remaining 60% of the families, at least one parent was *MM*.

Chapter 3

1. a. 2; b. 6; c. 11; d. 8; e. 7; f. 9; g. 12; h. 3; i. 5; j. 4; k. 1; l. 10.

3. One gene, 2 alleles, incomplete dominance; 1/2 *c^r c^w* (yellow): 1/4 *c^r c^r* (red): 1/4 *c^w c^w* (white).

5. Long is completely dominant to short. Flower color trait shows incomplete dominance of two alleles.

7. a. Single-gene inheritance with incomplete dominance. Heterozygotes have intermediate serum cholesterol levels; homozygotes have elevated levels. The following people must have the mutant allele but do not express it (incomplete penetrance): family 2 I-3 or I-4; family 4 I-1 or I-2. b. Other factors are involved, including environment (particularly diet) and other genes.

9. a. *ii* (phenotype O) or *i I^A* (phenotype A) or *i I^B* (phenotype B); b. *I^B I^B*, *I^B i* or *I^B I^A*; c. *ii* (phenotype O).

11. a. 1/4 spotted dotted: 1/2 marbled: 1/4 spotted; b. marbled and dotted.

13. a. Coat color is determined by three alleles of a single gene arranged in a dominance series with *C* (for chinchilla) > *c^h* (for himalaya) > *c^a* (for albino). b. Cross 1: *c^h c^a × c^h c^a;* Cross 2: *c^h c^a × c^a c^a;* Cross 3: *Cc^h × Cc^h;* Cross 4: *CC × c^h(c^h or c^a);* Cross 5: *Cc^a × Cc^a;* Cross 6: *c^h c^h × c^a c^a;* Cross 7: *Cc^a × c^a c^a;* Cross 8: *c^a c^a × c^a c^a;* Cross 9: *Cc^h × c^h c^h;* Cross 10: *Cc^a × c^h c^a.* c. 3/4 chinchilla (*CC, Cc^h*, and *Cc^a*) and 1/4 himalaya (*c^h c^a*).

15. a. 2/3 Curly: 1/3 normal; b. *Cy/Cy* is lethal; c. 90 Curly winged and 90 normal winged flies.

17. a. The 2:1 phenotypic ratio shows that the montezuma parents were heterozygous, *Mm* and homozygosity for *M* is lethal; b. 1/2 montezuma: 1/2 greenish, normal fin; c. 6/12 montezuma normal fin: 2/12 montezuma ruffled fin: 3/12 green normal fin: 1/12 green ruffled fin.

19. Incomplete penetrance or a spontaneous mutation during gamete or the father of the child is not the male parent of the couple.

21. Two genes are involved. The black mare was *AAbb* and the chestnut stallion was *aaBB*, the liver horses were *aabb* and the bay horses were *AaBb*.

23. a. There are two genes involved; homozygosity for the recessive allele of either or both genes causes yellow color. Green parent is *AABB;* yellow parent is *aabb*. b. *AaBb, aaBb, Aabb* and *aabb* in equal proportions: 1/4 green:3/4 yellow fruit.

25. Dominance relationships are between alleles of the same gene. Only one gene is involved. Epistasis involves two genes. The alleles at one gene affect the expression of a second gene.

27. 1/4 would appear to have O type blood, 3/8 have A, 3/8 have AB.

29.

	I-1	I-2	I-3	I-4	II-1	II-2	II-3	III-1	III-2
Phenotypes	AB	A	B	AB	O	O	AB	A	O
Genotypes	$I^A I^B$	I^A or $I^A I^A$	I^B or $I^B I^B$	$I^A I^B$	ii	I^B or $I^B I^B$	$I^A I^B$	$I^A i$	$I^A I^A$ or $I^A i$ or $I^B i$

	Hh	Hh	$H-$	$H-$	$H-$	hh	Hh	Hh	hh

One or both of I-3 and I-4 must carry h.

31. 2/6 yellow: 3/6 albino: and 1/6 agouti progeny.

33. a. $A^y aBbCc \times Aabbcc$; b. six phenotypes: albino, yellow, brown agouti, black agouti, brown, black.

35. a. 27/64 wild type, 37/64 mutant; b. $AA\ Bb\ Cc$.

37. a. Two genes are involved. $A-B-$ and $aa\ B-$ are WR, $A-bb$ is DR, and $aa\ bb$ is LR. b. For these true-breeding strains, WR-1 is $AA\ BB$; WR-2 is $aa\ BB$; DR is $AA\ bb$, and LR is $aa\ bb$. c. The cross was $Aa\ Bb$ (WR) $\times aa\ bb$ (LR).

39. 44/56.

Chapter 4

1. a. 13; b. 7; c. 11; d. 10; e. 12; f. 8; g. 9; h. 1; i. 6; j. 15; k. 3; l. 2; m. 16; n. 4; o. 14; p. 5.

3. a. 7 centromeres; b. 7 chromosome; c. 14 chromatids; d. 3 pairs; e. 4 metacentric and 3 acrocentric; f. females are XX.

5. a. iii; b. i; c. iv; d. ii; e. v.

7. a. 1, 1 → 2, 2, 2, 1, 1, b. yes, yes, yes, yes → no, no, no, no → yes; c. no, no, no, no → yes, yes, yes, yes → no; d. yes, yes, yes, yes → no, no, no, no → yes.

9. Meiosis produces 4 cells (n, haploid), each with 7 chromosomes.

11. a. Mitosis, meiosis I, II; b. mitosis, meiosis I; c. mitosis; d. meiosis II and meiosis I; e. meiosis I; f. none; g. meiosis I; h. meiosis II, mitosis; i. mitosis, meiosis I.

13. a. metaphase or early anaphase of meiosis I in a male (assuming X-Y sex determination in *Tenebrio molitor*); b. sister chromatids, centromeres, and telomeres (among others); c. five.

15. It is very realistic to assume that homologous chromosomes carry different alleles of some genes. In contrast, recombination almost always occurs between homologous chromosomes in any meiosis; thus the second assumption is much less realistic. The couple could potentially produce $2^{23} \times 2^{23} = 2^{46}$ or 70,368,744,177,664 different zygotic combinations.

17. Meiosis requires the pairing of homologous chromosomes during meiosis I.

19. a. 400 spermatozoa; b. 200; c. 100; d. 100; e. 100; f. none.

21. a. Only females; b. males; c. males; d. 1/5 ZZ males and 4/5 ZW females.

23. a. brown females and ivory-eyed males; b. females with brown eyes and males with ivory or brown eyes in a 1/2 to 1/2 ratio.

25. a. Nonbarred females and barred males; b. barred and nonbarred females and barred and nonbarred males.

27. The bag-winged females have one mutation on the X chromosome that has a dominant effect on wing structure and that also causes lethality in homozygous females or hemizygous males.

29.

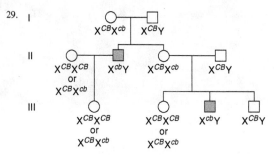

31. a. Recessive; b. autosomal; c. aa; d. Aa; e. Aa; f. Aa; g. Aa; h. Aa.

33. Vestigial wings is autosomal; body color is X-linked recessive.

35. a. X-linked dominant inheritance. b. Can exclude sex-linked recessive inheritance because affected females have unaffected sons. Can exclude autosomal recessive inheritance because the trait is rare and affected females have affected children with multiple husbands. Can exclude autosomal dominant inheritance because all the daughters but none of the sons of an affected male are affected. c. III-2 had four husbands and III-9 had six husbands.

37. a. 3; b. 1 or 3.

39. a. Purple is caused by homozygosity for a recessive allele of an autosomal gene (p), but the X-linked recessive white mutation is epistatic to p and to p^+. b. F_1 progeny: 1/2 white-eyed males and 1/2 wild-type (red) females; F_2 progeny: 1/4 white males, 1/4 white females, 3/16 red males, 3/16 red females, 1/16 purple males, 1/16 purple females.

41. a. Individual III-5; b. the BRCA2 mutation has a dominant effect on causing cancer; c. The data do not clearly distinguish between X-linked and autosomal inheritance BRCA2 is actually on autosome 13; d. The penetrance of the cancer phenotype is incomplete; e. The expressivity is variable; f. Ovarian cancer is sex-limited, the penetrance of breast cancer may be sex-influenced; g. low penetrance of the cancer phenotype, particularly among men.

Chapter 5

1. a. 8; b. 4; c. 1; d. 11; e. 2; f. 5; g. 6; h. 3; i. 10; j. 12; k. 9; l. 7.

3. a. parental gametes $B_1 D_1$ and $B_3 D_3$; b. recombinant gametes will be $B_1 D_3$ and $B_3 D_1$; c. the B and D DNA loci are linked.

5. a. $Oo\ Bb$; b. 9:3:3:1; c. not significant; d. between 0.5 and 0.1.

7. a. Notice that the null hypothesis is the same in both cases: that the genes are assorting independently; b. using 2 classes is a more sensitive test for linkage than using 4 classes; c. in a situation in which certain classes are sub-viable, you might see linkage with the 2 class test, but you would miss the even more important point that one allele causes reduced viability. This ability to see the relative viability of the alleles is an advantage to the 4 class method.

9. a. $Gs\ Bhd^+ / Gs^+\ Bhd\ ♀ \times Gs^+\ Bhd^+ / Y\ ♂ → 49\ Gs\ Bhd^+\ ♂:$ 48 $Gs^+\ Bhd\ ♂: 2\ Gs\ Bhd\ ♂: 1\ Gs^+\ Bhd^+\ ♂$. The rf = 3mu; b. genotypes, phenotypes and frequencies of the female progeny would be the same as their brothers.

11. 10%

13. a. A = normal pigmentation, a = albino allele, $Hbβ^A$ = normal globin, $Hbβ^S$ = sickle allele 49.5% $aHbβ^A$, 49.5% $AHbβ^A$, 0.5% $aHbβ^A$, 0.5% $AHbβ^A$; b. 49.5% $aHbβ^A$, 49.5% $AHbβ^A$, 0.5% $aHbβ^A$, 0.5% $AHbβ^A$; c. 0.0025.

15. a. 1/4 black, 1/2 albino, 1/4 brown; b. 34 m.u. apart.

17. a. Gametes: 20% Ab and aB, 30% AB and ab. F_2 generation: 59% $A-B-$, 16% $A-bb$ and $aa\ B-$, 9% $aa\ bb$. b. Gametes: 30% Ab and aB, 20% AB and ab. F_2 generation: 54% $A-B-$, 21% $A-bb$ and $aa\ B-$, 4% $aa\ bb$.

19. a. two genes are assorting independently; b. the two genes are on the same chromosome; yes; c. recombination occurs at the four

strand stage of meiosis, and so many crossovers occur between genes when they are far apart on the same chromosome that the linkage between alleles of these genes will be randomized; d. by summing up the values obtained for smaller distances separating other genes in between those at the ends.

21. The order of the genes is HIS4 − LEU2 − MAT − THR4.

23. the best map of these genes is:

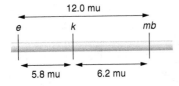

25. a. 360 $a^+b^+c^+$; 360 abc; 90 a^+bc; 90 ab^+c^+; 40 a^+b^+c; 40 abc^+; 10 a^+bc^+; 10 ab^+c; b. 500 $a^+b^+c^+$; 500 abc.

27. a. $sceccv$ / + + + and b / +; b. $sceccv$ / + + +, $sc−cv$ = 9 m.u., $ec−cv$ = 10.5 m.u.; c. predicted DCO = 0.009, observed DCO = 0.001, interference = 0.89.

29. a. 39%; b. 39%; c. 0.5%; d. 8%.

31. $\dfrac{dwp/pld^+\,rv^+\,rmp}{dwp^+/pld\,rv\,rmp^+}$ $rv−rmp$ 10 m.u.; $pld/dwp−rv$ 5 m.u.

33. a. 334;

35. a. First group: met^+lys^+ and met^-lys^-; second group: $met^+\,lys^+$, $met^+\,lys^-$, met^-lys^+, met^-lys^-. b. 5.5 m.u. c. met^-lys^+ and met^+lys^-.

37. a. 100% 4; b. 100% 2; c. 50% 0 and 50% 2; d. 40% 0, 20% 1, and 40% 2; e. 100% 0; f. 80% 0 and 20% 1; g. 2.

39. a. (Unordered tetrads): PD = 2 $his^-\,lys^+$ and 2 $his^+\,lys^-$; NPD = 2 $his^-\,lys^-$ and 2 $his^+\,lys^+$; T = 1 $his^-\,lys^+$, 1 $his^+\,lys^-$, 1 his^-lys^- and 1 $his^+\,lys^+$. b. 22.3 m.u. c. NCO = 222, SCO = 134; DCO = 44. d. 0.555 crossovers/meiosis. e. Two strand and three strand DCOs are missed. Map distance in map units = 1/2(T) + 3(NPD)/total asci; f. 27.8 m.u.

41. a. The sectors consist of $ade2^-/ade2^-$ cells generated by mitotic recombination. b. The sector size depends on when the mitotic recombination occurred during the growth of the colony. There should be many more small sectors because the mitotic recombinations creating them occur later in colony growth when there are many more cells.

43. a. Two mitotic crossovers occurred in succession in the same cell lineage. The first was between the sn and y genes, creating a patch of yellow tissue. The second was between the centromere and sn, creating a "clone within a clone" of yellow, singed cells. b. Yes.

Chapter 6

1. a. 6; b. 11; c. 9; d. 2; e. 4; f. 8; g. 10; h. 12; i. 3; j. 13; k. 5; l. 1; m. 7.

3. c.

5. Tube 1, nucleotides; tube 2, base pairs (without the sugar and phosphate) and sugar phosphate chains without the bases; tube 3, single strands of DNA.

7. a. 20% C; b. 30% T; c. 20% G.

9. Single stranded.

11. 5′.CAGAATGGTGCTCTGCTAT.3′.

13. 3′ GGGAACCTTGATGTTTCGGCTCTAATT 5′.

15. a. once every 4,096 nucleotides; b. once every 4,096 nucleotides; c. 256 nucleotides apart.

17. After one additional generation, 1/4 intermediate; after two additional generations, 1/8 intermediate.

19.

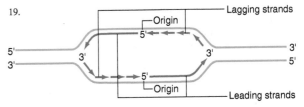

21. 5′ UAUACGAAUU 3′.

23. a. Relieves the stress of the overwound DNA ahead of the replication fork; b. unwinds the DNA; c. synthesizes a short RNA oligonucleotide; d. joins the sugar phosphate backbones.

25. The figure shows both strands of DNA are being replicated in the same direction relative to the replication fork.

27. a. no new DNAs will be formed; b. no new DNAs will be formed; c. the two DNA strands can pair with each other so two new DNA molecules will be formed; d. this single strand of DNA has two regions that have complementary base sequence so the DNA can form a so-called *hairpin loop* and the product will therefore be 5 nucleotides longer than the original:

29. Would not undergo recombination.

31. Regardless of which strands are cut during resolution (to result in crossing-over or no crossing-over) mismatches within the heteroduplex region can be corrected to the same allele, resulting in gene conversion.

33. If many short repeats are present in the double helix at the point where the invading strand is pairing, it is likely that the invading strand will not line up perfectly.

Chapter 7

1. 1. a, b, h; 2. b, c; 3. f, j; 4. g, j; 5. a, b, h; 6. f, i, k; 7. g, k; 8. d, i; 9. d, e, f, g, i.

3. The wild-type sequence is:
5′ ACCGTA**G**TCGAC**T**GGT**Δ**AACTTTGCGCG

5. 9.5×10^{-5}; higher than normal rate.

7. If phages induce resistance, several appear in random positions on each of the replica plates. If the mutations preexist, the resistant colonies would appear at the same locations on each of the three replica plates.

9. Female A has a white-eyed mutation on the X. Female B has a recessive lethal mutation on the X. Female C is mosaic with a lethal mutation on one strand and wild-type sequence on the other strand of one X chromosome, or she on the other strand of one X chromosome, or she is heterozygenes for an incompletely penetrant lethal mutation.

11. a. 857 essential X-linked genes; b. 37.6% of the genes on the X chromosome are essential; c. the X-ray induced mutation rate = 1.4 $\times$ 10^{-4} a 40-fold increase.

13. a. two-way mutagen; b. one-way mutagen; c. two-way mutagen; d. two-way mutagen; e. two-way mutagen.

15. a. nucleotide excision repair and the SOS-type error-prone repair; b. AP endonuclease and other enzymes in the base excision repair system could remove the damage and the SOS repair systems can work at AP sites, adding any of the 4 bases at random.

17. Yes; Liver converts substance X into a mutagen.

19. a. complementation test; − is a lack of complementation; + means that the two mutations complemented each other; b. 1 × 4 =−, 1 × 6 =+, 2 × 3 =+, 2 × 4 =+, 2 × 5 =+, 3 × 5 =+, 3 × 6 =+, 4 × 5 =+, 4 × 6 =+; c. 3 genes (1, 3, and 4), (2 and 6), (5).

21. a. Deletions do not revert. Also, deletions will fail to recombine with either of two *rII⁻* mutations that can recombine with each other to produce *rII⁺* phage. b. The length of the T4 chromosome predicts the number of nucleotide pairs. Recombination analysis with the mutants suggests the total map units in the T4 genome. Thus, Benzer could estimate the number of map units per nucleotide pair. c. *rII⁻* mutations in the same nucleotide pair cannot recombine with each other to produce *rII⁺* phage.

23. a. two; b. (1, 4), (2, 3, 5).

25. a. 3, 6, and 7 are deletions (nonreverting);

b.

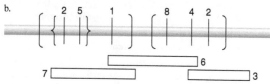

c. Use other deletions in crosses with mutants 2 and 5.

27. a. Parental ditype: All spores Arg⁻. Nonparental ditypes: 2 Arg⁻: 2 Arg⁺; b. Two of the PD spores grow on either ornithine, citrulline, arginosuccinate, or arginine; the other two grow with arginine only; NPD Arg⁻ spores grow with arginine only.

29. 45 purple: 16 green: 3 blue.

31. a. In all four crosses, there are two unlinked genes involved with complete dominance at both loci. b. (Each arrow represents a biochemical reaction catalyzed by one of the two gene products.) (Cross 1) colorless → blue → purple; (Cross 2) colorless1 → colorless2 → purple; (Cross 3) colorless1 → red and colorless2 → blue, with red + blue = purple; (Cross 4) colorless1 → purple and colorless2 → purple. c. Cross 2. d. F₂ only. (Cross 1) 2 purple: 1 blue: 1 white; (Cross 2) 1 purple: 1 white; (Cross 3) 2 purple: 1 red: 1 blue; (Cross 4) all purple.

33. a.   18   14   9   10   21

X → D → B → A → C → thymidine

b. 9 and 10 accumulates B; 10 and 14 accumulates D.

35 a. successful, immediate, prolonged; b. unsuccessful; c. successful, delayed, prolonged; d. successful, immediate, prolonged; e. unsuccessful; f. unsuccessful; g. successful, delayed, prolonged; h. unsuccessful; i. successful, immediate, short term; j. successful, immediate, prolonged.

37. a. two; b. 1/16 α1α1 β1β1: 1/8 α1α2 β1β1: 1/16 α2α2 β1β1: 1/8 α1α1 β1β2: 1/4 α1α2 β1β2: 1/8 α1α2 β2β2: 1/16 α1α1 β2β2: 1/8 α1α2 β2β2: 1/16 α2α2 β2 β2.

39. One chromosome with β β/δ δ; another with β/δ only (where / signifies a protein part of which, for example, the N-terminal part, is one type of globin and the other part the other type of globin.)

Chapter 8

1. a. 5; b. 10; c. 8; d. 12; e. 6; f. 2; g. 9; h. 14; i. 3; j. 13; k. 1; l. 7; m. 15; n. 11; o. 4; p. 16.

3. a. GU GU GU GU GU or UG UG UG UG;

b. GU UG GU UG GU UG GU UG GU;

c. GUG UGU GUG U etc.;

d. GUG UGU GUG UGU GUG UGU GUG UGU GU (depends on where you start);

e. GUG UGU GU or UGU GUG UG (depends on where you start).

5. Hbᶜ therefore precedes Hbˢ in the map of β-*globin* gene.

7. 5′ GGN GCA CCA AGG AAA 3′

9.

Stop Codon Change	UAA		UAG		UGA	
1ˢᵗ position	<u>A</u>AA	Lys	<u>A</u>AG	Lys	<u>A</u>GA	Arg
	<u>C</u>AA	Gln	<u>C</u>AG	Gln	<u>C</u>GA	Arg
	<u>G</u>AA	Glu	<u>G</u>AG	Glu	<u>G</u>GA	Gly
2ⁿᵈ position	U<u>U</u>A	Leu	U<u>U</u>G	Leu	U<u>U</u>A	Leu
	U<u>C</u>A	Ser	U<u>C</u>G	Ser	U<u>C</u>A	Ser
	U<u>G</u>A	STP	U<u>G</u>G	Trp	U<u>A</u>A	STP
3ʳᵈ position	UA<u>U</u>	Tyr	UA<u>A</u>	STP	UG<u>U</u>	Cys
	UA<u>C</u>	Tyr	UA<u>C</u>	Tyr	UG<u>C</u>	Cys
	UA<u>G</u>	STP	UA<u>U</u>	Tyr	UG<u>G</u>	Trp

11. a. UGG changed to UGA or UAG so the DNA change was G to A. b. If the second base of the Trp codon UGG changes to A, a UAG stop codon will result. If the third base of the Trp codon UGG changes to A, a UGA stop codon will result. Mutation of A to T in the first base of the Lys codon leads to UAA. If the Gly codon is GGA, mutation of the first G to T creates a UGA stop codon.

13. Three.

15. a. Mutant 1: transversion changes Arg to Pro; mutant 2: single-base-pair deletion changes Val to Trp and then stop; mutant 3: transition Thr (silent); mutant 4: single-base-pair insertion changes several amino acids then stop; mutant 5: transition changes Arg to stop; mutant 6: inversion changes identity of 6 amino acids. b. EMS: 1, 3, 5; Proflavin: 2, 4.

17. Required to add the appropriate ribonucleotide to a growing RNA chain.

19. Gene *F:* bottom strand; gene *G:* top strand.

21. Base pairing between the codon in the mRNA and the anticodon in the tRNA is responsible for aligning the tRNA that carries the appropriate amino acid to be added to the polypeptide chain.

23. a. Translation. b. Tyrosine (Tyr) is the next amino acid to be added to the C terminus of the growing polypeptide, which will be nine amino acids long when completed. c. The carboxy-terminus of the growing polypeptide chain is tryptophan. d. The first amino acid at the N terminus would be f-met in a prokaryotic cell and met in a eukaryotic cell. The mRNA would have a cap at its 5′ end and a poly-A tail at its 3′ end in a eukaryotic cell but not in a prokaryotic cell. If the mRNA were sufficiently long, it might encode several proteins in a prokaryote but not in a eukaryote.

25 a. 1431 base pairs; b. 5′ ACCCUGGACUAGUGGAAAGUUAACU-UAC 3′; c. N Pro Trp Thr Ser Gly Lys Leu Thr Tyr.C.

27. Mitochondria do not use the same genetic code; mutate the 5′ CUA 3′ codons in the mitochondrial gene to 5′ ACN 3′.

29. Order: c e i f a k h d b j g.

31. a. Very severe; b. mild; c. very severe; d. mild; e. no effect; f. mild to no effect; g. severe; h. severe or mild.

33. Mutations possibly causing a detectable change in protein size: d, e, g, and i. In protein amount (assumes all mutant proteins are equally stable): e, f, j, and k. In mRNA size: i and j. In mRNA amount (assumes all mutant mRNAs with poly-A tails are equally stable): f and j.

35. If the met⁺ phenotype is due to a true reversion, then: *met⁻ x met⁺→ met⁺ / met⁻ → 2 met⁺; 2 met⁻*. If there is an unlinked suppressor mutation: *met⁻ su⁻* (phenotypically met⁺) × *met⁺ su⁺* (wild type) → *met⁻ / met⁺; su⁻ / su⁺ →* 3/4 met⁺; 1/4 met⁻.

37. a. 3′ AUC 5′; b. 5′ CAG 3′, c. minimum two genes.

39. a. Missense mutations change identity of a particular amino acid inserted many times in many normal proteins but nonsense suppressors only make proteins longer b. (i) a mutation in a tRNA gene in a region other than that encoding the anticodon itself, so that the wrong aminoacyl-tRNA synthetase would sometimes recognize the tRNA and charge it with the wrong amino acid; (ii) a mutation in an aminoacyl-tRNA synthetase gene, making an enzyme that would sometimes put the wrong amino acid on a tRNA; (iii) a mutation in a gene encoding either a ribosomal protein, a ribosomal RNA or a translation factor that would make the ribosome more error-prone, inserting the wrong amino acid in the polypeptide; (iv) a mutation in a gene encoding a subunit of RNA polymerase that would sometimes cause the enzyme to transcribe the sequence incorrectly.

41. a. 5′ UUA 3′; b. 5′ UAG 3′ and 5′ UAA 3′ (due to wobble at the codon's 3′-most nucleotide); c. Gln, Lys, Glu, Ser, Leu, and Tyr.

Chapter 9

1. a. 10; b. 1; c. 9; d. 7; e. 6; f. 2; g. 8; h. 3; i. 5; j. 4.

3. Shorter molecules slip through pores more easily; large molecules get caught.

5. a. A; b. 10 kb; c. 10 kb.

7. a. 1.83 kb.

9. Selectable markers are genes that allow a vector to impart protection from an antibiotic on a host cell. When cells are transformed by a vector with a selectable marker, and then exposed to the appropriate antibiotic, only cells that have the vector will survive.

11. a. all; b. 1/4; c. none; d. 1/2 chance; e. 3/4.

13. a. Five; b. divide the number of base pairs in the genome by the average insert size, then multiply by 5.

15. After cloning: EcoRI: 42 and 2400 bp fragments; MboI: 705, 944, 500, and 300 bp or 905, 744, 500, and 300 bp fragments.

17. a. Alkaline phosphatase removes the 5′-phosphate groups so ligase can not join a hydroxyl group to the de-phosphorylated 5′ ends. The ligation with the non-phosphorylated vector reanneals to itself at a high frequency, leading to 99/100 blue colonies. The phosphorylated vector formed 99/100 white colonies, showing that almost all of the vectors had an insert; b. The dephosphorylation of the vector increased the number of clones (vector + insert) 100 fold; c. If the insert were dephosphorylated, it will not self-ligate, but the vector WILL self-ligate. The vector has the antibiotic resistance gene and ORI, so the "empty" vector will be propagated in *E. coli*, generating a high level of "background."

19. a. (1) 3.1, 6.9 kb; (2) 4.3, 4.0, 1.7 kb; (3) 1.5, 0.6, 1.0, 6.9 kb; (4) 4.3, 2.1, 1.9, 1.7 kb; (5) 3.1, 1.2, 4.0, 1.7 kb; b. The 6.9 kb fragment in the *Eco*RI+*Hin*dIII digest; the 2.1 and 1.9 kb fragments in the *Bam*HI+*Pst*I, and the 4.0 kb fragment in the *Eco*RI+*Bam*HI digest.

21. probes should be between about 15 and 18 nucleotides long; (i) if you knew the sequence of the protein from several bacterial species you could choose a very highly conserved region on which to base a probe; (ii) find a region of 5 or 6 contiguous amino acids with low degeneracy.

23. a. You wish to know whether the PKU syndrome in this patient is caused by a mutation in the phenylalanine hydroxylase gene; b. there are 300 template molecules in 1 ng of DNA; c. 110 ng of a 1 kb section of the genome after the PCR!

25. a. the chance that one of the two primers will anneal to a random region of DNA that is not the targeted CFTR exon would be $(1/4)^{18}$, or about 1 chance in 7×10^{10} so an 18 base sequence will be present once in every 70 billion nucleotides; b. (i) the chance probability of a 16 base sequence in random DNA is $(1/4)^{16}$, or 1 chance out of 4×10^9. (ii) the longer the primers the more expensive they are to synthesize, the longer the primers the more likely they are to anneal

with each other, if the primer is too long it can hybridize with DNA with which it is not perfectly matched. Thus, longer primers might anneal to other regions of the genome than the region you actually want to amplify; c. the 5′-end. mismatches at the 3′-end would prevent DNA polymerase from adding any new nucleotides to the chain.

27. In well studied organisms such as *C. elegans, D. melanogaster,* yeast and mice the entire DNA sequence of the genomes is now available. To study any region in these genomes design PCR primers based on the genomic sequence. Having the genome sequence of an organism increases the importance of PCR. Restriction digestions remain the basis for many important applications of DNA cloning.

29. a. newly synthesized strand: 5′ TAGCTAGGCTAGCCCTTTATCG 3′ template strand: 3′ ATCGATCCGATCGGGAAATAGC 5′ b. 5′ CGAUAAAGGGCUAGCCUAGCTA 3′; c. There are stop codons in each frame so it is unlikely that this is an exon sequence of a coding region.

31. a. This terminal ddA, which is linked to a green fluorescent label, therefore becomes the 3′ end of this molecule; b. 5′...ACCTATTTTACAGGAATT...3′; c. "Residue Position" indicates a peak at a specific location in the scan so the size of the single-stranded DNA fragment is represented by the residue position; d. The double peak at position 370 is most likely caused by the fact that the original DNA actually had two different DNA sequences. One chromosome carrys a T-A base pair at this location while the homologue had a G-C base pair.

Chapter 10

1. a. 6; b. 3; c. 2; d. 5; e. 1; f. 4.

3.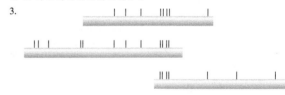

5. a. you could generate two sequencing primers that would hybridize in all of the clones to the BAC vector just on either side of the inserted monkey DNA. The same two primers would enable you to find thousands of different monkey STSs.

b.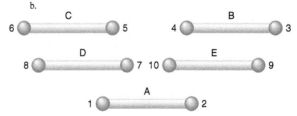

c. BAC clones C, B, and A. d. the contig could range from somewhat less than 300 kb long to somewhat less than 1500 kb long.

7. Recall that you can read approximately 500-800 nucleotides from a single sequencing reaction. If the repetitive sequence of DNA is longer than this size, then all of the data obtained from the reaction will be derived from the repeated sequence. If the repetitive sequence is repeated many times in the genome, you might not be able to tell from where in the genome the copy you have sequenced is derived. The hierarchical shotgun strategy. This strategy analyzes individual BACs that might contain only a single copy of the repetitive sequence, so shotgun sequencing of an entire BAC could proceed without complications. The whole genome shotgun strategy involves generating clones with known insert sizes of about 2 kb, 10 kb, and 200 kb. They then

sequence the two ends of each clone and retain the information that these two ends are related to each other (that is, one of the sequences is say ~200 kb away from the other sequence). Both types of sequencing strategies encounter major difficulties in dealing with tandemly repeated sequences. Regions around centromeres, for example, may have more than 1 Mb of tandemly repeated simple sequences.

9. some genomic sequences cannot be cloned (e.g. heterochromatin) and some sequences rearrange or delete when cloned (e.g. some tandemly arrayed repeats).

11. involves a single hybridization to a chromosome spread. FISH gives results quickly and can be used with any cloned piece of DNA.

13. the human genome contains a large amount of repeated DNA and introns can be quite large. There human genome also has many duplicated.

15. lack regulatory region information and intron DNA.

17. a. a difference in the amount of recombination in males and females; b. No, the same chromosomes are passed from generation to generation.

19. (i) centromeres and telomeres. (ii) Transposon-derived repeats have given rise to at least 47 different human genes. (iii) Certain genes have repeated sequences. (iv) Transposon-derived repeats have reshaped the genome by aiding the formation of chromosomal rearrangements.

21. a. the genome of yeast is very small. Yeast currently has a catalog tryptic peptides related to the genes which code for the as well as a catalog of >7,000 known protein-protein interactions and >500 protein-DNA interactions. b. The nematode is a fairly complex multi-cellular organism. c. The mouse is the closest model organism to humans.

23. a. suggesting that the protein is a transcription factor. b. the two genes arose by duplication.

25. the definition of 'gene' is somewhat imprecise; one gene can actually produce more than one type of protein, although the polypeptides produced by one gene are usually related to each other, and many genes are transcribed into RNAs that remain untranslated yet still have important functions. The most all-encompassing definition of 'gene' is a region of the chromosome that is transcribed into a discrete primary transcript that can subsequently be spliced or otherwise processed. It is possible to look for transcribed regions of the genome with techniques such as Northern blots or the sequencing of hundreds of thousands of clones from cDNA libraries. However, if a transcript is found only in very low abundance or if it is very small, these techniques do not ensure that it can be detected. Computer programs are much less successful in identifying genes with very short open-reading frames or the genes that are transcribed into very small non-coding RNAs.

27. a. If genes are vertically inherited, a cladogram that compared the DNA sequences of the gene should essentially match the accepted species cladogram, but if lateral gene transfer occurred then a cladogram of the protein sequences would unexpectedly show that the human gene was much closer in DNA sequence to the bacterial gene than to genes in more closely related species like primates or mammals. b. a gene of bacterial origin was found in humans and chimps, but not in any other primates or mammals. This suggests that the lateral transfer occurred before humans and chimps last shared a common ancestor (estimated to be about 5 million years ago), but before either of these two species last shared a common ancestor with any other current primate species (about 7 million years ago). c. if a large number of related species had a particular gene but one species in this group did not.

29. Not all human genes have been accurately identified. Genes that are rarely expressed or that have unusual codon usage patterns are difficult to find. The human proteome is much more complex and the human genome has more paralogs and chemical modifications of proteins.

31. a. Black—this gene is either, green—the mRNA for this gene accumulates to higher levels in normal tissue than in the tissue from the tumor, red—the mRNA for this gene accumulates to higher levels in cancerous tissue than in normal tissue, yellow—the mRNA for these genes accumulates to the same level in both kinds of tissue. b. a red signal.

Chapter 11

1. a. 5; b. 3; c. 8; d. 6; e. 2; f. 7; g. 1; h. 4.

3. Anonymous DNA markers are the DNA sequence of an individual. The terms dominant and recessive can only be used when discussing the phenotype of an organism, so in one sense this question is meaningless. Geneticists often say that DNA markers are inherited in a codominant fashion to denote that the both alleles can be seen in the DNA sequence.

5. a. Different numbers of simple sequence repeats; b. slippage of DNA polymerase during replication; c. a different mechanism: unequal crossing-over.

7. a. The polymorphism is within the short DNA sequence that is used as a probe; b. the polymorphism is in the nucleotide adjacent to the sequence used as a primer; c. the SNP polymorphism can be kilobases away from the probe sequence in a restriction site recognized by the restriction enzyme used to digest the genomic DNA.

9. The sequences of the ASOs would be

3′ GATATTTACCCGATCCGCA and 3′ GATATTTACGCGATC CGCA.

11. Sperm collected from man, eggs are collected from woman. After *in vetro* fertilization, embryos are allowed to develop to the eight-cell stage. A single cell from each eight-cell embryo is removed. DNA is prepared and genotype is analyzed using PCR and *Mst* II digestion. Embryos with the desired genotype are implanted into the woman's uterus.

13. Coworker 3 has the same DNA fingerprint as the crime sample and must be the perpetrator of the crime. The probability is essentially 100%.

15. a. Individuals A, B, C and E; b. Individuals D and F; c. 48 bp.

17. a. 10 kb; b. 10 kb; c. 0%; d. 50%.

19. Members of the disease family must be segregating two or more alleles at each DNA marker that is chosen.

21. a. 0% chance; b. 0.0075 probability of an affected child.

23. Mating W is not informative; mating X is informative – both parents are doubly heterozygous; mating Y is non-informative; mating Z is non-informative.

25. Identify sequences that are transcribed into RNA; use computational analysis to identify sequences that are conserved between distantly related species; use computational analysis to identify sequences that are open reading frames with appropriate codon usage and splice sites.

27. a. A, C and E, b. three different genes have been identified; c. Yes; d. fragments C and E; e. gene recognized by fragment E; f. If there is a mouse model of this disease you would transform the mice with the cDNA clone of the candidate gene and look for the normal human gene to rescue the mutant phenotype in the mice.

29. a. The disease is autosomal dominant; b. Yes, II-2, II-3 and III-1.

31. a. 12,500 different haplotypes; b. 156,250,000 possible diplotypes; c. The father's genotype is A25 C4 B7 / A23 C2 B35; the mother's genotype is A24 C5 B8 / A3 C9 B44; d. 1/4.

Chapter 12

1. a. 4; b. 9; c. 7; d. 8; e. 2; f. 3; g. 5; h. 1; i. 6.

3. Interphase: 40-fold compaction; metaphase: 10,000-fold compaction.

5. a. 1.2×10^8 molecules of H2A protein; b. during or just after S phase; c. more templates that the cells can transcribe simultaneously, allowing the more rapid production of histone proteins.

7. A deletion of one G band removes about 15 genes.

9. H1 is one the outside of the complex and locks the DNA to the core and interacts with H1 proteins from other nucleosomes to forming

the center of the coil that is thought to form the 300A fiber. The other histone proteins are coated with DNA and can not form the 300A fiber.

11. Mutate the DNA sequence so that the twelfth amino acid encoded is not lysine but another similar amino acid.

13. the Xist gene produces is a large, cis-acting mRNA causing inactivation of the X chromosome that produced it.

15. a. In the presence of a *Su(var)* mutant allele there will be fewer white patches in the eye and more red patches when the eyes are compared to a homozygous *Su(var)*⁺ fly. The situation would be reversed with more white patches and fewer red (wild type) patches if the fly were heterozygous for the *E(var)* mutation; b. the *Su(var)*⁺ genes encode proteins that establish and assist spreading of heterochromatin. The *E(var)*⁺ genes seem to encode proteins that restrict the spreading of heterochromatin.

17. These twin sisters could still be monozygotic twins. In the affected twin, the X^Dmd+ homolog was inactivated in the cells that are affected by muscular dystrophy. In the unaffected twin, the other X chromosome (X^Dmd) was inactivated in those same cells.

19. a. *OO* × *o*Y (orange females × black males), *oo* × *O*Y (black females × orange males), *Oo* × *o*Y (tortoiseshell females × black males), and *Oo* × *O*Y (tortoiseshell females × orange males); b. XXY Klinefelter males who are heterozygous *Oo;* c. an autosomal gene called the *white-spotting* or *piebald* gene causes the white spotting—a dominant allele of this gene causes white fur, but in heterozygotes this allele has variable expressivity so some patches have a color dictated by the functional alleles of the *orange* gene.

21. choice b.

23. a. alpha satellite DNA; b. Cohesin holds sister chromatids together until anaphase, kinetochores attach chromosomes to the spindle poles and contain motor proteins that move the separated chromosomes to the poles.

25. a. genes encoding cohesin proteins, genes encoding kinetochore proteins, genes encoding motor proteins that help chromosomes move on the spindle apparatus and genes encoding components of the spindle checkpoint that makes the beginning of anaphase dependent upon the proper connections of spindle fibers and kinetochores. Mutations that alter a centromere comprising a centromere might also have similar effects; b. look for colonies that contained many cells that had lost the YAC because of mitotic chromosome mis-segregation; mutate the centromeric DNA of this YAC using in vitro mutagenesis. If the centromere were disrupted the YAC would not segregate properly and would be lost.

27. a. your DNA probe must contain unique DNA found next to the repeated 5′ TTAGGG (telomere) sequences; b. the blurriness indicates that the hybridizing fragments from the end of the chromosome in a population of cells are not homogeneous in length. The number of repeat sequences at the telomere, and therefore the telomere length, varies from cell to cell, especially in actively dividing cells.

29. a. CENP-A mutant dies while the CENP-B mutant is viable. Chromosome loss at elevated temperature cannot be measured in CENP-A because the cell dies. The CENP-B mutant, on the other hand, shows increased chromosome loss; b. cells with a marker which is on a chromosome, or on an artificial linear chromosome (YAC), or on a circular plasmid containing a centromere.

31. a. Use the yeast CBF1 protein to make antibodies and then use these antibodies to probe the human cDNA expression library. Alternatively, you could use the cloned yeast gene as a probe to hybridize to clones in a human cDNA library; b. Label or tag the antibody (with fluorescence for example). You can determine the location of the protein in the cell.

33. digest the BAC, the YAC, and the genomic DNA with several restriction enzymes and compare the restriction patterns of each when they are hybridized with a probe containing the BAC or YAC DNA.

Chapter 13

1. a. 4; b. 8; c. 6; d. 5; e. 7; f. 3; g. 2; h. 1.

3. In a duplication, there would be a repeated set of bands; in a deletion, bands normally found would be missing.

5.

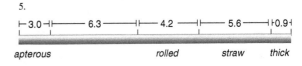

7.

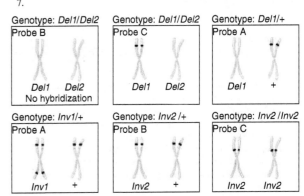

9. a. the parental types *y⁺ z¹ w⁺R spl⁺*/ Y (zeste) and *y z¹ w⁺R spl* / Y (yellow zeste split); b. crossing over anywhere between the *y* and *spl* genes; c. mispairing and unequal crossing over between the two copies of the *w⁺* gene; d. 5.9 mu.

11. a. 2, 4; b. 2, 4; c. 2; d. 1, 3.

13. a. 2 *URA3 ARG9* spores and 2 *ura3 arg9* spores;
   b. 2 spores die, 1 *URA3 ARG9* and one *ura3 arg9*;
   c. 4 viable spores, 2 *URA3 ARG9* spores and 2 *ura3 arg9* spores.

15. A two-strand double crossover with both crossovers in the inversion loop. One crossover must occur between *LEU2* and *HIS4*. The other crossover must occur on the other side of either of the two genes but still within the inversion loop.

17. a. 1, 3, 5 and 6; b. 2 and 4; c. 1 and 3; d. 5 and 6.

19. a. 1/4 fertile green, 1/4 fertile yellow-green, 1/4 semisterile green, 1/4 semisterile yellow-green; b. 1/2 fertile yellow-green, 1/2 semisterile green; c. from crossing-over events between the translocation chromosome and homologous region on the normal chromosome.

21. 1/2 *Lyra* males: 1/2 *Lyra⁺* (wild type) females.

23. the 11 base long primers must be 5′ GTTCGCATACG 3′ and 5′ GTGTACGCACG 3′.

25. the arrows show the positions of hybridization.

27. *Ds* is a defective transposable element and *Ac* is a complete, autonomous copy.

29. Use a probe made of DNA from the sequence preceding the 200 A residues to hybridize to genomic DNA on Southern blots or to chromosomes by *in situ* hybridization.

31. a. the black *K. waltii* genes are duplicated in *S. cerevisiae*.
   b. At some time after the evolutionary lines for these two species separated a portion of the *S. cerevisiae* genome was duplicated in a progenitor of *S. cerevisiae*. Over time one copy was lost of

many of the duplicated genes. Occasionally both copies of a gene were retained

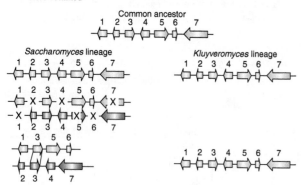

33. a. 7; b. sand oats: diploid, slender wild oats: tetraploid, cultivated oats: hexaploid; c. sand oats: 7, slender wild oats: 14, cultivated wild oats: 21; d. same answer as c.

35. a. (i) aneuploid, (ii) monosomic for chromosome 5, (iii) embryonic lethal; b. (i) aneuploid, (ii) trisomic for chromosomes 1 and 5, (iii) embryonic lethal; c. (i) euploid, (ii) autotriploid, (iii) viable but infertile; d. (i) euploid, (ii) autotetraploid, (iii) viable and fertile.

37. A: meiosis II in father; B: meiosis I in mother; C: meiosis I in father; D: meiosis II in mother.

39. You would actually expect more monosomies than trisomies, because meiotic nondisjunction would produce equal frequencies of monosomies and trisomies, but chromosome loss would produce only monosomies. The low frequency of monosomies observed is because monosomic zygotes usually arrest development so early that a pregnancy is not recognized. This may be due to a lower tolerance for imbalances involving only a single copy of a chromosome than for those involving three copies, or because recessive lethal mutations are carried on the remaining copy.

41. a. Mate putative mutants that are $ey\ ci^+ / ey^+\ ci$ with flies that are $ey\ ci / ey\ ci$. b. Nondisjunction during meiosis I will produce wild-type progeny; nondisjunction during meiosis II cannot be recognized. c. 2 eyeless: 2 cubitus interruptus: 1 eyeless, cubitus interruptus: 1 wild type. d. Mate putative mutants that are $ey\ ci^+/ ey^+\ ci$ with flies that have an unmarked attached chromosome 4. Nondisjunction during meiosis II would yield eyeless or cubitus interruptus progeny, but you could not recognize progeny resulting from nondisjunction during meiosis I. If the attached chromosome 4 carried two copies of ey and two copies of ci, you could recognize and discriminate some of the products of nondisjunction during the two meiotic divisions.

43. Treat with colchicine.

45. In autopolyploids, the banding patterns of homologs should be the same; in allopolyploids, different banding patterns will be seen for chromosomes from different species.

Chapter 14

1. a. 4; b. 5; c. 2; d. 7; e. 6; f. 3; g. 1.

3. 200 colonies on the first plate and 20 colonies on the second plate.

5. a. iv; b. iii; c. ii.

7. The $purE$ and $pepN$ genes will be cotransformed at a lower frequency if the $H.\ influenzae\ b$ pathogenic strain was used as a host donor strain.

9. plasmid transformation into *Shigella dysenteriae*, bacteriophage infection of *Staphylococcus*, *Streptococcus* or *E. coli* species and transposition of DNA (pathogenicity island) into *Vibrio cholerae*.

11. Do a mating between the mutant cell with 3-4 copies of F and a wild-type F⁻ recipient. A mutation in the F plasmid means the exconjugant will have the higher copy number. If the mutation is in a chromosomal gene the higher copy number phenotype would not be transferred into the recipient. You could isolate the F plasmid DNA from the mutant cell, and then transform this plasmid into new recipient cells. By examining the number of copies of the F factor in the transformed cells, you could tell whether the trait was carried by the plasmid.

13. a. (i) transformation, (ii) conjugation and (iii) transduction;. b. if the donor DNA used in the transformation includes plasmids recipient cells may take up the entire plasmid and acquire the characteristics conferred by the plasmid genes. Conjugation requires the presence of a conjugative plasmid in the donor cell. c. Bacteriophages are required for transduction. d. natural transformation with DNA fragments, conjugation with an Hfr and generalized transduction.

15. Transform the plasmid into a nontoxin-producing recipient strain and assay for toxin production.

17. order: *ilv bgl mtl*.

19. a.

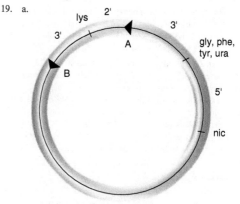

b.

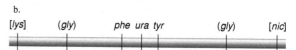

c. To map the *gly* gene with respect to other markers, select for Gly⁺ transductants on min + lys + phe + tyr + ura+ nic. Then score the other markers to determine which genes are cotransduced with Gly⁺ at the highest frequency.

21. this assay detects $recA^-$ mutants in the F⁻ cell based on the inability to form stable exconjugants.

23. a. *in vitro* portion; b. *in vivo*; c. *in vivo*; d. *in vitro*.

25. a. both; b. both; c. neither; d. both.

27. a.

		Trp	His	Ile	Met
mRNA	5'	UGG	CAU/C	AUU/C/A	AUG
nDNA mRNA-like	5'	TGG	CAT/C	ATT/C/A	ATG
nDNA template	3'	ACC	GTA/G	TAA/G/T	TAC

b.

		Trp	His	Ile	Met
mRNA	5'	UGA/G	CAU/C	AUC/U	AUG/A
mtDNA mRNA-lik	5'	TGA/G	CAT/C	ATC/T	ATG/A
mtDNA template	3'	ACT/C	GTA/G	TAG/A	TAC/T

29. a and d.

31. a. Introns would have to be removed, some of the codons in the nuclear gene would have to be changed since the genetic code in the nucleus and in mitochondria is not identical, a mitochondrial translational start site and a transcriptional termination site must be added, the open reading frame of the altered nuclear gene would have to be placed under the control of a mitochondrial promoter, and the cloned gene must be introduced into the yeast mitochondria. b. Such a strain can then be used to select for function of the mitochondrial genetic system in mutants that are unable to respire;

try to find arginine auxotrophs that could no longer make arginine because there was a DNA change that obliterated the function of the promoter. Such mutations allow analysis of the function of regulatory elements in the mitochondrial genome.

33. The small size of the sperm can mean that organelles are excluded; cells can degrade organelles or organellar DNA from the male parent; early zygotic mitoses distribute the male organelles to cells that will not become part of the embryo; the details of the fertilization process may prevent the paternal cell from contributing any organelles (only the sperm nucleus is allowed into the egg); and in some species that zygote destroys the paternal organelle after fertilization.

35. If the mutation is very debilitating to the cell, either because of the loss of energy metabolism in the case of mitochondria or of photosynthetic capability in the case of chloroplasts, a cell that is homoplasmic for the mutant genome will die.

37. a. The zygote that formed this plant was heteroplasmic, containing both wild type chloroplast genomes and mutant chloroplast genomes. These two types of genomes can segregate as tissue is propagated mitotically. b. many of the ovules generated on this branch are heteroplasmic and give rise to variegated plants. Some of the cells on the variegated branch gave rise to ovules that segregated one or the other chloroplast genomes. The phenotype of the progeny will reflect the type(s) of chloroplast genome(s) in the ovules; white leaved plants cannot make chlorophyll and since they cannot conduct photosynthesis they will die. c. part of the plant can conduct photosynthesis then these carbohydrates can be made and transported to tissues that are unable to conduct photosynthesis.

39. a. If one of the parental inbred lines is male sterile, then this line can not self-fertilize and the seed companies would not have to do anything more to prevent self-fertilization. b. the sterile inbred line in part a must also be homozygous for the recessive for the *rf* allele of *Restorer*. The other inbred line, the male parent supplying the pollen for the cross, would have to have at least one (and preferable two) dominant *Rf* alleles of *Restorer*. c. make a fertile "Maintainer" line that has mitochondria with a normal (non-CMS) genome but whose nuclear genomes are the same as the CMS plants and also *rf/rf*. The *rf/rf* CMS plants are used as the female parent (they can not produce pollen). When pollen from Maintainer plants fertilizes the CMS plants, the progeny will have CMS mitochondria and will also be *rf/rf*; in other words, these progeny will be identical to their maternal parents. d. farmers are now dependent upon the seed companies to provide their seed; the genetic variation of the corn crop overall is reduced.

41. a. The mother (I-1) may have had very low levels of mutant mitochondrial chromosomes or there may have been a spontaneous mutation either in the mitochondrial genome of the egg that gave rise to individual II-2 or in the early zygote of individual II-2. b. You could look at the mitochondrial DNA from somatic cells from various tissues in the mother. If the mutation occurred in her germline and was inherited by II-2, the mother's somatic cells would not show any defective DNA.

43. The variation in affected tissues is due to differences in where and when during development the mutation occurred. Variation in the severity of the disease can be due to the proportion of mutant genomes (the degree of heteroplasmy) in the cells of different tissues.

45. Gel electrophoresis is better suited for an overview of the differences between mitochondrial genomes. Deletions can be very large and might not be amplified by PCR. In addition, sequences to which primers bind might be deleted in some mutations

Chapter 15

1. a. 4; b. 8; c. 5; d. 2; e. 7; f. 1; g. 3; h. 6.

3. a. i, ii, iii; b. iv, v, vi.

5. Mutations in the promoter region can only act in cis to the structural genes immediately adjacent to this regulatory sequence. This promoter mutation will not affect the expression of a second, normal operon.

7. b.

9. Nonlysogenic recipient cell did not have the cI (repressor) protein, so incoming infecting phage could go into the lytic cycle.

11.

	β-*galactosidase*	*Permease*
a.	constitutive	constitutive
b.	constitutive	inducible
c.	inducible	inducible
d.	no expression	constitutive
e.	no expression	no expression

13.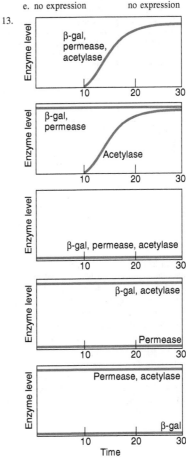

15. If the three genes make up an operon, they are cotranscribed to one mRNA and only one band should appear on a hybridization analysis using any of the three genes as a probe versus mRNA. If the genes are not part of an operon, there would be three differently sized hybridizing bands.

17. a. 4; b. 6; c. 7; d. 2; e. 3; f. 5; g. 1.

19. a. i, iii, v and vi, b. mutations ii, iii and iv; c. mutation 1 is i; mutation 6 is ii; mutation 2 is iii; mutation 4 is iv; mutation 5 is v; and mutation 3 is vi.

21. a. Mutations in O_2 or O_3 alone have only small effects on synthesis levels; b. Small DNA insertions between O_1 and O_2 may change the face and either change the ability of the repressor to bind one of the sites or change the ability of the bound repressor to bend the DNA leading to an O^c mutant phenotype; c. insensitive to a I^s repressor protein.

23. The protein-coding region of your gene must be in the same frame as the *lacZ* gene.

25. Seven His codons (CAC or CAU), in a row.

27. a. This seems to be a biosynthetic operon, the operon is repressible.

b.

Condition	Gene A	Gene B	Gene C	Gene D
Wildtype	completely repressible	constitutive	completely repressible	completely repressible
Nonsense in A	not expressed	constitutive	completely repressible	not expressed
Nonsense in B	partially repressible	not expressed	partially repressible	partially repressible
Nonsense in C	not expressed	constitutive	not expressed	not expressed
Nonsense in D	completely repressible	constitutive	completely repressible	not expressed
Deletion of region incl. E	partially repressible	constitutive	partially repressible	partially repressible
Deletion of F	partially repressible	constitutive	partially repressible	partially repressible
Deletion of G	not expressed	constitutive	not expressed	not expressed

c.

29. negative regulation.

31. a. two probes, one consists of labeled cDNA corresponding to the mRNA extracted from the culture grown at the higher osmolarity, and the other consists of cDNA corresponding to the mRNA in the culture grown at the lower osmolarity; b. each spot on the microarray would have a DNA sequence representing a single *E. coli* gene; c. use microarrays to compare the gene expression changes in cells grown under different osmotic conditions and those that are heat-shocked.

33. a. All of these turn out to be early genes; b. early genes; c. transcription of the large majority of *E. coli* genes would be drastically decreased; d. the *motA* gene prevents transcription of the middle genes, *asiA* should lower the transcription of middle and late T4 genes, the 55 gene should prevent the transcription of late transcripts but have little effect on the transcription of host genes; e. the *reg-A*-encoded ribonuclease is specifically required for the rapid destruction of T4 early mRNAs.

Chapter 16

1. a. 7; b. 4; c. 6; d. 2; e. 9; f. 8; g. 5; h. 3; i. 1.

3. include transcript processing (including alternate splicing of the RNA), export of mRNA from the nucleus, changes in the efficiency of translation (including miRNAs), chemical modification of the gene products and localization of the protein product in specific organelles.

5. a. i; b. ii.

7. a *GAL80* mutation in which the protein is not made or is made but cannot bind to the GAL4 protein will prevent repression and lead to constitutive synthesis. A *GAL4* mutation which inhibits binding to the GAL80 protein will also be constitutive. A mutation of the DNA at the binding site for the GAL4 protein will also give constitutive synthesis.

9. a. DNA binding; b. DNA binding; c. dimer formation; d. transcription activation; e. DNA binding.

11. If *Id* acts by quenching it interacts with *MyoD*, whereas if it blocks access to an enhancer it binds to DNA. Experimentally, look for binding to the regulatory DNA of a gene regulated by *MyoD*.

13. a. a *Drosophila* promoter sequence with the promoter added somewhere upstream of the DNA encoding the initiating AUG. Other helpful elements are a *Drosophila* poly-A addition sequence and a transcription termination signal downstream of the *lacZ* coding sequence; b. The type of construct you made is called an *enhancer trap*; these different insertions signal a position in the genome adjacent to a tissue-specific enhancer. In strains in which *lacZ* is expressed in the head, your construct must have integrated into the genome very near to an enhancer that helps activate transcription in the head. In other strains, your construct integrated into the genome near enhancers that are specific for other tissues like the thorax. Since the density of enhancer elements in the genome is low, most of the time new integrations of your construct would be located too far from an enhancer, so there would be no *lacZ* expression and no blue color.

15. differing levels of gene expression depending on their association with highly compacted, heterochromatic DNA vs. euchromatic; one example is Position Effect Variegation in *Drosophila*; another is Barr body formation in human females. Decompaction affects the location of the nucleosomes, and gives rise to DNase I hypersensitive sites where nucleosomes have been removed and the DNA is available for binding by RNA polymerase or regulatory proteins. Transcriptional silencing, on the other hand, involves methylation of the DNA.

17. Liver cell DNA has a DNaseI hypersensitive (DH) site 4 kb from 1 end of the *Eag*I fragment. This site is probably the promoter region for your gene.

19. a. 1, 2 and 4; b. 1 and 4; c. 1 and 4; d. 3.

21. a. half of his sons and half of his daughters will be affected; b. True; c. False; d. False.

23. {} represents an allele that is transcriptionally inactivated (imprinted); a. Bill Sr's genotype is 50K/{60K} and Joan's genotype (60K/{?}); b. Joan's genotype is 60K/{50K} and Bill Sr's genotype is 50K/{60K}.

25. a. The alleles of the gene are not expressed in the germ cells of male I-2. b. The allele of the gene from male I-2 will not be expressed in the somatic cells of II-2. c. The allele of the gene from male I-2 will be expressed in the germ cells of II-2. d. The allele of the gene from male I-2 will not be expressed in the somatic cells of II-3. e. The allele of the gene from male I-2 will not be expressed in the germ cells of II-3. f. The allele of the gene from male I-2 will be expressed in the germ cells of III-1. g. The allele of the gene from male I-2 will not be expressed in the germ cells of III-1.

27. Introns are spliced out, ribonuclease cleaves the primary transcript near the 3′ end and a poly-A tail is added, 5′ methl CAP is added.

29. The 5′ and 3′ untranslated regions could be cloned at the 5′ or 3′ ends of a reporter gene that is transformed back into *Drosophila* early embryos to see if either of the sequences affect the translatability of the reporter protein.

31. The protein in the fat cells may be post-translationally modified (for example, phosphorylated or de-phosphorylated) so that it is only active in fat cells. Alternatively, the protein may need a cofactor to be activated, and this cofactor is only transcribed in fat cells.

33. a. the difference in first detection of the mRNAs probably results from the different sensitivity in detecting mRNA versus protein. The difference in duration of the mRNA vs protein: the proteins are more stable than the mRNAs so they remain in the cells for several days longer; if the normal protein disappears at day 10.5 then the *lacZ* mRNA is more stable; or the β-galactosidase protein is more stable; or the transgene is transcribed until day 12; b. onset.

Chapter 17

1. a. 7; b. 6; c. 8; d. 2; e. 1; f. 9; g. 3; h. 5; i. 4.

3. a. a RAS mutant that stays in the GTP-bound state is permanently activated and will cause the cell to continue dividing. b. under the restrictive conditions the cells will not divide.

5. a. the effect of the T antigen is minimized. b. decrease the ability of p53 to function in cell cycle control. c. in a functional domain other than those that bind the T antigen and the transcription factor.

7. a. Use two different probes- one representing the specific sequence that you are analyzing and the other representing an unamplified control sequence. b. alterations in the chromosomal banding patterns in a karyotype analysis.

9. the role of diet, studies can be set up within the recent immigrant population vs. the United States-based native Indian population examining the effect of a Westernized diet vs. a diet resembling that of the ethnic group. Also, the effects of the same diets on non-Indian Westerners should be examined. To assess the role of genetic differences, you need to keep other factors, for example, diet, as constant as possible. You could look at the incidence in Indians and Americans who have similar diets.

11. order: d; a; b, c.

13. a. predisposition to colon cancer in this family could be an autosomal dominant trait. If this is true, then individuals II-2, and either I-1 or I-2 must have the mutation, but not express it. b. Individuals I-1, I-2 and II-2 are not among the high coffee consumers. Perhaps the predisposition to colon cancer is a combination of a particular genotype and the environmental factor of consumption of the special coffee.

15. Technique d.

17. If one PCR primer binds to one of the chromosomes at one side of the translocation while the other primer binds to the other chromosome on the other side of the breakpoint then your PCR primers will span the translocation. This would amplify a PCR fragment only if there were still cells in the blood that had the translocated chromosomes.

19. Both. These instabilities can be caused by somatic or germline mutations in genes such as *p53* or the genes for DNA repair enzymes, genome and karyotype instability can then result in additional problems that can contribute to cancer progression; mutations in DNA repair enzymes lead to a high rate of mutation and such mutations might inactivate a tumor suppressor gene or activate a protooncogene.

21. a. M (mitosis); b. M; c. S phase; d. G_1 phase.

23. three complementation groups.

25. cyclical regulation of and cyclical regulation of translation and cyclical control of posttranslational modifications.

27. a. 2; b. 3; c. 1.

29. In the M phase checkpoint molecules made by unattached kinetochores prevent the anaphase promoting complex (APC) from being activated. APC must become activated at the beginning of anaphase to destroy M phase cyclin, allowing cells to leave M phase. The activated APC adds ubiquitin to protein substrates. When this happens the ubiquinylated proteins are rapidly destroyed by the proteosome. One simple hypothesis is that cohesin is also targeted by the APC since it must be destroyed at the beginning of anaphase.

Chapter 18

1. a. 11; b. 4; c. 8; d. 7; e. 12; f. 9; g. 13; h. 3; i. l; j. 5; k. 6; 1. 10; m. 2.

3. a. In *C. elegans,* laser ablation at this early stage of development would almost certainly be lethal, while in mice the loss of one out of four early embryonic cells would have no effect; b. lethal to *C. elegans* and it is possible that the separated cells could develop into a mouse; c. in *C. elegans* would likely be lethal, in mice, such a fusion would be tolerated giving rise to a chimeric animal.

5. Make RNA preparations from homozygotes for the new null allele and then analyzing these preparations on Northern blots; RT-PCR or the mutation could be null but the gene would still be transcribed. Analyze protein extracts from the homozygous mutant animals by Western blot using the antibody against the rugose protein as a probe.

7. a.

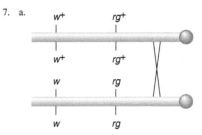

b. As a result of the mitotic crossover developing ommatidia in the eye would be simultaneously homozygous for the mutations in *rugose* and *white,* while adjacent ommatidia would be heterozygous for the wild type and mutant alleles of both genes. If the red ommatidia are abnormal even though their genotype predicts a normal structure, then the lack of rugose in the adjacent white ommatidia affects the red ommatidia; c. If these patches were normal in appearance, then rugose does not have an important role in eye development. If the white patch is abnormal, then rugose is important for eye development.

9. Mutate possible regulatory DNA elements.

11. Make DNA constructs that place a wild type genomic copy of gene X adjacent to *myo-2::GFP.* You then transform these constructs into worms that are homozygous for a null allele of gene X (and that did not contain any *GFP* source). The constructs form extrachromosomal arrays as described. Pharyngeal cells containing the arrays would be wild type for gene X and express GFP. Pharygeal cells that had lost the arrays would be homozygous mutant for gene X and would not express GFP.

13. a. If the mutation was due to an insertion of the transgene the MMTV *c-myc* gene should segregate with the phenotype; b. Clones containing the *c-myc* fusion could be identified by hybridization of MMTV sequences versus a library of genomic clones produced from the cells of the mutant mouse; c. The sequence of the gene into which the MMTV *c-myc* fusion inserted could be analyzed in the *ld* mutant to determine if there were mutations in the gene.

15. a. promoter, binding sites for transcription factors such as Bicoid and binding sites for other transcription factors that ensure the *hb* gene is transcribed in the proper cells in the mother; b. the amino acids in Hunchback that comprise DNA binding domains and domains involved in the transcriptional regulation of gap and pair rule genes; c. translational repression carried out by Nanos protein.

17. The cytoplasm from the anterior of a wild type embryo could be injected into the anterior end of a *bicoid* mutant embryo to see if there was rescue of the mutant phenotype. Alternately, purified *bicoid* mRNA injected into the anterior end of a *bicoid* mutant embryo would be a more definitive experiment. Finally, purified *bicoid* mRNA could be injected into the posterior end of a wild-type embryo.

19. a wild-type Knirps protein is needed to restrict the posterior limit of the zone of Kruppel expression; b. Hunchback protein would be seen throughout the embryo.

21. A mutation in the genes encoding a maternally supplied component which affects early development must be in the mother's genome. If the mutation affecting early development is in a gene whose transcription begins after fertilization then the mutation must be in the genome of the zygote (these are thus sometimes called "zygotic genes"). You would need two different kinds of genetic screens to make mutations either in the mothers' genome or the zygotes' genome.

23. a. the presence of PAR-3 and absence of PAR-2 from these cells indirectly dictates their ability to translate *glp-l* mRNA into GLP-1 protein; b. Such an interaction could occur through the extracellular domains of both proteins; c. receptor is the GLP-1 protein. Thus APX-1 would be the ligand; d. (i) the ablation of P_2 would make ABp and its descendants would have the same fate shown by ABa and its descendants, (ii) a null mutation of *apx-1* would have the same effect (iii) same, (iv) same.

Chapter 19

1. a. 3; b. 5; c. 8; d. 7; e. 6; f. 1; g. 9; h. 2; i. 4.

3. a, e.

5. a. the initial population is not in equilibrium; b. genotype frequencies in the F_1 will be 0.36 MM + 0.48 MN + 0.16 NN = 1, allele frequencies in the F_1 generation M = 0.6 and N = 0.4; c. the same as in part b.

7. Each allele frequency has a different set of genotype frequencies at equilibrium.

9. a. N = 0.1; b. 478 MN children on the island; c. N = 0.525.

11. a. p^2 + $2pq$ + q^2 + $2pr$ + r^2 + $2qr$ = 1; b. 0.516 A, 0.122 B, 0.075 AB and 0.287 O.

13. a. C = 8324/9049 = 0.92, c = 725/9049 = 0.08; b. this sample does not demonstrate Hardy-Weinberg equilibrium; c. the frequency of cP = 0.018, the frequency of c^d = 0.064, frequency of the C allele = 0.918; d. in boys C = 0.918 (normal vision), c^d = 0.064 (colorblind) and cP = 0.018 (colorblind). In the girls the genotype frequencies are: CC = 0.843 (normal vision), Cc^d = 0.118 (normal vision), CcP = 0.033 (normal vision), $cPcP$ = 3.3 × 10-4 (colorblind), c^dc^d = 0.004 (colorblind) and c^dcP = 0.002 (normal vision); e. the population is in equilibrium. As seen in part c, the allele frequency of C is the same in boys and girls and the allele frequency of c in the boys is the same as the total frequencies of c^d + cP in girls.

15. a. the genotype frequencies in the F_2 are 0.33 vg^+ vg^+ and 0.67 vg^+ vg; the allele frequencies in the F_2 for vg^+ = 0.33 + 1/2 (0.67) = 0.67 and for vg = 1/2 (0.67) = 0.33; b. genotype frequencies in the F_3 progeny are 0.449 vg^+ vg^+ + 0.442 vg^+ vg + 0.109 vg vg = 1, or 0.891 wild type and 0.109 vestigial; c. F_4 allele frequencies are vg^+ = 0.753 and vg = 0.249; d. If all of the F_4 flies are allowed to mate at random then there is no selection and the population will be in Hardy-Weinberg equilibrium −0.566 vg^+ vg^+ + 0.373 vg^+ vg + 0.062 vg vg = 1; vg^+ = 0.753 and vg = 0.247.

17. Selection against the homozygous recessive genotype will decrease the frequency of the recessive allele in the population, but it will never totally remove it, as the recessive allele is hidden in the heterozygote, recessive allele sometimes confers an advantage when present in the heterozygote, mutation can produce new recessive alleles in the population.

19. a. b = $\sqrt{0.25}$ = 0.5, B = 0.5; b. Δq for tank 1 = −0.1, q for all tanks = 0.5; Δq for tank 2 = 0; Δq for tank 3 = 0.05.

	Tank 1	Tank 2	Tank 3
b. Δq	−0.1	0.0	0.05
c. w_{Bb}	1.0	1.0	1.0
d. w_{bb}	<1.0	1.0	>1.0

21. a. fitness value (w) = 0 and the selection coefficient (s) = 1 for the affected genotype. There is no selection pressure against the carrier or the homozygous normal genotypes, so for both of these w = 1 and s = 0; b. Δq = −1.54 × 10^{-3}; c. 1.02 × 10^{-3}. This number (1.02 × 10^{-3}) is smaller than the observed q which is 0.04; d. CF^+/CF^- heterozygotes may be better able to survive outbreaks of cholera.

23. b.

25. a. Height has the highest heritability and weight has the lowest heritability; b. The data from the CDC is roughly in line with the conclusions from part a.

27. a. founder effect; b. advantages: genetic homogeneity and fewer genes that may affect a polygenic trait; disadvantages: some mutations are not found in the population that are in the general population.

29. a. 2n + 1 where n = number of genes; b. $(1/4)^n$ = 1/256, so n = 4.

Chapter 20

1. a. 4; b. 6; c. 5; d. 2; e. 1; f. 7; g. 3.

3. a, c.

5. a. The enzyme consists of an RNA molecule; b. the enzyme has both an RNA and a protein component.

7. a. Different constraints on the functions of each of the proteins; b. rates are more constant because these base changes do not affect function of the gene product.

9. Suggests there is some benefit to the CF allele in the heterozygous state.

11. Duplication followed by evolutionary divergence.

13. a. 240 million years; b. two; C allele arose 30 million years ago; B allele arose 1 million years ago; c. duplication of B: transposition; duplication of C: misalignment and crossing-over.

15. This gene was introduced from a different species.

17. a. Exons; b. genes.

19. They mediate genome rearrangements or contribute regulatory elements adjacent to a gene.

21. a. SINEs or LINEs; b. centromere satellite DNA.

23. a. The side effects suggest that the protease inhibitor is not completely specific to the HIV protease. Presumably the HIV protease may have distant evolutionary relationships with other proteases found in normal cells, b. Protease cleavage could be involved in the generation of a hormone like cortisol that could affect fat distribution. Many hormones are generated from prohormones by protease cleavage. c. Perhaps the indinavir sulfate affects the processes needed for energy metabolism, such as the function or the integrity of the mitochondria. This hypothesis could be tested by analyzing the energy content of the cells from patients treated with the drug.

Chapter 21

1. The elements of the system; the physical associations among the elements; the biological context of the system; how the association of the system's elements and their relation to changes in the biological context explain its emergent property.

3. genes that encode proteins and untranslated RNAs and the short DNA sequences that make up the control elements adjacent to the genes.

5. The sequences of the entire genomes of humans and other model organisms like E. coli, yeast and mice provide a genetics parts list of all the genes and the proteins they encode. The study of human genome defined the basic blocks of DNA, proteins and other molecules that systems biology hopes to fit together into networks. This also defined many of the complex molecular machines and protein networks, and enforced the idea that biological information is hierarchic. The Genome Projects also drive the development of powerful computational tools which make it possible to acquire, store, analyze, integrate, display and model biological information. The high-throughput platforms for genomics and proteomics enable the acquisition of global data sets of differing types of biological information.

7. What exactly is the biological system that he is perturbing? Does he know all of the elements in this system? Some of the cytokines may be the output of the system, but does he know all of the outputs? Or all of the inputs? If he is measuring protein levels, he has only one type of biological information. Also your friend is not looking at the other systems whose behaviors will be altered by the knockout perturbations. Your friend's research is not systems biology.

9. a. **True**; b. **True**; c. **True**; d. **True**; e. **True**.

Index

Page numbers followed by an *f* indicate figures; page numbers followed by a *t* refer to tables.